W9-BNP-905

MATHEMATICAL ANALYSIS

MATHEMATICAL ANALYSIS
BUSINESS AND ECONOMIC APPLICATIONS
SECOND EDITION

JEAN E. DRAPER
University of Arizona

JANE S. KLINGMAN
Xavier University

Revised by
JEAN DRAPER WEBER

HARPER & ROW, PUBLISHERS
NEW YORK   EVANSTON   SAN FRANCISCO   LONDON

CONTENTS

PREFACE TO THE SECOND EDITION

The second edition of this book follows the general outline of the first edition; the mathematical discussion of each topic is followed by a discussion of its applications in economics and business. There are, however, substantial changes and additions in content. The revised edition contains additional material on the following topics: sets; functions, including the addition of trigonometric functions; differentiation of composite functions; second-order difference equations; partitioned matrices; rank; and theory of simultaneous equations. Corresponding examples and problems are also included. A revised solutions manual is available to instructors adopting the text.

Thanks are extended to the many students and instructors who have offered suggestions for improving the book. Each suggestion has been carefully considered; many have been followed and all are appreciated. Special thanks are due David Monarchi for his careful reading of the complete manuscript and his many helpful comments.

The second author was unable to participate in the revisions for the second edition of the book. The first author accepts full responsibility for all changes made and for any errors remaining.

J. D. W.

PREFACE

This text offers the student an understanding of quantitative techniques both in their mathematical contexts and as they are applied to business and economic problems.

The material has been used in various stages of development in graduate and undergraduate quantitative analysis classes at The University of Wisconsin. It assumes reasonable facility with algebra; there is, however, an algebra review section at the end of the book for students whose skills in this area need sharpening. The text is designed for a one-year course, allowing perhaps for some omissions at the option of the instructor.

There are eight chapters: Graphical Representation, Differential Calculus: Functions of One Variable, Differential Calculus: Functions of More Than One Variable, Integral Calculus, Differential Equations, Difference Equations, Vectors and Matrices, and Applications of Matrix Algebra. Each chapter includes mathematical presentation of its subject and applications to business and economics. Each also includes many problems, for we believe that substantial practice in problem solving is essential in the study of mathematics. An extensive solutions manual providing complete calculations for all problems is available on request to instructors who adopt the text.

We wish to express our gratitude to the students who have used this material through its many drafts and whose comments and suggestions have been incorporated in the revisions. We would also like particularly to thank Myrna Edmonds for her patient and painstaking typing of the manuscript. Finally, we accept full responsibility for any errors that may remain.

J. E. D.

J. S. K.

INTRODUCTION

From the beginning of recorded history, cultural and scientific advances have depended on the use of symbols. The history of civilization can be viewed as the history of man's increasingly sophisticated use of symbols. Primitive man discovered that ideas are best developed and communicated through spoken and written language, that is, through the use of symbols representing mental images. As thinking in any area develops, the symbols used become increasingly abstract.

When the concepts to which symbols refer are essentially nonquantitative in nature, the symbols and their relationships can be studied in the general framework of logic and there is no need for mathematics as such. It is when symbols represent essentially quantitative concepts that mathematics is useful and, in fact, essential for analyzing their relationships. Mathematics is a branch of logic, the branch of logic that provides a systematic framework within which quantitative relationships can be studied. In pure mathematics definitions or axioms and assumptions are precisely stated symbolically and the analysis proceeds by deduction to obtain conclusions. Applied mathematics differs from pure mathematics in a very important respect—in pure mathematics symbols represent abstract concepts whose properties are assigned by definition, while in applied mathematics many symbols represent variables observed in the real world; the properties of these variables must be determined by observation, not by abstract definition, and then stated mathematically. In addition, the empirical

1

accuracy of the deductions of applied mathematics can be determined. Applied mathematical analysis thus is based on empirically determined definitions and assumptions from which empirically verifiable conclusions are obtained by deduction. Pure and applied mathematical analysis differ only with respect to the empirical aspect of the definitions and assumptions and conclusions, not with respect to the methods of deduction.

Because economics is concerned with concepts that are essentially quantitative in nature—for example, price, cost, wage rates, investment, income, and profit—much of economic analysis is inescapably mathematical in nature. Mathematics provides a logical, systematic framework within which quantitative relations can be studied. When economic variables are represented by symbols and their properties stated mathematically, mathematics provides the techniques for analyzing relations among the symbols and thus among the variables they represent. Much of economic analysis is therefore applied mathematical analysis.

In economic analysis, as in applied mathematics in general, deductions obtained by mathematical analysis are interpreted and evaluated empirically. It should be noted in this regard that if the deductions following from a set of definitions and assumptions are not correct with respect to empirical observation, mathematical analysis (if correctly performed) is not responsible and the difficulty is to be found in the definitions or assumptions. Mathematics enables the economist to be precise in defining relevant variables, to state clearly the assumptions made, to be logical in developing the analysis, and to consider a larger number of variables than might be feasible verbally. However, it does not and cannot prevent the omission or the empirically incorrect definition of relevant variables nor can it prevent empirically inaccurate or incomplete statements of assumptions. Mathematical analysis takes definitions and assumptions as given and obtains the conclusions that follow logically from them. Mathematical analysis is thus by nature logical, not empirical, and can be held responsible for conclusions only with respect to their logical validity given the definitions and assumptions on which they are based and not with respect to their empirical accuracy.

Thus if mathematical analysis is correctly performed, but its conclusions are empirically incorrect, the definitions and assumptions must be examined for accuracy and completeness. By providing a systematic framework for the deduction of empirically verifiable conclusions, mathematical analysis helps the economist determine the accuracy of his definitions and assumptions—if the conclusions are untenable, the definitions and assumptions must be examined and revised.

The purpose of this book is to help the student understand, appreciate, and perform applied mathematical analysis. Mathematical proofs are minimized except when they can be made heuristic. The book is organized so that a type of analysis is discussed first with respect to its mathematical (logical) procedure and then with respect to its applications in economics and business. The assumptions required for each type of analysis are emphasized and its applications are discussed in terms of these assumptions.

The subsequent sections of this chapter review some of the basic mathematical concepts and definitions used in later chapters.

■ SETS

A *set* is a collection of distinguishable well-defined objects or entities. The *def'n*
objects or entities belonging to a set are said to be *elements* of the set. A set is
determined either by a list of its elements or by specifying a rule that determines
whether a given object or entity belongs to the set. Such a rule is referred to as a
defining relation. Braces are used to denote a set; either the elements of the set or
its defining relation is written inside the braces.

Example

$A = \{a, b, c\}$ means that the set A consists of the elements a, b, and c.

$B = \{x : x$ is an odd integer$\}$ means that the set B consists of the odd integers.

$C = \{1, 2, 3, 4, 5, 6\}$ means that the set C consists of the numbers 1, 2, 3, 4, 5,
and 6.

$D = \{y : y$ is an integer$\}$ means that the set D consists of the integers.

The notation $x \in S$ means that the entity or object x is an element of the set *∈*
S. The notation $x \notin S$ means that x is not an element of the set S.

A defining relation that is satisfied by no element is said to define the *empty* *∅*
set, denoted by $\varnothing$.

Examples

Referring to the preceding example,

$$a \in A$$
$$b \notin B$$
$$4 \notin B$$
$$4 \in C$$
$$4 \in D$$
$$7 \notin C$$
$$7 \in B$$
$$7 \in D$$
$$d \notin A$$
$$d \notin D$$

$S = \{x : x$ is an odd number ending in 2$\} = \varnothing$

$P = \{y : y$ is an odd number that is the square of an even number$\} = \varnothing$

If every element of a set S is also an element of a set T, then S is said to be a *subset* of T. If there is at least one element in T that is not also in S, then S is a *proper subset* of T. The notation $S \subset T$ means that S is a subset of T; the notation $S \not\subset T$ means that S is not a subset of T. Note that the empty set is a subset of every set. If $S \subset T$ and $T \subset S$, then every element in S is also in T and vice versa and S and T are the same set. This is denoted $S = T$.

Example

Referring to the preceding examples,

$$A \not\subset B$$
$$B \subset D$$
$$B \not\subset C$$
$$C \subset D$$

The *union* of two sets S and T is the set consisting of the elements of S and the elements of T. The union of S and T, denoted by $S \cup T$, is described by

$$S \cup T = \{x : x \in S \text{ and/or } x \in T\}$$

Note that an element common to both sets is not counted twice in the union.

The *intersection* of two sets S and T is the set consisting of the elements that are common to S and T. The intersection of S and T is denoted by $S \cap T$ and is described by

$$S \cap T = \{x : x \in S \text{ and } x \in T\}$$

The *set difference* of two sets S and T is the set consisting of the elements of S that are not elements of T. The set difference of S and T is denoted by $S - T$ and is described by

$$S - T = \{x : x \in S \text{ and } x \notin T\}$$

A *universal set* or *universe* is a specified set that contains all the elements of interest for a particular discussion. If two sets have the property that their union is the universal set and their intersection is the null set, one set is said to be the *complement* of the other with respect to the universe. If U denotes the universal set, the complement of a given set S is denoted by S' and is described by

$$S' = U - S$$

A statement of complementation must be qualified unless the universal set is clearly understood. For example, if the complement of S is taken with respect to U and also with respect to V, the notation S'_U and S'_V is used.

Example

Referring to the preceding example,

$$B \cup D = D$$

$A \cup C = \{a, b, c, 1, 2, 3, 4, 5, 6\}$
$A \cap D = \varnothing$
$B \cap D = B$
$B \cap C = \{1, 3, 5\}$
$C \cap D = C$
$C - D = \varnothing$
$C - B = \{2, 4, 6\}$
$D - A = D$
$D - B = \{x : x \text{ is an even integer}\}$

If $U = \{x : x \text{ is an integer}\}$, then

$B'_U = \{x : x \text{ is an even integer}\}$
$D'_U = \varnothing$

If $V = \{1, 2, 3, 4, 5, 6, 7, 8, 9, 10\}$, then

$C'_V = \{7, 8, 9, 10\}$

If $W = \{x : x \text{ is a lowercase letter in the English alphabet}\}$, then

$A'_W = \{d, e, f, g, h, i, j, k, l, m, n, o, p, q, r, s, t, u, v, w, x, y, z\}$

Sets formed by unions, intersections, and complements are shown here diagrammatically; the shaded area is the set indicated below each diagram. This type of representation of a set is called a *Venn diagram*.

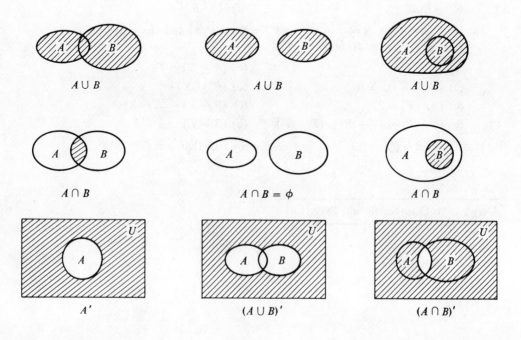

Problems

1. If A, B, and C are sets such that $A \subset B \subset C$, what is the relationship between $C - B$ and $C - A$?
2. Show that, in general, $(A \cap B)' = A' \cup B'$.
3. Show that, in general, $A \cap (B \cup C) = (A \cap B) \cup (A \cap C)$.
4. Show that $(S \cap T') \cup (S \cap T) = S \cap (S \cup T) = S \cup (S \cap T) = S$.
5. Show that $K \cup (L \cap M) = (K \cup L) \cap (K \cup M)$.
6. If $A \cap B = \varnothing$ and $A \cap C = \varnothing$, is it necessarily true that $B \cap C = \varnothing$?
7. If $A \neq B$ and $B \neq C$, is it necessarily true that $A \neq C$?
8. If $A \not\subset B$ and $B \not\subset C$, is it necessarily true that $A \not\subset C$?
9. If $A \subset C$ and $B \subset D$, is it necessarily true that $A \cup B \subset C \cup D$?
10. If $A \subset C$ and $B \subset D$, is it necessarily true that $A \cap B \subset C \cap D$?
11. If $S \cup T = \{1, 2, 3, 4\}$, $S \cap T = \{1, 3\}$, and $S - T = \{2\}$, find S and T.
12. If $A \cap B \neq \varnothing$, $A \cap C \neq \varnothing$, and $B \cap C \neq \varnothing$, is it necessarily true that $A \cap B \cap C \neq \varnothing$?
13. If U is a universal set, determine which of the following statements are incorrect and correct them.

    (a) $B \cup \varnothing = B$

    (b) $C \cap U = C$

    (c) $A \cup A' = U$

    (d) $B \cup U = U$

    (e) $D \cap \varnothing = \varnothing$

    (f) $A \cap A' = A$

    (g) $B \cap B = \varnothing$

    (h) $C \cup C = C$

    (i) $(D')' = U$

    (j) $(A - C) \cup C = A - C$

    (k) $B \cap (B - D) = B \cup D$

    (l) If $A = B'$, then $B = A'$

    (m) $(C - D)' = C' - D'$

    (n) $(A \cup D) - D = A - D$

14. If $A = \{e, f, g\}$ and $B = \{e, h\}$, find

    (a) $A - B$

    (b) $B - A$

    (c) $A \cap B$

    (d) $A \cup B$

15. If $R = \{w, x, y\}$, $S = \{u, v, w\}$, and $T = \{u, v, w, x\}$ and the universal set is $U = \{u, v, w, x, y, z\}$, find

    (a) $R' \cap T' \cap S'$

    (b) $(R - S) \cap T$

    (c) $(R' - T') \cup S$

    (d) $(R' \cup S')'$

    (e) $(S \cup T) - T'$

    (f) $(R - T) - (S - R)$

    (g) $(S - R) - [(T - R) \cup (T - S)]$

    (h) $(R - T) \cup S$

16. If $A \cap B = \varnothing$ and $A' = C$, is it necessarily true that $B \subset C$?

Answers to Odd-Numbered Problems

1. $C - B \subset C - A$
7. No
9. Yes

11. $S = \{1, 2, 3$
    $T = \{1, 3, 4\}$
13. (f) $A \cap A' = \emptyset$
    (g) $B \cap B = B$
    (i) $(D')' = D$
    (j) $(A - C) \cup C = A \cup C$
    (k) $B \cap (B - D) = B - D$
    (m) $(C - D)' = C' \cup D$
15. (a) $\{z\}$
    (b) $\{x\}$
    (c) S
    (d) $\{w\}$
    (e) T
    (f) $\{y\}$
    (g) $\emptyset$
    (h) S

■ VARIABLES

In mathematics a *constant* is a quantity that maintains a fixed value throughout a particular problem. An *absolute* or *numerical constant* retains the same value in all problems; an *arbitrary* or *parametric constant* (or a *parameter*) retains the same value throughout any particular problem but may assume different values in different problems. The *absolute* or *numerical value* of a constant a is denoted by $|a|$ and means the magnitude of a regardless of its algebraic sign. Thus $|+a| = |-a| = |a|$.

A *variable* is a quantity that assumes various values in a particular problem; the set of values which a variable assumes is its *range*. Thus in any problem there may be the following:

1. Quantities that are absolute constants and always retain the same value; such quantities are either numbers or symbols denoting numbers.

2. Quantities that are parameters and remain constant throughout the problem but may have different (constant) values for other problems; the value of a parameter depends on the particular situation represented in the problem.

3. Quantities that are variables in the problem and take on all possible values meaningful for the problem (frequently restricted to some or all positive values).

A variable may be either continuous or discrete. A *continuous variable* is one that may assume any value within a specified interval of real numbers (possibly all real numbers); successive values of a continuous variable thus may differ by infinitesimal amounts. A *discrete variable* is one that may assume only values specified in a countable range. Note that the number of points or values in any specified real interval, say between 5 and 10, is uncountable and no rule can be given for obtaining all possible such values. However, the number of integers or integer values in any specified interval is countable. The number of points on the real line (or on any part of the real line) is said to be a noncountable or nondenumerable infinity. The number of integers on the real line is a countable or denumerable infinity and any set obtained from the integers by a specified rule is also countable or denumerable.

In pure mathematics, usually the letters at the beginning of the alphabet are used to represent parameters and the letters at the end of the alphabet used to represent variables. However, in applied mathematics there are many exceptions to this convention, and a variable is frequently represented by the first letter of its name—for example, p for price, q for quantity, c for cost, s for savings, and so forth.

Examples

In the equation of a straight line,

$$\frac{x}{a} + \frac{y}{b} = 1$$

1 is a numerical constant, a and b are parameters, and x and y are variables.

a and b have constant numerical values within a given problem and are, therefore, parametric constants.

x and y may assume an infinite number of values within any particular problem and are, therefore, variables.

In the equation for the area of a circle,

$$A = \pi r^2$$

π is a numerical constant (approximately equal to 3.1416) and A and r are variables.

The only values of either constants or variables considered subsequently are *real numbers*. The real number system includes all the familiar types of numbers —rational numbers (positive and negative integers, fractions and decimal fractions) and irrational numbers that are roots of rational numbers and other numbers that cannot be expressed as fractions; it does not include even roots of negative numbers (which are called *imaginary numbers*) or numbers that have both real and imaginary parts (which are called *complex numbers*).

Examples

The equation $x^2 + 6 = 0$ has no real solution, since $\sqrt{-6}$ is an imaginary number.

> The equation $x^5 + 32 = 0$ has the real solution $x = -2$ (it also has four complex solutions not of interest for the present discussion).

The quotient $\dfrac{a}{b}$ of two numbers a and b is a number x such that $a = bx$. *quotient*

Division by zero is not permissible as a result of this definition. Note that if $b = 0$, $a = 0 \cdot x$, which is true only if $a = 0$, in which case x can be any number. Thus the expressions

$$\frac{a}{0} \quad \text{and} \quad \frac{0}{0}$$

are meaningless. To distinguish between $\dfrac{a}{0}$ and $\dfrac{0}{0}$, $\dfrac{a}{0}$ is sometimes said to be "undefined," $\dfrac{0}{0}$ is sometimes said to be "indeterminate."

Note that $\dfrac{0}{b} = 0$ for $b \neq 0$, since $\dfrac{0}{b}$ is the value of x for which $b \cdot x = 0$ and must be zero for $b \neq 0$. The symbol $\neq$ means "is unequal to." Other relationships involving inequalities are expressed as follows: $\neq$

> The notation $<$ indicates "less than"
> The notation $>$ indicates "greater than"
> The notation $\leq$ indicates "equal to or less than"
> The notation $\geq$ indicates "equal to or greater than"

$<$
$>$
$\leq$
$\geq$

■ RELATIONS AND FUNCTIONS

A set of ordered pairs of real numbers is referred to as a *binary relation*. The set of first elements of a binary relation is called the *domain* of the relation; the set of second elements is called the *range* of the relation. For a given set $\{(x, y)\}$, x and y are referred to as *variables*. The set of values variable x takes on is its domain and x is usually called the *independent variable*; the set of values variable y takes on is the range and y is usually called the *dependent variable*. When the number of variables is clear from the context, a binary relation may be referred to simply as a relation.

Example

> $S_1 = \{(1, 2), (2, 8), (2, 3)\}$ is a binary relation whose domain is $\{1, 2\}$ and whose range is $\{2, 3, 8\}$.
>
> $S_2 = \{(x, y) : x, y$ real numbers, $x \leq y\}$ is a binary relation some of whose members are $(2, 2)$, $(3, 4)$, $(5, 5)$, and $(8, 20)$. Note that $(2, 1)$, $(3, 2)$, and $(25, 20)$, for example, are not members of S_2.

$S_3 = \{(x, y) : y = x^2,\ x \in \mathcal{R}\}$ is a binary relation. ($\mathcal{R}$ denotes the set of all real numbers.) The domain of S_3 is $\mathcal{R}$ and the range is the set of all nonnegative real numbers.

$S_4 = \{(x, y) : y = x^2$ if $0 \le x \le 2$, $y = 3 - x$ if $2 < x < 3$, and $y = 3$ if $x = 3\}$ is a binary relation whose domain is the set $x : 0 \le x \le 3$ and whose range is the set $\{y : 0 \le y \le 4\}$.

def'n of a function

If a relation is such that to each element of the domain there corresponds one and only one element of the range, the relation is said to be a *function*. Functions constitute a subset of relations—all functions are relations, but not all relations are functions. Note that the relations S_3 and S_4 of the above example are functions, but the relations S_1 and S_2 are not functions. A special notation is used for functions to denote the element of the range corresponding to an element of the domain. If f denotes a function $\{(x, y)\}$, then the number y associated with a given x is denoted by $f(x)$, read "f of x." With this notation, the sets of pairs defining f may be written as $\{(x, f(x))\}$ where $y = f(x)$.

Example

Referring to the preceding example, S_3 and S_4 can be written, respectively, as

$S_3 = \{(x, f(x)) : f(x) = x^2,\ x \in \mathcal{R}\}$

$S_4 = \{(x, f(x)) : f(x) = x^2$ if $0 \le x \le 2$, $f(x) = 3 - x$ if $2 < x < 3$, and $f(x) = 3$ if $x = 3\}$

Other letters, for example, g, F, G, ϕ, and Γ, are also frequently used to indicate a name for a function. An equation such as $g(x) = x^2 + \dfrac{1}{x}$ provides a rule for finding the second member of a pair whose first member is x. Such an equation or formula is said to define the function, although the function is not the formula but is the set of ordered pairs $\{(x, g(x))\}$ or $\{(x, y)\}$. When a value of x is substituted in the formula for a function, the result is said to be the *function value* or the *value of the function* for that value of x.

In the case of a function involving two variables, whenever the value of the independent variable is specified the value of the dependent variable is determined. However, it is the independent variable whose value is thought of as being assigned arbitrarily (except for nonpermissible values), thus determining also the value of the dependent variable. It is conventional in applied mathematics to represent the independent variable by x and the dependent variable by y.

For most problems in analytic geometry and other branches of pure mathematics, the choice of independent and dependent variables is a matter of convenience and the conventional designation of x and y is concerned only with graphical representation, as discussed below. For example, in considering the equation

$$x - 4y^2 + 2y + 6 = 0$$

it is clearly more convenient to find pairs of points by regarding y as the independent and x as the dependent variable as follows:

$$x = 4y^2 - 2y - 6$$

When the variables are purely mathematical and do not represent quantities in a particular context, there is no other relevant basis for making the choice. However, when the variables do represent quantities in the context of a particular subject matter, the logic of the situation usually determines the choice of independent and dependent variables. For example, quantity produced is thought of as a primary determinant of total cost rather than vice versa. There are exceptions even in these types of problems; for example, price may be thought of as determining quantity demanded, or quantity demanded may be thought of as determining price.

Examples

If $f(x) = x^2 - x + 2$, then

$$f(z) = z^2 - z + 2$$

$$f(2) = 4 - 2 + 2 = 4$$

$$f(-3) = 9 + 3 + 2 = 14$$

$$f(0) = 0 - 0 + 2 = 2$$

$$f(a) = a^2 - a + 2$$

$$f(x + 2) = (x + 2)^2 - (x + 2) + 2$$

$$= (x^2 + 4x + 4) - (x + 2) + 2$$

$$= x^2 + 3x + 4$$

$$f(x + h) - f(x) = (x + h)^2 - (x + h) + 2 - (x^2 - x + 2)$$

$$= (x + h)(x + h) - (x + h) + 2 - (x^2 - x + 2)$$

$$= x^2 + 2xh + h^2 - x - h + 2 - x^2 + x - 2$$

$$= 2hx + h^2 - h$$

If $y = f(x) = \dfrac{x + 1}{x}$, then

$$f(1) = \frac{1 + 1}{1} = \frac{2}{1} = 2$$

$$f(-1) = \frac{-1 + 1}{-1} = \frac{0}{-1} = 0$$

$$f(0) = \frac{1}{0} \text{ (undefined)}$$

$$f(a + h) - f(a) = \frac{a + h + 1}{a + h} - \frac{a + 1}{a}$$

$$= \frac{a^2 + ah + a - a^2 - ah - a - h}{a(a + h)}$$

$$= -\frac{h}{a(a + h)}$$

If $y = f(x) = \dfrac{1 - x}{1 + x}$, find $x = f(y)$. Solving for x,

$$y = \frac{1 - x}{1 + x}$$

$$y(1 + x) = 1 - x$$

$$y + xy = 1 - x$$

$$y + xy + x - 1 = 0$$

$$x + xy = 1 - y$$

$$x(1 + y) = 1 - y$$

$$x = \frac{1 - y}{1 + y} = f(y)$$

If $f(x) = 10^x$ and $\phi(x) = \log_{10}x$, show that $f[\phi(x)] = \phi[f(x)] = x$.

$$f[\phi(x)] = 10^{\phi(x)} = 10^{\log_{10}x} = x$$

$$\phi[f(x)] = \log_{10} f(x) = \log_{10}10x = x$$

PROBLEMS

1. For each of the following relations state the domain and range and indicate whether the relation is a function.

   (a) $S = \{(1, 3), (2, 3), (2, 4), (3, 2), (4, 1), (5, 5)\}$

   (b) $A = \{(1, 3), (2, 3), (3, 3), (4, 3)\}$

   (c) $T = \{(x, y) : y = 4x + 1 \text{ if } 0 \leq x \leq 2, y = 10 - x^2 \text{ if } 2 < x \leq 3\}$

   (d) $B = \{(x, y) : y^2 = x, y \text{ is an integer and } |y| \leq 8\}$

2. For each of the following, determine if the set $\{(x, y)\}$ of pairs of real numbers formed according to the given rule is a function.

   (a) $y^2 = x$ (b) $y^3 = x$

   (c) $y^4 = x$ (d) $x^2 + y = 1$

   (e) $x + y^2 = 1$ (f) $x^2 + y^2 = 1$

   (g) $y = x^2 + 4$ (h) $xy = 1$

(i) $y = \dfrac{x^2 + 4}{x - 2}$

(j) $y = \dfrac{1}{x^2 - 6}$

(k) $x = \dfrac{1}{y^2 - y + 2}$

(l) $\dfrac{1}{y^2 + 2} = x$

ANSWERS TO ODD-NUMBERED PROBLEMS

1. (a) domain: $\{1, 2, 3, 4, 5\}$
    range: $\{1, 2, 3, 4, 5\}$
    not a function

  (b) domain: $\{1, 2, 3, 4\}$
    range: $\{3\}$
    a function

  (c) domain: $\{x : 0 \le x \le 3\}$
    range: $\{y : 1 \le y \le 9\}$
    a function

  (d) domain: $\{0, 1, 4, 9, 16, 25, 36, 49, 64\}$
    range: $\{0, \pm 1, \pm 2, \pm 3, \pm 4, \pm 5, \pm 6, \pm 7, \pm 8\}$
    not a function

☐ *INVERSE FUNCTIONS*

The domain and range of any relation may be interchanged to form a new relation. Each pair in the new relation is obtained by interchanging the elements of a corresponding pair in the original relation. Two such sets of pairs are said to be *inverse relations*; each relation is said to be the *inverse* of the other. If both relations are functions, they are called *inverse functions*. The inverse of a function f is denoted by the symbol f^{-1}. In this notation -1 is not an exponent; it means only that f^{-1} is the inverse of f. The inverse relation is a function if and only if the function is such that to each element of its range there corresponds one and only one element of its domain. If f^{-1} is the inverse function of f, then

$$f[f^{-1}(x)] = x \text{ for all } x \text{ in the domain of } f^{-1} \qquad f_0 f^{-1} = x$$

and

$$f^{-1}[f(x)] = x \text{ for all } x \text{ in the domain of } f \qquad f_0^{-1} f = x$$

Providing the algebra can be done, the relation $f^{-1}(x)$ can be found by solving $f[f^{-1}(x)] = x$ as though $f^{-1}(x)$ were a variable in the equation. When a domain is not specified it is assumed to be the set of all real numbers.

Examples

Let $g = \{(x, y) : y = 2x - 1\}$. Find the inverse relation and determine whether it is a function.

For every value of x there is one and only one y, so the inverse of g is a function:

$$y = 2x - 1$$
$$x = \tfrac{1}{2}(y + 1)$$

and

$$g^{-1} = \{(x, y) : y = \tfrac{1}{2}(x + 1)\}$$

Since the letters used to indicate the values of the domain and the range are arbitrary, x and y are used in their customary order.

Find the inverse of $f = \{(x, y) : y = x^2, x \geq 0\}$ and determine whether it is a function.

For every x there is one and only one y so the inverse of f is a function:

$$y = x^2$$
$$x = +\sqrt{y}$$

and

$$f^{-1} = \{(x, y) : y = \sqrt{x}\}$$

Note that if f has as its domain the set of all real numbers in the above example, f^{-1} is not a function since its domain is the set of all nonnegative real numbers and its range is the set of all real numbers.

A functional form can be obtained by the substitution of one form into another. If $y = f(x)$ and $u = g(y)$ and if $u = g[f(x)] = h(x)$, then h is called the *g composite of f*.

$$y = f(x)$$
$$u = g(y) \rightarrow y = f(x)$$
$$u = g[f(x)] = h(x) \qquad \therefore h \text{ is the } g \text{ composite of } f$$

Example

If $f(x) = x^2 - x - 1$ and $g(x) = x - 1$, then

$$f[g(x)] = (x - 1)^2 - (x - 1) - 1 = x^2 - 3x + 1$$

and

$$g[f(x)] = (x^2 - x - 1) - 1 = x^2 - x - 2$$

The above example illustrates the fact that, in general, $f[g(x)] \neq g[f(x)]$.

Example

If $g(x) = x^2 + 2$, then

$$g[g(x)] = (x^2 + 2)^2 + 2 = x^4 + 4x^2 + 6$$

PROBLEMS

1. If $f(x) = \dfrac{x^2}{3} - x$ and $g(t) = \dfrac{t^2 + 4}{3t}$, find

   (a) $f(7) - g(3)$ and (b) $\dfrac{f(3)}{g(2) + 1}$.

• 2. If $q(x) = p(x) + g(x)$ and $p(x) = \dfrac{x^2 - 7}{3}$, $g(x) = \dfrac{7}{x^2}$, find $q(2)$.

3. If $h(x) = x^{3/2}$ and $Q(x) = (x^2 + 1)^{-1}$, find $Q[h(x)]$.

4. If $h(y) = e^y$ and $Q(x) = x^2 + 4$, find $Q[h(y)]$.

• 5. If $h(x) = x^3 + 3x + 6$ and $g(y) = \dfrac{y}{1 + y}$, find $g[h(2)]$.

6. If $f(x) = \dfrac{8}{x^3}$, $g(x) = x^2$ and $Q(x) = x^3 - 10$, find $Q[f(-2) + g(2)]$.

.7. If $g(t) = t^2 + 3$ and $Q(t) = t^{-1}$, find $Q[g(t)]$.

' 8. If $f(t) = t^3 + a$ and $g(x) = x^{-3}$, find $g[f(t)]$.

9. If $f(t) = e^{t+\alpha}$, $h(t) = e^{b^2 t}$ and $g(y) = y^{b^2}$, find $\dfrac{g[f(t)]}{h(t)}$.

10. If $h(x) = \tfrac{4}{5} \ln x$ and $g(x) = e^{2x}$, find $h[g(10)]$.

• 11. If $g(h) = he^{1/h}$ and $F\left(\dfrac{1}{y}\right) = \dfrac{y^2}{y^2 + 1}$, find

   (a) $g[F(t)]$ and (b) $F[g(t)]$.

12. If $f(x) = x(x + 1)$, show that $f(x + h) - f(x) = h(2x + 1 + h)$.

13. If $f(x) = \dfrac{1}{x}$, show that $f(x + h) - f(x) = \dfrac{-h}{x^2 + hx}$.

— 14. If $g(y) = \dfrac{y}{1 - y}$, show that $\tfrac{1}{2}[g(y) + g(-y)] = g(y^2)$.

15. If $F(z) = \log z$, show that $F(xy) = F(x) + F(y)$.

- 16. If $\phi(R) = 2^R$, show that $\phi(R + 1) = 2\phi(R)$.

17. If $P(x) = \sqrt{x}$, show that $P(x + h) - P(x) = \dfrac{h}{\sqrt{x + h} + \sqrt{x}}$.

— 18. If $f(x) = x^2 - 1$ and $g(x) = 2x + 1$, show that $f[g(x)] = 4x(x + 1)$.

— 19. If $f(x) = \dfrac{x}{1 + x}$, show that $f(x) + f(-x) = 2f(-x^2)$.

• 20. If $g(y) = y^2$ and $h(y) = \dfrac{y}{1 - y}$, show that $h(y^2) = \dfrac{g(y)}{1 - g(y)}$.

21. If $Q(x) = 2 \ln x$ and $f(x) = x^{3/2}$, show that $Q[f(x)] = \frac{3}{2}Q(x)$.

• 22. If $f(x) = x^2$, show that $f(x - h) - f(x) = f(h) - 2hx$.

23. If $h(x) = x^{1/3}$, $g(x) = (x^9 + x^6)^{1/2}$, and $Q(x) = x(x + 1)^{1/2}$, show that $g[h(x)] = Q(x)$.

• 24. If $f(y) = \dfrac{y}{1 - y}$ and $g(y) = \dfrac{y}{1 + y}$, show that $f(y) - g(y) = 2f(y^2)$.

25. If $f(y) = \dfrac{1}{1 + y^2}$ and $g(y) = \dfrac{y^2}{1 + y^2}$, show that $f(y) + g(y) + \dfrac{g(y)}{f(y)} = \dfrac{1}{f(y)}$.

26. If $f(x) = \dfrac{x + 2}{x - 2}$, $g(x) = \dfrac{1 + x^2}{x}$, and $h(x) = \dfrac{1 - x}{1 + x}$, show that
$$f[g(x)] = \frac{1}{[h(x)]^2}.$$

• 27. If $f(x) = x - 1$ and $g(x) = \dfrac{1}{x + 1}$, show that $f(x^2)g(x) = f(x)$.

28. If $f(y) = \dfrac{2y}{1 + y}$ and $g(y) = \dfrac{-y}{1 - y}$, show that $f(y)g(y) = f(-y^2)$.

29. Determine for each of the following whether the inverse relation is a function; if it is not, alter the domain of the given function so that its inverse is a function.

(a) $\{(x, y) : y = x^2 + 1\}$ (b) $\{(x, y) : y = 4 - .x^2\}$
(c) $\{(w, z) : z = \sqrt{1 - w^2}\}$ (d) $\{(u, v) : v = |u|\}$

30. For each of the following functions find the inverse function $f^{-1}(x)$ and show that $f[f^{-1}(x)] = f^{-1}[f(x)] = x$.

(a) $f(x) = 3x + 2$ (b) $f(x) = x/(x - 4)$
(c) $f(x) = (x - 2)/(x + 2)$ (d) $f(x) = (x + 3)/x$

• 31. Find $f[g(x)]$ and $g[f(x)]$ for each of the following.
(a) $f(x) = 1/(x - 1)$ and $g(x) = x^2/(x^2 - 1)$
(b) $f(x) = x/(4 - x)$ and $g(x) = x/(x - 4)$
(c) $f(x) = g(x) = (x + 1)/(x - 1)$
(d) $f(x) = \sqrt{x - 1}$ and $g(x) = 1/(x + 1)$

32. If $f(x) = (ax + 1)/(bx - 1)$, find values of a and b such that f is its own inverse—that is, $f[f(x)] = x$.

ANSWERS TO ODD-NUMBERED PROBLEMS

1. (a) $\frac{71}{9}$, (b) 0
3. $(x^3 + 1)^{-1}$
5. $\frac{20}{21}$
7. $(t^2 + 3)^{-1}$

9. e^{ab^2}

11. (a) $\dfrac{1}{1+t^2} e^{1+t^2}$

   (b) $\dfrac{1}{1+t^2 \, e^{2/t}}$

29. (a) inverse a function if $x \geq 0$ or $x \leq 0$
   (b) inverse a function if $x \geq 0$ or $x \leq 0$
   (c) inverse a function if $0 \leq w \leq 1$
   (d) inverse a function if $u \geq 0$ or $u \leq 0$

31. (a) $f[g(x)] = x^2 - 1$; $g[f(x)] = 1/(2x - x^2)$
   (b) $f[g(x)] = x/(3x - 16)$; $g[f(x)] = x/(5x - 16)$
   (c) $f[g(x)] = g[f(x)] = x$
   (d) $f[g(x)] = \sqrt{-x/(x+1)}$; $g[f(x)] = (\sqrt{x-1} - 1)/(x-2)$

1

GRAPHICAL REPRESENTATION

■ 1.1 INTRODUCTION

It is to the French philosopher, René Descartes (1596–1650), that we owe a form of graphic analysis which enables us to plot algebraic equations in terms of geometric curves: to *see* relationships among such variables as price and quantity; direct, indirect, and total cost; savings, investment, and consumption. In addition, much of the theory of calculus can be presented in geometrical terms.

In order to relate algebra and geometry, and thus make possible this dual representation, use is made of a coordinate system which provides a means for locating specific points in a plane or in space. This correspondence may be established in many ways, but the system most commonly used is rectangular coordinates.

■ 1.2 RECTANGULAR COORDINATES

Two straight lines intersecting at right angles are used as lines of reference and a point is located in the plane of these lines by giving its perpendicular direction and distance from each of them. These two distances with signs indicating their directions are the *coordinates* of the point. The lines from which the distances are measured are *coordinate axes*, or (briefly) *axes*. The point of intersection of the axes is the *origin of coordinates*, or (briefly) the *origin*. The coordinate axes divide

19

the plane into four areas or regions called *quadrants*, numbered counterclockwise for reference as shown in Fig. 1.1.

Generally the horizontal line is called the *x-axis* and the vertical line is called the *y-axis*. The choice of positive directions is a matter of convenience and may be changed to simplify particular problems. However, it is customary to consider distances measured to the right of the y-axis as positive and those measured to the left as negative; similarly, it is customary to consider distances measured upward from the x-axis as positive and those measured downward as negative.

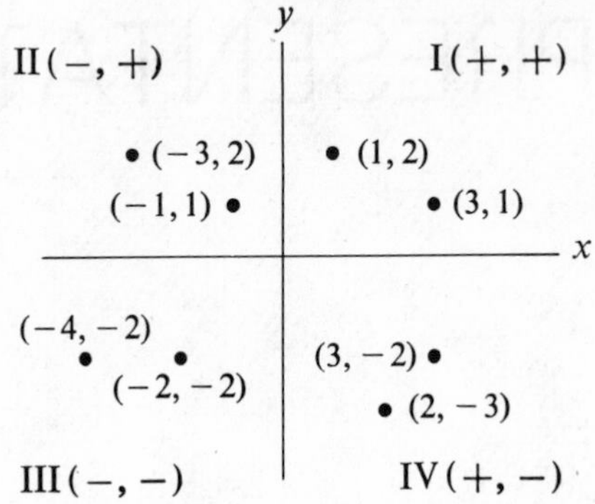

$$y$$

II$(-, +)$ I$(+, +)$

• $(-3, 2)$ • $(1, 2)$

$(-1, 1)$ •   • $(3, 1)$

———————————————— x

$(-4, -2)$

•   •

$(-2, -2)$ $(3, -2)$ •

     • $(2, -3)$

III$(-, -)$ IV$(+, -)$

FIGURE 1.1   The rectangular coordinate system.

Whenever convenient, the same unit of measure or scale is used on both axes when x and y represent variables having the same physical or geometrical characteristics or when they are given abstractly as numbers with no physical interpretation, as is frequently the case in analytic geometry. When the variables are measured in different units (for example, if x is quantity and y is total cost) the units of measure appropriate to the particular problem are used.

The *x-coordinate*, or *abscissa*, of a point is that coordinate which indicates the direction and distance of the point to the right or left of the y-axis; the *y-coordinate*, or *ordinate*, of a point is that coordinate which indicates the direction and distance of the point above or below the x-axis. The position of a point is indicated by writing its coordinates in parentheses in x, y order: (abscissa, ordinate). Locating a point when its coordinates are given is called *plotting* the point.

● **Fundamental Principle**

There is a one-to-one correspondence between number pairs and points in the plane in which they are represented—that is, to each pair of numbers (coordinates) there corresponds one and only one point and, conversely, to each point in the plane there corresponds one and only one pair of numbers. This is the basic convenience in establishing the rectangular coordinate system. The terms *point* and *coordinates of a point* are generally used interchangeably.

□   *SLOPE OF A STRAIGHT LINE*

If a straight line intersects the x-axis, its *angle of inclination* is the angle θ, shown in Fig. 1.2, which is measured counterclockwise from the positive direction of the x-axis to the line and thus is always between 0 and 180°.

If a line is parallel to the x-axis, its angle of inclination θ is defined to be 0°.

The *slope* of a line is the tangent of its angle of inclination and is usually denoted by m.

The *tangent* is one of the six trigonometric functions of an angle; the definition of the slope of a line is equivalent to the definition of the tangent of its angle of inclination. The trigonometric functions of an angle are defined in terms of a right triangle formed by the angle and a perpendicular to its adjacent side.

The tangent of 0° is 0—that is, $\tan 0° = 0$. If $0° < \theta < 180°$, let a line having angle of inclination θ intersect the x-axis at A. From any other point on the line

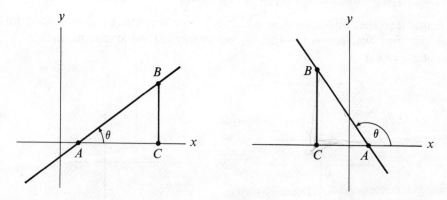

FIGURE 1.2

drop a perpendicular cutting the x-axis at C, as in Fig. 1.2. Now the tangent of θ, denoted $\tan \theta$, is defined by $\tan \theta = \dfrac{CB}{AC}$, where CB and AC are directed distances.

If (x_1, y_1) and (x_2, y_2) are any two distinct points on a straight line, then the slope of the line is

$$m = \tan \theta = \frac{y_2 - y_1}{x_2 - x_1} = \frac{\Delta y}{\Delta x}$$

It is customary, especially in calculus, to use the notation Δy, read delta y, to represent the difference $y_2 - y_1$. This symbol Δy denotes the change in y or the difference between two values of y. Do not think of Δy as delta times y. Similarly, Δx denotes $x_2 - x_1$.

It can be shown, by an argument based on properties of similar triangles, that the slope of a straight line is the same regardless of the two distinct points chosen for calculating it; correspondingly, the tangent of an angle is the same regardless of the point at which the perpendicular intersects the adjacent side, provided the point is not the intersection of the line and the x-axis.

Since

$$\frac{y_2 - y_1}{x_2 - x_1} = \frac{y_1 - y_2}{x_1 - x_2}$$

the slope of a line may be interpreted as the ratio of the directed change in vertical distance to the corresponding directed change in horizontal distance as a point moves along the line in either direction. In some problems (particularly in physics and engineering) $\Delta y = y_2 - y_1$ is called the _rise_ and $\Delta x = x_2 - x_1$ is called the _run_; then the slope is defined as the rise per unit of run—slope $= \dfrac{\text{rise}}{\text{run}} = \dfrac{\Delta y}{\Delta x}$.

If $y_1 = y_2$ and $x_1 \neq x_2$, the line through (x_1, y_1) and (x_2, y_2) is parallel to the x-axis, its angle of inclination θ is zero, and $\tan \theta = \dfrac{\Delta y}{\Delta x} = 0$.

If $x_1 = x_2$ and $y_1 \neq y_2$, the line through (x_1, y_1) and (x_2, y_2) is parallel to the y-axis, its angle of inclination θ is 90°, and $\tan \theta = \dfrac{\Delta y}{\Delta x}$ is undefined (see Fig. 1.3).

(Remember that an expression which involves division by zero is said to be _undefined_ or _indeterminate_—that is, no numerical value can meaningfully be assigned to it.)

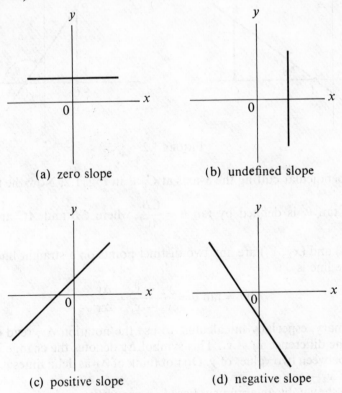

(a) zero slope

(b) undefined slope

(c) positive slope

(d) negative slope

FIGURE 1.3

SUMMARY: SLOPE

The slope of the x-axis is zero.

The slope of the y-axis is undefined.

If a line slopes upward to the right, Δx and Δy have the same sign and $\tan \theta = \dfrac{\Delta y}{\Delta x} > 0$; in this case $0 < \theta < 90°$.

If a line slopes downward to the right, Δx and Δy have opposite signs and $\tan \theta = \dfrac{\Delta y}{\Delta x} < 0$; in this case $90° < \theta < 180°$.

☐ PARALLEL, PERPENDICULAR, AND INTERSECTING LINES

Any two lines in a plane are either parallel or intersecting; lines that intersect at right angles are perpendicular. Two lines that are parallel have equal angles of inclination and therefore have equal slopes, and conversely.

Two lines that are perpendicular have slopes which are the negative reciprocals of each other, and conversely.

Example

The line $2x + 6y - 4 = 0$ has the indicated relationship to each of the following lines (note that $2x + 6y - 4 = 0$ can be written in the form $y = -\frac{1}{3}x + \frac{2}{3}$):

(a) $4x + 12y - 8 = 0$

$$12y = -4x + 8$$
$$y = -\tfrac{1}{3}x + \tfrac{2}{3} \qquad \text{coincident}$$

(b) $-3x + y - 4 = 0$

$$y = 3x + 4 \qquad \text{perpendicular}$$

(c) $x + 3y - 9 = 0$

$$3y = -x + 9$$
$$y = -\tfrac{1}{3}x + 3 \qquad \text{parallel}$$

(d) $2x + y - 4 = 0$

$$y = -2x + 4 \qquad \text{intersecting}$$

■ 1.3 STRAIGHT LINES

The rectangular coordinate system can be used to represent the geometric figures that correspond to equations in two variables (for example, equations in x and y). The geometric figure corresponding to an equation consists of all the points, and only those points, whose coordinates satisfy the equation; in particular, for every straight line in the coordinate plane there is a corresponding linear equation in two variables, and conversely.

An equation of the form

$$Ax + By + C = 0 \qquad (1)$$

where A, B, and C are constants and at least one of A and B is nonzero, is said to be *linear in x and y* and such an equation has a straight line as its geometrical representation. Equation (1) is also referred to as the *general equation of the first degree in two variables*.

The *degree of a variable* is the value of the positive integral power to which the variable is raised. The *degree of a term* of an equation in x and y is the sum of its degrees in x and y; that is, the sum of the powers to which x and y appear in the term. The degree of an equation is the degree of its term of greatest degree. For example, $x^3 + y^4 + 6 + y - 12 = 0$ is a fourth-degree equation; $4x^2 + y^4 + 2x^3y^3 - 21 = 0$ is a sixth-degree equation.

There are two aspects of the problem of correspondence between straight lines and linear equations: (1) given a linear equation, to graph the corresponding line, and (2) given (conditions determining) the line, to find the corresponding linear equation.

The coordinates x and y of every point (x, y) on a given line satisfy the equation corresponding to the line; conversely, the straight line that passes through all the points, and *only* through those points, whose coordinates satisfy the equation is called the *graph* or *locus* of the equation. However, since there are an infinite number of points on any given line or curve, establishing correspondence between algebraic equations and their geometrical representations point by point is clearly not feasible; it is the purpose of analytic geometry to develop methods using a minimum number of points for establishing this correspondence. In general, the more simple the algebraic equation (and thus its corresponding graph) the fewer points necessary for establishing meaningful correspondence.

A straight line, the simplest geometric curve, may be given uniquely by either of the following: (1) two points which lie on it, or (2) one point which lies on it and its slope.

One easy way to graph a straight line is to compute its intercepts. The *intercepts* of a line are the points where the line crosses the axes. Thus the *y-intercept* is the point determined by setting $x = 0$ in the equation of the line; similarly, the *x-intercept* is the point determined by setting $y = 0$ in the equation of the line.

Example

Graph the line $4x + 5y - 20 = 0$.

y-intercept	*x-intercept*
$x = 0$	$y = 0$
$4(0) + 5y - 20 = 0$	$4x + 5(0) - 20 = 0$
$5y = 20$	$4x = 20$
$y = 4$	$x = 5$
Intercept $(0, 4)$	Intercept $(5, 0)$

The intercepts may then be plotted and the line drawn through them, as shown in Fig. 1.4. As a check for accuracy, a third point is sometimes plotted as well. For example: Let $y = 2$.

$$4x + 5(2) - 20 = 0$$
$$4x - 10 = 0$$
$$x = \tfrac{10}{4} = \tfrac{5}{2}$$

The point is then (5/2, 2).

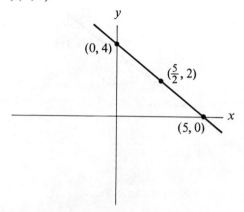

FIGURE 1.4

Depending upon the conditions that are given to determine a line, different formulas are more convenient for obtaining its equation. These formulas are all equivalent to the general equation for a straight line,

$$Ax + By + C = 0$$

and are generally easily transformed into it and into each other.

- **Two-Point Form**

One of the fundamental properties of a straight line is its constant slope; the slope can be determined using any two distinct points on a straight line. These two facts can be used to develop formulas for obtaining the equations of non-vertical straight lines as follows.

If (x_1, y_1) and (x_2, y_2) are two distinct points on a nonvertical straight line, then the slope m of the line is given by

$$m = \frac{y_2 - y_1}{x_2 - x_1}$$

If (x, y) is any other point (that is, a general point) on the straight line, then it and the point (x_1, y_1) can also be used to determine the slope m of the line,

$$m = \frac{y - y_1}{x - x_1}$$

and, since the slope is constant

$$\frac{y - y_1}{x - x_1} = \frac{y_2 - y_1}{x_2 - x_1}$$

or

$$y - y_1 = \frac{y_2 - y_1}{x_2 - x_1}(x - x_1) \qquad (1a)$$

See Fig. 1.5, noting that the labeling of the points is arbitrary and may be chosen for convenience.

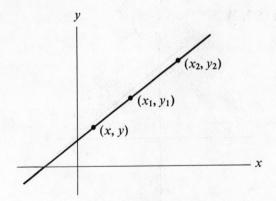

FIGURE 1.5

Equation (1a), referred to as the *two-point form* for a straight line, is generally most convenient for determining the equation of a straight line when two of its points are given.

Example

Find the equation of the line passing through the points (3, 4) and (−5, 2).

$$(x_1, y_1) = (3, 4) \qquad (x_2, y_2) = (-5, 2)$$

$$y - y_1 = \frac{y_2 - y_1}{x_2 - x_1}(x - x_1)$$

$$y - 4 = \left(\frac{2 - 4}{-5 - 3}\right)(x - 3)$$

$$y - 4 = \tfrac{1}{4}(x - 3)$$

$$x - 4y + 13 = 0$$

Check: Insert (3, 4) in $x - 4y + 13 = 0$:

$$3 - 4(4) + 13 = 0$$

$$0 = 0$$

Insert (−5, 2) in $x - 4y + 13 = 0$:

$$-5 - 4(2) + 13 = 0$$

$$0 = 0$$

● **Point-Slope Form**

Since the slope of a nonvertical line $m = \dfrac{y_2 - y_1}{x_2 - x_1}$, equation (1a) can be written

points-slope form

$$y - y_1 = m(x - x_1) \tag{1b}$$

Equation (1b), referred to as the *point-slope form* for a straight line, is generally most convenient for determining the equation of a straight line when one of the points on a line and its slope are given.

Example

Find the equation of the line passing through the point $(-1, 2)$ and having slope -4.

$$(x_1, y_1) = (-1, 2) \qquad m = -4$$
$$y - y_1 = m(x - x_1)$$
$$y - 2 = -4(x + 1)$$
$$= -4x - 4$$
$$4x + y + 2 = 0$$

Check: $m = -4$ in $4x + y + 2 = 0$. Insert $(-1, 2)$ in $4x + y + 2 = 0$:
$$-1(4) + 2 + 2 = 0$$
$$0 = 0$$

● **Slope-intercept Form**

For the special case when the point (x_1, y_1) is the y-intercept, denoted by $(0, b)$, equation (1b) can be written

$$\boxed{y = mx + b} \qquad \qquad (1c)$$

Equation (1c), referred to as the *slope-intercept form* for a straight line, is generally most convenient for determining the equation of a straight line when its y-intercept and slope are given.

Example

Find the equation of the line having y-intercept $(0, 5)$ and slope 3.
$$b = 5 \qquad m = 3$$
$$y = mx + b$$
$$= 3x + 5$$
$$3x - y + 5 = 0$$

Check: $m = 3$ in $3x - y + 5 = 0$. Insert $(0, 5)$ in $3x - y + 5 = 0$:
$$3(0) - 5 + 5 = 0$$
$$0 = 0$$

● **Intercept Form**

For the special case when the point (x_1, y_1) is the y-intercept, denoted by $(0, b)$, where $b \neq 0$, and the point (x_2, y_2) is the x-intercept, denoted by $(a, 0)$, where $a \neq 0$, then equation (1a) can be written

$$y - b = \frac{-b}{a}(x - 0)$$

$$\frac{y}{b} - 1 = -\frac{x}{a}$$

$$\boxed{\frac{x}{a} + \frac{y}{b} = 1}$$ (1d)

Equation (1d), referred to as the *intercept form* for a straight line, is generally most convenient for determining the equation of a straight line when its two intercepts are given.

Example

Find the equation of the line having intercepts $(0, -6)$ and $(4, 0)$.

$$b = -6 \qquad a = 4$$

$$\frac{x}{a} + \frac{y}{b} = 1$$

$$\frac{x}{4} + \frac{y}{-6} = 1$$

Multiplying by the lowest common denominator 12,

$$3x - 2y = 12$$
$$3x - 2y - 12 = 0$$

Check: Insert $(0, -6)$ in $3x - 2y - 12 = 0$:
$$3(0) - 2(-6) - 12 = 0$$
$$0 = 0$$

Insert $(4, 0)$ in $3x - 2y - 12 = 0$:
$$3(12) - 2(0) - 12 = 0$$
$$0 = 0$$

● **Vertical Lines**

Since the slope of a vertical line is undefined, the above formulas are not appropriate for obtaining the equations of vertical lines. A vertical line passing through the point (x_1, y_1) has the equation $x = x_1$.

Example

Find the equation of the vertical line passing through the point $(5, -4)$.

$$x = x_1 = 5$$

● **Horizontal Lines**

Since a horizontal line has zero slope, its equation may be obtained from the two-point, point-slope, or slope-intercept form. A horizontal line passing through the point (x_1, y_1) has the equation $y = y_1$.

horizontal line has equation $y = y_1$

Example

Find the equation of the horizontal line passing through the point $(-3, -2)$.
$$y = y_1 = -2$$

SUMMARY: STRAIGHT LINES

General form: $Ax + By + C = 0$

Two-point form: $y - y_1 = \dfrac{y_2 - y_1}{x_2 - x_1}(x - x_1)$

Point-slope form: $y - y_1 = m(x - x_1)$

Slope-intercept form: $y = mx + b$

Intercept form: $\dfrac{x}{a} + \dfrac{y}{b} = 1$

Vertical lines: $x = x_1$

Horizontal lines: $y = y_1$

slope $m = \dfrac{-A}{B}$

perpendicular = $m_1 m_2 = -1$

☐ **INTERSECTION OF TWO STRAIGHT LINES**

The coordinates of the point of intersection of two straight lines must satisfy the equations of both lines. Therefore, the point of intersection of two non-parallel lines can be found by solving their equations simultaneously.

The geometric property that two lines intersect corresponds to the algebraic condition that their equations be *independent* and *consistent*, and therefore have a *simultaneous solution*.

Consider two linear equations written in the form
$$A_1 x + B_1 y + C_1 = 0 \qquad A_2 x + B_2 y + C_2 = 0$$
where A_1, A_2, B_1, B_2, C_1, and C_2 are positive or negative constants.

● **Independent Equations**

These equations are *independent* if one cannot be obtained from the other by multiplication by a nonzero constant—that is, they are independent if the equality $\dfrac{A_1}{A_2} = \dfrac{B_1}{B_2} = \dfrac{C_1}{C_2}$ does not hold. If the equality does hold, the equations are *dependent*.

NOTE: Two equations that are dependent are equivalent—that is, they represent the same line and have the same graph, since any point that lies on one of the equations lies on the other also.

Example

The equations

$$3x + 5y + 10 = 0 \qquad 6x + 10y + 20 = 0$$

are dependent or equivalent, since the second equation is obtained by multiplying the first equation by 2; they have the same straight line as their graph.

● **Consistent Equations**

Equations are said to be *consistent* if they can hold simultaneously—that is, they are consistent if $\dfrac{A_1}{A_2} = \dfrac{B_1}{B_2} = \dfrac{C_1}{C_2}$ holds or if $\dfrac{A_1}{A_2} \neq \dfrac{B_1}{B_2}$. If $\dfrac{A_1}{A_2} = \dfrac{B_1}{B_2} = \dfrac{C_1}{C_2}$, the lines coincide and the equations are both consistent and dependent. If $\dfrac{A_1}{A_2} \neq \dfrac{B_1}{B_2}$, the lines have different slopes and thus intersect at just one point; such lines are consistent and independent. Two linear equations that are *inconsistent*—that is, not consistent—have parallel lines as their graphs.

Example

The equations

$$3x + 5y + 10 = 0 \qquad 6x + 10y + 15 = 0$$

are inconsistent (since $\frac{3}{6} = \frac{5}{10} \neq \frac{10}{15}$) and cannot both hold simultaneously; they have parallel lines as their graphs.

Note that the equations $A_1 x + B_1 y + C_1 = 0$ and $A_2 x + B_2 y + C_2 = 0$ can be written

$$y = \frac{A_1}{B_1} x + \frac{C_1}{B_1}$$

and

$$y = \frac{A_2}{B_2} x + \frac{C_2}{B_2}$$

Thus if $\dfrac{A_1}{A_2} = \dfrac{B_1}{B_2}$, the lines have the same slope. If $\dfrac{B_1}{B_2} = \dfrac{C_1}{C_2}$, the lines have the same intercept. If $\dfrac{A_1}{A_2} = \dfrac{B_1}{B_2} = \dfrac{C_1}{C_2}$, the lines have the same slope and the same intercept and are identical.

A point is said to be a *simultaneous solution* of two equations if its coordinates satisfy both equations; geometrically, two lines intersect (or coincide) at a point which is their simultaneous solution. Two straight lines have a unique simultaneous solution if they are intersecting (consistent and independent), no simultaneous solution if they are parallel (inconsistent), and infinitely many simultaneous solutions if they are coincident (consistent and dependent). These cases are illustrated in Fig. 1.6.

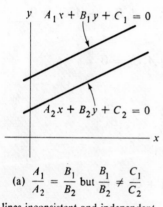

(a) $\dfrac{A_1}{A_2} = \dfrac{B_1}{B_2}$ but $\dfrac{B_1}{B_2} \neq \dfrac{C_1}{C_2}$

lines inconsistent and independent

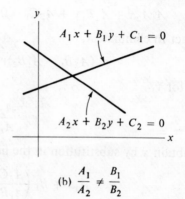

(b) $\dfrac{A_1}{A_2} \neq \dfrac{B_1}{B_2}$

lines consistent and independent

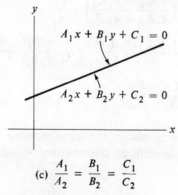

(c) $\dfrac{A_1}{A_2} = \dfrac{B_1}{B_2} = \dfrac{C_1}{C_2}$

lines consistent and dependent

FIGURE 1.6

Usually two linear equations can quite easily be solved simultaneously by elimination or substitution; in some cases the method of determinants (to be discussed in detail later) provides the solution more readily. To solve the equations

$$A_1 x + B_1 y + C_1 = 0 \qquad A_2 x + B_2 y + C_2 = 0$$

by *elimination*, multiply the first equation by A_2 and the second equation by A_1, subtract to eliminate x, solve for y, and obtain x by substitution in either equation.

(Alternatively, multiply the equations by B_2 and B_1, respectively, and eliminate y.)

To solve by *substitution*, obtain x in terms of y (or, alternatively, y in terms of x) from one equation, substitute in the other equation, and solve.

By either of these methods or, more directly, by the *method of determinants*, the solutions for x and y are

$$x = \frac{B_1 C_2 - B_2 C_1}{A_1 B_2 - A_2 B_1} \qquad y = \frac{A_2 C_1 - A_1 C_2}{A_1 B_2 - A_2 B_1}$$

provided $A_1 B_2 - A_2 B_1 \neq 0$.

For example, following the procedure for solution by elimination outlined above, multiply the first equation by A_2 and the second equation by A_1:

$$A_1 A_2 x + A_2 B_1 y + A_2 C_1 = 0 \qquad A_1 A_2 x + A_1 B_2 y + A_1 C_2 = 0$$

subtract to eliminate x,

$$(A_2 B_1 - A_1 B_2) y + A_2 C_1 - A_1 C_2 = 0$$

solve for y,

$$y = \frac{A_2 C_1 - A_1 C_2}{A_1 B_2 - A_2 B_1}$$

and obtain x by substitution in the first equation

$$A_1 x + B_1 \left(\frac{A_2 C_1 - A_1 C_2}{A_1 B_2 - A_2 B_1} \right) + C_1 = 0$$

$$x = \frac{B_1}{A_1} \left(\frac{A_2 C_1 - A_1 C_2}{A_1 B_2 - A_2 B_1} \right) - \frac{C_1}{A_1}$$

$$= \frac{-A_2 B_1 C_1 + A_1 B_1 C_2 - A_1 B_2 C_1 + A_2 B_1 C_1}{A_1 (A_1 B_2 - A_2 B_1)}$$

$$= \frac{B_1 C_2 - B_2 C_1}{A_1 B_2 - A_2 B_1}$$

In many cases it is easier to obtain the simultaneous solution for a particular pair of linear equations directly by elimination or substitution rather than by these formulas.

Examples

Find the point of intersection of the lines represented by the equations

$$3x - 4y + 6 = 0 \qquad x - 2y - 3 = 0$$

(see FIG. 1.7)

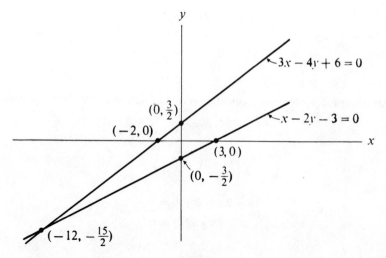

$$3x - 4y + 6 = 0$$

$$x - 2y - 3 = 0$$

$\left(0, \frac{3}{2}\right)$

$(-2, 0)$

$(3, 0)$

$\left(0, -\frac{3}{2}\right)$

$\left(-12, -\frac{15}{2}\right)$

FIGURE 1.7

Eliminating the x-term by multiplying the second equation by -3 and adding it to the first equation,

$$3x - 4y + 6 = 0$$
$$-3x + 6y + 9 = 0$$
$$2y + 15 = 0$$
$$2y = -15$$
$$y = -\tfrac{15}{2}$$

Substituting $y = -\tfrac{15}{2}$ in the first equation,

$$3x - 4(-\tfrac{15}{2}) + 6 = 0$$
$$3x + 30 + 6 = 0$$
$$3x = -36$$
$$x = -12$$

Answer: $(-12, -\tfrac{15}{2})$.

Check: Equation 1: $\quad 3(-12) - 4(-\tfrac{15}{2}) + 6 = 0$

$$-36 + 30 + 6 = 0$$
$$0 = 0$$

Equation 2: $\quad -12 - 2(-\tfrac{15}{2}) - 3 = 0$

$$-12 + 15 - 3 = 0$$
$$0 = 0$$

Alternatively, substituting for x obtained from the second equation in the first equation:

$$x = 2y + 3$$
$$3(2y + 3) - 4y + 6 = 0$$

$$6y + 9 - 4y + 6 = 0$$
$$2y + 15 = 0$$
$$2y = -15$$
$$y = -\tfrac{15}{2}$$

Substituting for y obtained from the second equation in the first equation:

$$y = \frac{x - 3}{2}$$

$$3x - 4\left(\frac{x - 3}{2}\right) + 6 = 0$$

$$3x - 2x + 6 + 6 = 0$$

$$x + 12 = 0$$

$$x = -12$$

Answer: $(-12, -\tfrac{15}{2})$, as above.

Using the formulas

$$x = \frac{B_1 C_2 - B_2 C_1}{A_1 B_2 - A_2 B_1} \qquad y = \frac{A_2 C_1 - A_1 C_2}{A_1 B_2 - A_2 B_1}$$

$$A_1 = 3, \quad B_1 = -4, \quad C_1 = 6 \qquad A_2 = 1, \quad B_2 = -2, \quad C_2 = -3$$

$$x = \frac{(-4)(-3) - (-2)(6)}{(3)(-2) - (1)(-4)}$$

$$= \frac{12 + 12}{-6 + 4} = \frac{24}{-2} = -12$$

$$y = \frac{(1)(6) - (3)(-3)}{(3)(-2) - (1)(-4)}$$

$$= \frac{6 + 9}{-6 + 4} = \frac{15}{-2}$$

Answer: $(-12, -\tfrac{15}{2})$, as above.

These equations are consistent and independent and have a **unique simultaneous** solution, the point $(-12, -\tfrac{15}{2})$.

Find the point of intersection of the lines represented by the equations

$$2x - 3y + 1 = 0 \qquad 4x - 6y + 12 = 0$$

Multiplying the first equation by 2 and rewriting the second equation,

$$4x - 6y + 2 = 0 \qquad 4x - 6y + 12 = 0$$

(see Fig. 1.8). These equations are inconsistent and do not have a simultaneous solution; they are represented by parallel lines.

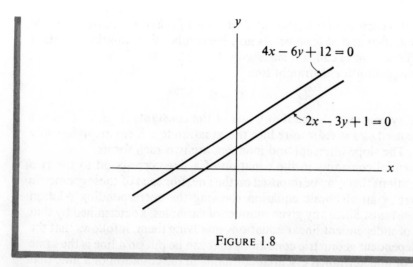

FIGURE 1.8

Find the point of intersection of the lines represented by the equations

$$2x - 3y + 1 = 0 \qquad 4x - 6y + 2 = 0$$

Multiplying the first equation by 2 and rewriting the second equation,

$$4x - 6y + 2 = 0 \qquad 4x - 6y + 2 = 0$$

(see Fig. 1.9). These equations are dependent and therefore equivalent and have

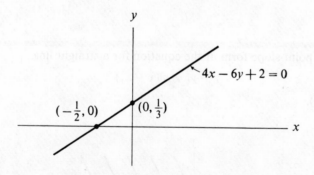

FIGURE 1.9

infinitely many simultaneous solutions; they are represented by the same straight line, every point of which is a simultaneous solution of the equations.

□ *FAMILIES OF LINES*

An important concept in both theoretical and applied mathematics is that of a family of straight lines or curves. The members of a family possess some geometric property (such as passing through a given point) in common, but differ in at least one other geometric property (such as having different slopes).

def'n of
parameter

Algebraically, this corresponds to the fact that some of the constants in a general equation are specified and at least one is not. Remember that an arbitrary (that is, unspecified) constant is called a *parameter*.

The general equation for a straight line

$$Ax + By + C = 0$$

has two arbitrary constants, since if any one of the constants A, B, or C is not zero, it may be used as a divisor to reduce the equation to a form involving only two constants. The slope intercept and intercept are two such forms.

The two essential constants in the equation of a line correspond to the two geometric conditions that may be imposed on the line. For each of these geometric conditions there is an algebraic equation showing the corresponding relation between the constants. Since any given number of variables is determined by that same number of independent linear equations involving them, it follows that the number of independent geometric conditions that can be put on a line is the same as the number of undetermined essential constants in the equation of a line, that is, two.

The general equation $Ax + By + C = 0$ with two essential parameters represents all lines in the plane. When one of the two constants is specified and the other is unspecified (that is, remains a parameter) a family of lines—such as all lines of a given slope, or all lines passing through a particular point—is represented by the equation. When both constants are specified, one particular line is represented by the equation.

Examples

Consider the point-slope form of the equation for a straight line

$$y - y_1 = m(x - x_1)$$

(see Fig. 1.10).

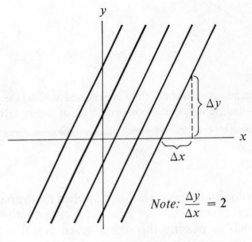

$$\Delta y$$

$$\Delta x$$

Note: $\dfrac{\Delta y}{\Delta x} = 2$

FIGURE 1.10

The two essential constants are expressed in this form of the equation as the slope m and the point (x_1, y_1). Suppose the condition that it is to have slope 2 is imposed on the line. This geometric condition corresponds to the algebraic equation

$$y - y_1 = 2(x - x_1)$$

The family of lines represented by this equation consists of an infinite number of lines parallel to each other and all having slope 2.

One further condition can be imposed on the line: Geometrically, a point through which it is to pass can be specified (as a special case, this point could be either the x-intercept or the y-intercept); algebraically, a pair of constant values can be assigned to the coordinates (x_1, y_1) (see Fig. 1.11). Suppose it is specified

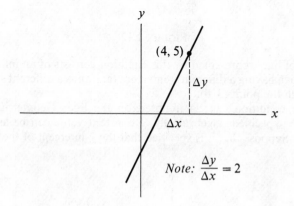

FIGURE 1.11

that the line is to pass through the point $(4, 5)$, that is, $(x_1, y_1) = (4, 5)$. Now a particular line is specified by the equation

$$y - 5 = 2(x - 4) \qquad \text{or} \qquad 2x - y - 3 = 0$$

which is obtained from the equations

$$m = 2 \qquad (x_1, y_1) = (4, 5)$$

corresponding to the imposed geometric conditions; this line has slope 2 and passes through the point $(4, 5)$.

Consider the intercept form of the equation for a straight line,

$$\frac{x}{a} + \frac{y}{b} = 1$$

(see Fig. 1.12).

The two essential constants are expressed in this form of the equation as the x-intercept $(a, 0)$ and the y-intercept $(0, b)$. Suppose the condition that it is to have the x-intercept $(3, 0)$ is imposed on the line. This geometric condition corresponds to the algebraic equation

$$\frac{x}{3} + \frac{y}{b} = 1$$

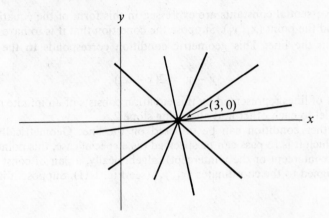

FIGURE 1.12

The family of lines represented by this equation consists of an infinite number of members, each having a different y-intercept (and thus a different slope) but all passing through the point $(3, 0)$.

One further condition can be imposed on the line: Geometrically, the y-intercept can be specified; algebraically, a constant value can be assigned to b (see Fig. 1.13). Suppose that it is specified that the y-intercept of the line is to be

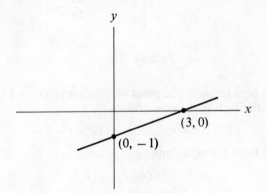

FIGURE 1.13

$(0, -1)$, that is, $b = -1$. Now a particular line is specified by the equation

$$\frac{x}{3} + \frac{y}{-1} = 1$$

or

$$x + \frac{3y}{-1} = 3$$

$$-x + 3y = -3$$

$$3y = x - 3$$

$$y = \frac{x - 3}{3}$$

$$x - 3y - 3 = 0$$

which is obtained from the two equations

$$a = 3 \qquad b = -1$$

corresponding to the imposed geometric conditions; this line has the x-intercept 3 and the y-intercept -1.

The idea of a general equation representing a large (frequently infinite) class of straight lines or curves and the specification of subclasses of this general class (that is, families) by imposing certain geometric (and therefore corresponding algebraic) conditions on the lines or curves is very useful in both theoretical and applied mathematics.

PROBLEMS

1. (a) Which of the following points lie on the line $3x + 4y - 10 = 0$?
   (i) $(1, 2)$ (ii) $(-2, 4)$
   (iii) $(10, -5)$ (iv) $(-25, 21)$
   (v) $(0, 0)$ (vi) $(\frac{22}{9}, \frac{2}{3})$
   (b) Graph the line indicating points above which lie on it.

2. For each of the following equations,
   (i) Graph using intercepts.
   (ii) Put into slope-intercept form.
   (iii) Put into intercept form—this form is inappropriate for one of the equations; which one and why?
   (a) $4y - 3x = 12$ (b) $5x - y = 10$
   (c) $2y + 3x + 2 = 0$ (d) $x - 3y = 0$

3. What relation (parallel, perpendicular, coincident, or intersecting) does the line $3x + 4y - 2 = 0$ have to each of the following lines?
   (a) $15x + 20y - 10 = 0$ (b) $8x - 6y + 5 = 0$
   (c) $9x + 12y + 7 = 0$ (d) $3x + y - 4 = 0$
   (e) $12x - 9y + 2 = 0$ (f) $2x + y - 6 = 0$

4. For each of the following pairs of points,
   (i) Find the slope of the line through the two points.
   (ii) Find the equation of the line using the slope.
   (iii) Find the equation of the line without using the slope.
   (iv) Graph the line.
   (a) $(0, 0)$ and $(6, 3)$ (b) $(\frac{10}{3}, 0)$ and $(0, \frac{5}{2})$
   (c) $(-7, 4)$ and $(8, 4)$ (d) $(3, -2)$ and $(3, 5)$
   (e) $(-1, -2)$ and $(4, 1)$ (f) $(-2, -3)$ and $(-5, -6)$

5. Find the equation of the line through the point $(3, -2)$ and perpendicular to the line through the points $(-1, -3)$ and $(3, 7)$.

6. Find the equation of the line through the point $(4, 3)$ and parallel to the line through the points $(0, -3)$ and $(6, 1)$.

7. Find the equation of the line through the point $(5, 15)$ and parallel to the line $y = x + 25$. What relation (parallel, perpendicular, coincident, or intersecting) does this line have to the line through the two points $(6, 0)$ and $(-2, 8)$?

8. Find the equation of the line which has intercept $(0, -3)$ and is perpendicular to the line through the points $(-2, -1)$ and $(2, 5)$.

9. Find the equation of the line which is parallel to the line through the points $(5, 6)$ and $(7, 8)$ and also passes through the intersection of the line having slope -2 through the point $(-4, -6)$ and the line having slope 3 through the point $(2, 2)$.

10. What relation (parallel, perpendicular, coincident, or intersecting) does the line $y - 2x - 4 = 0$ have to the following lines?
    (a) $y - x - 2 = 0$ (b) $4y - 8x - 16 = 0$
    (c) $5y - 10x - 4 = 0$ (d) $y - 3x - 4 = 0$
    (e) $2y + x - 6 = 0$

ANSWERS TO ODD-NUMBERED PROBLEMS

---

1. (ii), (iii), (vi)

3. (a) coincident
   (b) perpendicular
   (c) parallel
   (d) intersecting
   (e) perpendicular
   (f) intersecting

5. $2x + 5y + 4 = 0$

7. $x - y + 10 = 0$
   perpendicular

9. $x - y - 8 = 0$

■ 1.4 APPLICATIONS OF STRAIGHT LINES IN BUSINESS AND ECONOMICS

□ LINEAR DEMAND AND SUPPLY CURVES

In practice, some demand and supply equations are approximately linear for the relevant range; others are not linear. Even in the latter cases, linear equations may provide reasonably accurate representations of supply and demand for a limited range. In this section linear demand and supply equations are used for simplicity and clarity in illustrating certain types of analyses. Nonlinear equations are discussed in subsequent sections.

Figure 1.14(a) shows a more general representation of supply and demand curves. Figure 1.14(b) represents supply and demand as linear functions. It should be noted, as indicated in Fig. 1.14, that only the segments of the equations which fall in the first quadrant are pertinent to economic analysis. This is because supply, price, and quantity are, in general, either zero or positive. For example, in simpler forms of economic analysis:

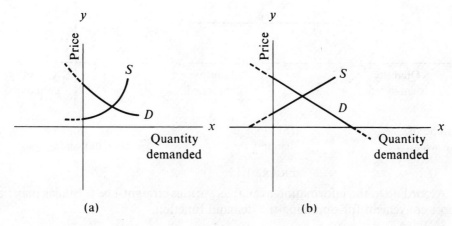

(a)   (b)

FIGURE 1.14

Negative supply implies that goods are not available in the market either because they are not produced or because they are withheld until a satisfactory price is offered.

Negative price implies that prices are paid to buyers for the removal of goods from the market.

Negative quantity demanded implies that price is so high as to preclude market activity until quantities are offered at a satisfactory price.

These cases can occur, but their incidence is infrequent and is considered only in more advanced economic analysis.

It is very important to realize that the straight line, mathematically, is perfectly general; the formulas for a straight line do not indicate the range of values of x and y which are to be considered. When it is specified, as it is for the present purpose, that only zero or positive values of x and y are of interest—and conversely, that negative prices or quantities are not meaningful—the range of values for x and y is restricted. These restrictions are based on the interpretation and meaning of the equation for a *particular application*; they are *not* based on its inherent mathematical properties. This must be kept in mind to avoid misinterpretations, particularly when more complicated equations are considered.

● **Linear Demand Curves**

In the usual case, the slope of a demand curve is negative—that is, as price increases, quantity demanded decreases, and as price decreases, quantity demanded increases. In certain cases, the slope of a demand curve may be zero—constant price regardless of demand. In other cases, the slope of a demand curve may be undefined—constant demand regardless of price. Figure 1.15 illustrates these three cases.

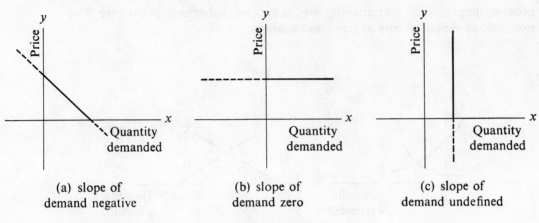

(a) slope of demand negative

(b) slope of demand zero

(c) slope of demand undefined

FIGURE 1.15

According to the information available, various straight-line formulas may be most convenient for obtaining the demand function.

Examples

10 watches are sold when the price is \$80; 20 watches are sold when the price is \$60. What is the demand equation?

$$y - y_1 = \frac{y_2 - y_1}{x_2 - x_1}(x - x_1)$$

$$x_1 = 10 \qquad y_1 = 80$$

$$x_2 = 20 \qquad y_2 = 60$$

$$y - 80 = \left(\frac{60 - 80}{20 - 10}\right)(x - 10)$$

$$= -2(x - 10)$$

$$2x + y - 100 = 0$$

(See Fig. 1.16.)

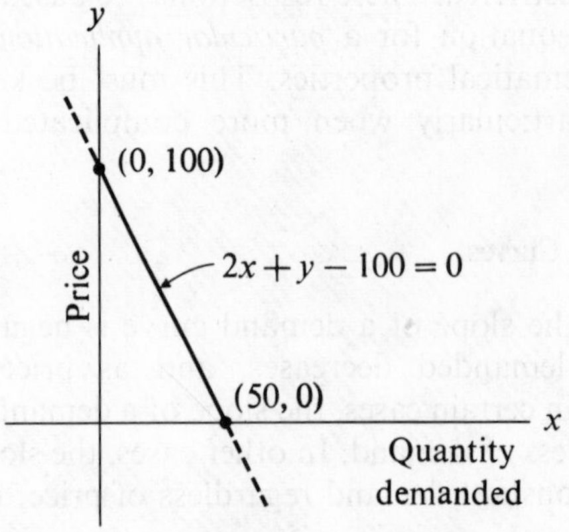

(0, 100)

$2x + y - 100 = 0$

(50, 0)

Quantity demanded

FIGURE 1.16

When the price is \$100, no watches are sold; when watches are free, 50 are demanded. What is the demand equation?

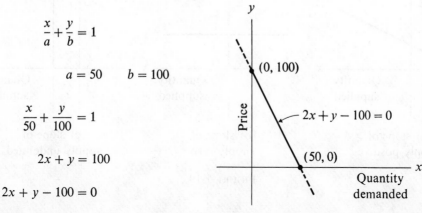

$$\frac{x}{a} + \frac{y}{b} = 1$$

$$a = 50 \qquad b = 100$$

$$\frac{x}{50} + \frac{y}{100} = 1$$

$$2x + y = 100$$

$$2x + y - 100 = 0$$

(See Fig. 1.17.)

FIGURE 1.17

Because they are considered necessary for national security 50 heavy-duty generators are bought every year, regardless of price. What is the demand equation?

$$x = x_1 = 50$$

(See Fig. 1.18.)

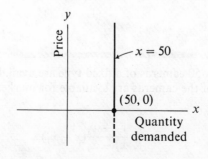

FIGURE 1.18

● **Linear Supply Curves**

In the usual case, the slope of the supply curve is positive—that is, as the price increases, quantity supplied increases and as price decreases, quantity supplied decreases. In certain cases, the slope of a supply curve may be zero—constant price regardless of supply. In other cases, the slope of a supply curve may be undefined—constant supply regardless of price (see Fig. 1.19).

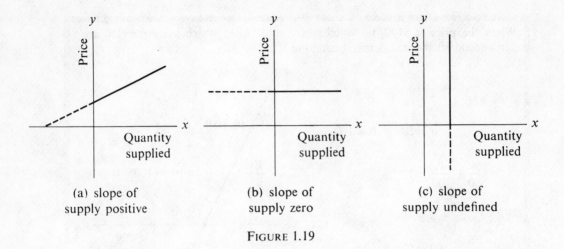

(a) slope of
supply positive

(b) slope of
supply zero

(c) slope of
supply undefined

FIGURE 1.19

As in the discussion of demand curves, y represents the price, in appropriate units, and x represents the quantity supplied, in appropriate units. Only positive values of x and y are of interest, as previously stated. Note that for the supply curve in case (a) the y-coordinate of the y-intercept may be positive, negative, or zero.

The x-coordinate of the x-intercept may be negative and, therefore, outside the range of values of interest. This is reasonable, since producers usually cease to supply a commodity before the price reaches zero.

Examples

When the price is \$50, 50 cameras of a fixed type are available for market; when the price is \$75, 100 of the cameras are available for market. What is the supply equation?

$$y - y_1 = \frac{y_2 - y_1}{x_2 - x_1}(x - x_1)$$

$$x_1 = 50 \qquad y_1 = 50$$

$$x_2 = 100 \qquad y_2 = 75$$

$$y - 50 = \left(\frac{75 - 50}{100 - 50}\right)(x - 50)$$

$$= \tfrac{1}{2}(x - 50)$$

$$x - 2y + 50 = 0$$

(See Fig. 1.20.)

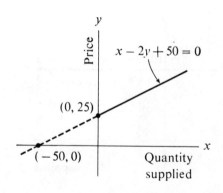

FIGURE 1.20

When the price is \$25, no cameras of a fixed type are available for market; for every \$10 increase in price, 20 more cameras are available for market. What is the supply equation?

$$y = mx + b \qquad m = \tfrac{1}{2} \qquad b = 25$$

$$y = \tfrac{1}{2}x + 25$$

$$x - 2y + 50 = 0$$

(See Fig. 1.21.)

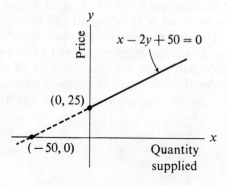

FIGURE 1.21

According to the terms of the contract between Company A and the telephone company, Company A pays the telephone company \$500 per month for long-distance calls of unlimited length of time. What is the supply equation?

$$y = y_1 = 500$$

(See Fig. 1.22.)

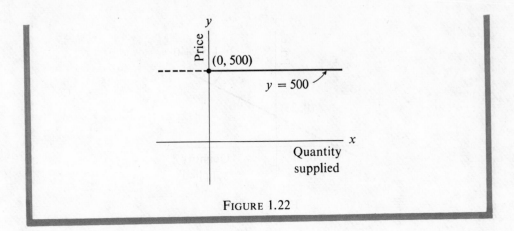

FIGURE 1.22

● Market Equilibrium

Market equilibrium is said to occur at that point (price) at which the quantity of a commodity demanded is equal to the quantity supplied, as in Fig. 1.23. Thus, provided the same units for x and y are used in both equations, the equilibrium amount and the equilibrium price correspond to the coordinates of the point of intersection of the demand and supply curves. Algebraically, the equilibrium amount and price are found by solving the supply and demand equations simultaneously (again, provided the same units for x and y are used in both equations).

In general, for an equilibrium to be meaningful, the values of both x and y must be positive or zero—that is, the demand and supply curves must intersect in the first quadrant. This occurs if and only if the y-coordinate of the y-intercept of the demand curve is greater than or equal to the y-coordinate of the y-intercept of the supply curve and the x-coordinate of the x-intercept of the demand curve is greater than or equal to the x-coordinate of the x-intercept of the supply curve. This can be seen geometrically in Fig. 1.23; the proof is given in Technical Note I.

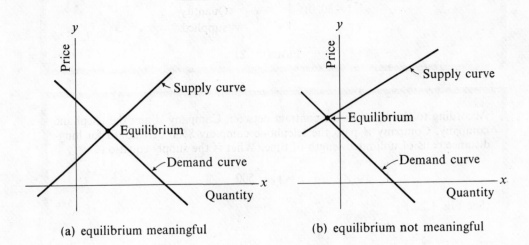

(a) equilibrium meaningful   (b) equilibrium not meaningful

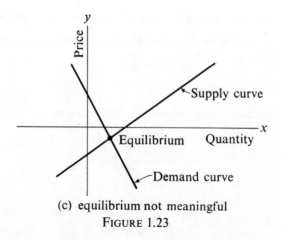

(c) equilibrium not meaningful

FIGURE 1.23

Examples

Find the point of equilibrium for the following demand and supply equations.

$$y = 10 - 2x$$

$$y = \tfrac{3}{2}x + 1$$

Solving the equations simultaneously by substitution,

$$10 - 2x = \tfrac{3}{2}x + 1$$

$$\tfrac{7}{2}x = 9$$

$$x = \tfrac{18}{7}$$

$$y = 10 - 2(\tfrac{18}{7})$$

$$= \tfrac{34}{7}$$

Answer: $(\tfrac{18}{7}, \tfrac{34}{7})$.
(See Fig. 1.24.)

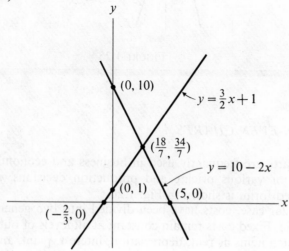

FIGURE 1.24

Find the point of equilibrium for the following demand and supply equations.

$$y = 5 - 3x$$

$$y = 4x + 12$$

Solving the equations simultaneously by substitution,

$$5 - 3x = 4x + 12$$

$$7x = -7$$

$$x = -1$$

$$y = 5 - 3(-1)$$

$$= 8$$

Answer: $(-1, 8)$ not meaningful equilibrium—note that $b_D = 5 < b_S = 12$. (See Fig. 1.25.)

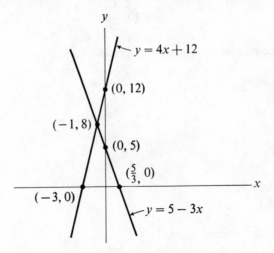

FIGURE 1.25

☐ BREAK-EVEN CHARTS

Break-even charts are frequently used in business and economics to analyze the implications of various pricing and production decisions. A break-even chart, in simplified form, is shown in Fig. 1.26.

In this particular case, costs have been divided into two general categories: fixed and variable. Fixed costs remain constant at all levels of output and commonly include such items as rent, depreciation, interest, plant, and equipment; variable costs are those which vary with output and include such items as labor, materials, and promotional expense. Total cost at any level of output is the sum of fixed cost and the variable cost at that level of output.

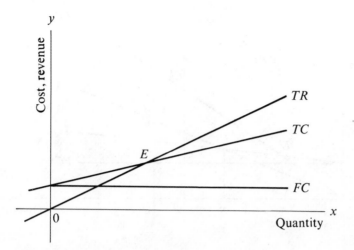

FIGURE 1.26

In Fig. 1.26 the straight line *FC* represents fixed cost. It is the straight line with the *y*-intercept equal to the constant fixed cost (that is, cost when output is zero) and slope zero.

The line *TC* represents total cost; its *y*-intercept is equal to fixed cost and its slope is equal to the increase in variable cost per unit increase in output. Note the assumption that variable cost is proportional to output over the relevant range.

The line *TR* represents total revenue to the firm for different quantities sold; its intercept is at the origin and its slope is equal to the price per unit, assuming that this price is constant for all quantities sold.

The break-even point *E* is that point at which the lines *TR* and *TC* intersect. It represents the quantity at which the producer just breaks even—that is, the quantity for which there is just sufficient revenue to cover costs.

Example

Break-even analysis is used more frequently in practice to demonstrate probable effects of changes than to determine what those changes should be.

In Fig. 1.27 suppose the firm decides that it could sell the same quantity of product, denoted by point *Q*, if the price per unit were increased so that total revenue would be raised from *TR* to *TR'*. *TC* remains the same, and the break-even point changes from *E* to *E'*.

At the original price, profit to the firm is represented by the area of triangle *EAB*; at the higher price, it is represented by the area of triangle *E'AC*.

If, on the other hand, the firm assumes that the increase in price resulting in *TR'* would reduce the quantity sold to that denoted by point *Q'*, the following would be indicated:

Total cost reduced from that denoted by *A* to *A'*
Total revenue reduced from that of point *C* to *C'*
Total profit changed from area *E'AC* to area *E'A'C'*

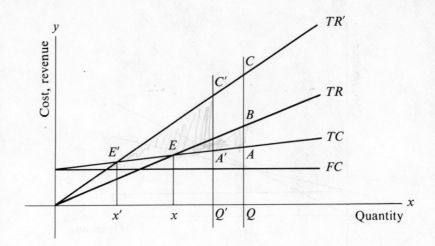

FIGURE 1.27

Since the profit area $E'A'C'$ is greater than the profit area EAB resulting from the larger quantity sold at the original price, the company might decide to increase the price even though sales would be expected to drop.

Break-even analysis may be used to study possible results of many combinations of factors involved in a particular problem.

□ THE CONSUMPTION FUNCTION

National income analysis provides an interesting example of the use of linear functions, since the consumption function is frequently assumed to be linear over relatively short periods or "in the short run." The analysis, in one of its simplest forms, is based on the following assumptions:

1.   There is some absolute amount of consumption necessary to maintain life, even though there may be no money income.

2.   Consumption is related to disposable income, that is, $C = f(y_d)$.

3.   When disposable income increases, consumption will also increase, but by a smaller amount. Stated mathematically, if

Δy_d represents an increase in disposable income

and

ΔC represents the resulting change in consumption

then

$\dfrac{\Delta C}{\Delta y_d}$ will be positive but less than one, that is, $0 < \dfrac{\Delta C}{\Delta y_d} < 1$.

4.   The proportion of an increment in disposable income which will be consumed is constant. This proportion is referred to as the "marginal propensity to consume."

These assumptions can be translated into the point-slope form of the equation for a straight line

$$C = a + by_d$$

where C represents consumption; a is fixed, basic consumption regardless of income; b is the marginal propensity to consume; and y_d is disposable income.

Example

In a simplified form of national income analysis, the following assumptions are made:

1. When national disposable income is 0, national consumption is 5 (in billions of dollars).

2. For the economy as a whole consumption is linearly related to national disposable income as follows:

At each level of disposable income, consumption equals 5 (in billions of dollars) plus 80% of disposable income.

What is the equation which expresses this relationship?

$$C = 5 + 0.8y_d$$

What is aggregate consumption when disposable income is 40 (in billions of dollars)?

$$C = 5 + 0.8(40) = 37$$

Graph the line representing aggregate consumption as a function of national disposable income. (See Fig. 1.28.)

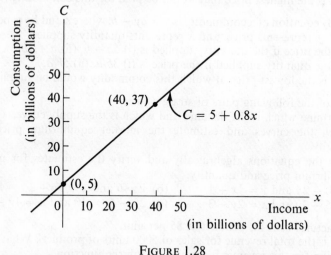

FIGURE 1.28

PROBLEMS

1. Which of the following equations represent demand curves, which represent supply curves, and which represent neither demand nor supply curves?

(Assume y represents price and x represents quantity.)

(a) $x - 2y = 0$ *Supply*
(b) $3x + 4y - 10 = 0$ *demand*
(c) $y - 4 = 0$ *supply, demand*
(d) $x - 3 = 0$ *supply y demand*
(e) $2x - 3y + 1 = 0$ *supply*
(f) $2x + 5y + 4 = 0$ *neither*
(g) $3x + 4y - 12 = 0$ *demand*
(h) $5x - y - 10 = 0$ *supply*
(i) $2y + 3x + 2 = 0$ *neither*
(j) $x - 3y = 0$ *supply*

2. The demand curve for a commodity is $x = 10 - y/4$. (Assume y represents price and x represents quantity demanded.)
   (a) Find the quantity demanded if the price is (i) 4, (ii) 16, (iii) 25.
   (b) Find the price if the quantity demanded is (i) 9, (ii) 7, (iii) 2.
   (c) What is the highest price that would be paid for this commodity?
   (d) What quantity would be demanded if the commodity were free?
   (e) Graph the curve.

3. The supply curve of a commodity is $x = 1.1y - 0.1$. (Assume y represents price and x represents quantity supplied.)
   (a) Find the price if the quantity supplied is (i) 1, (ii) 0.8, (iii) 0.5.
   (b) Find the quantity supplied if the price is (i) 8, (ii) 6, (iii) 4.1.
   (c) What is the lowest price at which this commodity would be supplied?
   (d) Graph the curve.

4. The demand equation of a commodity is $x = A - By$, where A and B are positive constants, y represents price, and x represents quantity demanded.
   (a) Find the price if the quantity demanded is $\dfrac{A}{3}$.
   (b) Find the quantity demanded if the price is $\dfrac{A}{2B}$.
   (c) Find the quantity demanded if the commodity is free.
   (d) What is the highest price that would be paid for this commodity?

5. The supply equation of a commodity is $x = ay - b$, where a and b are positive constants, y represents price, and x represents quantity supplied.
   (a) Find the price if the quantity supplied is (i) $5a - b$, (ii) $a + 2b$.
   (b) Find the quantity supplied if the price is (i) $3b/a$, (ii) $5b/a$.
   (c) What is the lowest price at which this commodity would be supplied?

6. For each of the following pairs of straight lines
   (i) Determine which is the demand and which is the supply curve.
   (ii) Graph the curves and estimate the market equilibrium price and quantity.
   (iii) Solve the equations algebraically and verify the estimates for market equilibrium price and quantity.
   (a) $y = 10 - 2x$ and $y = \frac{3}{2}x + 1$
   (b) $y = 6$ and $x = 3y - 3$
   (c) $x = 15 - 3y$ and $x = 2y - 3$
   (d) $2y + 3x = 10$ and $x = 4y - 6$

7. A manufacturer sells his product at $5 per unit.
   (a) What is the total revenue for sales of 5000 units of product? What is the equation for this revenue function? Graph the function.
   (b) Fixed costs are constant at $3000 regardless of the number of units of product involved. Superimpose the graph of this function on graph (a) above.
   (c) Total cost is equal to the sum of fixed costs and variable costs. In this company, variable costs are estimated at 40% of total revenue. What is the total cost when 5000 units of product are sold? Graph the function superimposed on graph (a).
   (d) What is the break-even point? Indicate this point on the graph, and solve

for the corresponding amount sold. Indicate on the graph the quantity at which the manufacturer will cover his fixed costs.

8. At a price of $5 per unit, a firm will supply 5000 plastic battery lanterns every month; at $3.50 per unit it will supply 2000 units. Determine the equation of the supply function for this product. Graph the equation.

9. (a) Graph the function $y = f(x) = 8 + 4x$.
   (b) Allow the intercept parameter 8 to change to 4, while the slope parameter 4 is unchanged. Graph this function on the same diagram.
   (c) Allow the slope parameter 4 in the original equation to change to 2, while the intercept parameter 8 remains unchanged. Graph this equation on the same diagram.

10. A firm has analyzed its sales and found that its customers will buy 20% more units of its products with each $2 reduction in the unit price. When the price is $12, the firm sells 500 units. What is the equation of the demand function for this product? Graph the equation.

11. (a) Assume that water is in unlimited supply in a municipality. The consumer pays $5.00 per month for water regardless of the amount used. Graph the demand and supply equations.
    (b) There is only one genuine painting by Rembrandt titled "The Night Watch." Assign arbitrary values to the painting and graph the demand and supply equations.

12. A bus company has learned that when the price of a short excursion trip is $5.00, 30 people will buy tickets; when the price is $8.00, only 10 tickets will be sold. Obtain the point-slope form of the equation for the demand function and graph the equation.

13. Identify which of the following equations represents a demand curve and which represents a supply curve; determine the equilibrium point and graph the curves.
    (I) $x + y = 5$
    (II) $2x - y = 5.5$

14. Change equation (II) in Problem 13 to $2x - y = 6$. Graph the equation and identify it as supply or demand. Has the equilibrium quantity involved increased or decreased relative to that in Problem 13?

ANSWERS TO ODD-NUMBERED PROBLEMS

1. (a) supply
   (b) demand
   (c) supply, demand
   (d) supply, demand
   (e) supply
   (f) neither
   (g) demand
   (h) supply
   (i) neither
   (j) supply

3. (a) (i) 1, (ii) 0.818, (iii) 0.545
   (b) (i) 8.7, (ii) 6.5, (iii) 4.41
   (c) 0.091

5. (a) (i) 5, (ii) $\dfrac{a + 3b}{a}$
   (b) (i) $2b$, (ii) $4b$
   (c) b/a

7. (a) $25,000
   $TR = 5x$
   (c) $13,000
   (d) break-even point at $x = 1000$; recovery of fixed costs at $x = 600$

13. (3.5, 1.5)

■ 1.5 NONLINEAR CURVES

A *polynomial* in x and y is the sum of a finite number of terms of the type kx^ry^s, where k is a constant and each of the exponents r and s is either a positive integer or zero. The *degree of* a *term* is $r + s$ and the *degree of the polynomial* is the degree of the term or terms of highest degree.

Equations of the form $f(x, y) = 0$, where $f(x, y)$ is a polynomial in x and y, are referred to as *algebraic*; the graphical representation of an algebraic equation is an *algebraic curve*. Any equation in x and y which is not algebraic is referred to as *transcendental*; the graphical representation of a transcendental equation is a *transcendental curve*. Included among the transcendental curves are the graphs of trigonometric, logarithmic, and exponential functions. Curves represented by algebraic equations of degree greater than two in x and y or by transcendental equations are referred to as *higher plane curves*. Any equation whose graph is not a straight line is referred to as *nonlinear*.

□ GENERAL METHODS OF GRAPHING

Graphing a straight line from its equation is a relatively simple problem, since any two distinct points uniquely determine a straight line. However, graphing more complicated equations is less straightforward. The graph representing any equation can be drawn fairly accurately if a sufficient number of points are plotted, but frequently so many points are required that this method is very laborious. Furthermore, plotting points in itself provides little or no information regarding the important properties of a curve.

From examining an equation, certain properties of the corresponding curve can be determined which will facilitate drawing the curve with a minimum of point plotting. Some of these properties are discussed below and their usefulness in graphing is illustrated. Following this general discussion, several particular types of curves and some of their applications in business and economics are discussed.

● Intercepts

The intercepts of a curve are the points at which it crosses the axes. The x-intercepts are obtained by setting $y = 0$ in the equation of the curve and solving for x; the y-intercepts are obtained by setting $x = 0$ in the equation of the curve and solving for y.

● Symmetry

Two points are *symmetric with respect to a line* if that line is the perpendicular bisector of the line segment joining the two points. Two points are symmetric with respect to a third point if that third point is the midpoint of the line segment joining the first two points. From these definitions it follows that the point (x, y) is a symmetric to the point

$(x, -y)$ with respect to the x-axis

$(-x, y)$ with respect to the y-axis

$(-x, -y)$ with respect to the origin

as shown in Fig. 1.29.

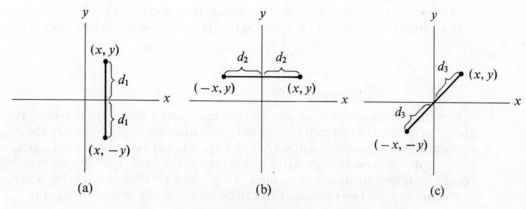

FIGURE 1.29 Symmetry with respect to (a) the x-axis,
(b) the y-axis, and (c) the origin.

Each of Figs. 1.30(a), (b), and (c) represents a type of symmetric curve as follows:

(a) A curve is symmetric to the x-axis if for each point (x, y) on the curve the symmetric point $(x, -y)$ is also on the curve—that is, if substitution of $-y$ for y does not change the form of the equation of the curve. For example, a curve is symmetric to the x-axis if it is represented by an algebraic equation in which y occurs only to even powers. Note, however, that there are algebraic curves symmetric to the x-axis whose equations contain odd powers of y. See the example below.

(b) A curve is symmetric to the y-axis if for each point (x, y) on the curve the symmetric point $(-x, y)$ is also on the curve—that is, if substitution of $-x$ for x does not change the form of the equation of the curve. For example, a curve is symmetric to the y-axis if it is represented by an algebraic equation in which x occurs only to even powers.

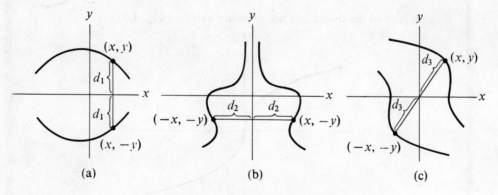

FIGURE 1.30 Symmetry with respect to (a) the x-axis,
(b) the y-axis, and (c) the origin.

(c) A curve is symmetric to the origin if for each point (x, y) on the curve, the symmetric point $(-x, -y)$ is also on the curve—that is, if substitution of $-x$ for x

and $-y$ for y does not change the form of the equation of the curve. For example, a curve is symmetric to the origin if it is represented by an algebraic equation each of whose terms is of even degree or each of whose terms is of odd degree.

In summary, the graph of an equation $f(x, y) = 0$ is symmetric with respect to

the x-axis if $f(x, y) = f(x, -y) = 0$

the y-axis if $f(x, y) = f(-x, y) = 0$

the origin if $f(x, y) = f(-x, -y) = 0$

Note that symmetry with respect to both the x and y axes implies symmetry about the origin, but symmetry about the origin does not imply symmetry about either axis. More generally, symmetry with respect to any two of the three (x-axis, y-axis, and origin) implies symmetry with respect to the third. Thus symmetry can occur with respect to none, one, or three of the x-axis, y-axis, and origin but never with respect to just two of them. This can be seen from the definitions above:

Substitution of $-y$ for y leaves equation unchanged (x-axis symmetry) and substitution of $-x$ for x leaves equation unchanged (y-axis symmetry)

$\underset{\not\Leftarrow}{\Rightarrow}$

Substitution of $-x$ for x and $-y$ for y leaves equation unchanged (symmetry to origin)

and similarly for the other two cases. (The symbol $\Rightarrow$ means "implies," the symbol $\not\Rightarrow$ means "does not imply," the symbol $\Leftarrow$ means "is implied by," the symbol $\not\Leftarrow$ means "is not implied by.")

Examples

The curve represented by the equation

$$3x^2y + y + x^3 = 0$$

is symmetric to the origin but not to either axis (see Fig. 1.31).

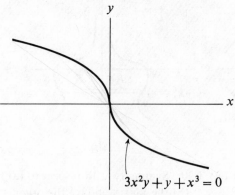

$$3x^2y + y + x^3 = 0$$

FIGURE 1.31

$f(x, -y) = -3x^2y - y + x^3$, so $f(x, -y) = 0$ is not the same equation as $f(x, y) = 0$ and $f(x, y) = 0$ is not symmetric to the x-axis.

$f(-x, y) = 3x^2y + y - x^3$, so $f(-x, y) = 0$ is not the same equation as $f(x, y) = 0$ and $f(x, y) = 0$ is not symmetric to the y-axis.

$f(-x, -y) = -3x^2y - y - x^3$, so $f(-x, -y) = 0$ is the same equation as $f(x, y) = 0$ and $f(x, y) = 0$ is symmetric to the origin.

The curve represented by the equation

$$2x^4 + x^2y + y + 6 = 0$$

is symmetric to the y-axis but not to either the x-axis or the origin (see Fig. 1.32).

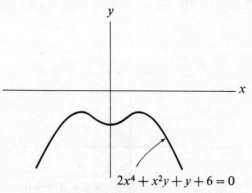

$$2x^4 + x^2y + y + 6 = 0$$

FIGURE 1.32

$f(x, -y) = 2x^4 - x^2y - y + 6$, so $f(x, -y) = 0$ is not the same equation as $f(x, y) = 0$ and $f(x, y) = 0$ is not symmetric to the x-axis.

$f(-x, y) = 2x^4 + x^2y + y + 6$, so $f(-x, y) = 0$ is the same equation as $f(x, y) = 0$ and $f(x, y) = 0$ is symmetric to the y-axis.

$f(-x, -y) = 2x^4 - x^2y - y + 6$, so $f(-x - y) = 0$ is not the same equation as $f(x, y) = 0$ and $f(x, y) = 0$ is not symmetric to the origin.

The curve represented by the equation

$$5x^2 - xy + 6x^3 = 0$$

is not symmetric to the x-axis, the y-axis, or the origin (see Fig. 1.33).

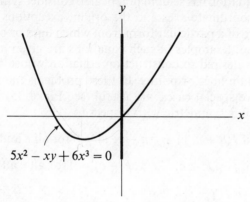

$$5x^2 - xy + 6x^3 = 0$$

FIGURE 1.33

$f(x, -y) = 5x^2 + xy + 6x^3$, so $f(x, -y) = 0$ is not the same equation as $f(x, y) = 0$ and $f(x, y) = 0$ is not symmetric to the x-axis.

$f(-x, y) = 5x^2 + xy - 6x^3$, so $f(-x, y) = 0$ is not the same equation as $f(x, y) = 0$ and $f(x, y) = 0$ is not symmetric to the y-axis.

$f(-x, -y) = 5x^2 - xy - 6x^3$, so $f(-x, -y) = 0$ is not the same equation as $f(x, y) = 0$ and $f(x, y) = 0$ is not symmetric to the origin.

The curve represented by the equation

$$x^3y + 3xy = 0$$

is symmetric to the x-axis, the y-axis, and the origin (see Fig. 1.34).

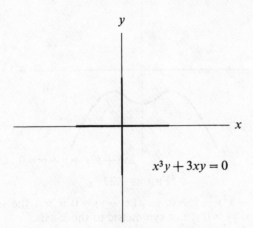

$$x^3y + 3xy = 0$$

FIGURE 1.34

$f(x, -y) = -x^3y - 3xy$, so $f(x, -y) = 0$ is the same equation as $f(x, y) = 0$ and $f(x, y) = 0$ is symmetric to the x-axis.

$f(-x, y) = -x^3y - 3xy$, so $f(-x, y) = 0$ is the same equation as $f(x, y) = 0$ and $f(x, y) = 0$ is symmetric to the y-axis.

$f(-x, -y) = x^3y + 3xy$, so $f(-x, -y) = 0$ is the same equation as $f(x, y) = 0$ and $f(x, y) = 0$ is symmetric to the origin.

In graphing an equation it is seldom practical to consider symmetry with respect to other than the coordinate axes and the origin; exceptions to this are curves whose equations are of a particular form from which lines or points of symmetry are readily identified. Examples of such equations are given in later sections.

Occasionally it is desired to construct an equation whose curve is symmetric with respect to certain lines or points. In these problems the following rules, of which the above are special cases, are useful (see Fig. 1.35): The graph of the equation $f(x, y) = 0$ is symmetric with respect to

the line $x = h$ if $f(h + c, y) = f(h - c, y) = 0$ for all c and y

the line $y = k$ if $f(x, k + c) = f(x, k - c) = 0$ for all c and x

the point (h, k) if $f(h + c, k + d) = f(h - c, k - d) = 0$ for all c and d

NOTE: Symmetry about the line $y = mx + b$ must be defined in terms of transformations. This procedure is discussed in later sections.

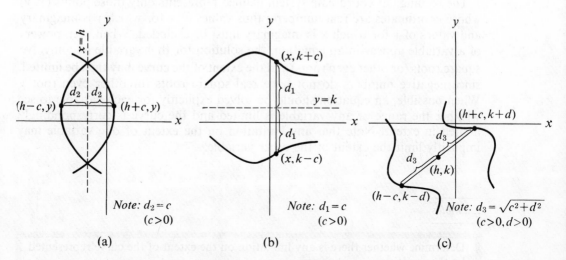

FIGURE 1.35 Symmetry with respect to (a) the line $x = h$,
(b) the line $y = k$, and (c) the point (h, k).

Symmetry with respect to the line $y = x$ is a property of inverse functions. Geometrically, the problem of finding the inverse function of $f(x)$ is the problem of viewing the graph of $y = f(x)$ with the x-axis and y-axis interchanged, which is equivalent to reflection about the line $y = x$. Thus the graph of the inverse of a function can be obtained by drawing a perpendicular from each point on the graph of the original function to the line $y = x$ and extending the perpendicular an equal distance beyond the line $y = x$. The points thus obtained are the graph of the inverse function $y = f^{-1}(x)$. (See Fig. 1.36.)

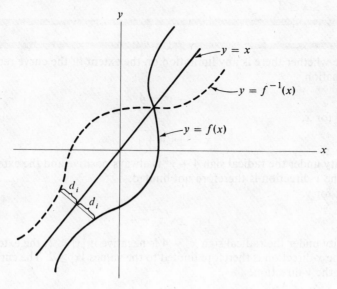

FIGURE 1.36 Symmetry with respect to the line $y = x$.

● **Extent**

The rectangular coordinate system defined represents only those points (x, y) whose coordinates are real numbers; thus values of x for which y is imaginary and values of y for which x is imaginary must be excluded. When even powers of a variable appear in an equation, the solution for that variable may involve square roots (or other even roots) and the extent of the curve may then be limited, since negative numbers do not have real square roots (or other even roots). When possible, an equation should be solved explicitly for each variable to see whether the range of any variable is limited and the curve is correspondingly limited in extent. Note that any limitation on the extent of one variable may implicitly limit the extent of the other variable.

Examples

Determine whether there is any limitation on the extent of the curve represented by the equation

$$x^2 + y^2 = 9$$

Solving for x,

$$x = \pm\sqrt{9 - y^2}$$

the quantity under the radical sign $9 - y^2$ is negative if $|y| > 3$; the extent of the curve in the y-direction is therefore limited to the interval $-3 \le y \le 3$.
Solving for y,

$$y = \pm\sqrt{9 - x^2}$$

and the extent of the curve in the x-direction is therefore similarly limited to the interval $-3 \le x \le 3$.

Determine whether there is any limitation on the extent of the curve represented by the equation

$$x^2 - y^2 = 4$$

Solving for x,

$$x = \pm\sqrt{4 + y^2}$$

the quantity under the radical sign $4 + y^2$ is always positive and the extent of the curve in the y-direction is therefore not limited.
Solving for y,

$$y = \pm\sqrt{x^2 - 4}$$

the quantity under the radical sign $x^2 - 4$ is negative if $|x| < 2$; the extent of the curve in the x-direction is therefore limited to the values $|x| \ge 2$. The curve is not limited in the y-direction.

● **Asymptotes**

A curve may have the property that a point can move along it so that the distance from the origin to the point increases without limit. If, as the distance (in some direction) of a point from the origin increases without limit, the distance between the point and a fixed straight line approaches zero through values of the same sign, <u>the line is called an *asymptote*</u> of the curve.

To show that a particular line is an asymptote of a particular curve it is necessary to show that the curve approaches arbitrarily close to the line as the distance from the origin increases without bound. This property involves the concept of limits, which will be discussed in succeeding sections.

In general, then, the line $y = mx + b$ is an asymptote of the curve $y = f(x)$ if

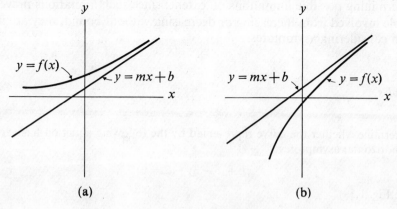

FIGURE 1.37 $f(x) \to mx + b$ as $x, y \to \infty$:
(a) from above, (b) from below.

$f(x)$ becomes arbitrarily close to $mx + b$ as x and y increase without bound. This may be written <u>$f(x) \to mx + b$ as $x, y \to \infty$</u>. (See Fig. 1.37.)

Asymptotes that are parallel to or coincident with one of the coordinate axes are frequently of particular interest in practice. These vertical and horizontal asymptotes are defined as follows (see Fig. 1.38).

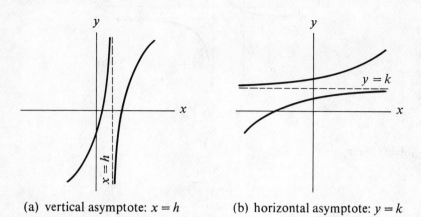

(a) vertical asymptote: $x = h$ (b) horizontal asymptote: $y = k$

FIGURE 1.38

The line $x = h$ is a *vertical asymptote* of the curve $y = f(x)$ if $x \to h$ as $y \to \infty$.

The line $y = k$ is a *horizontal asymptote* of the curve $y = f(x)$ if $y \to k$ as $x \to \infty$.

For purposes of graphing, it is helpful to determine the behavior of a curve with respect to each of its asymptotes, rather than just the existence of the asymptotes. Thus the equation should be examined as x and y in turn increase without bound ($x \to +\infty$, $y \to +\infty$) and as x and y in turn decrease without bound ($x \to -\infty$, $y \to -\infty$); the value of the variable which is not increasing or decreasing without bound should also be noted, in order to determine whether the curve is approaching its asymptote from the left or the right (vertical asymptotes) or from above or below (horizontal asymptotes). When investigating asymptotes, it is usually helpful to solve an equation explicitly first for one variable and then for the other variable, if possible. As noted above, this procedure is also useful in determining possible limitations on extent; since such limitations prevent the variable involved from increasing or decreasing without bound, they are important in considering asymptotes.

Examples

Determine whether the curve represented by the following equation has vertical or horizontal asymptotes:

$$xy + x - 3y - 2 = 0$$

(see Fig. 1.39).

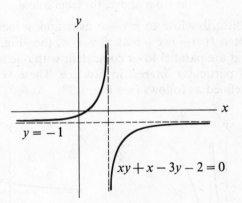

$$y = -1$$

$$xy + x - 3y - 2 = 0$$

FIGURE 1.39

Solving for x,

$$x = \frac{3y + 2}{y + 1}$$

as $y \to +\infty$, $x \to 3$, $x < 3$; as $y \to -\infty$, $x \to 3$, $x > 3$; thus $x = 3$ is an asymptote of the curve.

Solving for y,

$$y = \frac{x-2}{3-x}$$

as $x \to +\infty$, $y \to -1$, $y < -1$; as $x \to -\infty$, $y \to -1$, $y > -1$; thus $y = -1$ is an asymptote of the curve.

Determine whether the curve represented by the following equation has vertical or horizontal asymptotes:

$$x^2 - y - 1 = 0$$

(see Fig. 1.40).

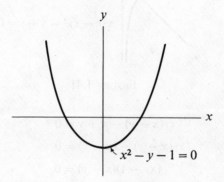

FIGURE 1.40

Solving for x,

$$x = \pm\sqrt{y+1}$$

as $y \to +\infty$, $x \to \pm\infty$; $y > -1$, so y cannot approach $-\infty$; thus the curve does not have a vertical asymptote.

Solving for y,

$$y = x^2 - 1$$

as $x \to +\infty$, $y \to +\infty$; as $x \to -\infty$, $y \to +\infty$ (as above); thus the curve does not have a horizontal asymptote.

● **Factorization**

If the left member of the equation $f(x, y) = 0$ can be written as the product of two or more factors, for example, if $f(x, y) = g(x, y) \cdot h(x, y) = 0$, then only those points (x, y) whose coordinates satisfy either $g(x, y) = 0$ or $h(x, y) = 0$ lie on the graph of $f(x, y) = 0$. Thus the graph of $f(x, y) = 0$ consists of the graphs of $g(x, y) = 0$ and $h(x, y) = 0$. It is important to check for factorization, since a factorable equation may be difficult to graph correctly if it is not factored.

Examples

Graph the equation

$$x^2y - xy^2 - x + y = 0$$

(see Fig. 1.41).

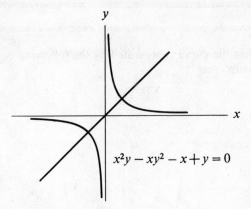

FIGURE 1.41

Factoring,

$$xy(x - y) - x + y = 0$$
$$xy(x - y) - (\dot{x} - y) = 0$$
$$(xy - 1)(x - y) = 0$$

Thus the graph of $x^2y - xy^2 - x + y = 0$ consists of the graphs of the curve $xy - 1 = 0$ and the straight line $x - y = 0$.

Graph the equation

$$2x^2 - 3xy - 2y^2 = 0$$

(see Fig. 1.42).

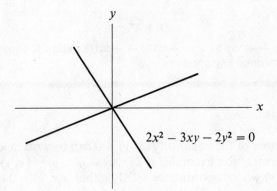

FIGURE 1.42

Factoring,

$$(2x + y)(x - 2y) = 0$$

Thus the graph of $2x^2 - 3xy - 2y^2 = 0$ consists of the graphs of $2x + y = 0$ and $x - 2y = 0$.

● Real Curve, Point Locus, or Imaginary Locus

Some equations are satisfied by the coordinates of only one point or of a finite number of points; the graphs of such equations are called *point loci*. Other equations are satisfied by the coordinates of no real point; since such equations have no graphical representation in a system of real axes, they are said to represent *imaginary loci*.

point loci

imaginary loci

Examples

The equation $x^2 + y^2 = 0$ is satisfied only by the point $(0, 0)$, and its graph is thus a point locus.

The equation $(x^2 - 4)^2 + (y^2 - 4)^2 = 0$ is satisfied only by the points $(2, 2)$, $(2, -2)$, $(-2, 2)$, and $(-2, -2)$, and its graph is thus a point locus.

The equation $x^2 + y^2 = -5$ is satisfied by no pair of real numbers x and y and its locus is thus imaginary.

SUMMARY: GENERAL METHODS OF GRAPHING

The following properties of curves are helpful in graphing:

1. Intercepts.   4. Asymptotes.
2. Symmetry.   5. Factorization.
3. Extent.   6. Real curve, point locus, or imaginary locus.

The following examples illustrate the use of these six properties in graphing a given equation. Although factorization occurs near the end of the list (because in practice factorable equations occur relatively infrequently), it should be checked first, as it may make investigation of some of the other properties unnecessary. The emphasis here is on determining properties of the curves from their equations; greater accuracy in graphing can be attained by plotting more points and, particularly, by methods of differential calculus to be discussed subsequently.

Examples

Graph the equation

$$y = (x + 2)(x - 3)^2$$

(see Fig. 1.43).

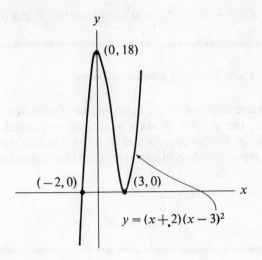

FIGURE 1.43

Intercepts: If $y = 0$, $x = -2$, 3; if $x = 0$, $y = 18$.

Symmetry: Not symmetric with respect to either axis or the origin.

Extent: No apparent limits.

Asymptotes: None (as $x \to +\infty$, $y \to +\infty$ and as $x \to -\infty$, $y \to -\infty$).

Factorization: Not factorable. [Note that factorability refers to the equation $f(x, y) = (x + 2)(x - 3)^2 - y = 0$, which is not factorable, although $y = f(x) = (x + 2)(x - 3)^2$ is, in fact, factored.]

Real point or imaginary locus: Real curve.

Graph the equation

$$xy - y - x - 2 = 0$$

(see Fig. 1.44).

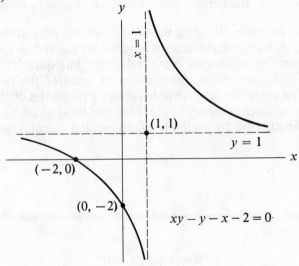

FIGURE 1.44

Intercepts: If $y = 0$, $x = -2$; if $x = 0$, $y = -2$.

Symmetry: Not symmetric with respect to either axis or the origin.

Extent: Solving for x,

$$x = \frac{y + 2}{y - 1}$$

No limitation on the extent of y except x is not defined for $y = 1$. Solving for y,

$$y = \frac{x + 2}{x - 1}$$

No limitation on the extent of x except y is not defined for $x = 1$.

Asymptotes: $x = \dfrac{y + 2}{y - 1}$ as $y \to +\infty$, $x \to 1$, $x > 1$; as $y \to -\infty$, $x \to 1$, $x < 1$; so $x = 1$ is an asymptote. $y = \dfrac{x + 2}{x - 1}$ as $x \to +\infty$, $y \to 1$, $y > 1$; as $x \to -\infty$, $y \to 1$, $y < 1$; so $y = 1$ is an asymptote.

Factorization: Not factorable.

Real, point, or imaginary locus: Real curve.

Graph the equation

$$xy + x^2 = 0$$

(see Fig. 1.45).

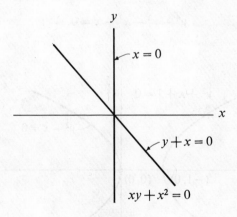

$x = 0$

x

$y + x = 0$

$xy + x^2 = 0$

FIGURE 1.45

$xy + x^2 = x(y + x) = 0$, so the graph consists of the two straight lines $x = 0$ and $y + x = 0$.

Graph the equation

$$y^3 + xy^2 - xy - x^2 = 0$$

(see Fig. 1.46).

$y^2(y + x) - x(y + x)$

$(y^2 - x)(y + x) = 0$

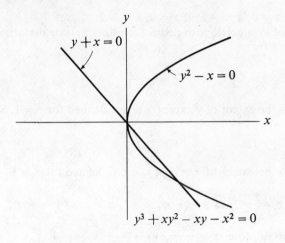

FIGURE 1.46

$y^3 + xy^2 - xy - x^2 = y^2(y + x) - x(y + x) = (y^2 - x)(y + x) = 0$, so the graph consists of the straight line $y + x = 0$ and the curve $y^2 - x = 0$.

Graph the equation

$$y^4 + y^2 - x^2 - x = 0$$

(see Fig. 1.47).

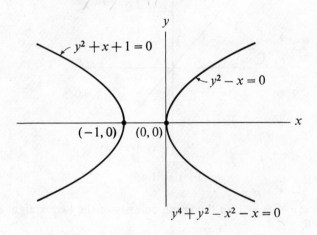

FIGURE 1.47

$y^4 + y^2 - x^2 - x = (y^2 + x)(y^2 - x) + (y^2 - x) = (y^2 - x)(y^2 + x + 1) = 0$, so the graph consists of the curves $y^2 - x = 0$ and $y^2 + x + 1 = 0$.

Graph the equation

$$x^2y - x^2 - 4y = 0$$

(see Fig. 1.48).

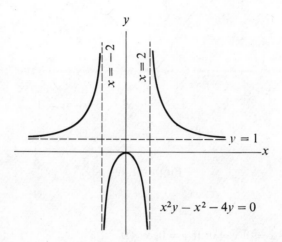

$x = -2$

$x = 2$

$y = 1$

$x^2y - x^2 - 4y = 0$

FIGURE 1.48

Intercepts: If $y = 0$, $x = 0$; if $x = 0$, $y = 0$.
Symmetry: Symmetric with respect to y-axis.
Extent: Solving for x,

$$x = \pm\sqrt{\frac{4y}{y-1}} = \pm 2\sqrt{\frac{y}{y-1}}$$

$\frac{y}{y-1}$ is negative if $0 < y < 1$ and is undefined if $y = 1$, so y is limited to the intervals $y \leq 0$ and $y > 1$. Solving for y, $y = \frac{x^2}{x^2 - 4}$, so there is no limitation on the extent of x except y is not defined for $x = \pm 2$.

Asymptotes: $x = \pm 2\sqrt{\frac{y}{y-1}}$. As $y \to +\infty$, $x \to \pm 2$, $x > |2|$; as $y \to -\infty$, $x \to \pm 2$, $x < |2|$; so $x = \pm 2$ are asymptotes. $y = \frac{x^2}{x^2 - 4}$. As $x \to +\infty$, $y \to 1$, $y > 1$; as $x \to -\infty$, $y \to 1$, $y > 1$, so $y = 1$ is an asymptote.
Factorization: Not factorable.
Real, point, or imaginary locus: Real curve.

Graph the equation

$$x^2y - x^2 + 4y = 0$$

(see Fig. 1.49).

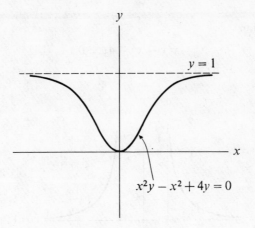

$$x^2y - x^2 + 4y = 0$$

FIGURE 1.49

Intercepts: If $x = 0$, $y = 0$; if $y = 0$, $x = 0$.
Symmetry: Symmetric with respect to y-axis.
Extent: Solving for x,

$$x = \pm\sqrt{\frac{4y}{1-y}} = \pm 2\sqrt{\frac{y}{1-y}}$$

$\dfrac{y}{1-y}$ is negative if $y < 0$ or $y > 1$ and is undefined if $y = 1$, so y is limited to the interval $0 \le y < 1$. Solving for y, $y = \dfrac{x^2}{x^2 + 4}$, so there is no limitation on the extent of x.

Asymptotes: $x = \pm 2\sqrt{\dfrac{y}{1-y}}$. y is limited in extent and cannot become large or small without bound. $y = \dfrac{x^2}{x^2 + 4}$. As $x \to +\infty$, $y \to 1$, $y < 1$; as $x \to -\infty$, $y \to 1$, $y < 1$, so $y = 1$ is an asymptote.
Factorization: Not factorable.
Real, point, or imaginary locus: Real curve.

Graph the equation

$$y^2 = x^3 - 4x$$

(see Fig. 1.50).

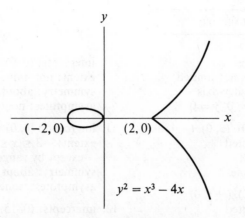

FIGURE 1.50

Intercepts: If $x = 0$, $y = 0$; if $y = 0$, $x = 0$, ± 2.
Symmetry: Symmetric with respect to the x-axis.
Extent: Solving for y,

$$y = \pm\sqrt{x(x^2 - 4)}$$

$x(x^2 - 4)$ is negative if $x < -2$ or $0 < x < 2$, so x is limited to the intervals $-2 \leq x \leq 0$ and $x \geq 2$. No obvious limitation on the extent of y.

Asymptotes: $y = \pm\sqrt{x^2(x^2 - 4)}$. As $x \to +\infty$, $y \to \pm\infty$; x cannot approach $-\infty$ because of the limitation on extent; so there are no asymptotes.
Factorization: Not factorable.
Real, point, or imaginary locus: Real curve.

PROBLEMS

Sketch the curves represented by the following equations; give intercepts, extent, symmetry, and asymptotes, as relevant.

1. $x^2 y = 10$

2. $xy^2 = -10$

3. $y = x(x - 3)(x + 4)$

4. $y = x^2(x^2 - 4x + 4)$

5. $y = x^4 - x^2$

6. $y = (x^2 - 1)(x^2 - 4)$

7. $y = x^3 - 4x$

8. $y = x^3(x - 1)(x + 6)$

9. $4y = x^3$

10. $y = x^2(x - 3)^2$

11. $y = x\sqrt{9 - x^2}$

12. $y = x^2\sqrt{9 - x^2}$

13. $y = (x - 3)(x^2 - 4x - 5)$

14. $y = x^2(x - 6)(x^2 - x - 6)$

ANSWERS TO ODD-NUMBERED PROBLEMS

1. intercepts: none
   extent: $y > 0$, x not limited
   symmetry: about y-axis
   asymptotes: $x = 0$, $y = 0$

3. intercepts: $(0, 0)$, $(3, 0)$, $(-4, 0)$
   extent: not limited
   symmetry: none
   asymptotes: none

5. intercepts: $(0, 0)$, $(\pm 1, 0)$
   extent: not limited
   symmetry: about y-axis
   asymptotes: none

7. intercepts: $(0, 0)$, $(\pm 2, 0)$
   extent: not limited
   symmetry: about origin
   asymptotes: none

9. intercepts: $(0, 0)$
   extent: not limited
   symmetry: about origin
   asymptotes: none

11. intercepts: $(0, 0)$, $(\pm 3, 0)$
    extent: $-3 \leq x \leq 3$, y not limited
      except by range of x
    symmetry: about origin
    asymptotes: none

13. intercepts: $(0, 15)$, $(3, 0)$, $(5, 0)$,
      $(-1, 0)$
    extent: not limited
    symmetry: none
    asymptotes: none

☐ *QUADRATIC EQUATIONS*

An equation of the form

$$Ax^2 + Bxy + Cy^2 + Dx + Ey + F = 0 \qquad (2)$$

where A, B, C, D, E, and F are constants and at least one of A, B, and C is non-zero, is said to be a *second-degree* or *quadratic equation*. An equation is said to be quadratic in a variable if that variable occurs to the second and no higher power. Equation (2) is the general equation of second degree in two variables.

The curves represented by equation (2) can generally be obtained by cutting a (double) cone with a plane and thus are known as *conic sections*. The four special forms of a conic section are (1) the circle, (2) the ellipse, (3) the parabola, and (4) the hyperbola (see Fig. 1.51). In addition to these curves, equation (2) may represent various types of *degenerate conics* (actually special cases of conic

*curves of
2nd degree equations
are conic
sections*

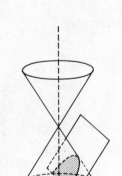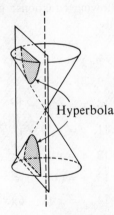

Parabola

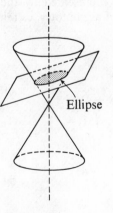

Hyperbola

Ellipse

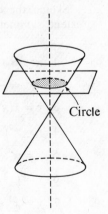

Circle

FIGURE 1.51   Conic sections.

sections): (1) two intersecting straight lines, (2) two parallel straight lines, (3) two coincident straight lines (that is, one straight line), (4) a point, or (5) no points at all.

Any conic section can be defined as the locus of a point that moves in such a way that the ratio of its distance from a fixed point (called its *focus*) to its distance from a fixed line (called its *directrix*) is a constant e (called its *eccentricity*). Conic sections can be classified into the four basic types according to the value of their eccentricity. (For a circle, $e = 0$; for an ellipse, $0 < e < 1$; for a parabola, $e = 1$; for a hyperbola, $e > 1$.)

There are many interesting scientific applications of conic sections. For example, the planets move in elliptic orbits about the sun with the sun at a focus; whispering galleries usually have elliptical ceilings arranged so that a person standing at one focus can hear a slight noise made at the other focus while someone standing between the two foci hears nothing; elliptic arches are frequently used in architecture. The cable of a suspension bridge hangs in the form of an arc of a parabola; a reflecting surface made by rotating a parabola about its axis will send the light out in parallel rays if the source of light is at the focus; the larger reflector in a reflecting telescope is usually parabolic; the path of a projectile, neglecting air resistance, is a parabola. The small reflector of a reflecting telescope is often a hyperbolic mirror (used to reflect the image to the eyepiece); the hyperbola can be used to locate an invisible source of sound, such as an enemy's guns, by considering two listening posts as the foci of a hyperbola and performing certain computations on the difference in time of arrival of the sound of the gun at the listening posts.

In economics and business certain types of parabolic and hyperbolic curves are appropriate for representing demand and supply functions, production functions, and many other relationships.

It is always possible to remove the xy-term from any second-degree equation, so that $B = 0$ and the general equation can be written

$$Ax^2 + Cy^2 + Dx + Ey + F = 0$$

The removal of the xy-term is accomplished by changing from one set of axes to a new set which can be obtained by rotating the original axes about the origin. The procedure will not be discussed in detail, as it is seldom necessary to use it in practice.

Essentially, absence of the xy-term in a second-degree equation indicates that the corresponding curve is symmetric to a line or lines (axes of the curve) parallel to one or both of the coordinate axes. A circle, by definition, always has this type of symmetry and $B = 0$ for a circle.

The type of conic section represented by a second-degree equation can be identified readily from an examination of its coefficients, whether or not the equation includes an xy-term. However, only if the equation contains no xy-term can it readily be put into an appropriate standard form from which properties useful for graphing and for other purposes can be obtained; degenerate cases can also be identified from the standard forms.

● **Identification of a Quadratic Equation**

The general quadratic equation

$$Ax^2 + Bxy + Cy^2 + Dx + Ey + F = 0$$

with at least one of A and C nonzero can be identified as a circle, ellipse, parabola, or hyperbola as follows:

> If $B = 0$ and $A = C$, the conic is a circle
> If $B^2 - 4AC < 0$, the conic is an ellipse
> If $B^2 - 4AC = 0$, the conic is a parabola
> If $B^2 - 4AC > 0$, the conic is a hyperbola

For the special case $B = 0$, with at least one of A and C nonzero, the above identification procedure can be reduced to the following:

if $B = 0$
then

> If $A = C$, the conic is a circle
> If $A \neq C$, but A and C have the same sign, the conic is an ellipse
> If $A = 0$ or $C = 0$ but not both, the conic is a parabola
> If A and C have opposite signs, the conic is a hyperbola

The standard forms for each of the four types of conic sections and their geometrical representations and properties are discussed in the following sections; the algebraic procedure known as "completing the square," which is used to put equations into these standard forms, is discussed in detail in Technical Note III.

● **The Circle**

Geometrically, a circle is the locus of points in a plane which are a fixed distance from a given point called the *center*. The distance of the points from the center is the *radius* of the circle. The general equation of a circle can be written

$$Ax^2 + Ay^2 + Dx + Ey + F = 0$$

(since $A = C$ and $B = 0$ in the general quadratic equation). As shown in Technical Note III, any equation that represents a circle can be written in the standard form

$$(x - h)^2 + (y - k)^2 = r^2$$

where (h, k) is the center of the circle and r is its radius, as shown in Fig. 1.52.

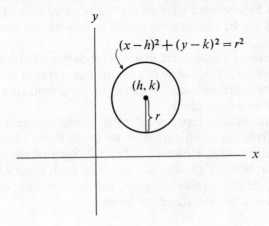

FIGURE 1.52

When an attempt is made to put an equation in the standard form for a circle, degenerate or imaginary loci can be detected from the indicated value of r^2:

If $r^2 < 0$, there is no real locus (imaginary radius)
If $r^2 = 0$, the locus is a point (zero radius)
If $r^2 > 0$, the locus is a circle

Example

Put the following equations into the appropriate standard form for a circle, check for degenerate or imaginary loci, and graph.
(a) $x^2 + y^2 - 4x - 6y + 19 = 0$.
(b) $2x^2 + 2y^2 + 16x - 4y + 17 = 0$.
(c) $x^2 + y^2 - 10x + 4y + 29 = 0$.

(a) $$(x^2 - 4x + 4) + (y^2 - 6y + 9) = -19 + 4 + 9$$
$$(x - 2)^2 + (y - 3)^2 = -6$$

$r^2 < 0$, so no real locus.

(b) $$2(x^2 + 8x + 16) + 2(y^2 - 2y + 1) = -17 + 32 + 2$$
$$(x + 4)^2 + (y - 1)^2 = \tfrac{17}{2}$$

Circle: center $(-4, 1)$, radius $\sqrt{\tfrac{17}{2}}$. See Fig. 1.53.

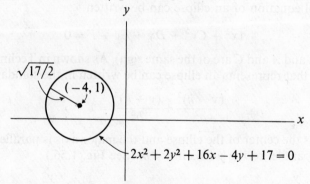

FIGURE 1.53

(c) $$(x^2 - 10x + 25) + (y^2 + 4y + 4) = -29 + 25 + 4$$
$$(x - 5)^2 + (y + 2)^2 = 0$$

Point: $(5, -2)$. See Fig. 1.54.

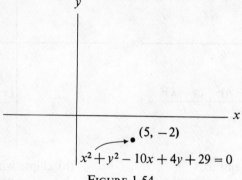

FIGURE 1.54

● **The Ellipse**

Geometrically, an ellipse is the locus of points in a plane the sum of whose distances from two fixed points (called *foci*) is constant. An ellipse has two (perpendicular) axes of symmetry; the longer of these is the *major axis*, the shorter is the *minor axis*; the point at which the axes intersect is the *center* of the ellipse (see Fig. 1.55).

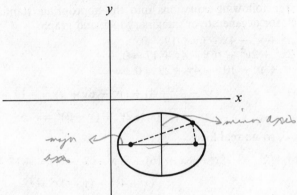

FIGURE 1.55

The general equation of an ellipse can be written

$$Ax^2 + Cy^2 + Dx + Ey + F = 0$$

(where $A \neq C$ and A and C are of the same sign). As shown in Technical Note III, any equation that represents an ellipse can be written in the standard form

$$\frac{(x-h)^2}{a^2} + \frac{(y-k)^2}{b^2} = 1$$

where (h, k) is the center of the ellipse and the major axis is parallel to the x-axis if $a > b$ and parallel to the y-axis if $a < b$. (See Fig. 1.56.)

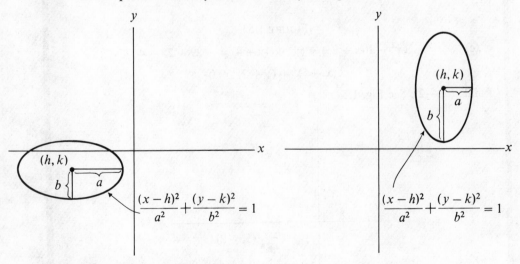

(a) ellipse with major axis parallel to x-axis $(a > b)$

(b) ellipse with major axis parallel to y-axis $(a < b)$

FIGURE 1.56

The length of the axis parallel to the x-axis is $2a$ and the length of the axis parallel to the y-axis is $2b$. When $a = b$, the ellipse becomes a circle with radius $r = a = b$.

When an equation is in the standard form for an ellipse, the locus is an ellipse. However,

If $\dfrac{(x - h)^2}{a^2} + \dfrac{(y - k)^2}{b^2} = C$, where $C < 0$, there is no real locus.

If $\dfrac{(x - h)^2}{a^2} + \dfrac{(y - k)^2}{b^2} = 0$, the locus is the point (h, k).

Example

Put the following equations into the appropriate standard form for an ellipse, check for degenerate or imaginary loci, and graph.

(a) $6x^2 + 4y^2 - 36x + 16y + 70 = 0$.
(b) $9x^2 + 2y^2 + 36x + 4y + 20 = 0$.
(c) $2x^2 + y^2 - 16x - 12y + 80 = 0$.

(a) $\qquad 6(x^2 - 6x + 9) + 4(y^2 + 4y + 4) = -70 + 54 + 16$

$$\frac{6(x^2 - 6x + 9)}{(6)(4)} + \frac{4(y^2 + 4y + 4)}{(6)(4)} = \frac{0}{(6)(4)}$$

$$\frac{(x - 3)^2}{2^2} + \frac{(y + 2)^2}{(\sqrt{6})^2} = 0$$

Point: $(3, -2)$. See Fig. 1.57.

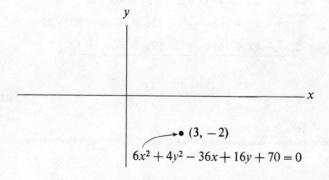

FIGURE 1.57

(b) $\qquad 9x^2 + 2y^2 + 36x + 4y + 20 = 0$

$$9(x^2 + 4x + 4) + 2(y^2 + 2y + 1) = -20 + 36 + 2$$

$$\frac{9(x^2 + 4x + 4)}{(9)(2)} + \frac{2(y^2 + 2y + 1)}{(9)(2)} = \frac{38 - 20}{(9)(2)}$$

$$\frac{(x+2)^2}{2} + \frac{(y+1)^2}{9} = \frac{18}{18}$$

$$\frac{(x+2)^2}{(\sqrt{2})^2} + \frac{(y+1)^2}{3^2} = 1$$

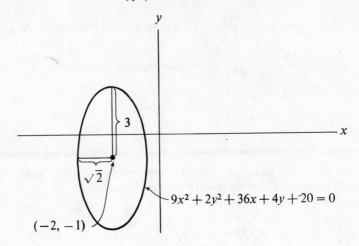

FIGURE 1.58

Ellipse: Center $(-2, -1)$, $a = \sqrt{2}$, $b = 3$.
Major axis $2(3) = 6$.
Minor axis $2\sqrt{2}$.
Major axis parallel to y-axis.
See Fig. 1.58.

(c)
$$2x^2 + y^2 - 16x - 12y + 80 = 0$$

$$2(x^2 - 8x + 16) + (y^2 - 12y + 36) = -80 + 32 + 36$$

$$\frac{2(x^2 - 8x + 16)}{2} + \frac{(y^2 - 12y + 36)}{2} = \frac{-12}{2}$$

$$\frac{(x-4)^2}{1^2} + \frac{(y-6)^2}{(\sqrt{2})^2} = -6$$

$-6 < 0$, so there is no real locus.

● The Parabola

Geometrically, a parabola is the locus of points in a plane which are equidistant from a fixed point (called the *focus*) and a fixed straight line (called the *directrix*). A parabola is symmetric about a line, called its *axis*; the point of intersection of the parabola and its axis is the *vertex* of the parabola (see Fig. 1.59).

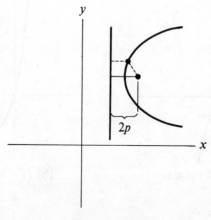

FIGURE 1.59

The general equation of a parabola can be written

$$Ax^2 + Dx + Ey + F = 0 \quad \text{if its axis is parallel to y-axis}$$

if the axis is parallel to the *y*-axis and

$$Cy^2 + Dx + Ey + F = 0 \quad \text{if its axis is parallel to x-axis}$$

if the axis is parallel to the *x*-axis. As shown in Technical Note III, any equation that represents a parabola can be written in the standard form

$$(x - h)^2 = 4p(y - k) \quad \text{axis is || to y-axis}$$

(h, k) is vertex of parabola

where (h, k) is the vertex of the parabola and the axis is parallel to the *y*-axis, or in the standard form

$$(y - k)^2 = 4p(x - h) \quad \text{axis is || to x-axis}$$

where (h, k) is the vertex of the parabola and the axis is parallel to the *x*-axis. The orientation and curvature of a parabola are determined by the sign and magnitude of p as follows:

For a parabola with axis parallel to the *y*-axis:

If $p < 0$, the parabola opens downward
If $p > 0$, the parabola opens upward

For a parabola with axis parallel to the *x*-axis:

If $p < 0$, the parabola opens to the left
If $p > 0$, the parabola opens to the right

(see Fig. 1.60). The distance between the point (focus) and the line (directrix)

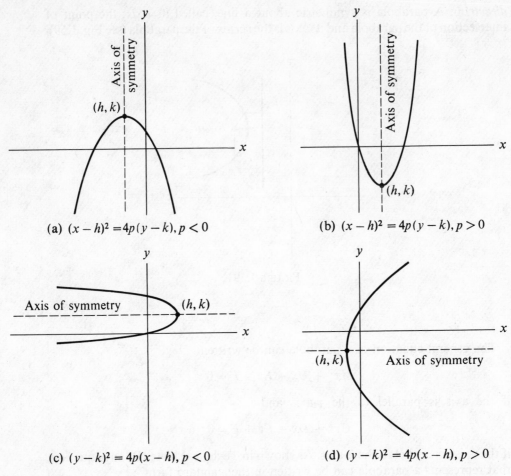

(a) $(x - h)^2 = 4p(y - k), p < 0$

(b) $(x - h)^2 = 4p(y - k), p > 0$

(c) $(y - k)^2 = 4p(x - h), p < 0$

(d) $(y - k)^2 = 4p(x - h), p > 0$

FIGURE 1.60

defining a parabola is $2p$ (distance from a point to a line is measured along the perpendicular); as shown in Fig. 1.61, the larger the value of p, the faster the parabola will open out.

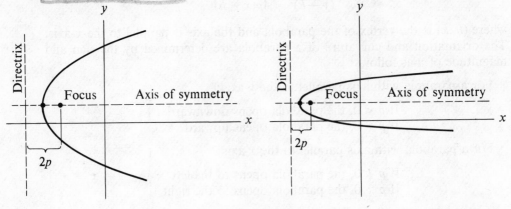

FIGURE 1.61

When an equation is in either standard form for a parabola, the locus is a parabola. However,

If $(x - h)^2 = C$, where $C < 0$, there is no real locus
If $(x - h)^2 = 0$, the locus is two coincident straight lines
(that is, geometrically, one straight line)
If $(x - h)(x - k) = 0$, the locus is two parallel lines

(and similarly for a parabola with axis parallel to the x-axis).

Example

Put the following equations into the appropriate standard form for a parabola, check for degenerate or imaginary loci, and graph.

(a) $y^2 - 8y + 17 = 0$.
(b) $x^2 - 4x + y + 14 = 0$.
(c) $x^2 - 7x + 12 = 0$.
(d) $y^2 - 10y + 25 = 0$.
(e) $y^2 - 2y - 6x + 19 = 0$.

Standard forms for parabolas:

$$(y - k)^2 = 4p(x - h) \qquad (x - h)^2 = 4p(y - k)$$

(a) $$y^2 - 8y + 17 = 0$$

$$(y^2 - 8y + 16) = -17 + 16$$
$$(y - 4)^2 = -1$$

$(y - k)^2 < 0$, so there is no real locus. Note that the x-term is missing in this example.

(b) $$x^2 - 4x + y + 14 = 0$$
$$x^2 - 4x + 4 = -y - 14 + 4$$
$$(x - 2)^2 = -(y + 10)$$

Parabola: Vertex $(2, -10)$, axis parallel to y-axis, parabola opens downward.

See Fig. 1.62. (Note that $4p = -1$.)

Note the distinction between example (a), where the locus is imaginary, and example (b), where the locus is real. In (a), the square of a number is said to be a negative constant, which is not possible for a real number. In (b), the square of a number is said to be the negative of a quantity involving a variable, which implies that the quantity $(y + 10)$ must be negative or zero; $y + 10$ is negative or zero if y is limited in extent to the interval $y \leq -10$, as shown in Fig. 1.62.

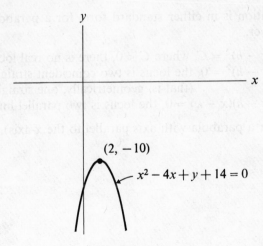

FIGURE 1.62

(c)
$$x^2 - 7x + 12 = 0$$
$$x^2 - 7x + \tfrac{49}{4} = -12 + \tfrac{49}{4}$$
$$(x - \tfrac{7}{2})^2 = \tfrac{1}{4}$$
$$x - \tfrac{7}{2} = \pm\sqrt{\tfrac{1}{4}}$$
$$x - \tfrac{7}{2} = \pm\tfrac{1}{2}$$
$$x = \pm\tfrac{1}{2} + \tfrac{7}{2}$$
$$= \tfrac{8}{2} \quad \text{or} \quad x - 4 = 0$$

and

$$x = \tfrac{6}{2} \quad \text{or} \quad x - 3 = 0$$

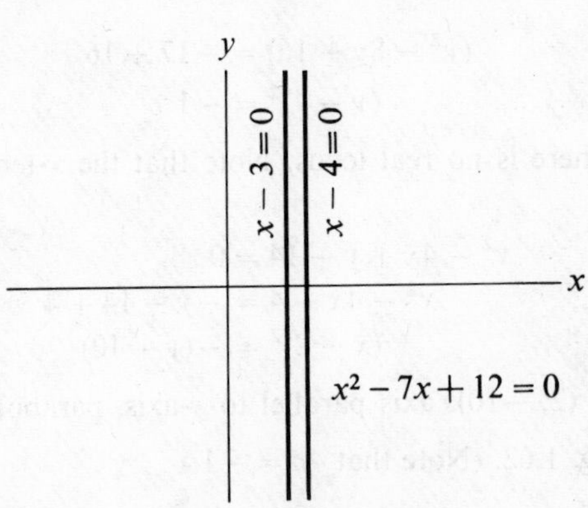

FIGURE 1.63

The locus is two parallel straight lines, parallel to the y-axis (see Fig. 1.63). Note that the y-term is missing in this example and the equation could have been factored $(x - 4)(x - 3) = 0$ without completing the square.

(d)
$$y^2 - 10y + 25 = 0$$
$$(y - 5)^2 = 0$$

The locus is two coincident straight lines (see Fig. 1.64). Note that the x-term is again missing.

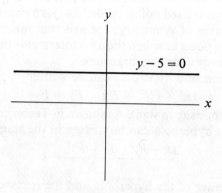

$$y - 5 = 0$$

FIGURE 1.64

(e)
$$y^2 - 2y - 6x + 19 = 0$$
$$(y^2 - 2y + 1) = 6x - 19 + 1$$
$$(y - 1)^2 = 6x - 18$$
$$(y - 1)^2 = 6(x - 3)$$

Parabola: Vertex (3, 1), axis parallel to x-axis, parabola opens to the right (see Fig. 1.65).

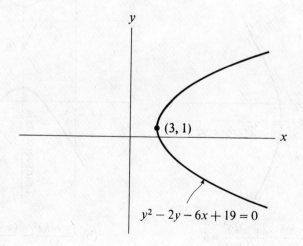

(3, 1)

$$y^2 - 2y - 6x + 19 = 0$$

FIGURE 1.65

● The Hyperbola

Geometrically, a hyperbola is the locus of points in a plane the difference of whose distances from two fixed points (called *foci*) is a constant. A hyperbola has two (perpendicular) axes of symmetry; the axis that intersects the hyperbola is its *transverse axis*; the point at which the axes intersect is the *center* of the hyperbola. A hyperbola always has two branches.

The general equation of a hyperbola can be written

$$Ax^2 + Cy^2 + Dx + Ey + F = 0$$

(where A and C are opposite in sign). As shown in Technical Note III, any equation that represents a hyperbola can be written in the standard form

$$\frac{(x - h)^2}{a^2} - \frac{(y - k)^2}{b^2} = 1$$

where (h, k) is the center of the hyperbola and the transverse axis is parallel to the x-axis, or in the standard form

$$\frac{(y - k)^2}{b^2} - \frac{(x - h)^2}{a^2} = 1$$

where (h, k) is the center of the hyperbola and the transverse axis is parallel to the y-axis. (See Fig. 1.66.)

Every hyperbola has a pair of intersecting straight lines as asymptotes; these asymptotes are given by the equations

$$\frac{x - h}{a} = \pm \frac{y - k}{b}$$

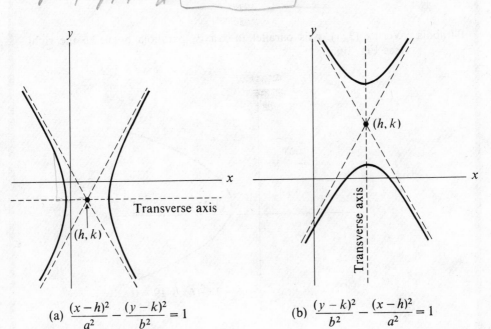

(a) $\dfrac{(x - h)^2}{a^2} - \dfrac{(y - k)^2}{b^2} = 1$ (b) $\dfrac{(y - k)^2}{b^2} - \dfrac{(x - h)^2}{a^2} = 1$

FIGURE 1.66

Note that the equations for these asymptotes can be obtained from the standard form by replacing 1 by 0, transposing the negative term, and taking square roots.

If $a = b$, the asymptotes of the hyperbola are perpendicular and the hyperbola is a *rectangular* or *equilateral hyperbola*. Equilateral hyperbolas are discussed in more detail below.

When an equation is in the standard form for a hyperbola, the locus is a hyperbola. However,

If $\dfrac{(x - h)^2}{a^2} - \dfrac{(y - k)^2}{b^2} = 0$, the locus is two intersecting straight lines,

$$\frac{x - h}{a} = \pm\frac{y - k}{b}$$

Note that these are also the equations for the asymptotes of the hyperbola.

There is no possibility of an imaginary locus in the case of a hyperbola. If, for example,

$$\frac{(x - h)^2}{a^2} - \frac{(y - k)^2}{b^2} = C \qquad \text{where } C < 0$$

then

$$\frac{(y - k)^2}{b^2} - \frac{(x - h)^2}{a^2} = C \qquad \text{where } C > 0$$

Example

Put the following equations into the appropriate standard form for a hyperbola, check for degenerate loci, and graph.
(a) $6x^2 - 12x - 4y^2 - 16y - 34 = 0$.
(b) $2y^2 - 12y - x^2 + 6x + 7 = 0$.
(c) $5x^2 + 20x - 3y^2 - 24y - 28 = 0$.

(a) $$6x^2 - 12x - 4y^2 - 16y - 34 = 0$$

$$(6x^2 - 12x) - (4y^2 + 16y) = 34$$

$$6(x^2 - 2x + 1) - 4(y^2 + 4y + 4) = 34 + 6 - 16$$

$$\frac{6(x - 1)^2}{(6)(4)} - \frac{4(y + 2)^2}{(6)(4)} = \frac{24}{(6)(4)}$$

$$\frac{(x - 1)^2}{2^2} - \frac{(y + 2)^2}{(\sqrt{6})^2} = 1$$

Hyperbola: Center $(1, -2)$, $a = 2$, $b = \sqrt{6}$, transverse axis parallel to the x-axis.

Asymptotes: $$\frac{x - 1}{2} = \pm\frac{y + 2}{\sqrt{6}}$$

$$y + 2 = \pm \frac{\sqrt{6}}{2}(x - 1)$$

Plotting the asymptotes:

$$y + 2 \approx 1.23(x - 1)$$

If $x = 0$, $y \approx -3.23$

If $y = 0$, $x \approx 2.63$

$$y + 2 \approx -1.23(x - 1)$$

If $x = 0$, $y \approx -0.77$

If $y = 0$, $x \approx -0.63$

(see Fig. 1.67).

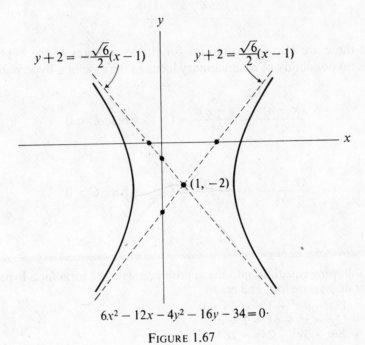

$$6x^2 - 12x - 4y^2 - 16y - 34 = 0 \cdot$$

FIGURE 1.67

NOTE: The symbol $\approx$ means "approximately equal to" and is used because of the approximation of $\sqrt{6}$.

(b)
$$2y^2 - 12y - x^2 + 6x + 7 = 0$$

$$2(y^2 - 6y + 9) - (x^2 - 6x + 9) = -7 + 18 - 9$$

$$\frac{2(y^2 - 6y + 9)}{(2)(1)} - \frac{(x^2 - 6x + 9)}{(2)(1)} = \frac{2}{(2)(1)}$$

$$\frac{(y - 3)^2}{1} - \frac{(x - 3)^2}{2} = \frac{2}{2}$$

$$\frac{(y - 3)^2}{1^2} - \frac{(x - 3)^2}{(\sqrt{2})^2} = 1$$

Hyperbola: Center $(3, 3)$; $a = \sqrt{2}$, $b = 1$, transverse axis parallel to y-axis.

Asymptotes: $y - 3 = \pm \dfrac{1}{\sqrt{2}}(x - 3)$

Plotting the asymptotes:

$$y - 3 \approx 0.71(x - 3) \qquad\qquad y - 3 \approx -0.71(x - 3)$$

If $x = 0$, $y \approx 0.87$ If $x = 0$, $y \approx 5.13$

If $y = 0$, $x \approx -1.23$ If $y = 0$, $x \approx 7.23$

See Fig. 1.68.

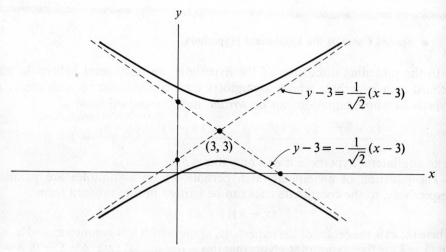

$$y - 3 = \frac{1}{\sqrt{2}}(x - 3)$$

$$(3, 3)$$

$$y - 3 = -\frac{1}{\sqrt{2}}(x - 3)$$

$$2y^2 - 12y - x^2 + 6x + 7 = 0$$

FIGURE 1.68

(c) $5x^2 + 20x - 3y^2 - 24y - 28 = 0$

$$5(x^2 + 4x + 4) - 3(y^2 + 8y + 16) = 28 + 20 - 48$$

$$\frac{(x + 2)^2}{(\sqrt{3})^2} - \frac{(y + 4)^2}{(\sqrt{5})^2} = 0$$

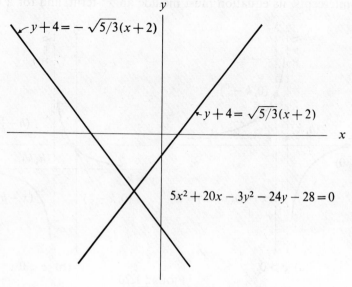

$$y + 4 = -\sqrt{5/3}(x + 2)$$

$$y + 4 = \sqrt{5/3}(x + 2)$$

$$5x^2 + 20x - 3y^2 - 24y - 28 = 0$$

FIGURE 1.69

The locus is two straight lines,

$$y + 4 = \pm\sqrt{\tfrac{5}{3}}(x + 2)$$

$y + 4 \approx 1.29(x + 2)$	$y + 4 \approx -1.29(x + 2)$
If $x = 0$, $y \approx -1.42$	If $x = 0$, $y \approx -6.58$
If $y = 0$, $x \approx 1.10$	If $y = 0$, $x \approx -5.10$

See Fig. 1.69.

● **Special Cases of the Equilateral Hyperbola**

In the preceding discussion of the hyperbola, an equilateral hyberpola was defined as a hyperbola whose asymptotes are perpendicular to each other. A hyperbola whose equation can be written in the standard form

$$\frac{(x - h)^2}{a^2} - \frac{(y - k)^2}{b^2} = 1 \quad \text{or} \quad \frac{(y - k)^2}{b^2} - \frac{(x - h)^2}{a^2} = 1$$

is an equilateral hyperbola if and only if $a = b$.

The equation of an equilateral hyperbola whose asymptotes are parallel, respectively, to the coordinate axes can be written in the standard form

$$(x - h)(y - k) = c$$

where (h, k) is the center of the hyperbola, about which it is symmetric, and $x = h$ and $y = k$ are the asymptotes. (Note that this is the special case $A = C = 0$, $B \neq 0$, of the general second-degree equation $Ax^2 + Bxy + Cy^2 + Dx + Ey + F = 0$.) If the asymptotes are considered as coordinate axes, the hyperbola has its two branches in the first and third quadrants if $c > 0$ and in the second and fourth quadrants if $c < 0$, as shown in Fig. 1.70. The intercepts of the hyperbola are the points $\left(h - \dfrac{c}{k}, 0\right)$ and $\left(0, k - \dfrac{c}{h}\right)$, where $h - \dfrac{c}{k}$ and $k - \dfrac{c}{h}$ may be positive or negative according to the values of h, k, and c. Note that this type of hyperbola has no more than one x-intercept and one y-intercept; for a hyperbola to have two x-intercepts, its equation must include an x^2-term, and for a hyperbola to

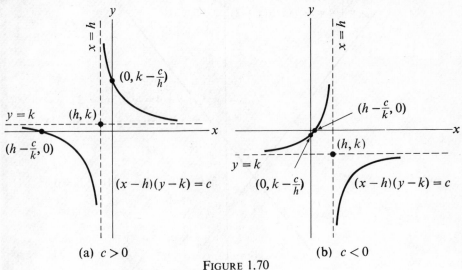

(a) $c > 0$ (b) $c < 0$

FIGURE 1.70

have two y-intercepts, its equation must include a y^2-term. Similarly, for a hyperbola to have one y-intercept, its equation must include an x-term and for a hyperbola to have one y-intercept, its equation must include a y-term.

The equation of an equilateral hyperbola whose asymptotes are the coordinate axes can be written in the standard form

$$xy = c$$

[Note that this is the special case $h = k = 0$ of the equation $(x - h)(y - k) = c$.]

This type of hyperbola has its center at the origin, about which it is symmetric; its branches occur in the first and third quadrants if $c > 0$ and in the second and fourth quadrants if $c < 0$. Since it is asymptotic to both coordinate axes, the hyperbola has no intercepts (see Fig. 1.71).

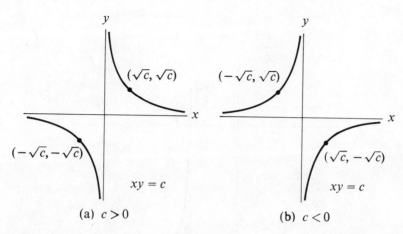

(a) $c > 0$ (b) $c < 0$

FIGURE 1.71

The equation $xy = c$ expresses an inversely proportional relationship between x and y—that is, as one variable increases, the other variable decreases proportionally. The variable y is said to be *inversely proportional* to the variable x, if there is a constant c such that

$$y = \frac{c}{x} \quad \text{or} \quad xy = c$$

By a generalization of this definition, the variable y is inversely proportional to a positive power n of a variable x, if there is a constant c, such that

$$y = \frac{c}{x^n} \quad \text{or} \quad x^n y = c$$

The curve corresponding to such an equation or to the analogous equation $xy^m = c$ is a *generalized equilateral hyperbola*, or *hyperbola of Fermat*. Its center is at the origin; its asymptotes are the coordinate axes.

If n or m is odd, the branches of the equilateral hyperbola are symmetric to the origin and are in the first and third quadrants if $c > 0$; the branches are in the second and fourth quadrants if $c < 0$. If $x^n y = c$ and n is even, the branches of the equilateral hyperbola are symmetric to the y-axis and are in the first and second quadrants if $c > 0$ and are in the third and fourth quadrants if $c < 0$. If $xy^m = c$ and m is even, the branches of the equilateral hyperbola are symmetric to the x-axis and are in the first and fourth quadrants if $c > 0$ and are in the second and third quadrants if $c < 0$.

Examples

Graph the equation

$$(x - 4)(y + 12) = 2$$

(see Fig. 1.72).

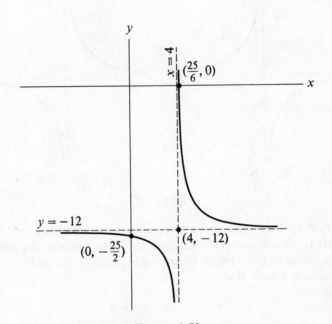

FIGURE 1.72

Equilateral hyperbola: Center $(4, -12)$.
                    Asymptotes $x = 4$, $y = -12$.
                    Lies in first and third quadrants of its asymptotes.

Graph the equation

$$(x - 2)y = -4$$

(see Fig. 1.73).

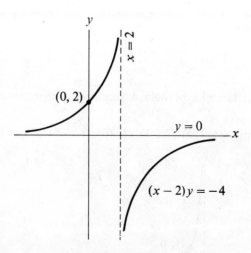

FIGURE 1.73

Equilateral hyperbola: Center $(2, 0)$.

Asymptotes $x = 2$, $y = 0$.

Lies in second and fourth quadrants of its asymptotes.

Graph the equation

$$x^3 y = 16$$

(see Fig. 1.74).

Generalized equilateral hyperbola, asymptotic to coordinate axes, symmetric to origin.

Points to aid graphing: $(2, 2)$, $(1, 16)$, $(\sqrt[3]{16}, 1)$, $(-2, -2)$, $(-1, -16)$, $(-\sqrt[3]{16}, -1)$ (note that $\sqrt[3]{16} \approx \frac{5}{2}$).

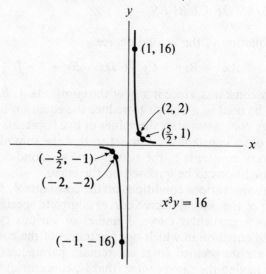

FIGURE 1.74

Graph the equation

$$xy^2 = 25$$

(See Fig. 1.75.)

Generalized equilateral hyperbola, asymptotic to coordinate axes, symmetric to x-axis.

Points to aid graphing: $(1, 5)$, $(25, 1)$, $(\frac{1}{4}, 10)$, $(1, -5)$, $(25, -1)$, $(\frac{1}{4}, -10)$.

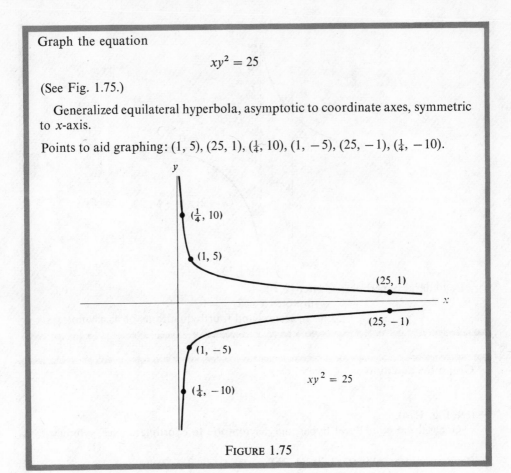

FIGURE 1.75

□ *FAMILIES OF CURVES*

The general equation of the second degree

$$Ax^2 + Bxy + Cy^2 + Dx + Ey + F = 0$$

has five arbitrary constants, since if any of the constants A, B, C, D, E, and F is not zero, it may be used as a divisor to reduce the equation to a form involving only five arbitrary constants; after the values of five constants are set arbitrarily, the value of the other constant must be set so that the sum of the terms is zero. These five arbitrary constants in the equation of a second-degree curve permit five geometric conditions to be imposed on the curve.

As discussed above, various conditions on the constants A, B, and C determine the general form of the second-degree curve; complete specification of the constants determines a particular curve. Families of various types of curves are represented by an equation in which one (or more) of the constants is specified and the others are unspecified (that is, remain parameters)—for example, a family of circles having the same center (that is, concentric) but different radii, or a family of parabolas having the same vertex but different degrees of curvature. Such families of curves will be discussed in more detail in later sections.

PROBLEMS

Identify the curves represented by the following equations; put each equation into the appropriate standard form and identify the parameters and properties thus obtained; sketch the curves.

1. $x^2 + y^2 - 6x - 2y - 6 = 0$

2. $y^2 - 6y + 9 = 0$

3. $3x^2 + 3y^2 - 6x + 4y = 1$

4. $y^2 - 10y = 0$

5. $xy - 4y = -4$

6. $x^2 - y^2 + 4x - 2y + 1 = 0$

7. $2x^2 + y^2 = 50$

8. $x^2 + y^2 - 4x - 2y + 5 = 0$

9. $4x^2 + 9y^2 - 16x - 18y + 133 = 0$

10. $xy + 3y = x + 6$

11. $3x^2 - y^2 - 12x - 6y = 0$

12. $x^2 - y^2 - 16 = 0$

13. $y = 3 + 2x - x^2$

14. $9x^2 + 25y^2 + 18x + 150y + 9 = 0$

15. $x^2 + 9y^2 - 8x + 7 = 0$

16. $16x^2 + y^2 - 32x - 6y + 25 = 0$

17. $y^2 - 3x^2 = 27$

18. $2x = 5y - y^2$

19. $5x^2 + 4y = 12$

20. $xy + 15y + 3x = 15$

21. $y^2 - 2y - 8x + 25 = 0$

22. $x^2 + y^2 - 4x - 2y + 6 = 0$

23. $y^2 - 4x^2 - 4y + 4 = 0$

24. $y^2 - 12y + 46 = 0$

25. $3y^2 + 2x = 0$

26. $xy - 6x + 2 = 0$

ANSWERS TO ODD-NUMBERED PROBLEMS

1. circle: $(x - 3)^2 + (y - 1)^2 = 4^2$
   center $(3, 1)$
   radius 4

3. circle: $(x - 1)^2 + (y + \frac{2}{3})^2 = (\frac{4}{3})^2$
   center $(1, -\frac{2}{3})$
   radius $\frac{4}{3}$

5. equilateral hyperbola: $y(x - 4) = -4$
   center $(4, 0)$
   asymptotes $x = 4$, $y = 0$
   second and fourth axes quadrants

7. ellipse: $\dfrac{(x - 0)^2}{5^2} + \dfrac{(y - 0)^2}{(5\sqrt{2})^2} = 1$
   center $(0, 0)$
   semiaxes $5\sqrt{2}$, 5
   major axis parallel to y-axis

9. ellipse with no real locus: $\dfrac{(x-2)^2}{3^2} + \dfrac{(y-1)^2}{2^2} = -3$

11. hyperbola: $\dfrac{(x-2)^2}{1^2} - \dfrac{(y+3)^2}{(\sqrt{3})^2} = 1$
center $(2, -3)$
asymptotes $\sqrt{3}x + y + 3 - 2\sqrt{3} = 0$ and $\sqrt{3}x - y - 3 - 2\sqrt{3} = 0$
transverse axis parallel to x-axis

13. parabola: $(x-1)^2 = -(y-4)$
vertex $(1, 4)$
axis parallel to y-axis, opens downward

15. ellipse: $\dfrac{(x-4)^2}{3^2} + \dfrac{(y-0)^2}{1^2} = 1$
center $(4, 0)$
semiaxes 3, 1
major axis parallel to x-axis

17. hyperbola: $\dfrac{(y-0)^2}{(3\sqrt{3})^2} - \dfrac{(x-0)^2}{3^2} = 1$
center $(0, 0)$
asymptotes $\sqrt{3}x + y = 0$ and $\sqrt{3}x - y = 0$
transverse axis parallel to y-axis

19. parabola: $(x-0)^2 = -\frac{4}{5}(y-3)$
vertex $(0, 3)$
axis parallel to y-axis, opens downward

21. parabola: $(y-1)^2 = 8(x-3)$
vertex $(3, 1)$
axis parallel to x-axis, opens to right

23. degenerate hyperbola: two intersecting lines $2x - y + 2 = 0$ and $2x + y - 2 = 0$

25. parabola: $(y-0)^2 = -\frac{2}{3}(x-0)$
vertex $(0, 0)$
axis parallel to x-axis, opens to left

■ 1.6 APPLICATIONS OF NONLINEAR CURVES IN BUSINESS AND ECONOMICS

☐ DEMAND AND SUPPLY CURVES

The first quadrant parts of various types of parabolas frequently are appropriate for representing demand and supply functions, as illustrated in Figs. 1.76 and 1.77. The first quadrant part of an equilateral hyperbola is frequently used to represent a demand function, as illustrated in Fig. 1.78.

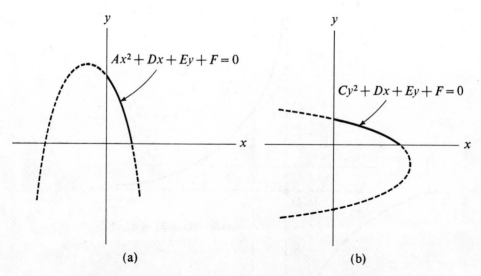

FIGURE 1.76   Examples of parabolic demand functions.

Note that each curve in Figs. 1.76, 1.77, and 1.78 is only one of a family of

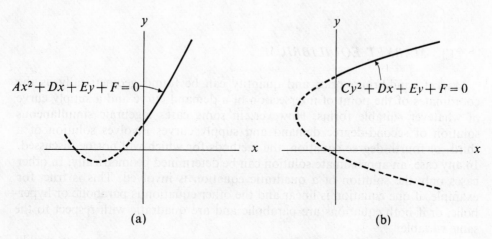

FIGURE 1.77   Examples of parabolic supply functions.

curves appropriate for representing the functions concerned. For example, the vertex of the parabola in Fig. 1.76(a) can lie anywhere in the second quadrant or on the positive y-axis, provided it has positive x- and y-intercepts. The conditions on the coefficients of the equation which specify the family of curves

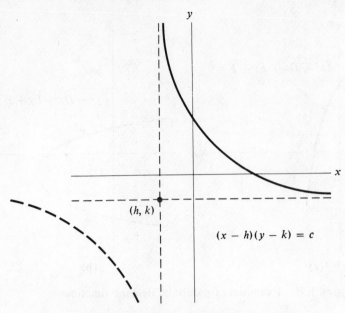

FIGURE 1.78   Example of a hyperbolic
demand function.

appropriate for representing a particular type of economic function can be determined from the corresponding standard form of the equation (see the Problems).

☐ MARKET EQUILIBRIUM

Market equilibrium price and quantity can be found geometrically as the coordinates of the point of intersection of a demand curve and a supply curve of whatever suitable forms. However, in some cases algebraic simultaneous solution of second-degree demand and supply curves involves solution of a third- or fourth-degree equation, the methods for which will not be discussed. In any case, an approximate solution can be determined geometrically. In other cases only the solution of a quadratic equation is involved. This is true, for example, if one equation is linear and the other equation is parabolic or hyperbolic, or if both equations are parabolic and are quadratic with respect to the same variable.

Unless a quadratic equation can be factored, its solution is most readily obtained by using the quadratic formula: The root(s) of a quadratic equation $ax^2 + bx + c = 0$ are given by

$$x = \frac{-b \pm \sqrt{b^2 - 4ac}}{2a}$$

This formula is obtained by the process of completing the square, as shown in Technical Note IV. Note that the number of real roots an equation has is determined by the value of $b^2 - 4ac$:

If $b^2 - 4ac < 0$, no real roots

If $b^2 - 4ac = 0$, one real root

If $b^2 - 4ac > 0$, two real roots

Examples

Find the equilibrium price and quantity for the following demand and supply equations (where x represents quantity and y represents price):

$$2x + y - 10 = 0$$

$$y^2 - 8x - 4 = 0$$

(see Fig. 1.79).

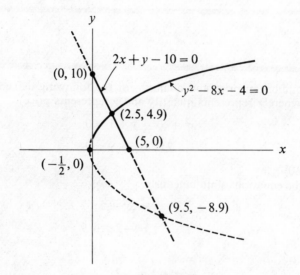

FIGURE 1.79

Solving the equations simultaneously,

$$2x = -y + 10 \text{ from the first equation}$$

$$8x = y^2 - 4 \text{ from the second equation}$$

so

$$y^2 - 4 = -4y + 40$$

$$y^2 + 4y - 44 = 0$$

and, using the quadratic formula,

$$y = \frac{-4 \pm \sqrt{16 - (4)(-44)}}{2}$$

$$= \frac{-4 \pm 4\sqrt{12}}{2}$$

$$= \frac{-4 \pm 8\sqrt{3}}{2}$$

$$= -2 \pm 4\sqrt{3}$$

$$x = \tfrac{1}{2}(-y + 10)$$

$$= \tfrac{1}{2}(12 \mp 4\sqrt{3})$$

$$= 6 \mp 2\sqrt{3}$$

$\sqrt{3} \approx 1.732$, so the approximate solutions are $(2.5, 4.9)$ and $(9.5, -8.9)$ and the approximate equilibrium point is $(2.5, 4.9)$.

Plotting the curves to verify the result geometrically:

$2x + y - 10 = 0$	$y^2 - 8x - 4 = 0$
If $x = 0$, $y = 10$	$y^2 = 8x + 4$
If $y = 0$, $x = 5$	$y^2 = 8(x + \tfrac{1}{2})$

Find the equilibrium price and quantity for the following demand and supply equations (where x represents quantity and y represents price):

$$x^2 + 5x - y + 1 = 0$$

$$2x^2 + y - 9 = 0$$

(see Fig. 1.80).

Solving the equations simultaneously,

$$y = x^2 + 5x + 1$$

$$= -2x^2 + 9$$

so

$$x^2 + 5x + 1 = -2x^2 + 9$$

$$3x^2 + 5x - 8 = 0$$

$$(3x + 8)(x - 1) = 0$$

$$x = -\tfrac{8}{3}, 1$$

$$y = -\tfrac{47}{9}, 7$$

The solutions are $(-\tfrac{8}{3}, -\tfrac{47}{9})$ and $(1, 7)$ and the equilibrium point is $(1, 7)$.

Plotting the curves to verify the result geometrically,

$x^2 + 5x - y + 1 = 0$	$2x^2 + y - 9 = 0$
$(x^2 + 5x + \tfrac{25}{4}) = y - 1 + \tfrac{25}{4}$	$2x^2 = -(y - 9)$
$(x + \tfrac{5}{2})^2 = y + \tfrac{21}{4}$	$x^2 = -\tfrac{1}{2}(y - 9)$

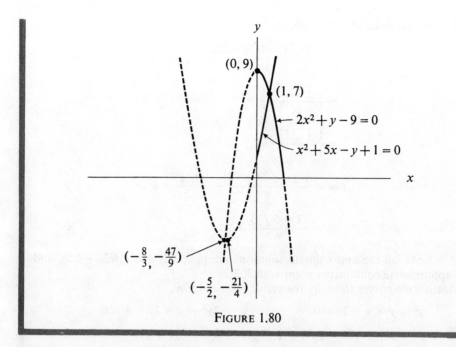

FIGURE 1.80

Find the equilibrium price and quantity for the following demand and supply equations (where x represents quantity and y represents price):

$$y^2 + y + x - 20 = 0$$
$$2y^2 - x - 3y - 4 = 0$$

(see Fig. 1.81).

Solving the equations simultaneously,

$$x = -y^2 - y + 20$$
$$= 2y^2 - 3y - 4$$

so

$$-y^2 - y + 20 = 2y^2 - 3y - 4$$
$$3y^2 - 2y - 24 = 0$$

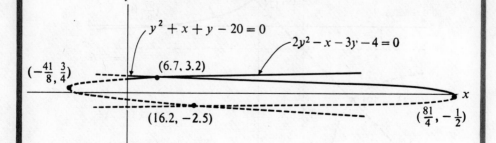

FIGURE 1.81

and, using the quadratic formula,

$$y = \frac{2 \pm \sqrt{4 - 4(3)(-24)}}{6}$$

$$= \frac{2 \pm 2\sqrt{73}}{6}$$

$$= \frac{1 \pm \sqrt{73}}{3}$$

$$x = -\frac{1 \pm 2\sqrt{73} + 73}{9} - \frac{1 \pm \sqrt{73}}{3} + 20$$

$$= -\frac{77 \pm 5\sqrt{73}}{9} + 20$$

$\sqrt{73} \approx 8.544$, so the approximate solutions are $(6.7, 3.2)$ and $(16.2, -2.5)$, and the approximate equilibrium point is $(6.7, 3.2)$.

Plotting the curves to verify the result geometrically,

$$y^2 + y + x - 20 = 0 \qquad\qquad 2y^2 - x - 3y - 4 = 0$$

$$y^2 + y + \tfrac{1}{4} = -x + 20 + \tfrac{1}{4} \qquad\qquad 2(y^2 - \tfrac{3}{2}y + \tfrac{9}{16}) = x + 4 + \tfrac{9}{8}$$

$$(y + \tfrac{1}{2})^2 = -(x - \tfrac{81}{4}) \qquad\qquad (y - \tfrac{3}{4})^2 = \tfrac{1}{2}(x + \tfrac{41}{8})$$

Find the market equilibrium price and quantity for the following demand and supply equations (where x represents quantity and y represents price):

$$(x + 12)(y + 6) = 169$$

$$x - y + 6 = 0$$

(see Fig. 1.82).

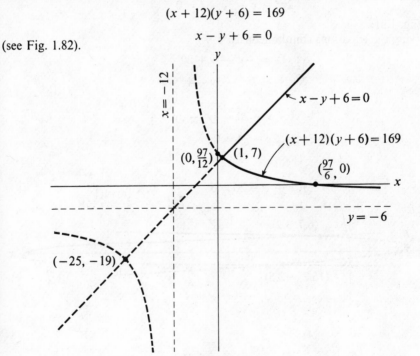

FIGURE 1.82

Solving the equations simultaneously,

$$y = x + 6 \qquad \text{from the second equation}$$

Substituting in the first equation,

$$(x + 12)(x + 12) = 169$$

$$x + 12 = \pm 13$$

$$x = 1, -25$$

$$y = 7, -19$$

The solutions are $(1, 7)$ and $(-25, -19)$ and the equilibrium point is $(1, 7)$. Plotting the curves to verify the result geometrically,

$x - y + 6 = 0$	$(x + 12)(y + 6) = 69$
If $x = 0$, $y = 6$	asymptotes $x = -12$, $y = -6$
If $y = 0$, $x = -6$	If $x = 0$, $y = \frac{97}{12}$
	If $y = 0$, $x = \frac{97}{6}$

☐ *PRODUCT TRANSFORMATION CURVES*

Some production processes will yield more than one output. Sheep raising is a classic example of such a process—two outputs, wool and mutton, can be produced in varying proportions by a single production process. Many industrial production processes can also yield more than one output—for example, commodities that are similar but of different type or quality. Production or product transformation curves express the relationship between the quantities of two different commodities produced by the same firm using common supplies of labor and raw materials. Note that the case of joint products is distinguished on a technical, not an organizational basis—the quantities of two or more products are technically or technologically interdependent. Cases in which a firm produces two or more technically independent products are excluded from analysis by product transformation curves.

A *product transformation curve* is defined as the locus of output quantity combinations which can be obtained from a given input. A product transformation curve is usually one of a family of possible product transformation curves, where the curves of the family correspond to various inputs. For example, Fig. 1.83 shows product transformation curves represented by the first-quadrant parts of four of a family of concentric circles; the farther a curve lies from the origin, the greater the input to which it corresponds.

If the two output quantities produced are x and y, the product transformation curve relating them must be such that as one quantity increases the other quantity decreases. To fulfill certain reasonable economic assumptions, which need not be discussed here, product transformation curves are usually also concave from below, as in Fig. 1.83.

In addition to circular product transformation curves, suitably located and oriented elliptic, parabolic, and hyperbolic curves are appropriate in some cases for representing product transformation curves, as illustrated in Figs. 1.84, 1.85, and 1.86. Note that for circular, elliptic, and parabolic product transformation

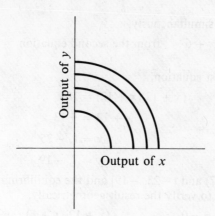

FIGURE 1.83 Members of a
family of circular product
transformation curves.

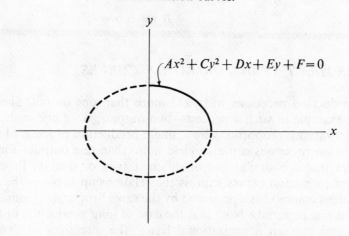

$$Ax^2 + Cy^2 + Dx + Ey + F = 0$$

FIGURE 1.84 Example of an elliptic
product transformation curve.

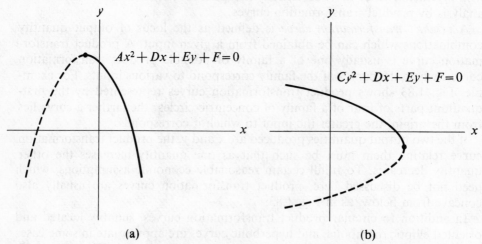

$$Ax^2 + Dx + Ey + F = 0$$

$$Cy^2 + Dx + Ey + F = 0$$

(a)　　　　　　　　　　　(b)

FIGURE 1.85 Examples of parabolic product transformation curves.

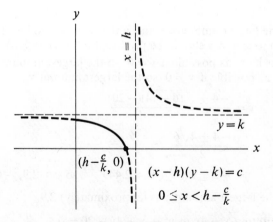

FIGURE 1.86 Example of a hyperbolic
product transformation curve.

curves the entire first-quadrant part of the curve is appropriate. However, for
hyperbolic product transformation curves the range is limited to the lower
branch of the hyperbola; this is usually stated as a restriction on the range of x:

$$0 \le x \le h - \frac{c}{k}$$

where $\left(h - \frac{c}{k}, 0\right)$ is the x-intercept.

Examples

A company produces amounts x and y of two different grades of steel using the
same production process. The product transformation curve for the input used

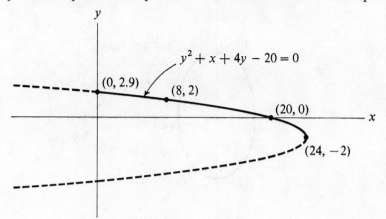

FIGURE. 1.87

is given by

$$y^2 + x + 4y - 20 = 0$$

(see Fig. 1.87).

(a) What are the largest amounts x and y that can be produced?

(b) What amounts x and y should be produced in order to have $x = 4y$?

(a) x is as large as possible if $y = 0$, so the largest amount x is 20. y is as large as possible if $x = 0$, so the largest amount y is

$$y = \frac{-4 \pm \sqrt{16 - (4)(-20)}}{2}$$

$$= \frac{-4 \pm 4\sqrt{6}}{2}$$

$$= -2 \pm 2\sqrt{6}; \sqrt{6} \approx 2.449 \qquad \text{so } y \approx 2.9, \; -6.9$$

and the largest amount y is (approximately) 2.9.

(b) Substituting $x = 4y$ in $y^2 + x + 4y - 20 = 0$,

$$y^2 + 4y + 4y - 20 = 0$$

$$y^2 + 8y - 20 = 0$$

$$(y + 10)(y - 2) = 0$$

$$y = -10, 2$$

So the amounts produced are $x = 8$, $y = 2$.

A company produces amounts x and y of two different kinds of candy using the same production process. The product transformation curve for the input used is given by

$$5x^2 + 2y^2 = 98$$

(see Fig. 1.88).

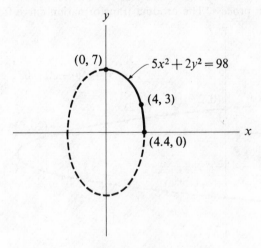

FIGURE 1.88

(a) What are the largest amounts x and y that can be produced?

(b) What amounts x and y should be produced in order to have $y = \frac{3}{4}x$?

(a) If $y = 0$,

$$5x^2 = 98$$

$$x^2 = \tfrac{98}{5}$$

$$x = \pm\sqrt{\tfrac{98}{5}} = \pm 7\sqrt{\tfrac{2}{5}} = \pm\tfrac{7}{5}\sqrt{10}$$

$$\sqrt{10} \approx 3.162 \qquad \text{so } x \approx \pm 4.4$$

So the largest amount x is (approximately) 4.4. If $x = 0$,

$$2y^2 = 98$$

$$y^2 = 49$$

$$y = \pm 7$$

So the largest amount y is 7.

(b) Substituting $y = \tfrac{3}{4}x$ in $5x^2 + 2y^2 = 98$,

$$5x^2 + 2(\tfrac{9}{16})x^2 = 98$$

$$\tfrac{49}{8}x^2 = 98$$

$$x^2 = 16$$

$$x = \pm 4, \; y = \pm 3$$

So the amounts produced are $x = 4$, $y = 3$.

A company produces amounts x and y of two petrochemicals using the same production process. The product transformation curve for the input used is given by

$$(x - 24)(y - 36) = 240, \; x < \tfrac{52}{3}$$

(see Fig. 1.89).

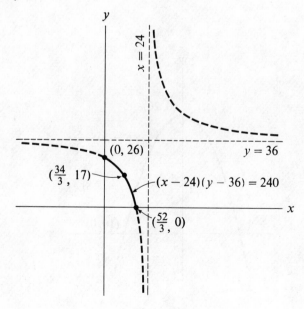

FIGURE 1.89

(a) What are the largest amounts x and y that can be produced?

(b) What amounts x and y should be produced to have $x = \frac{2}{3}y$?

(a) If $y = 0$,

$$x = -\frac{20}{3} + 24 = \frac{52}{3}$$

So the largest amount x is $\frac{52}{3}$. If $x = 0$,

$$y = -10 + 36 = 26$$

So the largest amount y is 26.

(b) Substituting $x = \frac{2}{3}y$ in $(x - 24)(y - 36) = 240$,

$$\left(\frac{2y}{3} - 24\right)(y - 36) = 240$$

$$(y - 36)(y - 36) = 360$$

$$y - 36 = \pm\sqrt{360}$$

$$\sqrt{360} = 6\sqrt{10} \approx 19.0$$

So $y = \pm\sqrt{360} + 36 \approx 55.17$. So the amounts produced are $x = \frac{34}{3}$, $y = 17$.

A company produces amounts x and y of two different textiles using the same production process. The product transformation curve for the input used is given by

$$y = 20 - \frac{x^2}{5}$$

(see Fig. 1.90).

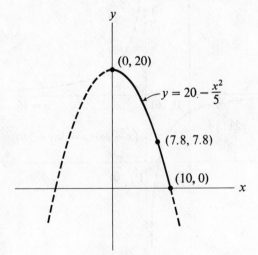

FIGURE 1.90

(a) What are the largest amounts x and y that can be produced?

(b) What amounts x and y should be produced to have $x = y$?

(a) If $y = 0$,

$$x^2 = 100$$

$$x = \pm 10$$

So the largest amount x is 10. If $x = 0$, $y = 20$, so the largest amount y is 20.

(b) Substituting $x = y$ in $y = 20 - \dfrac{x^2}{5}$,

$$5y = 100 - y^2$$

$$y^2 + 5y - 100 = 0$$

$$y = \frac{-5 \pm \sqrt{25 - (4)(-100)}}{2}$$

$$= \frac{-5 \pm 5\sqrt{17}}{2}$$

$$\sqrt{17} \approx 4.123 \qquad \text{so } y \approx 7.8, \ -12.8$$

So the amounts produced are $x = y = 7.8$

PROBLEMS

For each of the following pairs of equations (i) determine which equation represents a demand curve and which equation represents a supply curve, (ii) determine the market equilibrium quantity and price algebraically, and (iii) check geometrically (at least some of) the algebraically determined equilibrium points.

1. (a) $x = 16 - 2y$
   (b) $4x = 4y + y^2$

2. (a) $x = 130 - 4y$
   (b) $y = 10 + \dfrac{x}{5} + \dfrac{x^2}{100}$

3. (a) $y = 2 + \dfrac{x}{5} + \dfrac{x^2}{20}$
   (b) $y = \dfrac{30 - x}{4}$

4. (a) $y = 16 - x^2$
   (b) $y = 4 + x$

5. (a) $x = 32 - 4y - y^2$
   (b) $y = \dfrac{x}{20} + 1$

6. (a) $y = 9x + 12$
   (b) $y = 39 - 3x^2$

7. (a) $y = 6 + \dfrac{x^2}{4}$
   (b) $x = \sqrt{36 - y}$

8. (a) $y = (x + 2)^2$
   (b) $y = 39 - 3x^2$

9. (a) $y = 48 - 3x^2$
   (b) $y = x^2 + 4x + 16$

10. (a) $x = 84 - y^2$
    (b) $x = y + 4y^2$

11. (a) $x = 10y + 5y^2$
    (b) $x = 64 - 8y - 2y^2$

12. (a) $x = 10y + 4y^2$
    (b) $x = 96 - 8y - 2y^2$

13. (a) $(x + 16)(y + 12) = 480$
    (b) $y = 2x + 4$

14. (a) $x = 2y^2 - 2y - 6$
    (b) $x = -y^2 - y + 18$

15. (a) $y = 10 - 3x^2$
    (b) $y = 4 + x^2 + 2x$

16. (a) $xy = 30$
    (b) $3y - x = 9$

17. (a) $xy = 15$
    (b) $y = x + 2$

18. (a) $(x + 10)(y + 20) = 300$
    (b) $x = 2y - 8$

19. (a) $(x + 6)(y + 12) = 144$
    (b) $y = 2 + \dfrac{x}{2}$

20. (a) $(x + 12)(y + 6) = 169$
    (b) $x - y + 6 = 0$

21. (a) $(x + 5)(y + 6) = 80$
    (b) $y = \dfrac{x}{3} + 3$

22. (a) $(x + 1)y = 5$
    (b) $y = \dfrac{x}{4}$

23. (a) $x(y + 6) = 24$
    (b) $y - 2x + 4 = 0$

24. (a) $y(x + 3) = 18$
    (b) $y - 3x + 6 = 0$

25. (a) $(x + 4)(y + 2) = 24$
    (b) $y = 1 + \dfrac{x}{2}$

26. (a) $y = x^2 + 5x + 1$
    (b) $y + 2x^2 - 9 = 0$

27. (a) $x = 3y^2 - 3y - 2$
    (b) $x = 10 - y^2 - y$

28. (a) $(x + 10)(y + 5) = 225$
    (b) $x - y + 5 = 0$

Each of the following equations represents a product transformation curve for the amounts x and y, respectively, of two related commodities; find the largest amounts x and y that can be produced.

29. $x = 36 - 6y^2$

30. $y = 65 - 12x - 5x^2$

31. $y = 45 - 9x^2$

32. $x = 16 - 4y - 2y^2$

33. The production manager has decided that the marketing department can sell 126 units of product daily, and he wants to produce that much. If he assumes that all factors other than the number of employees and the resultant output remain constant within the range of this total production, the production function can be expressed by the equation

$$2x^2 + 4x - y = 0$$

with x representing the number of employees and y representing the units of production. The production manager claims that he will need 7 men to produce the 126 units. (a) Assuming that the equation is appropriate, is the production manager correct in his statement as to the number of men needed? (b) What type of curve does the equation represent? Graph the curve. (c) Draw up a schedule of units of production output per man employed in the range 1 through 7 employees. Indicate the change in the number of units produced through this range as each employee is added.

34. A company's operations research director believes that the short-run average cost of production can be expressed by the equation

$$x^2 - 16x - y + 68 = 0$$

with x representing the number of units produced and y representing the average cost per unit. He says that the average cost will be lowest when eight units are produced. (a) Is his statement correct? (b) What type of curve is represented? Graph the curve. (c) Draw up a schedule of values of y for the range $x = 4$ through $x = 12$ and indicate the amount of change in y for each change in x.

35. In national income analysis, the relationship between the supply of money and the amount of money demanded as a stock to be "held" is very important. The demand for a stock of money to be held, or the "liquidity preference," as Keynes called it, is often considered dependent upon three motives: (1) the transactions motive, (2) the precautionary motive, and (3) the speculative motive. In this problem, at a given level of national income, (1) and (2) above are assumed to be constant; (3) is considered to be a function of the interest rate as expressed by the equation $(x - 1)y = 4$, where x is the rate of interest ($\%$) and y is the demand for money to hold expressed in billions of dollars. (a) What type of curve does the equation express? Graph the curve. (b) Draw up a schedule of values for y, the amount of money demanded to be held (in billions of dollars) for the values of x from 2 through 7%. What is the value of y when $x = 100$ (in billions of dollars)? (c) Note and describe the segment of the curve which represents the "liquidity trap"—that segment in which the interest rate seems to lose its force as an effective factor in influencing the demand for money to hold.

36. According to convention, in the economic analysis discussed in Problem 35, the dependent variable (the demand for money to hold) is often assigned to the x-axis rather than the y-axis. An equation used to express Keynesian ideas concerning the relationship between the rate of interest and the money demanded to be held is then $x(y - 1) = 4$. (a) What type of curve does this equation represent? Graph the curve. (b) Draw up a schedule of values for the interest rate y for the values of x from 1 through 7 (in billions of dollars). What is the value of y when $x = 100$ (in billions of dollars)? (c) Note and describe the segment of the curve that represents the "liquidity trap."

37. Consider the parabola $y = \frac{1}{4}x^2 - x + 4$ and the equilateral hyperbola $(x + 2)(y - 2) = 4$. (a) Show that for $x = 0$ and for $x = 2$ both equations have the same value of y, but that for $x = 4$ and for $x = -2$ they have different values of y. (b) Show that the two equations have the same value of y only for $x = 0$ and for $x = 2$. (c) Sketch the two curves on the same set of axes.

38. A company produces x and y amounts of steel of two different grades, using the same resources; the product transformation curve is

$$y = 20 - \frac{300}{30 - x} \qquad (x < 30)$$

(a) Sketch the curve. (b) Determine the largest amounts of x and y that can be produced. (c) If the demand for grade x steel is twice that for grade y steel, determine the amounts the company should produce.

39. A company manufactures two grades of candy from the same resources. If x and y represent the quantities produced, the product transformation curve is

$$(x - 24)(y - 36) = 240 \qquad (x < 24)$$

(a) Sketch the curve. (b) Determine the largest amounts of x and y that can be produced. (c) If the demand for grade x candy is two-thirds that for grade y, determine the amounts the company should produce.

40. A company manufactures two grades of paper from the same resources; if x and y represent the quantities produced, the product transformation curve is

$$(x - 30)(y - 15) = 150 \qquad (x < 30)$$

(a) Sketch the curve. (b) If the demand for grade x paper is three times that for grade y paper, determine the amounts of paper the company should produce. (c) If the demand for grade y paper exceeds that for grade x paper by four units, determine the amounts the company should produce.

ANSWERS TO ODD-NUMBERED PROBLEMS

---

1. (a) demand
   (b) supply
   $E(8, 4)$

3. (a) supply
   (b) demand
   $E(6.91, 5.77)$

5. (a) demand
   (b) supply
   $E(20, 2)$

7. (a) supply
   (b) demand
   $E(4.90, 12)$

9. (a) demand
   (b) supply
   $E(2.37, 31.15)$

11. (a) supply
    (b) demand
    $E(40, 2)$

13. (a) demand
    (b) supply
    $E(4, 12)$

15. (a) demand
    (b) supply
    $E(1, 7)$

17. (a) demand
    (b) supply
    $E(3, 5)$

19. (a) demand
    (b) supply
    $E(3.22, 3.61)$

21. (a) demand
    (b) supply
    $E(3, 4)$

23. (a) demand
    (b) supply
    $E(3, 2)$

25. (a) demand
    (b) supply
    $E(2, 2)$

27. (a) supply
    (b) demand
    $E(4, 2)$

29. $x_{max} = 36$
    $y_{max} = \sqrt{6}$

31. $x_{max} = \sqrt{5}$
    $y_{max} = 45$

33. (a) yes
    (b) parabola, vertex $(-1, -2)$, axis parallel to y-axis
    (c)

Number of employees x	Total units produced y	Δy
1	6	
2	16	10
3	30	14
4	48	18
5	70	22
6	96	26
7	126	30

35. (a) equilateral hyperbola, transverse axis parallel to y-axis
    center $(1, 0)$
    lies in first and third quadrants of its asymptotes
    asymptotes: $x = 1$, $y = 0$
    intercept: $(0, -4)$

    (b)

Interest rate x	Amount of money demanded to be held y
1	
2	4
3	2
4	$\frac{4}{3}$
5	1
6	$\frac{4}{5}$
7	$\frac{2}{3}$
100	$\frac{4}{99}$

    (c) segment for which $x < 2$

39. (b) $x_{max} = 17\frac{1}{3}$, $y_{max} = 26$
    (c) $x = 11.36$, $y = 17.04$

☐ *PARETO'S LAW OF DISTRIBUTION OF INCOME*

The economist Vilfredo Pareto proposed the following law of distribution of income: The number of individuals N from a given population of size a whose income exceeds x is

$$N = \frac{a}{x^b}$$

where b is a population parameter, usually approximately 1.5. Note that this equation represents a generalized equilateral hyperbola and that it is appropriate only for the range $0 < N \le a$ and $0 < x <$ maximum income in the population (see Fig. 1.91).

For above-subsistence incomes, data indicate that Pareto's law is generally fairly accurate. Pareto suggested that the value of b is approximately 1.5; data indicate that this varies from population to population, but 1.5 is usually a good approximation.

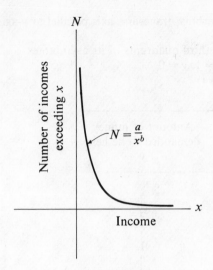

FIGURE 1.91

NOTE: The notation used in the following examples is reviewed in the next section, which deals with exponential and logarithmic functions. Note, however, that Pareto's law is represented by a power function, not an exponential function.

Examples

Pareto's law for the distribution of incomes for a particular group is

$$N = \frac{216 \times 10^{10}}{x^{3/2}}$$

(a) How many people are millionaires?
(b) How many people have incomes between 3600 and 10,000?
(c) What is the lowest income of the 80 people with the highest incomes?

(a) $N = \dfrac{216 \times 10^{10}}{(10^6)^{3/2}} = 2160$ millionaires

(b) The number with incomes exceeding 3600 is

$$N = \frac{216 \times 10^{10}}{(3600)^{3/2}} = \frac{216 \times 10^{10}}{6^3 \times 10^3} = 10^7$$

The number with incomes exceeding 10,000 is

$$N = \frac{216 \times 10^{10}}{(10^4)^{3/2}} = 216 \times 10^4$$

so the number with incomes between 3600 and 10,000 is
$10^7 - 216 \times 10^4 = (1000 - 216) \times 10^4 = 784 \times 10^4$ or   7,840,000

(c) $$80 = \frac{216 \times 10^{10}}{x^{3/2}}$$

$$x^{3/2} = \frac{216 \times 10^{10}}{80} = 27 \times 10^9$$

$$x = (27 \times 10^9)^{2/3} = 9 \times 10^6$$

or 9,000,000 is the lowest income of the 80 people with the highest incomes.

Pareto's law for the distribution of incomes for a given population is

$$N = \frac{16 \times 10^{12}}{x^{5/3}}$$

(a) How many people have incomes below 8000?
(b) How many people have incomes over 125,000 but less than 1,000,000?
(c) What is the lowest income of the 50 people with the highest incomes?

(a)
$$N = \frac{16 \times 10^{12}}{(8\times10^3)^{5/3}} = \frac{16 \times 10^{12}}{2^5 \times 10^5} = 5 \times 10^6$$

so 5×10^6 people have incomes above 8000 and $16 \times 10^{12} - 5 \times 10^6$ $= (16 \times 10^6 - 5) \times 10^6$ or 15,999,995,000,000 have incomes below 8000.

(b) The number with incomes over 125,000 is

$$N = \frac{16 \times 10^{12}}{(5^3 \times 10^3)^{5/3}} = \frac{16 \times 10^{12}}{5^5 \times 10^5} = \frac{16 \times 10^7}{5^5}$$

$$= 16 \times 2^5 \times 10^2 = 512 \times 10^2 \text{ or } 51,200$$

The number with incomes over 1,000,000 is

$$N = \frac{16 \times 10^{12}}{(10^6)^{5/3}} = 16 \times 10^2 \text{ or } 1600$$

So the number with incomes over 125,000 but less than 1,000,000 is $51,200 - 1600 = 49,600$

(c)
$$50 = \frac{16 \times 10^{12}}{x^{5/3}}$$

$$x^{5/3} = \frac{16 \times 10^{12}}{50} = 32 \times 10^{10}$$

$$x = (32 \times 10^{10})^{3/5} = 8 \times 10^6$$

or 8,000,000 is the lowest income of the 50 people with the highest incomes.

PROBLEMS

1. Pareto's law for the distribution of incomes is (for a particular group)

$$N = \frac{8 \times 10^8}{x^{3/2}}$$

(a) How many have incomes exceeding 1600?
(b) How many have incomes between 1600 and 3600?
(c) What is the lowest income of the 800 who have the highest incomes?

2. Pareto's law for the distribution of incomes is (for a particular group)

$$N = \frac{1.9 \times 10^{12}}{x^{1.70}}$$

(a) How many have incomes exceeding 50,000?
(b) How many have incomes between 25,000 and 50,000?
(c) What is the lowest income of the million who have the highest incomes?

3. Pareto's law for the distribution of incomes is (for a particular group)

$$N = \frac{100,000}{x^2}$$

(a) How many have incomes exceeding 15?
(b) How many have incomes between 50 and 75?
(c) What is the lowest income of the 5 who have the highest incomes?

4. Pareto's law for the distribution of incomes is (for a particular group)

$$N = \frac{32 \times 10^{10}}{x^{4/3}}$$

(a) How many have incomes between 125,000 and 1,000,000?
(b) What is the lowest income of the 200 who have the highest incomes?

5. Pareto's law for the distribution of incomes is (for a particular group)

$$N = \frac{625 \times 10^9}{x^{3/2}}$$

(a) How many have incomes between 2,500 and 10,000?
(b) What is the lowest income of the 5,000 who have the highest incomes?

6. Pareto's law for the distribution of incomes is (for a particular group)

$$N = \frac{6 \times 10^9}{x^{3/2}}$$

(a) How many have incomes exceeding 2,500?
(b) How many have incomes between 2,500 and 10,000?
(c) What is the lowest income of the 6 who have the highest incomes?

7. Pareto's law for the distribution of incomes is

$$N = \frac{a}{x^b}$$

(a) How many have incomes exceeding k?
(b) How many have incomes exceeding 100,000?
(c) What is the lowest income of the 10 who have the highest incomes?
(d) How many have incomes between s and t?
(e) How many have incomes between 500,000 and 1,500,000?

8. If the demand function is

$$y = \frac{17.6}{x^{1.43}}$$

(where x is quantity demanded and y is price):
(a) Find the price if the quantity demanded is 2.
(b) Find the quantity demanded if the price is 5.

9. If the demand function is

$$x = \frac{12.03}{y^{0.21}}$$

(where x is quantity demanded and y is price):
Find the price if the quantity demanded is (a) 6, (b) 3.3.
Find the quantity demanded if the price is (c) 100, (d) 67.

10. If the demand function is

$$x = \frac{a}{y^b}$$

(where x is quantity demanded and y is price):
Find the price if the quantity demanded is (a) $5a$, (b) 1.
Find the quantity demanded if the price is (c) 1, (d) a.

ANSWERS TO ODD-NUMBERED PROBLEMS

1. (a) 12,500
   (b) 8796
   (c) 10,000

3. (a) 444
   (b) 22
   (c) 141

5. (a) 4,375,000
   (b) 250,000

7. (a) $\dfrac{a}{k^b}$

   (b) $\dfrac{a}{10^{5b}}$

   (c) $\left(\dfrac{a}{10}\right)^{1/b}$

   (d) $\dfrac{a(t^b - s^b)}{s^b t^b}$

   (e) $\dfrac{a(3^b - 1)}{(15 \times 10^5)^b}$

9. (a) 27.455
   (b) 473.21
   (c) 4.574
   (d) 4.975

■ 1.7 EXPONENTIAL AND LOGARITHMIC CURVES

☐ EXPONENTIAL FUNCTIONS

A function having a variable base and a constant exponent is a *power function*. For example, $y = x^a$ is a power function, where x is the base and a is the exponent. Many examples of power functions have been discussed in previous sections. A function having a constant base and a variable exponent is an *exponential function*. For example, $y = a^x$ is an exponential function, where a is the base and x is the exponent.

$y = x^a$

$y = a^x$

The following rules of exponents are applicable to both power functions and exponential functions.

If x, y, and z are positive real numbers,

Rule	*Example*
1. $x^m x^n = x^{m+n}$	$10^2 \times 10^3 = 10^5$

2. $(x^m)^n = x^{mn}$ $\qquad\qquad$ $(2^4)^6 = 2^{24}$

3. $(xyz)^m = x^m y^m z^m$ $\qquad$ $(2 \times 4 \times 5)^6 = 2^6 \times 4^6 \times 5^6$

4. $\left(\dfrac{x}{y}\right)^m = \dfrac{x^m}{y^m}$ $\qquad\qquad$ $\left(\dfrac{3}{8}\right)^4 = \dfrac{3^4}{8^4}$

5. $x^{-m} = \dfrac{1}{x^m}$ $\qquad\qquad$ $5^{-6} = \dfrac{1}{5^6}$

6. $\dfrac{x^m}{x^n} = x^{m-n} = \dfrac{1}{x^{n-m}}$ $\qquad$ $\dfrac{4^5}{4^8} = 4^{-3} = \dfrac{1}{4^3}$

7. $x^{1/n} = \sqrt[n]{x}$, where n is a positive integer, $\qquad$ $7^{1/3} = \sqrt[3]{7}$
   read the nth root of x

8. $x^{m/n} = \sqrt[n]{x^m} = (\sqrt[n]{x})^m$, where m and n are $\qquad$ $9^{5/8} = \sqrt[8]{9^5} = (\sqrt[8]{9})^5$
   integers, $n > 0$, read the mth power of
   the nth root of x.

NOTE: By definition, if $x \neq 0$, $x^0 = 1$; that is, any base to the zero power is 1.

One very convenient use of exponents is in the representation of numbers which are very large or very small in absolute value, by expressing them as a constant multiplied by an exponent of 10. For example, 80,000 can be written 8×10^4; 5,000,000 can be written 5×10^6. Similarly, the fraction 0.002 can be written 2×10^{-3}; the fraction 0.00000000096 can be written 9.6×10^{-10}. This representation of numbers is referred to as *scientific notation*; the significant digits in the number are conventionally expressed with one digit to the left of the decimal point. This notation was used in the examples of Pareto's law, but the convention concerning decimal points was violated for convenience of calculation.

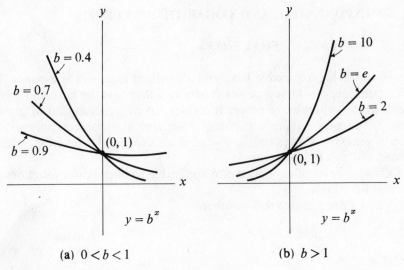

(a) $0 < b < 1$ $\qquad\qquad\qquad\qquad$ (b) $b > 1$

FIGURE 1.92

The simplest exponential functions are of the form $y = b^x$, $b > 0$. The curve representing the function $y = b^x$ lies entirely in the first two quadrants; it is monotonically decreasing if $0 < b < 1$ and monotonically increasing if $b > 1$; in both cases the curve is asymptotic to the x-axis and has y-intercept $(0, 1)$. The parameter b determines the curvature of the function (see Fig. 1.92).

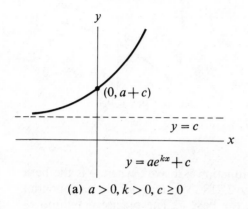

(a) $a > 0, k > 0, c \geq 0$

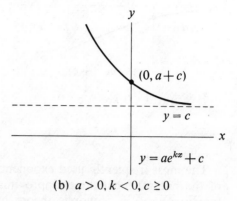

(b) $a > 0, k < 0, c \geq 0$

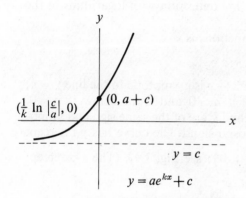

(c) $a > 0, k > 0, c \leq 0, |c| < a$

(if $|c| > a$, intercepts negative)

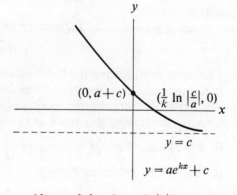

(d) $a > 0, k < 0, c \leq 0, |c| < a$

(if $|c| > a$, intercepts negative)

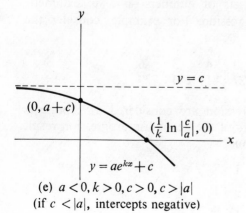

(e) $a < 0, k > 0, c > 0, c > |a|$

(if $c < |a|$, intercepts negative)

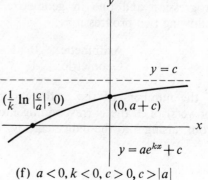

(f) $a < 0, k < 0, c > 0, c > |a|$

(if $c < |a|$, intercepts negative)

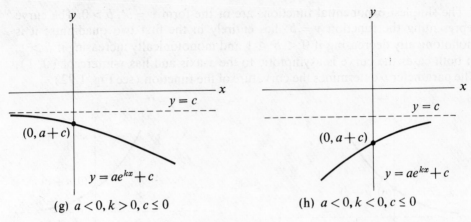

(g) $a < 0, k > 0, c \leq 0$ (h) $a < 0, k < 0, c \leq 0$

FIGURE 1.93

The most frequently used exponential function is $y = e^x$, where e is the base of the natural logarithms, approximately 2.718. Virtually all the exponential functions used in economic theory have the base e. The precise definition of this base and its advantages are discussed in connection with logarithms in the following sections.

A more general form for exponential functions is

$$y = ae^{kx} + c$$

The curve representing the function $y = ae^{kx} + c$ is asymptotic to the line $y = c$; it approaches its asymptote from above if $a > 0$ and from below if $a < 0$. The curve is monotonically increasing if a and k are of the same sign and monotonically decreasing if a and k are of opposite signs. The curve has y-intercept $(0, a + c)$ and, if $c < 0$, x-intercept $\left(\frac{1}{k} \ln \left|\frac{c}{a}\right|, 0\right)$; see Fig. 1.93. (The x-intercept is obtained in Technical Note V.)

☐ *LOGARITHMIC FUNCTIONS*

In 1614, John Napier wrote the first treatise on logarithms. He based his discussion on the comparison of two sets of numbers—one in arithmetic progression and one in geometric progression. For example, consider the following two progressions:

Arithmetic: 0   1   2   3   4   5   6 . . .
Geometric: 1   3   9   27   81   243 729 . . .

If the numbers of the arithmetic progression are considered as exponents (powers) of 3, the corresponding numbers of the geometric progression result from raising 3 to the indicated power. Thus

$$3^0 = 1$$

$$3^1 = 3$$

$$3^2 = 9$$

$$3^3 = 27$$

and so forth. Furthermore, the two progressions indicate that to multiply, it is necessary only to add exponents: $3^2 \times 3^3 = 3^{2+3} = 3^5$. And to divide, it is necessary only to subtract exponents: $3^5 \div 3^2 = 3^{5-2} = 3^3$. This idea is the basis for the computational short cuts possible using logarithms.

By definition, the *logarithm* of a positive number y to a positive base b, other than 1, is the exponent x to which the base must be raised to obtain the number. Thus, if $b > 0$, $b \neq 1$, and b, x, and y are related by the equation

$$y = b^x \tag{3}$$

then x, the exponent of b, is the logarithm of y to the base b. This relation may also be expressed by the equation

$$x = \log_b y \tag{4}$$

Equations (3) and (4) express the same relationship between b, x, and y in exponential and logarithmic forms, respectively, and are inverse functions—that is, if y is an exponential function of x, then x is a logarithmic function of y.

Although the base of a logarithm can be any positive number other than 1, in practice the base is almost always either 10 (common or Briggsian logarithms) or $e \approx 2.718$ (natural or Naperian logarithms). The base e is defined in terms of limits as follows:

$$e = \lim_{n \to \infty} \left(1 + \frac{1}{n}\right)^n$$

The concept of limits is discussed in detail later; for present purposes it is sufficient to note that e can be approximated as accurately as desired by increasing n in the expression $\left(1 + \frac{1}{n}\right)^n$.

In some cases, common logarithms are more convenient for computational work; natural logarithms are more convenient for theoretical work. By convention, $\log x$ denotes the common logarithm of x and $\ln x$ denotes the natural logarithm of x. If any other base is meant it is specified.

The use of logarithms can save considerable work in computations involving numbers that are very large or very small in absolute value. The essential properties of logarithms are summarized in the following rules:

If x and y are positive real numbers,

Rule	Example
1. $\log_b(xy) = \log_b x + \log_b y$	$\log_4 10 = \log_4 5 + \log_4 2$
2. $\log_b \left(\dfrac{x}{y}\right) = \log_b x - \log_b y$	$\log_8 \left(\tfrac{5}{6}\right) = \log_8 5 - \log_8 6$
3. $\log_b x^n = n \log_b x$	$\log_5 3^2 = 2 \log_5 3$

4. $\log_b \sqrt[n]{x} = \dfrac{1}{n}\log_b x$ $\qquad\qquad\qquad$ $\log_9 \sqrt[6]{2} = \frac{1}{6}\log_9 2$

5. $\log_a x = \log_a b \, \log_b x = \left(\dfrac{1}{\log_b a}\right)\log_b x$ $\quad$ $\log_{10} 14 = (\log_{10} 2)(\log_2 14)$

$$= \left(\dfrac{1}{\log_2 10}\right)\log_2 14$$

The simplest logarithmic functions, mentioned above, are of form

$$y = \log_b x, \qquad b > 0 \text{ and } b \neq 1$$

The curve representing the function $y = \log_b x$ lies entirely in the first and fourth quadrants; it is monotonically decreasing if $0 < b < 1$ and monotonically increasing if $b > 1$; in both cases the curve is asymptotic to the y-axis and has x-intercept $(1, 0)$. The parameter b determines the curvature of the function (see Fig. 1.94).

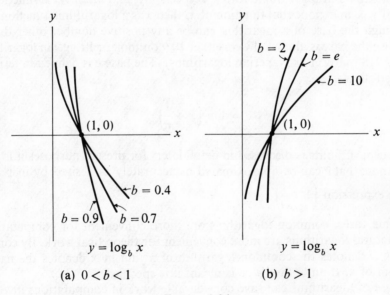

(a) $0 < b < 1$ $\qquad\qquad\qquad\qquad$ (b) $b > 1$

FIGURE 1.94

Since $y = b^x$ and $y = \log_b x$ are inverse functions, the graph of either one of these families of curves (or of one particular curve for some specified value of b) can be obtained from the graph of the other geometrically by reflection about the line $y = x$. (Recall that reflection of a curve about a line consists of obtaining the curve that is symmetric to the given curve with respect to the line; see Fig. 1.95.)

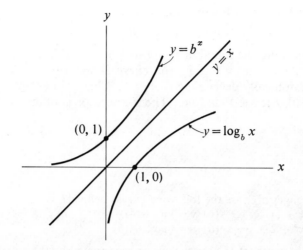

FIGURE 1.95

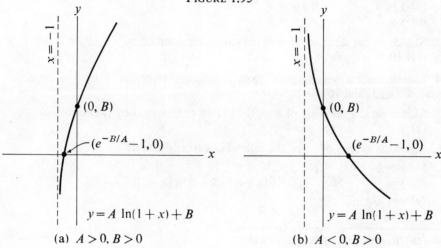

(a) $A > 0, B > 0$　　　　　　　(b) $A < 0, B > 0$

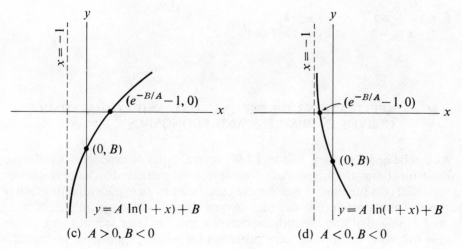

(c) $A > 0, B < 0$　　　　　　　(d) $A < 0, B < 0$

FIGURE 1.96

A more general form for logarithmic functions is

$$y = A \ln(1 + x) + B, \ x > -1$$

The curve representing the function $y = A \ln(1 + x) + B$ lies to the right of and is asymptotic to the line $x = -1$; the curve is monotonically increasing if $A > 0$ and monotonically decreasing if $A < 0$. It has x-intercept $(e^{-B/A} - 1, 0)$ and y-intercept $(0, B)$; see Fig. 1.96. (The x-intercept is obtained in Technical Note V.)

PROBLEMS

1. For what ranges of x are the following curves defined?
   (a) $y = \ln(x + 1)$ (b) $y = \ln(x - 4)$
   (c) $y = \ln(x^3 + 27)$ (d) $y = \ln(x^4 - 16)$

2. Sketch on the same set of axes the curves represented by the equations
   (a) $y = 2^x$ (b) $y = 2^{-x}$
   (c) $y = 2^{x/2}$ (d) $y = 2^{2x}$

3. Sketch on the same set of axes the curves represented by $y = a^x$ for $a = 2, e, 3,$ and 10.

4. Sketch on the same set of axes the curves represented by $y = \log_a x$ for $a = 2, e, 3,$ and 10.

5. Sketch on the same set of axes the curves represented by the equations
   (a) $y = 3^x$ (b) $y = \log_3 x$

6. For what ranges of x are the following curves defined?
   (a) $y = \frac{1}{2} \ln (1 - x^2)$ (b) $y = \sqrt{36 - x^2}$
   (c) $y = \sqrt{x^2 - 36}$ (d) $y = -3 - 6 \ln (x - 2)$
   (e) $y = \sqrt{x - 27}$

ANSWERS TO ODD-NUMBERED PROBLEMS

1. (a) $x > -1$ (b) $x > 4$
   (c) $x > -3$ (d) $x < -2$ and $x > 2$

■ **1.8 APPLICATIONS OF EXPONENTIAL AND LOGARITHMIC CURVES IN BUSINESS AND ECONOMICS**

As can be noted in Figs. 1.93 and 1.96, several types of exponential and logarithmic functions are appropriate for representing demand or supply curves; exponential cost functions—representing total cost as an exponential function of number of units produced—are also frequently used. Many examples of these uses of exponential and logarithmic curves appear in later sections; the immediately following sections concern problems for which exponential or logarithmic functions are uniquely appropriate.

□ COMPOUND INTEREST

If the interest rate is $100i\%$ per year payable (that is, compounded) k times per year, an amount of money x (the principal) becomes after n years

$$y = x\left(1 + \frac{i}{k}\right)^{nk}$$

(when k is large, $y \approx xe^{in}$, where $e \approx 2.718$ is the base of the natural logarithms).

This formula can be developed as follows: If the interest at rate $100i\%$ is payable yearly, then the amount (principal plus interest) y_1 at the end of the first year is

$$y_1 = x + ix = x(1 + i)$$

The amount y_2 after 2 years is

$$y_2 = [x(1 + i)][1 + i] = x(1 + i)^2$$

The amount y_3 after 3 years is

$$y_3 = [x(1 + i)^2][1 + i] = x(1 + i)^3$$

$$\vdots$$

The amount y_n after n years is

$$y_n = x(1 + i)^n$$

If interest is payable k times per year, then the rate of interest in any one period is $100\dfrac{i}{k}\%$ and the number of periods is nk. Thus the amount after n years is

$$y = x\left(1 + \frac{i}{k}\right)^{nk}$$

Example

A man deposits $5000 at 4% interest. How much has he (principal plus interest) after 10 years (a) if interest is payable yearly, and (b) if interest is payable quarterly?

(a)
$$y = x(1 + i)^n$$

$$= 5000(1 + 0.04)^{10}$$

$$\log y = \log 5000 + 10 \log 1.04$$

$$= 3.69897 + (10)(0.01703)$$

$$= 3.86927$$

$$y = \$7400.67$$

(b)
$$y = x \left(1 + \frac{i}{k}\right)^{nk}$$
$$= 5000 \left(1 + \frac{0.04}{4}\right)^{40}$$
$$\log y = \log 5000 + 40 \log 1.01$$
$$= 3.69897 + 40(0.00432)$$
$$= 3.87177$$
$$y = \$7443.33$$

□ GROWTH FUNCTIONS

There are many relationships in business and economics which are appropriately represented by curves referred to as growth functions—for example, number of employees as a function of annual sales (in dollars) of a company, amount of finished stock as a function of days after beginning a production run, sales as a function of advertising expenditure, maintenance cost as a function of number of hours a machine is run, sales as a function of length of time a product has been on the market, and so forth.

The basic property of the variety of curves referred to as growth functions is that they are monotonically increasing. Growth functions may or may not have an upper asymptote (although usually for business and economic applications absence of an upper asymptote is reasonable only when relatively short periods of time are considered) and they may be of various shapes. Three particular types of growth functions are discussed below: (1) very simple functions originally developed to describe certain types of biological growth and appropriate only for growth that does not have an upper asymptote, (2) Gompertz functions used to describe growth that starts rather slowly and approaches an upper asymptote, and (3) learning functions originally used by psychologists to describe human learning and appropriate for growth that begins rapidly, levels off, and approaches an asymptote.

● Biological Growth Curves

Many laws of biological growth are represented by the equation

$$N = N_0 R^t$$

where N is the number of individuals in the population at time t, N_0 is the initial number of individuals in the population (at time zero), and $R > 0$ is the rate of growth, as in Fig. 1.97. This equation is based on the model of a population each of whose members produces $R - 1$ additional members in each unit of time and none of whose members die. (This situation is approximated for certain laboratory cultures, at least for limited periods of time.) The

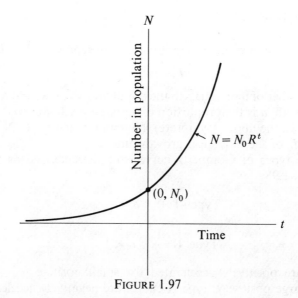

FIGURE 1.97

equation can be developed as follows:

Time	Number in Population
0	N_0
1	$N_0 + N_0(R - 1) = N_0R$
2	$N_0R + N_0R(R - 1) = N_0R^2$
3	$N_0R^2 + N_0R^2(R - 1) = N_0R^3$
.	.
.	.
.	.
t	$N_0R^{t-1} + N_0R^{t-1}(R - 1) = N_0R^t$

Organization theorists have claimed that the function $N = N_0R^t$ is appropriate for describing the early growth of a rapidly developing company; because it has no upper asymptote, the function is inappropriate for describing biological or organizational growth for an indefinite period of time. In addition, the behavior of the curve, as illustrated in the example below, indicates that it should be used with extreme caution in theoretical analysis.

Example

The National Aerospace Research Organization is beginning its operations with a staff of 5 men. At the end of each year of its operation, each employee will hire 3 assistants. How many employees will National Aerospace Research Organization have after 10 years of operation?

$$N = N_0R^t$$

$$= (5)(3^{10})$$

$$= 295,245 \text{ employees after 10 years}$$

● **Gompertz Curves**

Gompertz curves, named for their originator, are represented by the equation

$$N = ca^{R^t}$$

where N is the number of individuals in the population at time t and $R\,(0 < R < 1)$ is the rate of growth, a is the proportion of initial growth, and c is the growth at maturity (that is, the upper asymptote). Note that when $t = 0$, $N = ca$, which corresponds to N_0 of the biological growth function.

The two basic types of Gompertz curves are characterized as follows and illustrated in Fig. 1.98:

$$\text{Type \quad I}: 0 < a < \frac{1}{e}$$

$$\text{Type \quad II}: \frac{1}{e} \leq a < 1$$

Type I curves are positively accelerated for small positive t and negatively accelerated for large positive t; type II curves are negatively accelerated for all positive t. The precise definitions of positive and negative acceleration are discussed later; essentially, positively accelerated means increasing at an increasing rate and negatively accelerated means increasing at a decreasing rate.

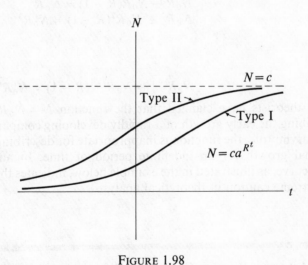

FIGURE 1.98

Gompertz curves have been used extensively by psychologists to describe various aspects of human growth and development, including some types of learning. Organization theorists have found Gompertz curves appropriate for describing the growth of many types of organizations. They are also appropriate for many other functions in business and economics, for example, total revenue and production functions.

Example

On the basis of expected sales and data for similar companies, the Personnel Director of National Industries predicts that the number of employees can be described by the equation

$$N = 200(0.04)^{0.5^t}$$

where N is the number of employees after t years. Assuming he is correct, how many employees will National Industries have after 3 years? How many employees did the company employ initially? How many will it employ when it reaches its maximum size?

The company employs $(200)(0.04) = 8$ people initially and 200 at maximum size. After 3 years it employs

$$N = (200)(0.04)^{0.5^3}$$

$$\log N = \log 200 + 0.5^3 \log 0.04$$

$$= 2.30103 + (0.125)(-1.39794)$$

$$= 2.12629$$

$$N = 133.75 \qquad \text{or approximately 134 people}$$

● **Learning Curves**

Because of their extensive use by psychologists to describe learning, exponential curves of the form

$$y = c - ae^{-kx}$$

where c, a, and k are positive, are frequently referred to as learning curves. [Note that this is case (f) of the general form $y = ae^{kx} + c$ discussed previously.] Clark Hull used the special case $c = a$ of this function as one of the basic equations in his reinforcement theory of learning to describe the relationship between strength of learning y and number of reinforcements x.

The function $y = c - ae^{-kx}$ rises rapidly at first, flattens out, and then approaches its asymptote $y = c$ (see Fig. 1.99). These curves have been found to be appropriate for representing various cost and production functions.

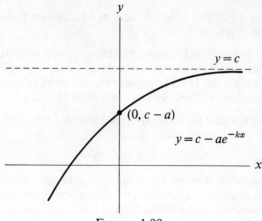

FIGURE 1.99

Examples

If the number of items y manufactured per day x days after the beginning of a production run is given by

$$y = 200(1 - e^{-0.1x})$$

how many items are manufactured per day 10 days after beginning the run and what per cent of the maximum is this?

$$y = 200(1 - e^{-1})$$
$$= 200(1 - 0.368)$$
$$= 200(0.632)$$
$$= 126.4 \text{ or approximately 126 items, } 63.2\% \text{ of the maximum.}$$

If the yearly maintenance cost y of a computer is related to its average monthly use x (in hundreds of hours) by the equation

$$y = 35,000 - 25,000e^{-0.02x}$$

what is the yearly maintenance cost for 200 hours average monthly use?

$$y = 35,000 - 25,000e^{-0.04}$$
$$= 35,000 - 25,000(0.135)$$
$$= 35,000 - 3375$$
$$= \$31,625 \text{ yearly maintenance}$$

PROBLEMS

1. Chem Corporation has $10,000 to deposit and expects to leave the deposit for 20 years. Two options are available: 5% interest payable semiannually and $4\frac{1}{2}\%$ interest payable quarterly. Which option should Chem Corporation choose?

2. In order to have $20,000 after 20 years at 6% interest payable yearly, how much must be deposited?

3. The National Professional Society has been formed with 10 original members. The rules state that each member may invite 2 people to join at the beginning of each year. If each member always takes advantage of this rule, how many members will the society have after 15 years?

4. Monthly total revenue (in dollars) for a particular firm can be described by the equation

$$R = 1000(.10)^{0.8p}$$

where p is the amount spent for promotion and advertising. What is total revenue when nothing is spent for promotion and advertising? What is the maximum attainable total revenue? What is total revenue if $20 is spent for promotion and advertising?

5. Production costs (in hundreds of dollars) for a firm are described by the equation

$$C = 100 - 70e^{-0.02x}$$

where x is the number of units of output. To what do the firm's fixed costs amount? When output is 100 units, what proportion of the production costs are fixed?

6. One job on a production line consists of screwing a small screw into a metal plate. For a typical employee, the number of plates completed per hour is described by the equation

$$y = 50 - 40e^{-0.30x}$$

where x is number of hours the employee has worked on the production line. (a) How many plates can an employee complete the first hour? (b) How many the fifth hour?

7. The number of firms in a particular industry is described by the equation

$$N = 5(.5)^{0.75t}$$

where t is the number of years since the industry began. How many firms were there in the industry after 5 years? How many firms were in the industry originally? How many firms will there be when the industry reaches maximum size?

8. In order to have $10,000 after $6,000 has been deposited for 25 years with interest payable yearly, what interest rate must be paid?

9. For a 10-year deposit, what interest rate payable annually is equivalent to 5% interest payable quarterly?

10. General Corporation has three regional offices each of which has three district offices each of which has three divisional offices each of which has three supervisors. If every supervisor has a copy of the company's sales records, how many copies of these records are there?

ANSWERS TO ODD-NUMBERED PROBLEMS

---

1. 5% payable semiannually ($26,841) rather than $4\frac{1}{2}$% payable quarterly ($24,480)

3. 327,680

5. $3000 fixed costs
   33.14% of production costs are fixed for 100 units output

7. 3.45 (approximately 3) firms after 5 years
   3 firms originally
   6 firms at maximum size

9. 5.1%

■ 1.9 TRIGONOMETRIC CURVES

The trigonometric functions of an angle θ are the sine of θ ($\sin \theta$), the cosine of θ ($\cos \theta$), the tangent of θ ($\tan \theta$), the cosecant of θ ($\csc \theta$), the secant of θ ($\sec \theta$), and the cotangent of θ ($\cot \theta$). When the angle θ is at the center of a circle of radius r and is measured counterclockwise, as in Fig. 1.100, the trigonometric functions of θ are defined by the equations

$$\sin \theta = \frac{a}{r} \qquad \csc \theta = \frac{r}{a}$$

$$\cos \theta = \frac{b}{r} \qquad \sec \theta = \frac{r}{b}$$

$$\tan \theta = \frac{a}{b} \qquad \ctn \theta = \frac{b}{a}$$

The sin and cos are said to be cofunctions, as are the sec and csc and the tan and cot. The trigonometric functions are defined similarly for negative angles, that is, angles measured clockwise from the positive x-axis.

Since $r^2 = a^2 + b^2$ (Pythagorean theorem), it can easily be shown that

$$\sin^2\theta + \cos^2\theta = 1$$
$$1 + \cot^2\theta = \csc^2\theta$$
$$1 + \tan^2\theta = \sec^2\theta$$

Various additional trigonometric identities can be proved.

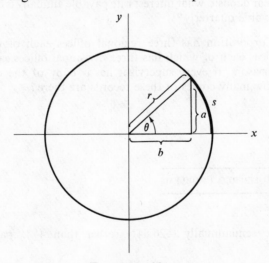

FIGURE 1.100

An angle θ may be measured in degrees or in radians; in calculus radian measure is usually more convenient. The number of radians, θ_r, in the angle θ (see Fig. 1.100) is defined by

$$\theta_r = \frac{s}{r} \quad \text{or} \quad s = r\theta$$

When the number of degrees θ_d in the angle θ is 360, $s = 2\pi r$, since the circumference of a circle is $2\pi r$. Therefore the number of radians in a circle is 2π and π radians equal $180°$. Thus $\theta_r = \dfrac{\pi \theta_d}{180}$.

Example

If $\theta_d = 200°$, $\theta_r = \dfrac{200\pi}{180} = \dfrac{10\pi}{9}$

If $\theta_d = -35°$, $\theta_r = \dfrac{-35\pi}{180} = -\dfrac{7\pi}{36}$

If $\theta_d = 300°$, $\theta_r = \dfrac{300\pi}{180} = \dfrac{5\pi}{3}$

The following table gives the radian measure and the values of the sine, cosine, and tangent for several frequently occurring angles:

Degrees	0	30	45	60	90	180	270	360
Radians	0	$\dfrac{\pi}{6}$	$\dfrac{\pi}{4}$	$\dfrac{\pi}{3}$	$\dfrac{\pi}{2}$	π	$\dfrac{3\pi}{2}$	2π
Sine	0	$\tfrac{1}{2}$	$\dfrac{\sqrt{2}}{2}$	$\dfrac{\sqrt{3}}{2}$	1	0	-1	0
Cosine	1	$\dfrac{\sqrt{3}}{2}$	$\dfrac{\sqrt{2}}{2}$	$\tfrac{1}{2}$	0	-1	0	1
Tangent	0	$\dfrac{\sqrt{3}}{3}$	1	$\sqrt{3}$	Not defined	0	Not defined	0

The graphs of the sine, cosine, and tangent functions are given in Fig. 1.101. Note that the function $\sin x$ is defined and is continuous for all values of x. Sin x is a periodic function with the period 2π, because $\sin(x + 2\pi) = \sin x$; that is, when the value of x is increased by one period, the value of y is repeated. The function $\cos x$ is also defined and continuous for all values of x and is periodic with period 2π. The graph of $y = \cos x$ can be obtained from the graph of $y = \sin x$ by taking the line $x = \dfrac{\pi}{2}$ as the y-axis; that is, the graph of $y = \cos x$ is the same as the graph of $y = \sin x$ when that graph is shifted to the right by $\dfrac{\pi}{2}$ radians. The function $\tan x$ is discontinuous for all values of x such that $x = (n + \tfrac{1}{2})\pi$, where n is any positive or negative integer; $\tan x$ is periodic with period π.

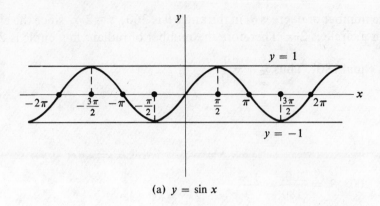

(a) $y = \sin x$

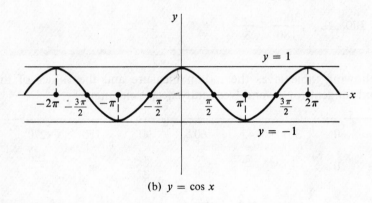

(b) $y = \cos x$

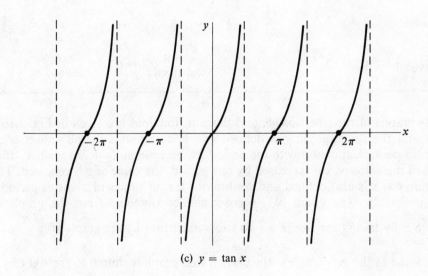

(c) $y = \tan x$

FIGURE 1.101

Any trigonometric function of the angle $\left(k\dfrac{\pi}{2} \pm \theta\right)$ is equal to ($\pm$) the same function of θ if k is even and is equal to ($\pm$) the cofunction of θ if k is odd, where the sign is that of the original function of $\left(k\dfrac{\pi}{2} \pm \theta\right)$. The signs of the trigonometric functions for the four quadrants are summarized below:

Function	Quadrant I	Quadrant II	Quadrant III	Quadrant IV
sin, csc	+	+	−	−
cos, sec	+	−	−	+
tan, cot	+	−	+	−

Note, for example, that $\sin(-\theta) = -\sin\theta$, $\cos(-\theta) = +\cos\theta$, $\tan(-\theta) = -\tan\theta$. Tables of the trigonometric functions are available for $0° \le \theta \le 90°$ and these tables may be used, with the above formulas, to obtain the trigonometric functions of any angle.

Example

Find the value of the following trigonometric functions:

$$\cos 120° = \cos\left(1 \cdot \frac{\pi}{2} + 30°\right) = \pm\sin 30° = -\frac{1}{2}$$

$$\sec 135° = \sec\left(1 \cdot \frac{\pi}{2} + 45°\right) = \pm\cos 45° = -\frac{\sqrt{2}}{2}$$

$$\tan 330° = \tan\left(3 \cdot \frac{\pi}{2} + 60°\right) = \pm\cot 60° = \pm\frac{1}{\tan 60°} = -\frac{1}{\sqrt{3}} = -\frac{\sqrt{3}}{3}$$

$$\cot 150° = \cot\left(1 \cdot \frac{\pi}{2} + 60°\right) = \pm\tan 60° = -\sqrt{3}$$

It is frequently more convenient to define points in the polar coordinate system than in the rectangular coordinate system. In particular, in calculus trigonometric functions are almost always expressed in terms of polar coordinates. To the point (x, y) in rectangular coordinates is associated the point $(r\cos\theta, r\sin\theta)$ in polar coordinates, where r and θ are determined as follows: If (x, y) is a point in the real plane, then (x, y) lies on the circle centered at the origin with radius $r = \sqrt{x^2 + y^2}$; that is, (x, y) satisfies the equation of the circle $x^2 + y^2 = r^2$. (See Fig. 1.102.) The point (x, y) can thus be determined completely by specifying the radius r of the circle centered at $(0, 0)$ on which it lies and the angle θ formed by moving counterclockwise from the positive x-axis along the circumference of the circle to the point (x, y). The numbers (r, θ) are called the *polar coordinates* of the point (x, y). The polar and rectangular coordinates are related as follows:

$$x = r \cos \theta \qquad \tan \theta = \frac{y}{x}$$

$$y = r \sin \theta \qquad \sin \theta = \frac{y}{\sqrt{x^2 + y^2}}$$

$$r = \sqrt{x^2 + y^2} \qquad \cos \theta = \frac{x}{\sqrt{x^2 + y^2}}$$

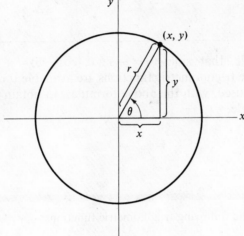

Figure 1.102

These relations are used to change from one system of coordinates to the other.

Examples

Find polar coordinates for the following points given in rectangular coordinates.

(a) $(0, \sqrt{2})$
(b) $(1, 1)$

(a)
$$(x, y) = (0, \sqrt{2})$$
$$r = \sqrt{0 + 2} = \sqrt{2}$$
$$\cos \theta = 0$$
$$\sin \theta = 1$$
$$\theta = \frac{\pi}{2}$$

Polar coordinates $(r, \theta) = \left(\sqrt{2}, \frac{\pi}{2} \right).$

(b)

$$(x, y) = (1, 1)$$

$$r = \sqrt{1 + 1} = \sqrt{2}$$

$$\cos \theta = \frac{1}{\sqrt{2}} = \frac{\sqrt{2}}{2}$$

$$\sin \theta = \frac{1}{\sqrt{2}} = \frac{\sqrt{2}}{2}$$

$$\theta = \frac{\pi}{4}$$

Polar coordinates $(r, \theta) = \left(\sqrt{2}, \frac{\pi}{4} \right)$.

Find rectangular coordinates for the following points given in polar coordinates.

(a) $\left(3, \frac{\pi}{2} \right)$

(b) $\left(\sqrt{2}, \frac{\pi}{6} \right)$

(a)

$$(r, \theta) = \left(3, \frac{\pi}{2} \right)$$

$$r \cos \theta = (3)(0) = 0$$

$$r \sin \theta = (3)(1) = 3$$

$$(x, y) = (0, 3)$$

(b)

$$(r, \theta) = \left(\sqrt{2}, \frac{\pi}{6} \right)$$

$$r \cos \theta = (\sqrt{2})\left(\frac{\sqrt{3}}{2} \right) = \frac{\sqrt{6}}{2}$$

$$r \sin \theta = (\sqrt{2})\left(\frac{1}{2} \right) = \frac{\sqrt{2}}{2}$$

Note that the polar coordinates of a point are not unique and may be expressed in various ways. For example, $\left(3, \frac{\pi}{6} \right)$, $\left(3, -\frac{11\pi}{6} \right)$, and $\left(-3, \frac{7\pi}{6} \right)$ all denote the same point. Because of this indefiniteness in the representation of a point in polar coordinates, a polar equation may be written in various alternative forms. In general, if $f(r, \theta) = 0$ is the equation of a curve in polar coordinates, the curve may be represented by any one of the equations

$$f[(-1)^n r, \theta + n\pi] = 0 \qquad \text{where } n = 0, \pm 1, \pm 2, \ldots$$

Example

The equation $r = \sin \dfrac{\theta}{2}$ has three other distinct alternative forms which may be found from $(-1)^n r = \sin\left(\dfrac{\theta}{2} + n\dfrac{\pi}{2}\right)$ by taking $n = 1, 2, 3$.

$$\text{if } n = 1, \; (-1)r = \sin\left(\frac{\theta}{2} + \frac{\pi}{2}\right) = \cos\frac{\theta}{2} \text{ or } r = -\cos\frac{\theta}{2}$$

$$\text{if } n = 2, \; (-1)^2 r = \sin\left(\frac{\theta}{2} + \pi\right) = -\sin\frac{\theta}{2} \text{ or } r = -\sin\frac{\theta}{2}$$

$$\text{if } n = 3, \; (-1)^3 r = \sin\left(\frac{\theta}{2} + \frac{3\pi}{2}\right) = -\cos\frac{\theta}{2} \text{ or } r = \cos\frac{\theta}{2}$$

The relations between polar and rectangular coordinates can be used to change an equation from one system of coordinates to the other. After an equation is expressed in polar coordinates, alternative forms can be obtained using the rule above.

Examples

Find the equation in rectangular coordinates of the curve whose equation in polar coordinates is $r = \dfrac{4}{1 + 2\cos\theta}$.

$$\sqrt{x^2 + y^2} = \frac{4}{1 + \dfrac{2x}{\sqrt{x^2 + y^2}}}$$

$$\sqrt{x^2 + y^2} = \frac{4}{\dfrac{\sqrt{x^2 + y^2} + 2x}{\sqrt{x^2 + y^2}}}$$

$$1 = \frac{4}{\sqrt{x^2 + y^2} + 2x}$$

$$\sqrt{x^2 + y^2} = 4 - 2x$$

$$x^2 + y^2 = 16 - 16x + 4x^2$$

$$3x^2 - y^2 - 16x + 16 = 0 \qquad \text{(hyperbola)}$$

Find the equation in polar coordinates of the curve whose equation in rectangular coordinates is $Ax + By + C = 0$.

$$Ar\cos\theta + Br\sin\theta + C = 0$$

$$r(A\cos\theta + B\sin\theta) + C = 0$$

Alternatively, for $n = 1$,

$$(-1)^1 r(A \cos(\theta + \pi) + B \sin(\theta + \pi)) + C = 0$$
$$-r(-A \cos \theta - B \sin \theta) + C = 0$$
$$r(A \cos \theta + B \sin \theta) + C = 0$$

The equation is also unchanged for $n = 2$ and thus, in this case, the representation of the equation in polar coordinates is unique.

PROBLEMS

1. Determine the number of radians in each of the following angles given in degrees.
   (a) $\theta = -240°$ (b) $\theta = 70°$
   (c) $\theta = 120°$ (d) $\theta = -40°$
   (e) $\theta = -100°$ (f) $\theta = 315°$

2. Find the value of the following trigonometric functions.
   (a) $\sin 210°$ (b) $\csc 240°$
   (c) $\tan 225°$ (d) $\cos 300°$

3. Find polar coordinates for the following points given in rectangular coordinates.
   (a) $(1, \sqrt{3})$ (b) $(-1, -1)$
   (c) $(3, 3\sqrt{3})$ (d) $(-1, 0)$

4. Find rectangular coordinates for the following points given in polar coordinates.

   (a) $\left(4, \dfrac{\pi}{3}\right)$ (b) $(-2, \pi)$

   (c) $\left(3, \dfrac{\pi}{6}\right)$ (d) $\left(-1, \dfrac{\pi}{2}\right)$

Find the equation in rectangular coordinates that corresponds to each of the following equations given in polar coordinates.

5. $r = 5$

6. $r = \sin \theta + \cos \theta$

7. $r = \dfrac{2}{2 - \cos \theta}$

8. $r = 1 + \cos \theta$

9. $r = a \cos \theta$

10. $r = a \sin \theta$

11. $r = \theta$

12. $r = a \sec \theta$

13. $r^2 = a^2 \cot \theta$

14. $r = \tan \theta \sec \theta$

15. $r^3 = a^3 \csc \theta$

16. $r = a \tan^2 \theta$

17. $r^2 = \theta$

18. $\theta = \dfrac{\pi}{2}$

Find the equation in polar coordinates that corresponds to each of the following equations given in rectangular coordinates.

19. $y^2 = 4ax$

20. $x^2 + y^2 = a^2$

21. $x^2 + y^2 = x + y$

22. $y = x$

23. $y^3 = ax^2$

24. $(x^2 + y^2)^2 = a^2(x^2 - y^2)$

25. $2xy = a^2$

26. $y = x^2$

27. $xy^2 = a$

28. $x + y = a$

1. (a) $s = -\dfrac{4\pi}{3}$ (b) $s = \dfrac{7\pi}{18}$

   (c) $s = \dfrac{2\pi}{3}$ (d) $s = -\dfrac{2\pi}{9}$

   (e) $s = -\dfrac{5\pi}{9}$ (f) $s = \dfrac{7\pi}{4}$

3. (a) $\left(2, \dfrac{\pi}{6}\right)$ (b) $\left(\sqrt{2}, \dfrac{5\pi}{4}\right)$

   (c) $\left(6, \dfrac{\pi}{3}\right)$ (d) $(1, \pi)$

5. $x^2 + y^2 = 25$ 17. $y = x \tan(x^2 + y^2)$

7. $2\sqrt{x^2 + y^2} - x - 2 = 0$ 19. $r = 4a \cot \theta \csc \theta$

9. $x^2 + y^2 - ax = 0$ 21. $r = \cos \theta + \sin \theta$

11. $y = x \tan(\sqrt{x^2 + y^2})$ 23. $r = a \cot^2\theta \csc \theta$

13. $a^2x = y(x^2 + y^2)$ 25. $r^2 = \tfrac{1}{2}a^2 \sec \theta \csc \theta$

15. $x^2y + y^3 = a^3$ 27. $r^3 = a \sec \theta \csc^2 \theta$

■ 1.10 APPLICATIONS OF TRIGONOMETRIC CURVES IN BUSINESS AND ECONOMICS

Many economic phenomena can be described in part by sine or cosine functions. In the study of business cycles, seasonal or other cyclic variations are described by sine or cosine functions. In spectral analysis—the method most frequently used currently to analyze periodicity or cyclic variation in time series —the detrended series is analyzed in terms of cosine functions. Spectral analysis, and even less complicated types of analysis of cyclic variation, involve statistical problems beyond the scope of the present discussion. However, these analyses are an application of trigonometric curves, and the logic on which they are based is intuitively reasonable: A series is described in terms of components representing trends and cyclic variations.

TECHNICAL NOTE I

Two linear equations of the form

$$A_1x + B_1y + C_1 = 0 \qquad A_2x + B_2y + C_2 = 0$$

have the simultaneous solution (x, y), where

$$x = \frac{B_1C_2 - B_2C_1}{A_1B_2 - A_2B_1} \qquad y = \frac{A_2C_1 - A_1C_2}{A_1B_2 - A_2B_1}$$

provided $A_1B_2 - A_2B_1 \neq 0$.

Thus if the nonvertical demand and supply curves

$$y = m_D x + b_D \qquad y = m_S x + b_S$$

(where the subscripts D and S distinguish demand and supply curves) are written

$$m_D x - y + b_D = 0 \qquad m_S x - y + b_S = 0$$

then the equilibrium quantity and price are

$$x = \frac{b_D - b_S}{m_S - m_D} \qquad y = \frac{b_D m_S - b_S m_D}{m_S - m_D}$$

since $m_S - m_D \neq 0$. Since $m_D < 0$, $m_S > 0$, $y_D > 0$, and y_S is unrestricted, $m_S - m_D > 0$ and $x \geq 0$ if $b_D - b_S \geq 0$—that is, if $b_D > b_S$, which is the first condition stated for equilibrium in the first quadrant; $y \geq 0$ if

$$b_D m_S - b_S m_D \geq 0$$

or

$$b_D m_S \geq b_S m_D$$

$$\frac{b_D}{m_D} \leq \frac{b_S}{m_S} \quad \text{(since } m_D < 0\text{)}$$

$$\frac{-b_D}{m_D} \geq \frac{-b_S}{m_S}$$

which is the second condition stated for equilibrium in the first quadrant, since the x-coordinate of the x-intercept of the line $y = mx + b$ is $-\dfrac{b}{m}$.

TECHNICAL NOTE II

The type of conic section represented by a second-degree equation, $Ax^2 + Bxy + Cy^2 + Dx + Ey + F = 0$, can be determined from certain conditions on the coefficients as summarized in Table 1.1.

Table 1.1

Case	Conditions on the coefficients	Type of conic
Proper conic, $\bar{D} \neq 0$	$\bar{C} > 0$; I, $\bar{D}$ opposite in sign, $A = C$, $B = 0$ (no xy-term)	Circle
	$\bar{C} > 0$; I, $\bar{D}$ opposite in sign	Ellipse
	$\bar{C} < 0$	Hyperbola
	$\bar{C} = 0$	Parabola
	$\bar{C} > 0$; I, $\bar{D}$ same in sign	No real locus
Degenerate conic, $\bar{D} = 0$	$\bar{C} < 0$	Two intersecting lines
	$\bar{C} = 0$, $J < 0$	Two parallel lines
	$\bar{C} = 0$, $J = 0$	Two coincident lines
	$\bar{C} > 0$	A point
	$\bar{C} = 0$, $J > 0$	No real locus

In this table,

$$I = A + C$$

$$\bar{C} = AC - \frac{B^2}{4}$$

$$J = AC + CF + AF - \frac{E^2}{4} - \frac{D^2}{4} - \frac{B^2}{4}$$

$$\bar{D} = ACF + \frac{BED}{4} - \frac{CD^2}{4} - \frac{AE^2}{4} - \frac{FB^2}{4}$$

In many cases it can be assumed (owing to the nature of the application) that the given equation represents a proper conic (that is, $\bar{D} \neq 0$) and a real locus (that is, I and $\bar{D}$ opposite in sign if $\bar{C} > 0$). In such cases it is necessary only to compute $\bar{C}$ and note the coefficients A, C, and B in order to determine which type of conic section is represented by the equation.

TECHNICAL NOTE III COMPLETING THE SQUARE

In many problems it is convenient to have an equation written so that variables which occur in terms of second degree occur only as terms of a perfect square; this is accomplished by putting the terms of the perfect square(s) on one side and all other terms on the other side of the equation and adding the appropriate constant terms to both sides of the equation.

The process of completing the square is based on the formula $(x + a)^2 = x^2 + 2ax + a^2$. Thus, given $x^2 + cx$, take half the coefficient of x and square it to complete the square: $x^2 + cx + \left(\frac{c}{2}\right)^2$. Any constant term added to one side of an equation must, of course, be added also to the other side in order to preserve the equality. Completing the square is the essential step in putting a second-degree equation into the appropriate standard form.

If $ax^2 + bx + cy + d = 0$, then the terms to be included in the perfect square are ax^2 and bx; thus

$$a\left(x^2 + \frac{b}{a}x\right) = -cy - d$$

$$a\left(x^2 + \frac{b}{a}x + \frac{b^2}{4a^2}\right) = -cy - d + \frac{b^2}{4a}$$

$$\left(x + \frac{b}{2a}\right)^2 = -\frac{c}{a}\left(y + \frac{d}{c} - \frac{b^2}{4ac}\right)$$

Examples

Complete the square for the equation

$$3x^2 + 4x + 2y - 4 = 0$$

$$3(x^2 + \tfrac{4}{3}x + \tfrac{4}{9}) = -2y + 4 + \tfrac{4}{3}$$

$$(x + \tfrac{2}{3})^2 = -\tfrac{2}{3}(y - \tfrac{8}{3})$$

If $ax^2 + by^2 + cx + dy + e = 0$, then the terms to be included in the perfect squares are ax^2, cx, by^2, and dy; thus

$$a\left(x^2 + \frac{c}{a}x\right) + b\left(y^2 + \frac{d}{b}y\right) = -e$$

$$a\left(x^2 + \frac{c}{a}x + \frac{c^2}{4a^2}\right) + b\left(y^2 + \frac{d}{b}y + \frac{d^2}{4b^2}\right) = -e + \frac{c^2}{4a} + \frac{d^2}{4b}$$

$$\frac{\left(x + \frac{c}{2a}\right)^2}{b} + \frac{\left(y + \frac{d}{2b}\right)^2}{a} = \frac{1}{ab}\left(\frac{c^2}{4a} + \frac{d^2}{4b} - e\right) = \frac{c^2}{4a^2b} + \frac{d^2}{4ab^2} - \frac{e}{ab}$$

Complete the squares for the equation

$$3x^2 + 4y^2 - 6x + 7y - 10 = 0$$

$$3(x^2 - 2x) + 4(y^2 + \tfrac{7}{4}y) = 10$$

$$3(x^2 - 2x + 1) + 4(y^2 + \tfrac{7}{4}y + \tfrac{49}{64}) = 10 + 3 + \tfrac{49}{16}$$

$$\frac{(x-1)^2}{4} + \frac{(y + \tfrac{7}{8})^2}{3} = \tfrac{1}{12}(13 + \tfrac{49}{16}) = \tfrac{257}{192}$$

The essential aspect of the process of completing the square is the addition of the appropriate constant terms so that groups of terms form perfect squares; the most convenient form of writing the constant coefficients depends on the particular problem.

A second-degree equation can be put into the appropriate standard form for the type of conic it represents by the process of completing the square.

The circle:

$$Ax^2 + Ay^2 + Dx + Ey + F = 0$$

$$A\left(x^2 + \frac{D}{A}x + \frac{D^2}{4A^2}\right) + A\left(y^2 + \frac{E}{A}y + \frac{E^2}{4A^2}\right) = \frac{D^2}{4A} + \frac{E^2}{4A} - F$$

$$\left(x + \frac{D}{2A}\right)^2 + \left(y + \frac{E}{2A}\right)^2 = \frac{D^2}{4A^2} + \frac{E^2}{4A^2} - \frac{F}{A}$$

which is of the form $(x - h)^2 + (y - k)^2 = r^2$, where

$$h = -\frac{D}{2A} \qquad k = -\frac{E}{2A} \qquad r^2 = \frac{D^2}{4A^2} + \frac{E^2}{4A^2} - \frac{F}{A}$$

The ellipse: $Ax^2 + Cy^2 + Dx + Ey + F = 0$, A and C same sign:

$$A\left(x^2 + \frac{D}{A}x + \frac{D^2}{4A^2}\right) + C\left(y^2 + \frac{E}{C}y + \frac{E^2}{4C^2}\right) = \frac{D^2}{4A} + \frac{E^2}{4C} - F$$

Denoting $\frac{D^2}{4A} + \frac{E^2}{4C} - F$ by k,

$$\frac{\left(x + \frac{D}{2A}\right)^2}{\frac{k}{A}} + \frac{\left(y + \frac{E}{2C}\right)^2}{\frac{k}{C}} = 1$$

which is of the form

$$\frac{(x-h)^2}{a^2} + \frac{(y-k)^2}{b^2} = 1$$

where

$$h = -\frac{D}{2A} \qquad k = -\frac{E}{2C}$$

The parabola: $Ax^2 + Dx + Ey + F = 0$

$$A\left(x^2 + \frac{D}{A}x + \frac{D^2}{4A^2}\right) = -E\left(y + \frac{F}{E} - \frac{D^2}{4AE}\right)$$

$$\left(x + \frac{D}{2A}\right)^2 = -\frac{E}{A}\left(y - \frac{D^2 - 4AF}{4AE}\right)$$

which is of the form $(x - h)^2 = 4p(y - k)$, where

$$h = -\frac{D}{2A} \qquad k = \frac{D^2 - 4AF}{4AE} \qquad 4p = -\frac{E}{A}$$

(and similarly for the parabola $Cy^2 + Dx + Ey + F = 0$).

The hyperbola: $Ax^2 + Cy^2 + Dx + Ey + F = 0$, A and C opposite in sign:

$$A\left(x^2 + \frac{D}{A}x + \frac{D^2}{4A^2}\right) + C\left(y^2 + \frac{E}{C}y + \frac{E^2}{4C^2}\right) = \frac{D^2}{4A} + \frac{E^2}{4C} - F$$

Denoting $\dfrac{D^2}{4A} + \dfrac{E^2}{4C} - F$ by k,

$$\frac{\left(x + \dfrac{D}{2A}\right)^2}{\dfrac{k}{A}} + \frac{\left(y + \dfrac{E}{2C}\right)^2}{\dfrac{k}{C}} = 1$$

which is of the form

$$\frac{(x-h)^2}{a^2} - \frac{(y-k)^2}{b^2} = 1$$

or

$$\frac{(y-k)^2}{b^2} - \frac{(x-h)^2}{a^2} = 1$$

since A and C are opposite in sign, where

$$h = -\frac{D}{2A} \qquad k = -\frac{E}{2C}$$

The various properties of particular second-degree curves can, of course, be obtained by identifying the appropriate type of conic section and then substituting appropriate numerical values in the corresponding formulas given above, rather than by putting each equation into standard form.

TECHNICAL NOTE IV

The formula for the roots of a quadratic equation is obtained by completing the square as follows:

$$ax^2 + bx + c = 0$$

$$a\left(x^2 + \frac{bx}{a} + \frac{b^2}{4a^2}\right) = -c + \frac{b^2}{4a}$$

$$\left(x + \frac{b}{2a}\right)^2 = \frac{b^2 - 4ac}{4a^2}$$

$$x + \frac{b}{2a} = \pm\sqrt{\frac{b^2 - 4ac}{4a^2}}$$

$$x = \frac{-b \pm \sqrt{b^2 - 4ac}}{2a}$$

TECHNICAL NOTE V

To obtain the x-intercept for the curve $y = ae^{kx} + c$: Let $y = 0$; then

$$ae^{kx} = -c$$

$$e^{kx} = -\frac{c}{a}$$

$$\ln\left(-\frac{c}{a}\right) = kx$$

$$x = \frac{1}{k}\ln\left(-\frac{c}{a}\right)$$

In order for $\ln\left(-\frac{c}{a}\right)$ to be defined,

$$c \leq 0, a > 0 \quad \text{(cases c and d)}$$

or

$$c \geq 0, a < 0 \quad \text{(cases e and f)}$$

Note in Fig. 1.93 that only cases (c), (d), (e), and (f) have x-intercepts and that

$$\frac{1}{k}\ln\left(-\frac{c}{a}\right) > 0 \text{ if } a > 0, c \leq 0, k < 0, a > |c| \quad \text{(case d)}$$

$$a < 0, c \geq 0, k > 0, c > |a| \quad \text{(case e)}$$

$$\frac{1}{k}\ln\left(-\frac{c}{a}\right) < 0 \text{ if } a > 0, c \leq 0, k > 0, a > |c| \quad \text{(case c)}$$

$$a < 0, c \geq 0, k < 0, c > |a| \quad \text{(case f)}$$

To obtain the x-intercept for the curve $y = A \ln(1 + x) + B$: Let $y = 0$; then

$$A \ln(1 + x) = -B$$

$$\ln(1 + x) = -\frac{B}{A}$$

$$e^{-(B/A)} = 1 + x$$

$$x = e^{-(B/A)} - 1$$

and

$$e^{-(B/A)} - 1 > 0 \qquad \text{if } \frac{B}{A} < 0$$

That is,

$$A > 0, B < 0 \qquad \text{(case c)}$$

or

$$A < 0, B > 0 \qquad \text{(case b)}$$

$$e^{-(B/A)} - 1 = 0 \qquad \text{if } \frac{B}{A} = 0$$

That is,

$$B = 0$$

$$e^{-(B/A)} - 1 < 0 \qquad \text{if } \frac{B}{A} > 0$$

That is,

$$A > 0, B > 0 \qquad \text{(case a)}$$

or

$$A < 0, B < 0 \qquad \text{(case d)}$$

2

DIFFERENTIAL
CALCULUS:
FUNCTIONS OF
ONE VARIABLE

■ 2.1 **INTRODUCTION**

Calculus is concerned with the mathematical analysis of movement and change. Because everything in the world changes, calculus has applications in virtually all areas of scientific inquiry. It is nearly impossible to exaggerate the importance of calculus, particularly differential calculus, as a basis for almost all mathematical analysis.

As a distinctly new mathematical method, calculus was developed in the seventeenth century by Sir Isaac Newton and Gottfried Leibnitz, working independently. For Newton, calculus originated in attempts to solve certain problems connected with his work in physics and astronomy: finding the velocity of a moving body, the work done by force, the center of mass of a body. For Leibnitz, calculus originated in attempts to solve certain problems in geometry: finding the tangent to a curve, the length of a portion of a curve, the area bounded by one or more curves, the volume of a solid.

The basic operations of calculus are differentiation and integration; these operations are the reverse of each other, as are addition and subtraction and multiplication and division. Differentiation is concerned essentially with determining the rate of change of a given function. Integration is concerned essentially with the inverse problem of finding a function when its rate of change is given.

The analogy of a moving-picture film is frequently used in discussing the processes of differentiation and integration. A moving-picture film is a series of (static) pictures, each at least slightly different from the others—each frame depicts the subjects in given positions at a particular instant of time. When the film is run through a projector at proper speed, the pictures are summed up and the illusion of motion is created. Similarly, differentiation essentially breaks up a function into many infinitesimally small (static) pieces and thus analyzes it at a particular point of time or for a particular value of the independent variable; integration, on the other hand, sums up the infinitesimally small pieces to obtain the function.

When relations among variables are stated in equations, calculus can be used to analyze these relations. Calculus has been used by physicists, astronomers, chemists, and engineers almost since its development; more recently, calculus has also been used by biological, social, and behavioral scientists.

Since analysis in business and economics is frequently concerned with change, calculus is an extremely valuable tool for business executives and economists. Marginal analysis is perhaps the most direct application of calculus in business and economics; marginal rate of change or variation on the margin is expressed analytically as the first derivative of the relevant function. Differential calculus is also the method by which maxima or minima of functions are obtained. Thus problems of maximizing profit or minimizing cost under various assumptions can be solved using calculus. Mathematical programming, which is concerned with maximizing or minimizing a function subject to constraints, is used increasingly in business and economics; the methods used in mathematical programming, for example, in linear programming, are applications of differential calculus.

The idea of the rate of change of a function, which is the basis of differential calculus, is discussed in the following paragraphs. The applications of this concept to marginal analysis and to various problems of maximization and minimization are discussed in some detail in following chapters.

The simplest type of functional relationship between two variables is represented by a straight line and corresponds to a *constant*, or *uniform*, rate of change in the dependent variable with respect to change in the independent variable. A *variable* rate of change in the dependent variable with respect to change in the independent variable is represented by a curvilinear (or nonlinear) function. The *average variable* rate of change is the average value over an interval of the variable rate of change.

For many analyses the most important concept is that of *instantaneous* rate of change—the variable rate of change at a particular instant of time or for a particular value of the independent variable. Instantaneous rate of change is obtained by differentiation and is, in fact, the first derivative of the function evaluated at the point of interest. The concept of instantaneous change is the basis of marginal analysis in economics; marginal analysis considers the effect on the dependent variable of small changes in the independent variable—that is, variation on the margin.

The mathematical definition and derivation of instantaneous or marginal rate of change are discussed in detail later; the concept can perhaps best be understood intuitively in terms of an example of physical movement. If a car is driven from city A to city B always at the same speed, then the rate of change in its distance from city A is constant with respect to change in time since leaving city *A*—the car is traveling at a constant or uniform rate. However, the car occasionally slows down for curves, towns, traffic, and so forth—it travels at a variable rate. Suppose the trip from city *A* to city *B* takes 5 hours; the number of miles traveled each hour could be averaged to obtain the average variable rate of travel per hour. There is clearly another rate of travel of interest to drivers and traffic policemen—the rate of travel at a particular instant of time. It is this instantaneous rate that is obtained by differential calculus.

Although instantaneous rate of change is perhaps most readily understood in terms of physical motion, it can be generalized to any type of functional relationship. For example, total cost is a function of the quantity produced and usually changes at a variable rate as the quantity produced changes. The rate of change of total cost as quantity produced changes is the marginal cost and is the first derivative of total cost; marginal cost is a function of the quantity produced and can be evaluated for any quantity of interest.

The first derivative—that is, the rate of change—of a function can be used to determine its stationary points, if any. A function increases (positive rate of change) until it reaches a maximum and then decreases (negative rate of change); similarly, a function decreases until it reaches a minimum and then increases. This basic method for determining the maxima and minima of a function by differentiation has been developed and generalized for use in problems of varying complexity and, as noted above, is the basis of the methods of mathematical programming.

Calculus, as noted, is concerned with infinitesimally small changes in the independent and dependent variables. Mathematically, such changes are defined using the concepts of limits and continuity; thus the following sections concern the mathematical concepts of limits and continuity which provide the foundation for the theory of calculus.

■ 2.2 LIMITS

The concept of a limit seems to be one of the most troublesome in mathematics. The idea of approaching a point or value as closely as specified and still never reaching it apparently is not intuitively appealing. In fact, however, limit-type concepts are frequently used in nonmathematical thinking and conversation. For example, the theoretical maximum production of a machine or of a factory is a limit—the ideal (or limiting) performance which is never attained in practice but which can be approached arbitrarily closely. This same idea applies to the performance of any mechanical or electronic device for which engineers can calculate an ideal (or limiting) performance and also, for example, to profits under ideal conditions, gas mileage under ideal conditions and operation, and so forth. Similarly, there are lower limits of cost, waste, spoilage, and so forth.

The mathematical concept of a limit is fundamental in understanding differential calculus and is discussed in some detail below. It is also used in later sections concerning series and indeterminate forms.

Consider a function $f(x)$ and let the independent variable x assume values near a given constant a; then the function $f(x)$ assumes a corresponding set of values. Suppose that when x is close to a, the corresponding values of $f(x)$ are close to some constant A. Moreover, suppose that the values of $f(x)$ can be made to differ arbitrarily little from A by taking values of x that are sufficiently close to a and that this is true for all such values of x (except, perhaps, for $x = a$). Then $f(x)$ is said to approach the *limit* A as x approaches a. More concisely, the definitions of the limit of a variable and the limit of a function are as follows.

A variable x is said to approach a constant a as a limit when x varies in such a way that the absolute difference $|x - a|$ becomes and remains less than any preassigned positive number, however small this number is chosen. This is indicated by the notation

$$\lim x = a \quad \text{or} \quad x \to a$$

Example

If x assumes the sequence of values

$$\tfrac{1}{2}, \tfrac{3}{4}, \tfrac{7}{8}, \tfrac{15}{16}, \ldots, \frac{2^n - 1}{2^n}, \ldots$$

then $x \to 1$. But if x assumes the sequence of values

$$\tfrac{1}{2}, -\tfrac{3}{4}, \tfrac{7}{8}, -\tfrac{15}{16}, \ldots, (-1)^{n-1}\frac{2^n - 1}{2^n}, \ldots$$

then x does not approach a limit.

If the function $f(x)$ approaches a constant A when x approaches a in whatever manner without assuming the value a, A is said to be the limit of $f(x)$ as x approaches a. This is indicated by the notation

$$\lim_{x \to a} f(x) = A \quad \text{or} f(x) \to A \quad \text{as } x \to a$$

Example

If $f(x) = 2x + 5, \lim_{x \to 0} f(x) = 5$, since, for example,

$$f(1) = 7 \qquad\qquad f(-1) = 3$$
$$f(\tfrac{1}{2}) = 6 \qquad\qquad f(-\tfrac{1}{2}) = 4$$
$$f(\tfrac{1}{4}) = 5\tfrac{1}{2} \qquad\qquad f(-\tfrac{1}{4}) = 4\tfrac{1}{2}$$
$$f(\tfrac{1}{100}) = 5\tfrac{1}{50} \qquad\qquad f(-\tfrac{1}{100}) = 4\tfrac{49}{50}$$
$$f(\tfrac{1}{1000}) = 5\tfrac{1}{500} \qquad\qquad f(-\tfrac{1}{1000}) = 4\tfrac{499}{500}$$
$$\text{etc.} \qquad\qquad\qquad \text{etc.}$$

The following two statements of the definition of the limit of a function are equivalent to the definition given above.

A function $f(x)$ is said to approach a limit A as x approaches a if the absolute difference between $f(x)$ and A is less than an arbitrarily small positive number for all values of x that are sufficiently close to a and for which $x \neq a$.

A function $f(x)$ approaches a limit A as x approaches a if, and only if, for each $\varepsilon > 0$ there exists a δ such that whenever $0 < |x - a| < \delta$, $|f(x) - A| < \varepsilon$.

It is implied in the above discussion of limits that both x and $f(x)$ approach finite constants (a and A, respectively) as limits. It is also possible, however, for either one or both of x and $f(x)$ to become arbitrarily large or arbitrarily small. These types of limiting behavior are defined as follows.

If the difference between a function $f(x)$ and a constant A is less in absolute value than an arbitrarily small positive number for all positive values of x that are sufficiently large, then $f(x)$ is said to approach A as a limit when x becomes positively infinite, that is, increases without limit. This is indicated by the notation

$$\lim_{x \to \infty} f(x) = A \qquad \text{or } f(x) \to A \quad \text{as } x \to \infty$$

NOTE: The notation $\lim\limits_{x \to +\infty} f(x) = A$ or $f(x) \to A$ as $x \to +\infty$ is sometimes used. However, as for numbers, ∞ is understood to mean $+\infty$, and the plus sign is usually omitted for convenience.

Example

If $f(x) = 1 - \dfrac{1}{x}$, then $\lim\limits_{x \to \infty} f(x) = 1$, since, for example,

$$f(1) = 0$$

$$f(5) = \tfrac{4}{5}$$

$$f(20) = \tfrac{19}{20}$$

$$f(100) = \tfrac{99}{100}$$

$$f(1000) = \tfrac{999}{1000}$$

$$f(10,000) = \tfrac{9999}{10,000}$$

etc.

Similarly, the limit of $f(x)$ may be defined when x becomes negatively infinite (that is, decreases without limit) by using numerically large negative values of x. This is indicated by the notation

$$\lim_{x \to -\infty} f(x) = A' \qquad \text{or } f(x) \to A' \quad \text{as } x \to -\infty$$

Example

If $f(x) = 1 - \dfrac{1}{x}$, then

$$\lim_{x \to -\infty} f(x) = 1$$

If a function $f(x)$ is greater than an arbitrarily large positive number for all values of x that are sufficiently near a constant a and for which $x \neq a$, then $f(x)$ is said to become positively infinite (that is, increases without limit) as x approaches a. This is indicated by the notation

$$\lim_{x \to a} f(x) = \infty \qquad \text{or } f(x) \to \infty \quad \text{as } x \to a$$

Similarily, $f(x)$ becomes negatively infinite (that is, decreases without limit) when it assumes numerically large negative values. This is indicated by the notation

$$\lim_{x \to a} f(x) = -\infty \qquad \text{or } f(x) \to -\infty \quad \text{as } x \to a$$

Example

If $f(x) = \dfrac{1}{(x-2)^2}$, then

$$\lim_{x \to 2} f(x) = \infty$$

If a function $f(x)$ is greater than an arbitrarily large positive number for all positive values of x that are sufficiently large, then $f(x)$ is said to become positively infinite (that is, increases without limit) as x becomes positively infinite (that is, increases without limit). This is indicated by the notation

$$\lim_{x \to \infty} f(x) = \infty \qquad \text{or } f(x) \to \infty \quad \text{as } x \to \infty$$

The cases indicated by the following notation are defined similarly:

$$\lim_{x \to \infty} f(x) = -\infty \qquad \text{or } f(x) \to -\infty \quad \text{as } x \to \infty$$

$$\lim_{x \to -\infty} f(x) = \infty \qquad \text{or } f(x) \to \infty \quad \text{as } x \to -\infty$$

$$\lim_{x \to -\infty} f(x) = -\infty \qquad \text{or } f(x) \to -\infty \quad \text{as } x \to -\infty$$

Examples

If $f(x) = x^4 - 4$, then

$$\lim_{x \to \infty} f(x) = \infty \quad \text{and} \quad \lim_{x \to -\infty} f(x) = \infty$$

If $f(x) = x^3 - 8$, then

$$\lim_{x \to \infty} f(x) = \infty \quad \text{and} \quad \lim_{x \to -\infty} f(x) = -\infty$$

In some cases a function may approach either of two different limits, depending on whether the variable approaches its limit through values larger or smaller than that limit; in such a case, the limit is not defined (does not exist) but the right-hand and left-hand limits exist.

The *right-hand limit* of a function is the value the function approaches when the variable approaches its limit through decreasing values (that is, from the right); this type of limiting behavior is indicated by the notation

$$\lim_{x \to a^+} f(x) = A^+ \quad \text{or} f(x) \to A^+ \quad \text{as } x \to a^+$$

The *left-hand limit* of a function is the value the function approaches when the variable approaches its limit through increasing values (that is, from the left); this is indicated by the notation

$$\lim_{x \to a^-} f(x) = A^- \quad \text{or} f(x) \to A^- \quad \text{as } x \to a^-$$

Thus the limit of a function exists if and only if its right-hand and left-hand limits exist and are identical; in that case

$$\lim_{x \to a^+} f(x) = \lim_{x \to a^-} f(x) = \lim_{x \to a} f(x)$$

Examples

If $f(t) = [t] = $ largest integer in t, then

$$\lim_{t \to 3^+} f(t) = 3 \quad \text{and} \quad \lim_{t \to 3^-} f(t) = 2$$

Thus $\lim_{t \to 3} f(x)$ is not defined.

It might seem intuitively that the limit of this function $f(t)$ as $t \to 3$ should be 3. However, when t is arbitrarily close to 3 some of the values of $[t]$ are 2 (when $t < 3$), others are 3 (when $t > 3$)—thus the values of t are not close to any one value A when t is arbitrarily close to 3 and $\lim_{t \to 3} [t]$ does not exist, although the right-hand and left-hand limits do exist. This is indicated in Fig. 2.1 by the unbroken horizontal lines between successive integer values of t. [That is, $f(t)$

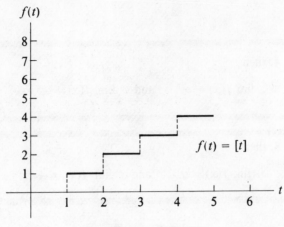

FIGURE 2.1

approaches 2 as t approaches 3 from the left; $f(t)$ approaches 3 as t approaches 3 from the right.] Clearly there is nothing unique about the integer 3; in fact, $f(t)$ does not have a limit (although it has right-hand and left-hand limits) as t approaches any integer value; $f(t)$ does, however, have the limit $[t]$ as t approaches any noninteger value.

If $f(t) = \dfrac{1}{t}$, then

$$\lim_{t\to 0^+} f(t) = \infty \qquad \text{and} \qquad \lim_{t\to 0^-} f(t) = -\infty$$

(see Fig. 2.2).

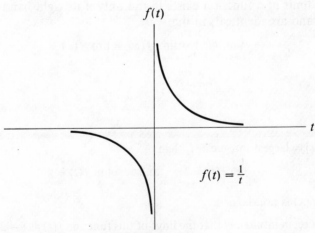

FIGURE 2.2

Thus $\lim_{t\to 0} f(t)$ is not defined; as t approaches 0 from above, $f(t)$ becomes positively infinite; as t approaches 0 from below, $f(t)$ becomes negatively infinite.

It is also possible that even right-hand and left-hand limits do not exist; this is the case, for example, for the sine and cosine functions which are oscillatory in nature.

□ PROPERTIES OF LIMITS

The following properties of limits are useful in evaluating the limit of a function.

If K is a constant and $\lim_{x \to a} f(x) = b$ and $\lim_{x \to a} g(x) = c$, then

1. $\lim_{x \to a} K = K$.

That is, the limit of a constant is equal to that constant. For purposes of interpreting the following properties of limits, a constant may be thought of as a special type of function—that is, a function that assumes only one value. Thus the following statements are valid (as special cases) if some or all of the functions are constants.

2. $\lim_{x \to a} [f(x) \pm g(x)] = \lim_{x \to a} f(x) \pm \lim_{x \to a} g(x) = b \pm c$.

That is, the limit of the sum (or difference) of two functions is equal to the sum (or difference) of their limits.

NOTE: This rule applies to the sum or difference of any finite number of functions—that is, if $\lim_{x \to a} f_i(x) = a_i$ for $i = 1, 2, \ldots, n$, then

$$\lim_{x \to a} \left(\sum_{i=1}^{n} f_i(x) \right) = \sum_{i=1}^{n} \lim_{x \to a} f_i(x) = \sum_{i=1}^{n} a_i$$

3. $\lim_{x \to a} [f(x) \cdot g(x)] = [\lim_{x \to a} f(x)][\lim_{x \to a} g(x)] = bc$.

That is, the limit of the product of two functions is equal to the product of their limits.

NOTE: This rule applies to the product of any finite number of functions—that is, if $\lim_{x \to a} f_i(x) = a_i$ for $i = 1, 2, \ldots, n$, then

$$\lim_{x \to a} \left(\prod_{i=1}^{n} f_i(x) \right) = \prod_{i=1}^{n} \lim_{x \to a} f_i(x) = \prod_{i=1}^{n} a_i$$

4. $\lim_{x \to a} \dfrac{f(x)}{g(x)} = \dfrac{\lim_{x \to a} f(x)}{\lim_{x \to a} g(x)} = \dfrac{b}{c}$ if $c \neq 0$.

That is, the limit of the quotient of two functions is equal to the quotient of their limits, provided the limit of the divisor is not zero.

5. $\lim_{x \to a} [f(x)]^n = [\lim_{x \to a} f(x)]^n = b^n$.

That is, the limit of the nth power of any function is equal to the nth power of the limit of the function. (This follows from rule 3 applied to the product of n equal factors.)

6. $\lim\limits_{x \to a} (\sqrt[n]{f(x)}) = \sqrt[n]{\lim\limits_{x \to a} f(x)} = \sqrt[n]{b}.$

That is, the limit of the principal nth root of a positive function is equal to the principal nth root of the limit of that function. (This follows from rule 4.)

Examples

$$\lim_{x \to 2} (x^3 - 3x + 5) = \lim_{x \to 2} x^3 - \lim_{x \to 2} 3x + \lim_{x \to 2} 5 \qquad \text{(rule 2)}$$
$$= (\lim_{x \to 2} x)^3 - 3(\lim_{x \to 2} x) + 5 \qquad \text{(rules 1, 3, 5)}$$
$$= 2^3 - 3(2) + 5 = 7.$$

$$\lim_{x \to 2} \left(\frac{x^2 \sqrt{x + 2}}{x^2 + 1} \right) = \frac{\lim\limits_{x \to 2} x^2 \sqrt{\lim\limits_{x \to 2}(x + 2)}}{\lim\limits_{x \to 2}(x^2 + 1)} \qquad \text{(rules 1, 2, 3, 4, 5, 6)}$$
$$= \frac{2^2 \sqrt{4}}{4 + 1} = \frac{8}{5}.$$

$$\lim_{x \to \infty} \left(\frac{2}{x^2 + 1} \right) = 0. \qquad \text{(rules 1, 2, 4, 5)}$$

$$\lim_{x \to 0} \left(1 + \frac{1}{x^2} \right) = \infty. \qquad \text{(rules 1, 2, 4, 5)}$$

$$\lim_{x \to -1} \left(\frac{x^2 + 1}{x^2 + x + 1} \right) = 2. \qquad \text{(rules 1, 2, 4, 5)}$$

$$\lim_{x \to \infty} \left(4 - \frac{2}{x + 1} \right) = 4. \qquad \text{(rules 1, 2, 4)}$$

In applying rule 4 concerning the limit of a quotient, it may happen that the quotient of the limits takes the meaningless form $\frac{0}{0}$. This is one of the indeterminate forms to be discussed in some detail in a later section; however, in this case it is frequently possible to obtain a determinate limit for the original quotient if a different and very simple procedure is used. The procedure essentially is to divide both the numerator and the denominator by an expression which in the limit is equal to zero, thereby obtaining an expression having a limit.

Examples

If $f(x) = \dfrac{x^2 - 4}{x - 2}$, then $\lim\limits_{x \to 2} f(x)$ is the indeterminate form $\dfrac{0}{0}$. But if $x \neq 2$, both numerator and denominator can be divided by $x - 2 : \dfrac{(x + 2)(x - 2)}{x - 2}$. Then $f(x) = \dfrac{x^2 - 4}{x - 2} = x + 2$.

Recall that in evaluating $\lim\limits_{x \to 2} f(x)$ it is not the value of $f(x)$ at $x = 2$ but only the values of $f(x)$ for x close to 2 which are of interest. For those values $f(x) = x + 2$ and $\lim\limits_{x \to 2} f(x) = \lim\limits_{x \to 2} (x + 2) = 4$. Thus, even though $f(x)$ is undefined at $x = 2$, it has the limit 4 as $x \to 2$.

If $F(h) = \dfrac{(2 + h)^2 - 4}{h}$, then $\lim\limits_{h \to 0} F(h)$ is the indeterminate form $\dfrac{0}{0}$. However, for $h \neq 0$, $F(h) = \dfrac{4 + 4h + h^2 - 4}{h} = \dfrac{4h + h^2}{h} = 4 + h$ and thus $\lim\limits_{h \to 0} F(h) = 4$.

Another type of indeterminate form that can arise as a result of applying rule 4 is $\dfrac{\infty}{\infty}$. This is also one of the indeterminate forms to be discussed in later sections; however, in this case it is frequently possible to obtain a determinate limit for the original quotient if both the numerator and denominator are divided by the highest power of the variable which appears in the denominator.

Examples

If $f(x) = \dfrac{2x^3 + x^2 - 3}{x^3 + x + 2}$, then $\lim\limits_{x \to \infty} f(x)$ is the indeterminate form $\dfrac{\infty}{\infty}$. However, if both the numerator and denominator are divided by x^3, then

$$f(x) = \frac{2x^3 + x^2 - 3}{x^3 + x + 2} = \frac{2 + \dfrac{1}{x} - \dfrac{3}{x^3}}{1 + \dfrac{1}{x^2} + \dfrac{2}{x^3}}$$

and thus $\lim\limits_{x \to \infty} f(x) = 2$, since as $x \to \infty$, $\dfrac{1}{x} \to 0$, $\dfrac{1}{x^2} \to 0$, $\dfrac{2}{x^3} \to 0$, and $\dfrac{3}{x^3} \to 0$.

If $f(x) = \dfrac{x + \dfrac{1}{x}}{2x - \dfrac{1}{x}}$, then $\lim\limits_{x \to \infty} f(x)$ is the indeterminate form $\dfrac{\infty}{\infty}$. However, if both

the numerator and denominator are divided by x, then

$$f(x) = \frac{x + \dfrac{1}{x}}{2x - \dfrac{1}{x}} = \frac{1 + \dfrac{1}{x^2}}{2 - \dfrac{1}{x^2}}$$

and thus $\lim\limits_{x \to \infty} f(x) = \frac{1}{2}$, since $\dfrac{1}{x^2} \to 0$ as $x \to \infty$.

PROBLEMS

Evaluate the following limits.

1. $\lim\limits_{t \to 0} \dfrac{3t - 5}{t + 2}$

2. $\lim\limits_{t \to \infty} \dfrac{3t^2 - 5t + 4}{t^2 + 2}$

3. $\lim\limits_{h \to 0} a^{x+h}$

4. $\lim\limits_{h \to 0} 2^{-h}$

5. $\lim\limits_{x \to 2} x^{-4}$

6. $\lim\limits_{x \to -2} x^4$

7. $\lim\limits_{x \to -\infty} 2^x$

8. $\lim\limits_{x \to \infty} 2^{-x}$

9. $\lim\limits_{t \to \infty} e^{-t}$

10. $\lim\limits_{t \to 0} \dfrac{e^t + e^{-t}}{2}$

11. $\lim\limits_{x \to 0} \dfrac{x - y}{x + y}$

12. $\lim\limits_{x \to 0} \dfrac{2^x - 2^{-x}}{2^x + 2^{-x}}$

13. $\lim\limits_{y \to 0} \dfrac{x - y}{x + y}$

14. $\lim\limits_{x \to \infty} \dfrac{x^3 - 2x + 5}{2x^3 - 7}$

15. $\lim\limits_{x \to \infty} \dfrac{x^2 + a^2}{x^3 + a^3}$

16. $\lim\limits_{x \to 0} \dfrac{x^3 - 5x + 6}{x^2 - 2x + 3}$

17. $\lim\limits_{x \to \infty} \dfrac{1}{1 + 2^{1/x}}$

18. $\lim\limits_{x \to -\infty} \dfrac{1}{1 + 2^{1/x}}$

19. $\lim\limits_{x \to 0^+} \dfrac{1}{1 + 2^{1/x}}$

20. $\lim\limits_{x \to 0^-} \dfrac{1}{1 + 2^{1/x}}$

21. $\lim\limits_{x \to -2} x^3$

22. $\lim\limits_{x \to 2} x^{-3}$

23. $\lim\limits_{x \to a} \dfrac{ax + 10}{x}$

24. $\lim\limits_{x \to \infty} \dfrac{1}{1 + e^{1/x}}$

25. $\lim\limits_{x \to 0^-} \dfrac{1}{1 + e^{1/x}}$

26. $\lim\limits_{x \to 0^+} \dfrac{1}{1 + e^{1/x}}$

27. $\lim\limits_{x \to 0} \dfrac{x + e^{x^2+3} + x^2}{e^3 + x}$

28. $\lim\limits_{x \to 0} \dfrac{x}{1 + e^x}$

29. $\lim\limits_{h \to 1} \dfrac{e^{-h}}{h^3 + 4h + 5}$

30. $\lim\limits_{t \to 2} \dfrac{t^2 + 4}{(t + 2)(t + 3)}$

31. $\lim\limits_{t \to \infty} e^{1/t} + 5$

32. $\lim\limits_{t \to 0} \dfrac{e^t - e^{-2t} - e^{3t^2}}{10}$

33. $\lim\limits_{x \to 4} \dfrac{x^2 - 16}{(x - 4)^2}$

34. $\lim\limits_{x \to -4} \dfrac{x^2 - 16}{(x - 4)^2}$

35. $\lim\limits_{x \to 4} \dfrac{x^2 - 16}{(x + 4)^2}$

36. $\lim\limits_{x \to 0} \dfrac{h^{-x} + h^x}{x}$

37. $\lim_{t \to 2} e^{-t+2}$

38. $\lim_{h \to 0} \dfrac{e^{-h} - e^{2h}}{3}$

39. $\lim_{x \to \infty} 1 + 3^{1/x}$

40. $\lim_{y \to 0} \dfrac{x - y + 3}{x + y - 6}$

41. $\lim_{x \to 3} \dfrac{x^3 - 3x^2 + 2x - 6}{x + 4}$

42. $\lim_{h \to 0} \dfrac{(h + 1)e^{-h}}{h^2 + 1}$

43. $\lim_{x \to \infty} e^{1/x}$

44. $\lim_{y \to 0} \dfrac{x^2 - y^2 + 2}{x^3 - y}$

45. $\lim_{x \to 2} \dfrac{x^4 - 6x - 4}{x + 1}$

46. $\lim_{t \to \infty} \dfrac{t^3 + 4t^2 + 10}{5t^2 + 12t}$

47. $\lim_{h \to \infty} \dfrac{1 + e^{1/h}}{e^h}$

48. $\lim_{h \to -\infty} \dfrac{1 + e^{1/h}}{e^h}$

49. $\lim_{h \to 2} \dfrac{x - h}{x + h}$

50. $\lim_{t \to 2} \dfrac{t^2 - 6t + 8}{t^2 - 5t + 6}$

→51. $\lim_{h \to \infty} \dfrac{h^4 + 5h^5}{3h + 2h^6}$

52. $\lim_{t \to 0} \dfrac{e^{-t}}{1 + e^{1/t}}$

53. $\lim_{t \to -3} \dfrac{t^2 - t - 12}{t^2 + 4t + 3}$

54. $\lim_{x \to 0} \dfrac{x^2 + 2ax + a^2}{a^3}$

55. $\lim_{x \to 0^+} \dfrac{2 - e^x}{e^{1/x}}$

56. $\lim_{x \to 0^-} \dfrac{2 - e^x}{e^{1/x}}$

Answers to Odd-Numbered Problems

1. $-\frac{5}{2}$
3. a^x
5. $\frac{1}{16}$
7. 0
9. 0
11. -1

13. 1
15. 0
17. $\frac{1}{2}$
19. 0
21. -8
23. $\dfrac{a^2 + 10}{a}$

25. 1
27. 1
29. $\dfrac{1}{10e}$
31. 6
33. ∞
35. 0

37. 1
39. 2
41. 0
43. 1
45. 0
47. 0

49. $\dfrac{x - 2}{x + 2}$
51. 0
53. $\frac{7}{2}$
55. 0

■ 2.3 CONTINUITY

In the definition of $\lim_{x \to a} f(x)$ the value of $f(x)$ for $x = a$ is not specified; that is, this limit depends only on the values of $f(x)$ in the neighborhood of (i.e., close to) $x = a$ but not on the value of $f(x)$ at $x = a$. Thus $\lim_{x \to a} f(x)$ may or may not be equal to $f(a)$. The case where $\lim_{x \to a} f(x)$ exists and the value $f(a)$ exists and is equal to $\lim_{x \to a} f(x)$ is of special interest and importance. In particular, a function $f(x)$ is said to be *continuous at $x = a$* if

1. $f(a)$ exists.

2. $\lim_{x \to a} f(x)$ exists.

3. $\lim_{x \to a} f(x) = f(a)$.

NOTE: When a limit is said to exist, this should be understood to mean that the limit exists finitely. Possible confusion arises because, even though, for example, the expression $\lim_{x \to a} A = \infty$ is written, this does not mean A approaches a number designated by ∞, but only that A becomes arbitrarily large as x approaches a. It should be remembered that ∞ is *not* a number and should not be thought of as one, even though for convenience it is used similarly in some expressions.

A function $f(x)$ is said to be *continuous in* (or on) *an interval* $b \leq x \leq c$ (or $b < x < c$) if it is continuous at every point of the interval.

A function that is not continuous at a point $x = a$ is said to be *discontinuous at $x = a$.*

From the definition of continuity it follows that the graph of a function that is continuous on an interval consists of an unbroken curve (that is, a curve that can be drawn without raising the pen from the paper) over that interval. Continuity of the curves discussed in the preceding sections concerning graphical representation was tacitly assumed. In subsequent sections this assumption, which makes it possible to sketch a curve by plotting relatively few points and drawing an unbroken curve through them, will be justified for several (large) classes of curves.

The three conditions that must be satisfied for a function to be continuous can be violated in various ways, resulting in different types of discontinuities. In general, four types of discontinuities occur.

1. A function $f(x)$ is said to have an *infinite discontinuity* at $x = a$ if $f(x)$ becomes infinite (positively or negatively) as $x \to a$. That is, $f(a)$ is not defined and $\lim_{x \to a} f(x)$ does not exist.

2. A function $f(x)$ is said to have a *finite discontinuity* at $x = a$ if $f(x)$ remains finite but changes abruptly at $x = a$. That is, $f(a)$ is defined but $\lim_{x \to a} f(x)$ does not exist [although, in general, the right-hand and left-hand limits exist and $f(a)$ is equal to one of them].

3. A function $f(x)$ is said to have a *missing-point discontinuity* at $x = a$ if $f(a)$ is not defined but $\lim_{x \to a} f(x)$ exists.

4. A *discrete function* is defined only for a finite number of values of x in any interval and is thus discontinuous at all other (infinitely many) values of x in the interval. Since x assumes only discrete values, the concept of a limit is not appropriate for discrete functions.

Graphically, the curves representing functions having different types of discontinuities are quite different in appearance: The curve representing a function having an infinite discontinuity at $x = a$ approaches $x = a$ as an asymptote; the curve representing a function having a finite discontinuity at $x = a$ has an abrupt jump or step at $x = a$; the curve representing a function having a missing-point discontinuity at $x = a$ appears to be continuous, but the single point $x = a$ is missing; the curve representing a discrete function consists of discrete points and thus is not a curve in the usual sense.

A missing-point discontinuity at $x = a$ occurs because $f(a)$ is not defined; this type of discontinuity may be removed by defining

$$f(a) = \lim_{x \to a} f(x)$$

since all three conditions of the definition of a continuous function at $x = a$ are thus satisfied. It is possible for a function to have more than one missing-point discontinuity; as long as the number of these discontinuities is finite, they may be removed by the procedure described. Note that there is also the logical possibility (although a practical example is difficult to construct) that there is a discontinuity at $x = a$ because $f(a)$, although defined, is not equal to $\lim_{x \to a} f(x)$. Such a discontinuity is not removable, since $f(a)$ is already defined and cannot therefore be defined as equal to $\lim_{x \to a} f(x)$.

Although missing-point discontinuities are removable, finite and infinite discontinuities are not removable. This is the case because the definition of a function is an arbitrary set of rules; adding another rule to this set, provided it is compatible with the others, is perfectly permissible, and this is all that is required to remove a missing-point discontinuity. On the other hand, finite and infinite discontinuities occur because the function in question does not approach a limit under the specified conditions; a limit either exists or does not exist as a mathematical fact associated with the nature of the function in question and cannot be defined into existence. Thus there is no way to remove a discontinuity resulting from the nonexistence of a limit.

Examples

The function $f(x) = \dfrac{1}{(x - 2)^2}$ has an infinite discontinuity at $x = 2$, since $f(x) \to \infty$ as $x \to 2$ and $f(2)$ is undefined. However, this function is continuous at all values of x other than $x = 2$ (see Fig. 2.3).

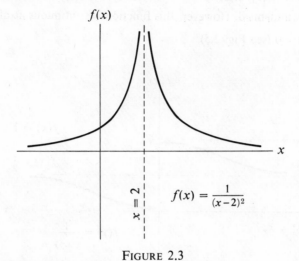

FIGURE 2.3

The function $f(x) = \dfrac{4x}{4-x^2}$ has infinite discontinuities at $x = \pm 2$, since $f(x) \to \infty$ as $x \to 2^-$, $f(x) \to -\infty$ as $x \to 2^+$, $f(x) \to \infty$ as $x \to -2^-$, and $f(x) \to -\infty$ as $x \to -2^+$ and $f(+2)$ and $f(-2)$ are undefined. However, this function is continuous at all values of x other than $x = \pm 2$ (see Fig. 2.4).

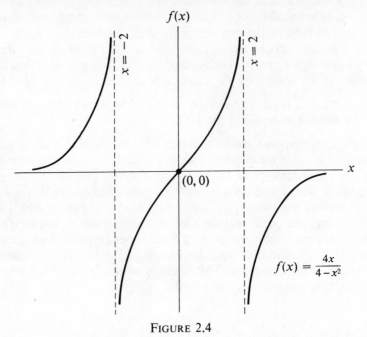

FIGURE 2.4

The function $f(x) = \dfrac{1}{1 + 2^{1/x}}$ has a finite discontinuity (that is, "jump") at $x = 0$ since $\lim\limits_{x \to 0} f(x)$ is undefined. However, this function is continuous at all values of x other than $x = 0$ (see Fig. 2.5).

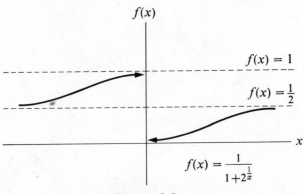

FIGURE 2.5

The function $f(x) = \dfrac{x^3 - 2x^2 - 3x + 6}{x - 2}$ is undefined and thus discontinuous when $x = 2$ (see Fig. 2.6). However, for $x \neq 2$,

$$f(x) = \frac{x^3 - 2x^2 - 3x + 6}{x - 2} = \frac{(x^2 - 3)(x - 2)}{x - 2} = x^2 - 3$$

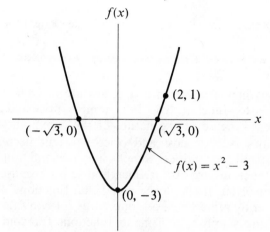

FIGURE 2.6

and $\lim\limits_{x \to 2} f(x) = 1$. Thus if, by definition,

$$f(2) = \lim_{x \to 2} f(x) = 1$$

then $f(x)$ is continuous for all x and its graph is the parabola

$$y = x^2 - 3$$

The function $f(x) = \dfrac{x^2 - 9}{x + 3}$ is undefined and thus discontinuous when $x = -3$

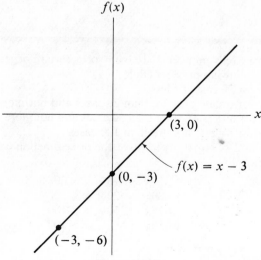

FIGURE 2.7

(see Fig. 2.7). However, for $x \neq -3$,

$$f(x) = \frac{x^2 - 9}{x + 3} = x - 3$$

and $\lim\limits_{x \to -3} f(x) = -6$. Thus if, by definition,

$$f(-3) = \lim\limits_{x \to -3} f(x) = -6$$

then $f(x)$ is continuous for all x and its graph is the straight line

$$y = x - 3$$

Many functions in business and economics are discrete or have finite discontinuities of the step-function type. For example, price and cost functions are frequently discrete because of the nature of the commodity involved and/or have discontinuities because cost and price per unit decrease (or increase) abruptly for particular quantities. Supply and demand functions and many other economic functions are also frequently discrete because of the nature of the commodity involved. It should be noted that functions which are, in fact, discrete are frequently represented as continuous for convenience; this applies, for example, to the supply and demand functions for commodities sold in units—such as refrigerators, eggs, light bulbs, chairs, lawn mowers, cars, and so forth. Representation as continuous of a function which is by nature discrete makes possible the use of many tools of analysis not otherwise applicable. However, in interpreting the results of such analyses, the basic discreteness should not be forgotten—for example, it is inappropriate to discuss the price of 1.632 refrigerators or the wages of 29.2 workers.

Examples

A wholesale grocer sells number 2 size cans of a certain vegetable in case lots according to the following price schedule:

$2.50 per case for 20 cases or less
$2.00 per case for orders of more than 20 cases and not more than 50 cases
$1.75 per case for orders of more than 50 cases and not more than 100 cases
$1.50 per case for orders of more than 100 cases

If y is total price and x is quantity in cases, the price function can be represented as follows algebraically

$$y = \begin{cases} 2.50x & 0 \leq x \leq 20 \\ 2.00x & 20 < x \leq 50 \\ 1.75x & 50 < x \leq 100 \\ 1.50x & x > 100 \end{cases}$$

and geometrically as shown in Fig. 2.8.

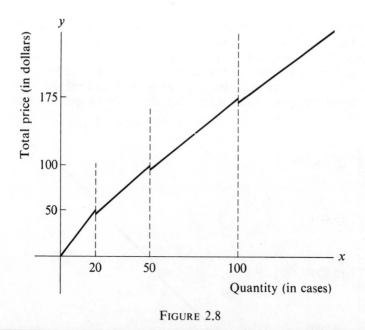

FIGURE 2.8

A company sells printed business stationery only in boxes of 200 sheets at $2.25 per box. If y is total price and x is number of boxes, the price function can be represented algebraically by the equation

$$y = 2.25x \qquad \text{for} \quad x = 1, 2, 3, \ldots$$

and geometrically by the graph of Fig. 2.9. This function is discrete, since it is defined only for integer values of x.

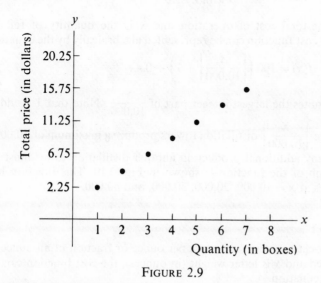

FIGURE 2.9

An oil refinery has 5 distillation towers and operates as many of them as needed to process the raw materials available. The overhead cost of operating each distillation tower (operator, maintenance, and so forth) is $100 per week; in addition, the cost of raw materials is $0.40 per gallon of refined oil. Each distillation tower can process raw materials yielding 10,000 gallons of refined oil

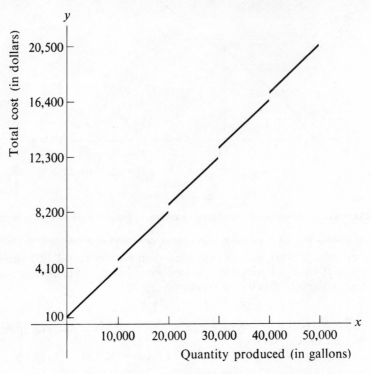

FIGURE 2.10

per week. If y is the total cost of operation and x is the quantity of refined oil (in gallons), the cost function can be represented algebraically by the equation

$$f(x) = 100 \left(\left[\frac{x}{10,000} \right] + 1 \right) + 0.4x$$

where $\left[\dfrac{x}{10,000} \right]$ denotes the largest integer part of $\dfrac{x}{10,000}$. Note that 1 is added

to $\left[\dfrac{x}{10,000} \right]$ because $\left[\dfrac{x}{10,000} \right]$ distillation towers produce a maximum of $10,000x$ gallons. Thus for any additional production another distillation tower must be operated. The graph of the function is shown in Fig. 2.10. This function has finite discontinuities at $x = 10,000$, $20,000$, $30,000$, and $40,000$.

United States first-class postage is 8 cents per ounce or fraction of an ounce. If y is postage required and x is letter weight (in ounces), the cost function can be represented by the equation

$$y = 0.08([x] + 1)$$

where [x] denotes the largest integer part of x. The graph of the function is shown in Fig. 2.11. This function has finite discontinuities at all integer values of x.

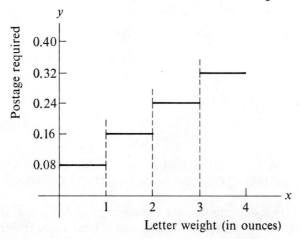

FIGURE 2.11

A stationery store sells Christmas cards for 10 cents each or $1.00 for a box of 12 (see Fig. 2.12). If y is price and x is number of cards sold, the price function can be represented by the equation

$$y = \left[\frac{x}{12}\right] + 0.10\left(x - 12\left[\frac{x}{12}\right]\right) \quad \text{for } x = 1, 2, 3, \ldots$$

where $\left[\dfrac{x}{12}\right]$ denotes the largest integer part of $\dfrac{x}{12}$. This function is discrete since it is defined only for integer values of x; it is also nonmonotonic, owing to discounting for larger quantities purchased.

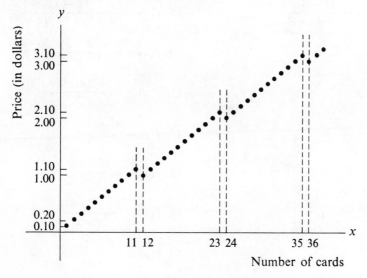

FIGURE 2.12

The following properties of continuous functions follow from the definition of a continuous function and the properties of limits.

If $f(x)$ and $g(x)$ are two functions that are continuous at $x = a$, then

$$F(x) = f(x) + g(x)$$
$$G(x) = f(x) - g(x)$$
$$H(x) = f(x) \cdot g(x)$$

are also continuous at $x = a$. If $g(a) \neq 0$, then

$$I(x) = \frac{f(x)}{g(x)}$$

is also continuous at $x = a$. [Note that if $g(a) = 0$, then $I(a)$ is undefined.]

The following properties can also be proved (but by more advanced arguments):

If a function $f(x)$ is continuous in a closed interval $b \leq x \leq c$, then

1. $f(x)$ has a greatest value (maximum) and a least value (minimum) in the interval.

2. $f(x)$ cannot go from one value to another in the interval without assuming every intermediate value at least once.

3. If $f(b)$ and $f(c)$ are opposite in sign, then there exists at least one value $x = a$ in the interval such that $f(a) = 0$.

PROBLEMS

Determine the values of x for which the following functions are discontinuous. Identify the removable discontinuities and give appropriate definitions for removing them.

1. $f(x) = \dfrac{3x + 5}{x^2 + 4x + 4}$

2. $f(x) = \dfrac{x - 2}{x + 1}$

3. $f(x) = \dfrac{x^2 - 1}{x - 1}$

4. $f(x) = \dfrac{x^2 + 4}{x^2 - x - 2}$

5. $f(x) = \log(2x - 5)$

6. $f(x) = \dfrac{1}{2^x - 1}$

7. $f(x) = \dfrac{1}{x(x - 2)}$

8. $f(x) = \sqrt{\dfrac{x + 1}{x - 1}}$

9. $f(x) = \dfrac{(x - 1)^2}{(x - 1)(x^2 - 4x + 5)}$

10. $f(x) = \log\left(\dfrac{x - 2}{x}\right)$

11. $f(x) = \dfrac{x^2 + 5x + 6}{x + 2}$

12. $f(x) = \dfrac{x^2 - 3}{x^2 - 4}$

13. $f(x) = \dfrac{x^2 - 2x}{x^3 - x^2 + x}$

14. $f(x) = \dfrac{x^2 - 5x + 6}{x - 2}$

15. $f(x) = \dfrac{x^2 + 1}{x^3 - 4x}$

16. $f(x) = \dfrac{4x}{4 - x^2}$

17. $f(x) = \dfrac{1}{4x^2 - 16}$

18. $f(x) = \dfrac{x - 2}{(x - 2)(x^2 + 2x + 10)}$

19. $f(x) = \dfrac{1}{e^{4x} - 1}$

20. $f(x) = \dfrac{x - 2}{(x - 2)(x^2 + 2x - 3)}$

21. $f(x) = \dfrac{e^x + 2x^2}{2e^{3x} - 2}$

22. $f(x) = \dfrac{x^2 - 5x + 6}{(x - 2)(x^2 - 3x + 5)}$

23. $f(x) = \dfrac{1}{e^x - 1}$

24. $f(x) = \dfrac{x^2 - 3}{x^2 - 16}$

25. $f(x) = \dfrac{(x - 3)^3}{(x - 3)(x^2 - 2x + 6)}$

26. $f(x) = \dfrac{x^2 + 2x - 8}{x + 4}$

27. $f(x) = \dfrac{1}{3e^{3x} - 3}$

28. $f(x) = \dfrac{(x + 5)^2(x + 3)}{(x + 5)(x^2 - 4x + 8)}$

29. $f(x) = \dfrac{x^2 + 5x + 6}{x + 2}$

30. $f(x) = \dfrac{x^2 + 3x + 6}{x^2 - 1}$

31. $f(x) = \dfrac{10}{e^{6x} - 1}$

32. $f(x) = \dfrac{x^2 + x - 2}{x^2 + 27x + 50}$

33. $f(x) = \dfrac{x^2 + 10x + 1}{x^2 - 9}$

34. $f(x) = \dfrac{x^2 - 5x + 4}{x - 4}$

35. $f(x) = \ln(x^2 - 6)$

36. $f(x) = \dfrac{x^2 - 5x + 6}{(x - 2)(x^2 - 2x - 3)}$

37. $f(x) = \dfrac{2x^2 + 3x}{x^3 - 9x}$

38. $f(x) = \dfrac{1}{3e^x - 3}$

39. $f(x) = \dfrac{e^x + 4x}{3e^{4x} - 3}$

40. $f(x) = \dfrac{x^2 + 5x + 4}{(x + 4)(x^2 - 6x + 10)}$

41. $f(x) = \dfrac{x^2 - 1}{x + 1} \qquad \text{for } x \neq -1$
$ = -2 \qquad \text{for } x = -1$
Is $f(x)$ continuous at $x = -1$?

42. $f(x) = \dfrac{x^2 + 3x - 10}{x - 2} \quad \text{for } x \neq 2.$

What value should be assigned to $f(2)$ to make $f(x)$ continuous at $x = 2$?

43. $f(x) = \sqrt[3]{x}$. Is $f(x)$ continuous at $x = 0$?

44. $f(x) = \dfrac{x^2 - 7x + 12}{x - 3} \qquad \text{for } x \neq 3$
$ = 1 \qquad \text{for } x = 3$
Is $f(x)$ continuous at $x = 3$?

ANSWERS TO ODD-NUMBERED PROBLEMS

1. $x = -2$

3. $x = 1, f(1) = 2$

5. $x = \frac{5}{2}$

7. $x = 0, x = 2$

9. $x = 1, f(1) = 0$

11. $x = -2, f(-2) = 1$

13. $x = 0, f(0) = -2$

15. $x = 0, x = \pm 2$

17. $x = \pm 2$

19. $x = 0$

21. $x = 0$

23. $x = 0$

25. $x = 3, f(3) = 0$

27. $x = 0$

29. $x = -2, f(-2) = 1$

31. $x = 0$

33. $x = \pm 3$

35. $x = \pm \sqrt{6}$

37. $x = \pm 3, x = 0, f(0) = -\frac{1}{3}$

39. $x = 0$

41. continuous

43. continuous

■ **2.4 DEFINITION OF A DERIVATIVE**

. In the discussion of straight lines, the slope m of a straight line is defined as the tangent of its angle of inclination or, equivalently, as the ratio of the change in vertical distance (rise) to the change in horizontal distance (run) as a point moves along the line in either direction (see Fig. 2.13).

$$m = \tan \theta = \frac{y_2 - y_1}{x_2 - x_1} = \frac{\Delta y}{\Delta x}$$

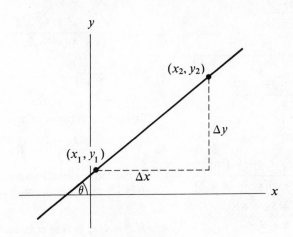

FIGURE 2.13

The slope of any given straight line is a constant—that is, the rate of change of y as x changes is constant throughout the length of the line. However, for less simple curves this is not the case, and the slope must thus be determined for each particular point of interest.

Suppose that (x_1, y_1) and (x_2, y_2) are any two points on the curve $y = f(x)$. Then the slope of the line (called a secant) joining (x_1, y_1) and (x_2, y_2) is

$$m_{\text{sec}} = \frac{y_2 - y_1}{x_2 - x_1} = \frac{\Delta y}{\Delta x}$$

Suppose now that the point (x_1, y_1) is held fixed while the point (x_2, y_2) is moved along the curve $y = f(x)$ toward the point (x_1, y_1); as the point (x_2, y_2) is moved along the curve $f(x)$ the slope of the line joining (x_1, y_1) and (x_2, y_2) will, in general, vary. However, it may happen, and does happen for most curves encountered in practice, that as the point (x_2, y_2) moves closer and closer to the point (x_1, y_1), the slope of the secant line varies by smaller and smaller amounts and, in fact, approaches a constant limiting value. When this happens, the limiting value is said to be the slope of the tangent to the curve at (x_1, y_1) or the slope of the curve at (x_1, y_1) (see Fig. 2.14).

More concisely, if, as the point (x_2, y_2) approaches the point (x_1, y_1) along the curve $y = f(x)$, the slope of the secant line approaches a constant limiting value, then this limiting value is said to be the slope of the tangent to the curve at (x_1, y_1) or, briefly, the slope of the curve at (x_1, y_1). That is,

$$\lim_{\Delta x \to 0} m_{\text{sec}} = \lim_{\Delta x \to 0} \frac{\Delta y}{\Delta x} = \text{slope of curve at } (x_1, y_1)$$

The slope of the tangent to a curve at a given point is the *first derivative* of the curve at the given point.

It is customary in defining the first derivative to use the notation (x, y) for the stationary point (x_1, y_1) and the notation $(x + \Delta x, y + \Delta y)$ for the moving point (x_2, y_2). Then

$$\frac{dy}{dx} = \lim_{\Delta x \to 0} \frac{\Delta y}{\Delta x} = \lim_{\Delta x \to 0} \frac{f(x + \Delta x) - f(x)}{\Delta x}$$

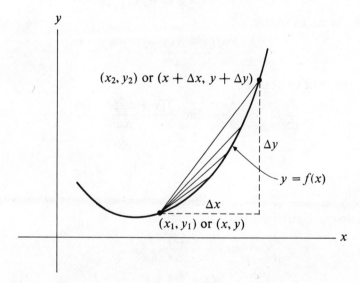

FIGURE 2.14

is the first derivative with respect to x of the function $y = f(x)$. This limit may exist for some values of x and fail to exist for other values of x. At each point (x, y) where this limit does exist, the function $y = f(x)$ is said to have a derivative or to be *differentiable* and $\frac{dy}{dx}$ is said to be the *first derivative* or the derivative of $y = f(x)$. The process of obtaining the first derivative of a function is referred to as *differentiation*. Various types of notation, in addition to $\frac{dy}{dx}$, are used to denote the first derivative of $y = f(x)$ with respect to x. The most common of these are

$$f'(x) \qquad y' \qquad \frac{d}{dx}(y) \qquad D_x y \qquad D_x(y)$$

It should be noted that the first derivative of a function with respect to x is, in general, another function of x and must be evaluated for particular values of interest. This corresponds to the fact stated above that, except for straight lines, curves do not in general have the same slope at different points.

From the definition of a derivative and the properties of limits, rules for obtaining the derivatives of various types of functions have been obtained. These are given subsequently. However, it is instructive to obtain the derivatives of several relatively simple functions directly from the definition.

The steps for obtaining a derivative directly are as follows:

1. Consider the function $y = f(x)$.

2. Give increments to x and y to obtain

$$y + \Delta y = f(x + \Delta x)$$

3. Subtract to obtain

$$\Delta y = f(x + \Delta x) - f(x)$$

4. Divide by Δx to obtain

$$\frac{\Delta y}{\Delta x} = \frac{f(x + \Delta x) - f(x)}{\Delta x}$$

5. Take the limit to obtain

$$\frac{dy}{dx} = \lim_{\Delta x \to 0} \frac{\Delta y}{\Delta x} = \lim_{\Delta x \to 0} \frac{f(x + \Delta x) - f(x)}{\Delta x}$$

Examples

Find the first derivative of $y = 4x + 1$.

$$\frac{dy}{dx} = \lim_{\Delta x \to 0} \frac{f(x + \Delta x) - f(x)}{\Delta x}$$

$$= \lim_{\Delta x \to 0} \frac{4(x + \Delta x) + 1 - 4x - 1}{\Delta x}$$

$$= \lim_{\Delta x \to 0} \frac{4\Delta x}{\Delta x}$$

$$= \lim_{\Delta x \to 0} 4 = 4$$

Note that $y = 4x + 1$ represents a straight line and thus $\frac{dy}{dx}$ is a constant.

Find the first derivative of $y = x^3 - 12x + 13$.

$$\frac{dy}{dx} = \lim_{\Delta x \to 0} \frac{f(x + \Delta x) - f(x)}{\Delta x}$$

$$= \lim_{\Delta x \to 0} \frac{(x + \Delta x)^3 - 12(x + \Delta x) + 13 - x^3 + 12x - 13}{\Delta x}$$

[NOTE: $(a + b)^3 = a^3 + 3a^2 b + 3ab^2 + b^3$]

$$= \lim_{\Delta x \to 0} \frac{3x^2(\Delta x) + 3x(\Delta x)^2 + (\Delta x)^3 - 12(\Delta x)}{\Delta x}$$

$$= \lim_{\Delta x \to 0} [3x^2 + 3x(\Delta x) + (\Delta x)^2 - 12]$$

$$= 3x^2 - 12$$

Note that $\frac{dy}{dx}$ is a function of x and can be evaluated for any value of x which is of interest.

Find the first derivative of $y = x^2 + \frac{1}{x}$ for $x \neq 0$.

$$\frac{dy}{dx} = \lim_{\Delta x \to 0} \frac{f(x + \Delta x) - f(x)}{\Delta x}$$

$$= \lim_{\Delta x \to 0} \frac{(x + \Delta x)^2 + \dfrac{1}{x + \Delta x} - x^2 - \dfrac{1}{x}}{\Delta x}$$

$$= \lim_{\Delta x \to 0} \frac{2x(\Delta x) + (\Delta x)^2 + \dfrac{x - x - \Delta x}{x(x + \Delta x)}}{\Delta x}$$

$$= \lim_{\Delta x \to 0} \left[2x + \Delta x - \frac{1}{x(x + \Delta x)} \right]$$

$$= 2x - \frac{1}{x^2} \text{ for } x \neq 0$$

Note that again $\frac{dy}{dx}$ is a function of x and can be evaluated for any value of $x \neq 0$ that is of interest.

For each of the following functions $f(x)$, find the first derivative $f'(x)$ using the definition

$$f'(x) = \lim_{\Delta x \to 0} \frac{f(x + \Delta x) - f(x)}{\Delta x}$$

1. $f(x) = x^2 - x + 1$ 2. $f(x) = \dfrac{1}{x^2}$ 3. $f(x) = \sqrt{2x}$

4. $f(x) = x - \dfrac{1}{x}$ 5. $f(x) = 6 - 2x^3$ 6. $f(x) = 5x^4 - 2$

ANSWERS TO ODD-NUMBERED PROBLEMS

1. $2x - 1$ 3. $\dfrac{1}{\sqrt{2x}}$ 5. $-6x^2$

□ INTERPRETATION OF THE FIRST DERIVATIVE

Although the geometrical interpretation of the first derivative has historical significance and is perhaps the most intuitive approach, other interpretations are equally valid and sometimes are more useful in applications.

Two of the classical interpretations of a derivative are in terms of the velocity of a moving body and the rate of change of a function. Both of these interpretations originated in the study of various problems in physics and mathematics; however, they have since been applied in many fields. For example, marginal analysis in economics can be more readily understood in terms of the rate of change of a function.

● Velocity of a Moving Body

Consider a body (or a particle) moving along a straight-line path. Let t denote the time measured from some fixed instant and let s denote the distance of the particle from some fixed origin on the line, considered positive or negative according to the direction from the origin. Suppose that the distance from the origin is given in terms of the time by a function $s = f(t)$, called the *law of motion*. [For example, think of the body or particle as being a car that is driven along a straight road in such a way that its distance from the starting point is given as a function of t by $s = f(t)$.]

At a certain time t_1, let the particle be at a distance s_1 from the origin 0, and suppose that during the following time interval Δt it moves a distance Δs farther from the origin (see Fig. 2.15).

If the ratio $\dfrac{\Delta s}{\Delta t}$ is constant, so that equal distances are always traversed in equal intervals of time, the motion is said to be *uniform* and the ratio $\frac{\Delta s}{\Delta t}$ is called the *velocity* at any instant. The term *speed* is used frequently to mean the magnitude—that is, absolute value—of the velocity.

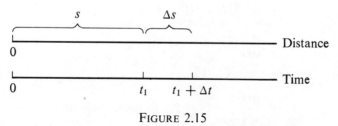

FIGURE 2.15

If, however, the motion is not uniform, the ratio $\frac{\Delta s}{\Delta t}$ varies as Δt varies and is no longer the velocity of the particle at any instant. It is instead the *average velocity* of the particle during the particular time interval Δt:

$$\text{Average velocity during interval } \Delta t = \frac{\Delta s}{\Delta t}$$

As the time interval Δt approaches zero, this average velocity $\frac{\Delta s}{\Delta t}$ may approach a limit. If so, this limit is said to be the *instantaneous velocity* at time t_1:

$$\text{Instantaneous velocity} = \lim_{\Delta t \to 0} \frac{\Delta s}{\Delta t}$$

But, by definition, $\lim\limits_{\Delta t \to 0} \frac{\Delta s}{\Delta t}$ is the first derivative of $f(t)$ at the point $t = t_1$. Thus at an instant t_1 the velocity of a particle moving in a straight line according to the law of motion $s = f(t)$, where s is the directed distance from a fixed origin and t is the time, is given by the value of the derivative of s with respect to t for $t = t_1$.

Examples

The distance of a train from its starting point when it is traveling along a straight track is given by the equation

$$s = 16t^2 + 2t$$

where s is distance in miles and t is time in hours. Find (a) the distance traveled and (b) the velocity after 2 hours.

   (a) $s = 16t^2 + 2t$. So after 2 hours, $s = 64 + 4 = 68$ miles traveled.
   (b) $s = 16t^2 + 2t$.

$$\frac{ds}{dt} = \lim_{\Delta t \to 0} \frac{f(t + \Delta t) - f(t)}{\Delta t}$$

$$= \lim_{\Delta t \to 0} \frac{16(t + \Delta t)^2 + 2(t + \Delta t) - 16t^2 - 2t}{\Delta t}$$

$$= \lim_{\Delta t \to 0} \frac{32t(\Delta t) + 16(\Delta t)^2 + 2(\Delta t)}{\Delta t}$$

$$= \lim_{\Delta t \to 0} [32t + 16(\Delta t) + 2]$$

$$= \lim_{\Delta t \to 0} (32t + 2)$$

and the velocity after 2 hours is

$$\frac{ds}{dt}\bigg|_{t=2} = 64 + 2 = 66 \text{ miles per hour}$$

(The notation $\dfrac{ds}{dt}\bigg|_{t=2}$ means the function $\dfrac{ds}{dt}$ evaluated for $t = 2$.)

One of the attractions at a carnival is a "prove your strength" bell, which rings if a lever is hit with sufficient strength to propel an iron ball up a vertical shaft to hit the bell. When the lever is hit with a force of 50 lb, the distance of the ball from the bottom of the shaft is given by

$$s = 40t - 32t^2$$

where s is distance in feet and t is time in minutes. (a) If the bell is at the top of a 15-ft shaft, is a force of 50 lb sufficient to ring it? (b) How far from the bottom of the shaft is the ball after 30 seconds, 45 seconds, 1 minute, and 75 seconds?

(a) Velocity $\dfrac{ds}{dt}$ is zero when the ball is at the top of the shaft, so solving the equation $\dfrac{ds}{dt} = 0$ provides the time the ball travels up the shaft before coming back down.

$$\frac{ds}{dt} = \lim_{\Delta t \to 0} \frac{f(t + \Delta t) - f(t)}{\Delta t}$$

$$= \lim_{\Delta t \to 0} \frac{40(t + \Delta t) - 32(t + \Delta t)^2 - 40t + 32t^2}{\Delta t}$$

$$= \lim_{\Delta t \to 0} \frac{40(\Delta t) - 64t(\Delta t) - 32(\Delta t)^2}{\Delta t}$$

$$= \lim_{\Delta t \to 0} [40 - 64t - 32(\Delta t)]$$

$$= 40 - 64t$$

If $\dfrac{ds}{dt} = 0$, $t = \frac{40}{64} = \frac{5}{8}$ minutes (or 37.5 seconds) and $s = 40(\frac{5}{8}) - 32(\frac{25}{64}) = 12.5$ feet, so the force is not sufficient to ring the bell 15 feet up the shaft. (See Fig. 2.16.)

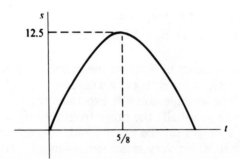

FIGURE 2.16

(b) If $t = 30$ seconds $= \frac{1}{2}$, $s = 40(\frac{1}{2}) - 32(\frac{1}{4}) = 12$ feet (on the way up)

    If $t = 45$ seconds $= \frac{3}{4}$, $s = 40(\frac{3}{4}) - 32(\frac{9}{16}) = 12$ feet (on the way down)

    If $t = 1$, $s = 40 - 32 = 8$ feet (on the way down)

    If $t = 75$ seconds $= \frac{5}{4}$, $s = 40(\frac{5}{4}) - 32(\frac{25}{16}) = 0$ (ball back down)

● **Rate of Change of a Function**

Let p and q denote the measures of two related variables and regard q as a function of p—that is, $q = f(p)$. If the ratio $\frac{\Delta q}{\Delta p}$ of corresponding changes in the two quantities has the same value for all values of Δp, it is called the *rate of change* of q with respect to p and q is said to change uniformly with respect to p. But if the ratio $\frac{\Delta q}{\Delta p}$ is not constant as Δp changes, q does not change uniformly, and $\frac{\Delta q}{\Delta p}$ is then called the *average rate of change* of q with respect to p over the interval Δp.

If the ratio $\frac{\Delta q}{\Delta p}$ approaches a limit when Δp approaches zero, then this limit is said to be the *instantaneous rate of change* of q with respect to p.

From the definition of the derivative, it follows that the instantaneous rate of change of a variable quantity q with respect to a related variable quantity p is given by the derivative $\frac{dq}{dp}$ of q with respect to p.

It is customary to use the expression "rate of change of a function" as equivalent to the derivative of the function.

If the variable q can be expressed as a function of the variable time t, then the derivative $\frac{dq}{dt}$ of q with respect to t gives the *time rate of change* of q. Thus the velocity of a particle is the time rate of change of its distance from the origin.

The interpretation of a derivative in terms of the rate of change of a function is frequently applicable in economics, as discussed below.

☐ *APPLICATIONS OF THE DERIVATIVE*
IN BUSINESS AND ECONOMICS

It is customary in economics to describe the variation of one quantity y with respect to another quantity x in terms of two concepts—an *average* concept and a *marginal* concept. The average concept expresses the variation of y over a whole range of values of x, usually the range from zero up to a certain selected value. The marginal concept, on the other hand, concerns the variation of y " on the margin "—that is, for very small variations of x from a given value. The marginal concept is thus precise only when it is considered in the limiting sense, as the variations in x approach zero.

The economic concepts of average and marginal variation correspond to the more general concepts of the average rate of change of a function over an interval and the instantaneous rate of change (that is, the derivative) of a function.

Average and marginal variations in quantities are essential considerations in the development of both microeconomic and macroeconomic theory. Examples of the application of the derivative in both microeconomic theory (cost, revenue, elasticity) and macroeconomic theory (income, consumption, savings) are discussed below; additional examples are given in later sections.

● **Cost**

Suppose the total cost y of producing and marketing x units of a commodity is given by the function

$$y = F(x)$$

Then the *average cost* per unit is

$$\frac{y}{x} = \frac{F(x)}{x}$$

If output is increased by an amount Δx from a certain level x and if the corresponding increase in cost is Δy, then the average increase in cost per unit increase in output is $\dfrac{\Delta y}{\Delta x}$ and marginal cost is defined as

$$\lim_{\Delta x \to 0} \frac{\Delta y}{\Delta x} = \frac{dy}{dx} = F'(x)$$

That is, marginal cost is the derivative $F'(x)$ of the total cost function $y = F(x)$ with respect to x and is the rate of increase in total cost with increase in output.

Example

Consider the total cost function

$$y = 20 + 2x + 0.5x^2$$

where y denotes total cost and x denotes quantity produced. Average cost is

$$\frac{y}{x} = \frac{20}{x} + 2 + 0.5x$$

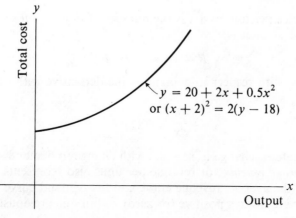

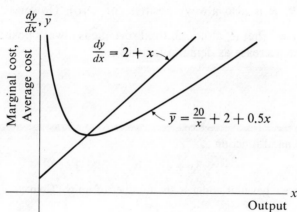

FIGURE 2.17

and marginal cost is

$$\frac{dy}{dx} = 2 + x$$

Thus total cost increases as output increases; average cost per unit decreases and then increases as output increases; and marginal cost (rate of increase in total cost) increases as output increases (see Fig. 2.17).

NOTE: Derivatives are given in these examples without any explanation of how they were obtained. The method of the preceding section or the rules given in the next section can be used to verify the derivations.

● **Revenue**

For any given demand function

$$y = f(x)$$

where y is the price per unit and x is the number of units, *total revenue* R is the product of x and y—that is,

$$R = xy = x \cdot f(x)$$

Marginal revenue with respect to demand is the derivative with respect to x of total revenue,

$$\frac{dR}{dx} = R'(x)$$

and is thus the rate of change in revenue with change in demand.

Note that *average revenue*, or revenue per unit, also represents the price per unit, y—that is, the average revenue curve and the demand curve are identical.

Since x and y are always positive (or zero) within our previously stated analytical framework, R is also always positive (or zero). However, $\frac{dR}{dx}$ may be positive or negative—that is, although total revenue is always positive (or zero), it may increase or decrease as demand increases.

Example

Consider the demand function

$$3x + 4y = 10$$

where y is the price per unit and x is the number of units. Then

$$y = \tfrac{5}{2} - \tfrac{3}{4}x$$

Total revenue is

$$R = \tfrac{5}{2}x - \tfrac{3}{4}x^2$$

and marginal revenue is

$$\frac{dR}{dx} = \tfrac{5}{2} - \tfrac{3}{2}x$$

Thus total revenue increases and then decreases as quantity increases; both average revenue and marginal revenue decrease (linearly) as quantity increases. Note that the average and marginal revenue curves have the same y-intercept and that, apart from this common point, the marginal revenue curve lies below the average revenue curve. Note also that the marginal revenue curve intersects the x-axis at the output for which total revenue is greatest and that the average revenue curve intersects the x-axis at twice that output. These are general properties for linear demand functions, as is the fact that the magnitude of the slope of the average revenue curve is one-half the magnitude of the slope of the marginal revenue curve (see Fig. 2.18).

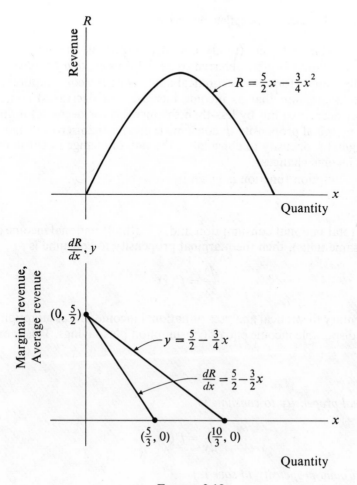

FIGURE 2.18

● **Elasticity**

The *point elasticity* of the function $y = f(x)$ at the point x is the proportional rate of change in y per unit change in x:

$$\frac{Ey}{Ex} = \frac{\dfrac{dy}{y}}{\dfrac{dx}{x}} = \frac{x}{y} \cdot \frac{dy}{dx}$$

Note that the elasticity of a function is independent of the units in which the variables are measured. This results from the definition of elasticity in terms of proportional changes, which are necessarily independent of units of measurement.

The point elasticity of demand, supply, cost, productivity, and other functions is an important concept in economic theory. Detailed examples of these and other applications of derivatives are discussed in subsequent sections, following the discussion of the techniques of differentiation.

● **National Income, Consumption, and Savings**

The relationship between (total) national disposable income and (total) national consumption is often referred to as the *consumption function*.

Essentially, simple forms of theoretical analysis of the consumption function rest on the assumption that as income increases (or decreases) consumption increases (or decreases) but by less than the increase (or decrease) in income— that is, the marginal propensity to consume is greater than zero but less than 1, where marginal propensity to consume is the rate of change in consumption as disposable income changes.

If the consumption function is given by

$$c = f(x)$$

where c is total national consumption and x is (total) national income (c and x are in the same units), then the marginal propensity to consume is

$$\frac{dc}{dx} = f'(x)$$

In elementary theoretical analyses of national income, the assumption is often made that disposable income equals consumption plus savings. This is expressed as

$$x = c + s$$

The marginal propensity to consume is

$$\frac{dc}{dx} = f'(x)$$

and *the marginal propensity to save* is

$$\frac{ds}{dx} = 1 - \frac{dc}{dx}$$

In national income analysis investment is considered as capital formation, and represents an increase in real capital as typified by equipment, buildings, inventories, and so forth.

Investment and consumption are assumed to be related in such a way that an initial investment expenditure may result in an increase in income of several times that amount. A precise numerical relationship for this relationship is given by the multiplier. The multiplier is the ratio of the ultimate increase in income over the increase in investment that gave rise to it.

The *multiplier k* is related to the marginal propensity to consume and is given by

$$k = \frac{1}{1 - \dfrac{dc}{dx}} = \frac{1}{\dfrac{ds}{dx}}$$

Note that if $\frac{dc}{dx} = 0$, then $k = 1$—that is, if none of the additional income is spent, the total increase in income is equal to the initial expenditure; if $\frac{dc}{dx} \rightarrow 1$,

$k \to \infty$—that is, if all the additional income is spent, the total increase in income becomes infinitely large.

Example

Suppose the consumption function is

$$c = 10 + 0.8x + 0.5\sqrt{x}$$

where c is total consumption and x is total disposable income. Then the amount saved is

$$s = x - c$$

$$= x - (10 + 0.8x + 0.5\sqrt{x})$$

$$= -10 + 0.2x - 0.5\sqrt{x}$$

The marginal propensity to consume is

$$\frac{dc}{dx} = f'(x) = 0.8 + \frac{0.25}{\sqrt{x}}$$

and the marginal propensity to save is

$$\frac{ds}{dx} = 0.2 - \frac{0.25}{\sqrt{x}}$$

(Note that $\frac{dc}{dx} + \frac{ds}{dx} = 1$; see Fig. 2.19) The multiplier is

$$k = \frac{1}{0.2 - \dfrac{0.25}{\sqrt{x}}}$$

Note that $\frac{dc}{dx}$ and k are decreasing functions of x and $\frac{ds}{dx}$ is an increasing function of x.

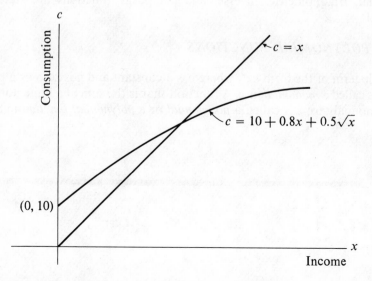

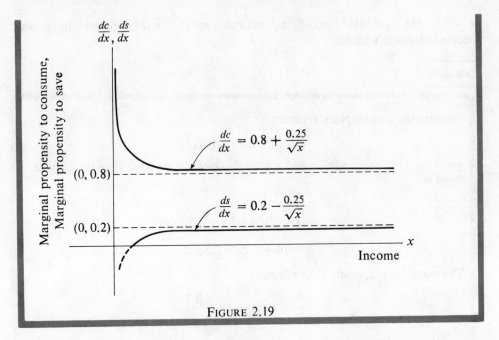

FIGURE 2.19

NOTE: For certain economic analyses, it is more appropriate to consider income as a function of consumption rather than consumption as a function of income. In this case, income is plotted on the y-axis, and consumption on the x-axis.

■ 2.5 RULES FOR DIFFERENTIATION

In practice, rules for differentiating particular types of functions are used in order to avoid repeating the procedure for obtaining derivatives directly. The rules for differentiation are obtained by the usual procedure, as shown in Technical Note I.

In this section, rules for differentiating polynomial, algebraic, logarithmic, exponential, trigonometric, inverse, and composite functions are stated and illustrated.

□ POLYNOMIAL FUNCTIONS

A single term of the form cx^n, where c is a constant and n is zero or a positive integer, is called a *monomial* in x. A function that is the sum of a finite number of such monomial terms is called a *polynomial* or a *polynomial function* in x.

Example

$$f(x) = x^4 + x^3 + 2x$$
$$g(x) = 8x^3 + 1$$
$$h(x) = 4x$$

$\Phi(x) = 6$

are polynomial functions in x.

The derivatives of polynomial functions are obtained using the following formulas:

Rule 1. The derivative of a constant is zero: If $y = c$,

$$\frac{dy}{dx} = 0$$

The derivative of the product of a constant and a differentiable function is the product of the constant and the derivative of the function: If $y = cu$, where $u = f(x)$ is a differentiable function of x,

$$\frac{dy}{dx} = c\frac{du}{dx}$$

Rule 2. The derivative of the nth power of a variable is the product of n and the $(n-1)$st power of the variable: If $y = x^n$,

$$\frac{ay}{dx} = nx^{n-1}$$

for any positive integer n.

Examples

If $y = 6$, $\dfrac{dy}{dx} = 0$.

If $y = 6x^4$, $\dfrac{dy}{dx} = 6(4)x^3 = 24x^3$.

If $y = 10x$, $\dfrac{dy}{dx} = 10(1)x^{1-1} = 10x^0 = 10$.

Rule 3. The derivative of the sum of a finite number of differentiable functions is the sum of their derivatives: If $y = u + v$, where $u = f(x)$ and $v = g(x)$ are differentiable functions of x,

$$\frac{dy}{dx} = \frac{du}{dx} + \frac{dv}{dx}$$

In general, if $y = \sum_{i=1}^{n} u_i$, where $u_i = f_i(x)$ are differentiable functions of x for

$i = 1, 2, \ldots, n$, then

$$\frac{dy}{dx} = \sum_{i=1}^{n} \frac{du_i}{dx}$$

Examples

If $y = 3x^2 + 4x + 2$,

$$\frac{dy}{dx} = 6x + 4$$

If $y = x^8 + 6x^5 + x^4 + x^2 + x$,

$$\frac{dy}{dx} = 8x^7 + 30x^4 + 4x^3 + 2x + 1$$

● **Summary of Rules for Derivatives of Polynomial Functions**

The derivative of a monomial in x is

$$\frac{d}{dx}(cx^n) = cnx^{n-1}$$

and the derivative of the sum of a finite number of such terms (that is, the derivative of a polynomial) is the sum of the derivatives of the terms:

$$\frac{d}{dx}\left(\sum_{i=1}^{n} c_i x^{n_i}\right) = \sum_{i=1}^{n} c_i n_i x^{n_i - 1}$$

☐ *ALGEBRAIC FUNCTIONS*

The formulas in this section apply to the products, quotients, powers, and roots of differentiable functions.

Rule 4. The derivative of the product of two differentiable functions is equal to the first function times the derivative of the second function plus the second function times the derivative of the first function. Similarly, the product of more than two differentiable functions is the sum of the products of the derivative of each function and the other functions. If $y = uv$, where $u = f(x)$ and $v = g(x)$ are differentiable functions of x,

$$\frac{dy}{dx} = u\frac{dv}{dx} + v\frac{du}{dx}$$

In general, if $y = \prod_{i=1}^{n} u_i$, where $u_i = f_i(x)$ are differentiable functions of x for $i = 1, 2, \ldots, n$, then

$$\frac{d}{dx}\left(\prod_{i=1}^{n} u_i\right) = \sum_{i=1}^{n}\left[f_i'(x)\prod_{\substack{j=1 \\ j \neq i}}^{n} u_j\right]$$

Examples

If $y = (x^3 + 4)(x + 3)$,

$$\frac{dy}{dx}(uv) = u\frac{dv}{dx} + v\frac{du}{dx}$$

and

$$\frac{du}{dx} = 3x^2 + 0$$

$$\frac{dv}{dx} = 1(x^{1-1}) = 1$$

$$\frac{dy}{dx} = (x^3 + 4)(1) + (x + 3)(3x^2)$$

$$= x^3 + 4 + 3x^3 + 9x^2$$

$$= 4x^3 + 9x^2 + 4$$

If $y = (x + 3)(2x + 3)(x^2 + 1)$,

$$\frac{dy}{dx} = (2x + 3)(x^2 + 1) + 2(x + 3)(x^2 + 1) + 2x(x + 3)(2x + 3)$$

$$= (4x + 9)(x^2 + 1) + 2x(2x^2 + 9x + 9)$$

$$= 4x^3 + 9x^2 + 4x + 9 + 4x^3 + 18x^2 + 18x$$

$$= 8x^3 + 27x^2 + 22x + 9$$

Rule 5. The derivative of the quotient of two differentiable functions is the quotient of the product of the denominator and the derivative of the numerator minus the product of the numerator and the derivative of the denominator divided by the square of the denominator: If $y = \frac{u}{v}$, where $u = f(x)$ and $v = g(x)$ are differentiable functions of x,

$$\frac{dy}{dx} = \frac{v\frac{du}{dx} - u\frac{dv}{dx}}{v^2}$$

Examples

If $y = \dfrac{x^2 - 4x + 1}{x - 6}$,

$$u = x^2 - 4x + 1 \qquad v = x - 6$$

$$\frac{du}{dx} = 2x - 4 \qquad \frac{dv}{dx} = 1$$

and

$$\frac{dy}{dx} = \frac{(x - 6)(2x - 4) - (x^2 - 4x + 1)(1)}{(x - 6)^2}$$

$$= \frac{2x^2 - 16x + 24 - x^2 + 4x - 1}{(x - 6)^2}$$

$$= \frac{x^2 - 12x + 23}{(x - 6)^2}$$

If $y = \dfrac{4}{x^6}$,

$$u = 4 \qquad v = x^6$$

$$\frac{du}{dx} = 0 \qquad \frac{dv}{dx} = 6x^5$$

and

$$\frac{dy}{dx} = \frac{(x^6)(0) - 4(6x^5)}{(x^6)^2}$$

$$= \frac{-24x^5}{x^{12}}$$

$$= \frac{-24}{x^7}$$

Rule 6. The derivative of the nth power of a differentiable function is the product of n, the $(n - 1)$st power of the function and the derivative of the function: If $y = u^n$, where $u = f(x)$ is a differentiable function of x and n is any real number (positive or negative, integer or noninteger),

$$\frac{dy}{dx} = nu^{n-1} \frac{du}{dx}$$

Special Case: If $u = f(x) = x$, then $u^n = x^n$ and

$$\frac{dy}{dx} = nu^{n-1} = nx^{n-1}$$

for any real number n. (This special case is a generalization of Rule 2, in which n is a positive integer.)

Examples

If $y = (x^2 + 3)^3$,

$$\frac{dy}{dx} = 3(x^2 + 3)^2(2x)$$

$$= 6x(x^2 + 3)^2$$

If $y = (x + 3)^{-1/3}$,

$$\frac{dy}{dx} = -\tfrac{1}{3}(x + 3)^{-4/3}$$

$$= \frac{-1}{3(x + 3)^{4/3}}$$

If $y = \left(\dfrac{x + 1}{x - 1}\right)^2$,

$$\frac{dy}{dx}(u^n) = nu^{n-1}\frac{du}{dx}$$

but note that $u = \dfrac{x + 1}{x - 1}$ is a fraction and thus Rule 5 must be used to obtain $\dfrac{du}{dx}$.

$$\frac{du}{dx} = \frac{(x - 1) - (x + 1)}{(x - 1)^2}$$

$$= \frac{-2}{(x - 1)^2}$$

and thus

$$\frac{dy}{dx} = 2\left(\frac{x + 1}{x - 1}\right)\left(\frac{-2}{(x - 1)^2}\right)$$

$$= \frac{-4(x + 1)}{(x - 1)^3}$$

If $y = (x + 1)^2(x^2 + 1)^{-3}$,

$$\frac{dy}{dx}(uv) = u\frac{dv}{dx} + v\frac{du}{dx}$$

but note that $u = (x + 1)^2$ and $v = (x^2 + 1)^{-3}$ and thus Rule 6 must be used to obtain $\dfrac{du}{dx}$ and $\dfrac{dv}{dx}$.

$$\frac{dy}{dx} = (x + 1)^2(-3)(x^2 + 1)^{-4}(2x) + (x^2 + 1)^{-3}(2)(x + 1)$$

$$= (x + 1)(x^2 + 1)^{-4}[-6x(x + 1) + 2(x^2 + 1)]$$

$$= (x + 1)(x^2 + 1)^{-4}(-4x^2 - 6x + 2)$$

$$= \frac{-2(x + 1)(2x^2 + 3x - 1)}{(x^2 + 1)^4}$$

If $y = (x^2 - x)^{-2}$,

$$\frac{dy}{dx} = -2(x^2 - x)^{-3}(2x - 1)$$

$$= -2(2x - 1)\frac{1}{(x^2 - x)^3}$$

$$= \frac{2(1 - 2x)}{x^3(x - 1)^3}$$

If $y = x^2(x + 1)^{-1}$,

$$\frac{dy}{dx} = 2x(x + 1)^{-1} + x^2(-1)(x + 1)^{-2}$$

$$= (x + 1)^{-2}[2x(x + 1) - x^2]$$

$$= (x + 1)^{-2}(2x^2 + 2x - x^2)$$

$$= (x + 1)^{-2}(x^2 + 2x)$$

$$= \frac{x(x + 2)}{(x + 1)^2}$$

If $y = (x + x^{-1})^2$,

$$\frac{dy}{dx} = 2(x + x^{-1})(1 - x^{-2})$$

$$= 2(x - x^{-1} + x^{-1} - x^{-3})$$

$$= 2(x - x^{-3})$$

$$= 2x^{-3}(x^4 - 1)$$

$$= \frac{2(x^4 - 1)}{x^3}$$

If $y = 2x(3x^2 + 1)^{-1}$,

$$\frac{dy}{dx} = 2(3x^2 + 1)^{-1} + 2x(-1)(3x^2 + 1)^{-2}(6x)$$

$$= 2(3x^2 + 1)^{-2}(3x^2 + 1 - 6x^2)$$

$$= 2(3x^2 + 1)^{-2}(1 - 3x^2)$$

$$= \frac{2(1 - 3x^2)}{(3x^2 + 1)^2}$$

PROBLEMS

Find the first derivative with respect to x for each of the following functions $y = f(x)$.

1. $y = 2x^3 + 4x^2 - 5x + 8$

2. $y = -5 + 3x - \frac{3}{2}x^2 - 7x^3$

3. $y = (2x^2 + 4x - 5)^6$

4. $y = \frac{1}{5}x^{5/2} + \frac{1}{3}x^{3/2}$

5. $y = (1 - x^2)^{1/2}$

6. $y = \frac{6}{x} + \frac{4}{x^2} - \frac{3}{x^3}$

7. $y = (x^3 - 3x)^4$

8. $y = (x + x^{-1})^2$

9. $y = (x - 1)^3(x + 2)^4$

10. $y = (x + 2)^2(2 - x)^3$

11. $y = (x + 1)^2(x^2 + 1)^{-3}$

12. $y = \frac{2x + 1}{x^2 - 1}$

13. $y = \frac{x}{x^2 + 1}$

14. $y = \left(\frac{x + 1}{x - 1}\right)^2$

15. $y = (x^2 - x)^{-2}$

16. $y = x^2(x + 1)^{-1}$

17. $y = \frac{1}{(x^2 - 9)^{1/2}}$

18. $y = \frac{1}{(16 - x^2)^{1/2}}$

19. $y = \frac{x}{(x + 1)^{1/2}}$

20. $y = \frac{(x^2 + 2)^{1/2}}{x}$

21. $y = \frac{2x}{(x^5 + 10)^{1/8}}$

22. $y = (x + 2)^3(x^2 + 1)^{-1}$

23. $y = \left(\frac{x^2 + 10}{x}\right)^{10}$

24. $y = \frac{3}{(x^3 - 4)^{2/3}}$

25. $y = \frac{(x^2 + 1)^{1/2}}{(2x + 4)^{1/4}}$

26. $y = (x + 2)^{-3/2}(3x^2 + 1)$

27. $y = x^3(x^2 + 3)^{-1}$

28. $y = x^6 + x^{4/3} + 6x^{1/2}$

ANSWERS TO ODD-NUMBERED PROBLEMS

1. $6x^2 + 8x - 5$

3. $24(x + 1)(2x^2 + 4x - 5)^5$

5. $-x(1 - x^2)^{-1/2}$

7. $12x^3(x^2 - 1)(x^2 - 3)^3$

9. $(x - 1)^2(x + 2)^3(7x + 2)$

11. $-2(x + 1)(x^2 + 1)^{-4}(2x^2 + 3x - 1)$

13. $\dfrac{1 - x^2}{(x^2 + 1)^2}$

15. $-2x^{-3}(x - 1)^{-3}(2x - 1)$

17. $\dfrac{-x}{(x^2 - 9)^{3/2}}$

19. $\dfrac{x + 2}{2(x + 1)^{3/2}}$

21. $(x^5 + 10)^{-9/8}(\frac{3}{4}x^5 + 20)$

23. $10\left(\dfrac{x^2 - 10}{x^2}\right)\left(\dfrac{x^2 + 10}{x}\right)^9$

25. $\dfrac{3x^2 + 8x - 1}{2(x^2 + 1)^{1/2}(2x + 4)^{5/4}}$

27. $x^2(x^2 + 9)(x^2 + 3)^{-2}$

☐ *LOGARITHMIC FUNCTIONS*

The notation "ln" denotes natural logarithms; the base of the natural logarithms is defined by $e = \lim\limits_{n \to \infty}\left(1 + \dfrac{1}{n}\right)^n$, and is approximately 2.718. The notation "log" denotes common logarithms (base 10); if any other base is meant it is specified.

Rule 7. If $y = \log_a u$, where $u = f(x)$ is a differentiable function of x,

$$\frac{dy}{dx} = \frac{\log_a e}{u}\frac{du}{dx}$$

Examples

If $y = \log\dfrac{x}{x + 1}$,

$$\frac{dy}{dx} = \frac{\log e}{\dfrac{x}{x + 1}}\left(\frac{x + 1 - x}{(x + 1)^2}\right)$$

$$= \frac{\log e}{x(x + 1)}$$

If $y = \sqrt{\log x}$,

$$\frac{dy}{dx} = \frac{1}{2}(\log x)^{-1/2}\frac{\log e}{x}$$

$$= \frac{\log e}{2x\sqrt{\log x}}$$

If $y = (\log x^2)^3$,

$$\frac{dy}{dx} = 3(\log x^2)^2\left(\frac{\log e}{x^2}\right)(2x)$$

$$= \frac{6(\log x^2)^2 \log e}{x}$$

Special Case: If $y = \ln u$, where $u = f(x)$ is a differentiable function of x,

$$\frac{dy}{dx} = \frac{1}{u}\frac{du}{dx}$$

Examples

If $y = \ln\sqrt{x^2 - 1}$,

$$\frac{dy}{dx} = \left(\frac{1}{\sqrt{x^2 - 1}}\right)(\tfrac{1}{2})(x^2 - 1)^{-1/2}(2x)$$

$$= \frac{x}{x^2 - 1}$$

If $y = \dfrac{\ln x}{x}$,

$$\frac{dy}{dx} = \frac{\left(\frac{1}{x}\right)x - \ln x}{x^2}$$

$$= \frac{1 - \ln x}{x^2}$$

If $y = \ln(x + \sqrt{x^2 + 4})$,

$$\frac{dy}{dx} = \frac{1}{x + \sqrt{x^2 + 4}}\,[1 + \tfrac{1}{2}(x^2 + 4)^{-1/2}(2x)]$$

$$= \frac{1 + \dfrac{x}{\sqrt{x^2 + 4}}}{x + \sqrt{x^2 + 4}}$$

$$= \frac{\dfrac{x + \sqrt{x^2 + 4}}{\sqrt{x^2 + 4}}}{x + \sqrt{x^2 + 4}}$$

$$= \frac{1}{\sqrt{x^2 + 4}}$$

□ **EXPONENTIAL FUNCTIONS**

Rule 8. If $y = a^u$, where $u = f(x)$ is a differentiable function of x,

$$\frac{dy}{dx} = a^u \ln a \,\frac{du}{dx}$$

Examples

If $y = 2^{-x}$,

$$\frac{dy}{dx} = 2^{-x}(\ln 2)(-1)$$

$$= -2^{-x}\ln 2$$

If $y = 10^{x^2 - x}$,

$$\frac{dy}{dx} = 10^{x^2 - x}(\ln 10)(2x - 1)$$

$$= (2x - 1)10^{x^2 - x}\ln 10$$

If $y = a^x x^a$,

$$\frac{dy}{dx} = a^x(\ln a)x^a + a^x a x^{a-1}$$

$$= a^x x^{a-1}(a + x \ln a)$$

Special Case: If $y = e^u$, where $u = f(x)$ is a differentiable function of **x**,

$$\frac{dy}{dx} = e^u \frac{du}{dx}$$

Examples

If $y = \dfrac{e^x}{x}$,

$$\frac{dy}{dx} = \frac{xe^x - e^x}{x^2}$$

$$= \frac{e^x(x - 1)}{x^2}$$

If $y = \dfrac{e^x - e^{-x}}{e^x + e^{-x}}$,

$$\frac{dy}{dx} = \frac{(e^x + e^{-x})^2 - (e^x - e^{-x})^2}{(e^x + e^{-x})^2}$$

$$= \frac{e^{2x} + 2 + e^{-2x} - e^{2x} + 2 - e^{-2x}}{(e^x + e^{-x})^2} = \frac{4}{(e^x + e^{-x})^2}$$

If $y = x^5 e^{-3 \ln x} = x^2$,

$$\frac{dy}{dx} = 2x$$

Rule 9. If $y = u^v$, where $u = f(x)$ and $v = g(x)$ are differentiable functions of x, differentiate $\ln y = v \ln u$ to obtain

$$\frac{dy}{dx} = vu^{v-1} \frac{du}{dx} + u^v \ln u \frac{dv}{dx}$$

Note that Rule 8 is a special case of Rule 9 where $u = a$. Differentiating algebraic functions is frequently simpler if logarithms are used.

Examples

If $y = x^{x^2}$,

$$\ln y = x^2 \ln x$$

$$\frac{1}{y}\frac{dy}{dx} = 2x \ln x + x^2 \left(\frac{1}{x}\right)$$

$$= x(2 \ln x + 1)$$

$$\frac{dy}{dx} = x^{x^2+1}(1 + 2 \ln x)$$

If $y = x^{e^x}$,

$$\ln y = e^x \ln x$$

$$\frac{1}{y}\frac{dy}{dx} = e^x \ln x + e^x \left(\frac{1}{x}\right)$$

$$= e^x \left(\ln x + \frac{1}{x}\right)$$

$$\frac{dy}{dx} = x^{e^x} e^x \left(\frac{1}{x} + \ln x\right)$$

If $y = \dfrac{(2x+1)^2}{(x^2+2)^3}$,

$$\ln y = 2 \ln(2x+1) - 3 \ln(x^2+2)$$

$$\frac{1}{y}\frac{dy}{dx} = 2 \left(\frac{2}{2x+1}\right) - 3 \left(\frac{2x}{x^2+2}\right)$$

$$\frac{dy}{dx} = \frac{(2x+1)^2}{(x^2+1)^3} \left(\frac{4}{2x+1} - \frac{6x}{x^2+2}\right)$$

$$= \frac{(2x+1)^2}{(x^2+2)^3} \left(\frac{4x^2 + 8 - 12x^2 - 6x}{(2x+1)(x^2+2)} \right)$$

$$= \frac{(2x+1)(8 - 6x - 8x^2)}{(x^2+2)^4}$$

If $y = \dfrac{\sqrt{1-x^2}}{(x+1)^{2/3}}$,

$$\ln y = \tfrac{1}{2} \ln(1-x^2) - \tfrac{2}{3} \ln(x+1)$$

$$\frac{1}{y}\frac{dy}{dx} = \tfrac{1}{2}\left(\frac{-2x}{1-x^2} \right) - \tfrac{2}{3}\left(\frac{1}{x+1} \right)$$

$$= \frac{-3x - 2(1-x)}{3(1-x^2)}$$

$$\frac{dy}{dx} = \frac{(1-x^2)^{1/2}}{(x+1)^{2/3}} \left(\frac{-x-2}{3(1-x^2)} \right)$$

$$= -\frac{x+2}{3(x+1)^{2/3}(1-x^2)^{1/2}}$$

□ *TRIGONOMETRIC FUNCTIONS*

Rule 10. If $y = \sin u$, where $u = f(x)$ is a differentiable function of x,

$$\frac{dy}{dx} = \cos u \frac{du}{dx}$$

Examples

If $y = \sin(x^2 + \theta)$,

$$\frac{dy}{dx} = 2x \cos(x^2 + \theta)$$

If $y = \sin^2 3x$,

$$\frac{dy}{dx} = 2(\sin 3x)(\cos 3x)(3)$$

$$= 6 \sin 3x \cos 3x$$

The derivatives of the cosine, tangent, secant, cosecant, and cotangent functions can be obtained using Rule 10.

Examples

$y = \cos u$, where $u = f(x)$, can be written $y = \sin\left(\dfrac{\pi}{2} - u\right)$ and

$$\frac{dy}{dx} = \cos\left(\frac{\pi}{2} - u\right)\left(-\frac{du}{dx}\right)$$

$$= -\sin u \, \frac{du}{dx}$$

$y = \tan u$, where $u = f(x)$, can be written $y = \dfrac{\sin u}{\cos u}$ and

$$\frac{dy}{dx} = \frac{\cos^2 u \, \dfrac{du}{dx} + \sin^2 u \, \dfrac{du}{dx}}{\cos^2 u}$$

but $\cos^2 u + \sin^2 u = 1$ and

$$\frac{dy}{dx} = \frac{\dfrac{du}{dx}}{\cos^2 u} = \sec^2 u \, \frac{du}{dx}$$

Similarly,

$$y = \sec u = \frac{1}{\cos u}$$

$$y = \csc u = \frac{1}{\sin u}$$

$$y = \cot u = \frac{1}{\tan u}$$

can be differentiated to obtain the derivatives of the secant, cosecant, and cotangent functions. The derivatives of the six trigonometric functions are given by

$$\frac{d}{dx}(\sin u) = \cos u \, \frac{du}{dx} \qquad \frac{d}{dx}(\csc u) = -\csc u \cot u \, \frac{du}{dx}$$

$$\frac{d}{dx}(\cos u) = -\sin u \, \frac{du}{dx} \qquad \frac{d}{dx}(\sec u) = \sec u \tan u \, \frac{du}{dx}$$

$$\frac{d}{dx}(\tan u) = \sec^2 u \, \frac{du}{dx} \qquad \frac{d}{dx}(\cot u) = -\csc^2 u \, \frac{du}{dx}$$

Examples

If $y = \cos x + \sec x$,

$$\frac{dy}{dx} = -\sin x + \sec x \tan x$$

$$= \sin x(\sec^2 x - 1)$$

If $y = (1 + \cot x)^2$,

$$\frac{dy}{dx} = 2(1 + \cot x)(-\csc^2 x)$$

$$= -2 \csc^2 x(1 + \cot x)$$

☐ *INVERSE FUNCTIONS*

If $y = f(x)$ can be solved for x, giving $x = g(y)$, then $f(x)$ and $g(y)$ are inverse relations.

Rule 11. The derivative of the inverse of a function is equal to the reciprocal of the derivative of the function. If $y = f(x)$ and $x = g(y)$ are inverse differentiable functions,

$$\frac{dy}{dx} = \frac{1}{\dfrac{dx}{dy}}$$

or

$$\frac{df(x)}{dx} = \frac{1}{\dfrac{dg(y)}{dy}}$$

Examples

If $x = y + \frac{1}{3}y^3 + \frac{1}{5}y^5$, find $\dfrac{dy}{dx}$.

$$\frac{dx}{dy} = 1 + y^2 + y^4$$

$$\frac{dy}{dx} = \frac{1}{\dfrac{dx}{dy}} = \frac{1}{1 + y^2 + y^4}$$

If $x = y^{1/2} + y^{1/3}$, find $\dfrac{dy}{dx}$.

$$\frac{dx}{dy} = \frac{1}{2}y^{-1/2} + \frac{1}{3}y^{-2/3}$$

$$\frac{dy}{dx} = \frac{1}{\dfrac{dx}{dy}} = \frac{1}{\frac{1}{2}y^{-1/2} + \frac{1}{3}y^{-2/3}}$$

$$= \frac{6y^{2/3}}{3y^{1/6} + 2}$$

PROBLEMS

Find the first derivative of each of the following functions.

1. $y = \log(1 - 2t)$

2. $y = \ln\left(\dfrac{1 - 4x}{1 + 4x}\right)$

3. $R = \log_a(a^2 - x^2)^3$

4. $t = 6^{-2u}$

5. $y = e^x \ln x$

6. $y = \dfrac{\sqrt{x + 1}}{\sqrt[3]{x + 2}}$

7. $t = e^{\ln x}$ $= x$ $t'(a) = 1$

8. $y = a^x e^x$

9. $y = \log(x^3 - 3x)^{1/3}$

10. $y = t^2 \ln t$

11. $y = 2 \ln\left(\sqrt{\dfrac{1 - t^2}{t}}\right)$

12. $y = 25^{3x^3 - 6}$

13. $y = e^{-1/x}$

14. $y = x^{x^3}$

15. $y = x^{e^{x^2 + 1}}$ $= e^{x^2 + 1} \ln x$

16. $y = \dfrac{(x + 1)^6}{(x^2 + 2x + 2)^3}$

17. $y = 2x^2 e^{x^2 + 3}$

18. $y = \log_5(x^3 + x^2)^6$

19. $y = x^{2x^4 + x}$

20. $y = \log_b(b - x^3)^2$

21. $y = \left(\dfrac{x + 3}{x - 1}\right)^2$

22. $y = e^{\ln x^2}$

23. $y = 16^{x^2 - 2x}$ $\ln' 16 = 0$ $0 \cdot (m) = 0$

24. $y = x^{x^4}$

25. $y = e^{x^2 + 4x + 3}$

26. $y = e^{\ln(x + 3)}$

27. $y = \log_8(6 - x^2)^4$

28. $y = x^{x^3 + 2}$

29. $y = 2 \ln(x^3 + 4x^2)^{1/4}$

30. $y = (x^2 + 4)^2 e^{x^2 + 1}$

31. $y = \frac{1}{3}e^{3 \ln x}$ $\quad e^{3\ln x} = \left(e^{\ln x}\right)^3 = (x)^3$

32. $y = xe^{\ln(x^2 + 5)}$

33. $y = x^2 e^{x^2 + 4x + 2}$

34. $y = e^{\ln(x^4 + 3x^2 + 10)}$

35. $y = \dfrac{\csc x}{x}$

36. $y = \dfrac{\sin x - \cos x}{x}$

37. $y = x^2 \cot x$

38. $y = \tan x \csc x$

$\sin^2 3x + \cos^2 3x = 1$

39. $y = \sin 3x \tan 3x$

40. $y = \cot(x^2 + 1)$

41. $y = x + \cot x$

42. $y = \dfrac{x + \sin x}{x}$

43. $y = \cos^2 2x$ $x^2 / \cos x | 2x |$

44. $y = \sin x \cos x$

45. $y = \sin^2 x + \cos^2 x = 1$ $y'(x) = 0$

46. $y = x \sin x$

47. $y = \dfrac{\sin x}{x}$

48. $y = x^2 - \cos x$

49. $y = \dfrac{\tan x}{(1 + x)^2}$

50. $y = \sin x^2$

51. $y = \tan 3x$

52. $y = \tan x + \sec 2x$

53. $y = \dfrac{\sin x}{\sec x}$

54. $y = \cos x \csc x$

55. $y = \sec^2 3x$

56. $y = \dfrac{x}{\sec x}$

57. $y = \dfrac{1}{1 + \cot x}$

58. $y = \dfrac{\cot x}{1 + x^2}$

ANSWERS TO ODD-NUMBERED PROBLEMS

1. $\dfrac{2 \log e}{2t - 1}$

3. $\dfrac{6x \log_a e}{x^2 - a^2}$

5. $\dfrac{e^x}{x}(1 + x \ln x)$

7. 1

9. $\dfrac{(x^2 - 1)\log e}{x(x^2 - 3)}$

11. $\dfrac{t^2 + 1}{t(t^2 - 1)}$

13. $\dfrac{1}{x^2}\, e^{-1/x}$

15. $x^{e^{x^2+1}}(e^{x^2+1})\left(\dfrac{1}{x} + 2x \ln x\right)$

17. $4x(x^2 + 1)e^{x^2+3}$

19. $x^{2x^4+x}[2x^3 + 1 + (8x^3 + 1)\ln x]$

21. $\dfrac{-8(x + 3)}{(x - 1)^3}$

23. $2(x - 1)16^{x^2-2x} \ln 16$

25. $(2x + 4)e^{x^2+4x+3}$

27. $\dfrac{-8x \log_8 e}{6 - x^2}$

29. $\dfrac{3x + 8}{2(x^2 + 4x)}$

31. x^2

33. $2x(x + 1)^2 e^{x^2+4x+2}$

35. $\dfrac{-\csc x(1 + x \cot x)}{x^2}$

37. $2x \cot x - x^2 \csc^2 x$

39. $3 \sin 3x(1 + \sec^2 3x)$

41. $1 - \csc^2 x$

43. $-4 \cos 2x \sin 2x$

45. 0

47. $\dfrac{x \cos x - \sin x}{x^2}$

49. $\dfrac{(1 + x)\sec^2 x - 2 \tan x}{(1 + x)^3}$

51. $3 \sec^2 3x$

53. $\cos^2 x - \sin^2 x$

55. $6 \sec^2 3x \tan 3x$

57. $\dfrac{1}{(\sin x + \cos x)^2}$

☐ *COMPOSITE FUNCTIONS*

If y is a function of u and u is a function of x, then y is a function of a function or a *composite function*; the derivative of y with respect to x is the product of the derivative of y with respect to u and the derivative of u with respect to x.

Rule 12. If $y = \Phi(u)$ and $u = F(x)$, that is, $y = \Phi[F(x)] = f(x)$,

$$\frac{dy}{dx} = \frac{dy}{du} \cdot \frac{du}{dx}$$

(This is sometimes called the *chain rule of differentiation*.)

Note that Rules 6, 7, 8, 9, and 10 are special cases of Rule 12.

Examples

If $y = u^{2/3}$ and $u = x^2 + 1$, find $\dfrac{dy}{dx}$.

$$\frac{dy}{du} = \tfrac{2}{3}u^{-1/3}$$

$$= \frac{2}{3(x^2 + 1)^{1/3}}$$

$$\frac{du}{dx} = 2x$$

$$\frac{dy}{dx} = \frac{dy}{du} \cdot \frac{du}{dx} = \frac{4x}{3(x^2 + 1)^{1/3}}$$

Alternatively,

$$y = u^{2/3} = (x^2 + 1)^{2/3}$$

$$\frac{dy}{dx} = \tfrac{2}{3}(x^2 + 1)^{-1/3}(2x)$$

$$= \frac{4x}{3(x^2 + 1)^{1/3}}$$

If $y = \dfrac{z^2}{z^2 + 1}$ and $z = \sqrt{2u + 1}$, find $\dfrac{dy}{du}$.

$$\frac{dy}{dz} = \frac{2z(z^2 + 1) - z^2(2z)}{(z^2 + 1)^2}$$

$$= \frac{2z}{(z^2 + 1)^2}$$

$$= \frac{2\sqrt{2u + 1}}{(2u + 2)^2}$$

$$= \frac{\sqrt{2u + 1}}{2(u + 1)^2}$$

$$\frac{dz}{du} = \frac{1}{2}(2u + 1)^{-1/2}(2)$$

$$= \frac{1}{\sqrt{2u + 1}}$$

$$\frac{dy}{du} = \frac{dy}{dz} \cdot \frac{dz}{du} = \frac{1}{2(u + 1)^2}$$

Alternatively,

$$y = \frac{z^2}{z^2 + 1} = \frac{2u + 1}{2u + 2}$$

$$\frac{dy}{dx} = \frac{2(2u + 2) - (2u + 1)(2)}{2(u + 2)^2}$$

$$= \frac{2}{(2u + 2)^2}$$

$$= \frac{1}{2(u + 1)^2}$$

If $y = \ln(w^3 - 1)$ and $w = z^2 - 1$, find $\dfrac{dy}{dz}$.

$$\frac{dy}{dw} = \frac{3w^2}{w^3 - 1} = \frac{3(z^2 - 1)^2}{(z^2 - 1)^3 - 1}$$

$$\frac{dw}{dz} = 2z$$

$$\frac{dy}{dz} = \frac{dy}{dw} \cdot \frac{dw}{dz} = \frac{6z(z^2 - 1)^2}{(z^2 - 1)^3 - 1}$$

Alternatively,

$$y = \ln(w^3 - 1) = \ln[(z^2 - 1)^3 - 1]$$

$$\frac{dy}{dz} = \frac{3(z^2 - 1)^2(2z)}{(z^2 - 1)^3 - 1}$$

$$= \frac{6z(z^2 - 1)^2}{(z^2 - 1)^3 - 1}$$

PROBLEMS

Determine $\dfrac{dy}{dx}$ for each of the following functions.

1. $x = \sqrt{1 - 2y}$

2. $x = \sqrt[3]{4 - 9y}$

3. $x = (2 - 3y^2)^3$

4. $x = \left(a - \dfrac{b}{y}\right)^2$

5. $x = y\sqrt{a^2 + y^2}$

6. $x = \dfrac{a - y}{a + y}$

7. $x = y\sqrt{a + by}$

8. $x = \dfrac{b}{a}\sqrt{a^2 - y^2}$

9. $x = \ln(ay^2 + b)$

• 10. $x = \dfrac{e^y - e^{-y}}{e^y + e^{-y}}$

• 11. $x = \dfrac{2}{e^y}$

, 12. $x = \dfrac{\ln y}{y}$

13. $x = y^2 e^{-y}$

• 14. $x = \ln(y^2 e^y)$

15. $x = \ln(\sqrt{\cos 2y})$

16. $x = \dfrac{4}{\sqrt{\sec y}}$

17. $x = \ln\left(\dfrac{1 + \sin y}{1 - \sin y}\right)^{1/2}$

18. $x = (\sin 2y)^{1/2}$

19. $y = u^6$; $u = 1 + 2\sqrt{x}$

20. $y = u \sin u$; $u = \ln x$

21. $y = u^2 \cos u$; $u = ax^2$

22. $y = \dfrac{a - u}{a + u}$; $u = \dfrac{b - x}{b + x}$

23. If $y = x^4 + 5$ and $x = \log z$, find $\dfrac{dy}{dz}$

24. If $y = e^{3u}$ and $u = 2x^2 - 3x$, find $\dfrac{dy}{dx}$

25. If $u = \ln(y + 4)$ and $y = x^2$, find $\dfrac{du}{dx}$

26. If $x = \dfrac{4y + 2}{y + 6}$ and $y = u^3 + 10u$, find $\dfrac{dx}{du}$

27. If $y = e^t + 6$ and $t = \ln(x^2 + 6x)$, find $\dfrac{dy}{dx}$

28. If $y = \dfrac{4t - 8}{t + 4}$ and $t = x^2 - 4$, find $\dfrac{dy}{dx}$

ANSWERS TO ODD-NUMBERED PROBLEMS

1. $-(1 - 2y)^{1/2}$

3. $-\dfrac{1}{18y(2 - 3y^2)^2}$

5. $\dfrac{(a^2 + y^2)^{1/2}}{a^2 + 2y^2}$

7. $\dfrac{2(a + by)^{1/2}}{2a + 3by}$

9. $\dfrac{ay^2 + b}{2ay}$

11. $-\frac{1}{2}e^y$

13. $\dfrac{e^y}{y(2 - y)}$

15. $-\cot 2y$

17. $\cos y$

19. $\dfrac{6(1 + 2\sqrt{x})^5}{\sqrt{x}}$

21. $2a^2 x^3(2 \cos ax^2 - ax^2 \sin ax^2)$

23. $\dfrac{4(\log z)^3}{z} \log e$

27. $2x + 6$

25. $\dfrac{2x}{x^2 + 4}$

● **Summary of Procedure for Differentiation**

1. Determine whether the entire function to be differentiated is a sum or difference of functions; a product or quotient of functions; a logarithmic, exponential, or trigonometric function of a function; a power of a function; a composite function; or some combination of these.

2. Differentiate using the appropriate rule for the entire function and the appropriate rules for the different parts of the function.

Examples

Find the first derivative of $y = x^2 + \ln x^3$.
   The entire function is the sum of two functions

$$y = u(x) + v(x) \qquad \text{where } u(x) = x^2$$
$$v(x) = \ln x^3$$

Thus $\dfrac{dy}{dx} = \dfrac{du}{dx} + \dfrac{dv}{dx}$ (Rule 3).

   $u = x^2$ is differentiated using Rule 2 and $v = \ln x^3$ is differentiated using Rules 2 and 7.

$$\frac{du}{dx} = 2x \quad \text{and} \quad \frac{dv}{dx} = \frac{3}{x}$$

Thus

$$\frac{dy}{dx} = 2x + \frac{3}{x}$$

Find the first derivative of $e^{x^2 + 2}(x + 1)^2$.
   The entire function is the product of two functions

$$y = u(x) \cdot v(x) \qquad \text{where } u(x) = e^{x^2 + 2}$$
$$v(x) = (x + 1)^2$$

Thus $\dfrac{dy}{dx} = u\dfrac{dv}{dx} + v\dfrac{du}{dx}$ (Rule 4).

   $u = e^{x^2 + 2}$ is differentiated using Rules 1, 2, 3, and 8 and $v = (x + 1)^2$ is differentiated using Rules 1, 2, 3, and 6.

$$\frac{du}{dx} = 2xe^{x^2+2}$$

$$\frac{dv}{dx} = 2(x + 1)$$

Thus

$$\frac{dy}{dx} = 2e^{x^2+2}(x + 1) + (x + 1)^2 e^{x^2+2}$$

$$= (x + 1)e^{x^2+2}(2 + x + 1)$$

$$= (x + 1)(x + 3)e^{x^2+2}$$

Find the first derivative of $y = x^{\tan x}$.

The entire function is a function raised to a functional power

$$y = u(x)^{v(x)} \qquad \text{where } u(x) = x$$

$$v(x) = \tan x$$

Thus $\dfrac{dv}{dx} = vu^{v-1}\dfrac{du}{dx} + (\ln u) u^v \dfrac{dv}{dx}$ (Rule 9).

$u = x$ is differentiated using Rule 2 and $v = \tan x$ is differentiated using Rule 10.

$$\frac{du}{dx} = 1 \quad \text{and} \quad \frac{dv}{dx} = \sec^2 x$$

Thus

$$\frac{dy}{dx} = (\tan x)x^{(\tan x)-1} + (\ln x)x^{\tan x}(\sec^2 x)$$

$$= x^{\tan x}\left(\frac{\tan x}{x} + \cos^2 x \ln x\right)$$

PROBLEMS

Obtain the first derivative of each of the following functions.

1. $y = \dfrac{2}{x + 1}$

2. $s = \dfrac{\theta + 4}{\theta}$

3. $y = \ln(x + \sqrt{1 + x^2})$

4. $y = \dfrac{2}{e^x}$

5. $y = \dfrac{x^3 + 1}{x}$

6. $y = \dfrac{3}{x^2 + 2}$

7. $s = \dfrac{1}{1 - 2t}$

8. $y = \dfrac{x^2}{4 - x^2}$

9. $y = e^{ax} \sin bx$

10. $y = \dfrac{x}{x^2 + 1}$

11. $y = \dfrac{ax + b}{bx + d}$

12. $y = \ln\left(\tan \dfrac{x}{2}\right)$

13. $y = \ln^3 x$

14. $y = \log\left(\dfrac{2}{x}\right)$

15. $y = 10^{nx}$

16. $y = \ln(ax^2 + b)$

17. $s = e^{-t} \cos 2t$

18. $y = \frac{1}{3} \tan^3\theta - \tan\theta + \theta$

19. $s = \dfrac{a + bt + ct^2}{\sqrt{t}}$

20. $z = \dfrac{a + bx + cx^2}{x}$

21. $z = a^{2y}$

22. $y = e^{x^2}$

23. $y = x^x$

24. $y = x^n(a + bx)^m$

25. $y = x^{\sin x}$

26. $y = x^{\sqrt{x}}$

27. $s = \left(\dfrac{a}{t}\right)^t$

28. $y = (\cos x)^x$

Answers to Odd-Numbered Problems

1. $-\dfrac{2}{(x + 1)^2}$

3. $\dfrac{1}{\sqrt{1 + x^2}}$

5. $\dfrac{2x^3 - 1}{x^2}$

7. $\dfrac{2}{(1 - 2t)^2}$

9. $e^{ax}(a \sin bx + b \cos bx)$

11. $\dfrac{ad - bc}{(cx + d)^2}$

13. $\dfrac{3 \ln^2 x}{x}$

15. $n(\ln 10)10^{nx}$

17. $-e^{-t}(2 \sin 2t + \cos 2t)$

19. $-\dfrac{a}{2t\sqrt{t}} + \dfrac{b}{2\sqrt{t}} + \dfrac{3c\sqrt{t}}{2}$ $= \dfrac{-a + bt + 3t}{2t\sqrt{t}}$

21. $2a^{2y} \ln a$

23. $x^x(1 + \ln x)$

25. $x^{\sin x}\left(\dfrac{\sin x}{x} + \cos x \ln x\right)$

27. $\left(\dfrac{a}{t}\right)^t\left(\ln\left(\dfrac{a}{t}\right) - 1\right)$

□ *SUMMARY*

● **Polynomial Functions**

Rule 1. If $y = c, \dfrac{dy}{dx} = 0$

If $y = cu$, where $u = f(x), \dfrac{dy}{dx} = c\dfrac{du}{dx}$

Rule 2. If $y = x^n, \dfrac{dy}{dx} = nx^{n-1}$

Rule 3. If $y = u + v$, where $u = f(x)$ and $v = g(x)$,

$$\frac{dy}{dx} = \frac{du}{dx} + \frac{dv}{dx}$$

● **Algebraic Functions**

Rule 4. If $y = uv$, where $u = f(x)$ and $v = g(x)$,

$$\frac{dy}{dx} = u\frac{dv}{dx} + v\frac{du}{dx}$$

Rule 5. If $y = \dfrac{u}{v}$, where $u = f(x)$ and $v = g(x)$,

$$\frac{dy}{dx} = \frac{v\dfrac{du}{dx} - u\dfrac{dv}{dx}}{v^2}$$

Rule 6. If $y = u^n$, where $u = f(x)$,

$$\frac{dy}{dx} = nu^{n-1}\frac{du}{dx}$$

Special Case: If $u = f(x) = x$, then $u^n = x^n$ and $\dfrac{dy}{dx} = nu^{n-1} = nx^{n-1}$.

● **Logarithmic Functions**

Rule 7. If $y = \log_a u$, where $u = f(x)$,

$$\frac{dy}{dx} = \frac{\log_a e}{u}\frac{du}{dx}$$

Special Case: If $a = e$, then $y = \ln u$ and $\dfrac{dy}{dx} = \dfrac{1}{u}\dfrac{du}{dx}$.

● **Exponential Functions**

Rule 8. If $y = a^u$, where $u = f(x)$,

$$\frac{dy}{dx} = a^u \ln a\,\frac{du}{dx}$$

Special Case: If $a = e$, then $y = e^u$ and $\dfrac{dy}{dx} = e^u\dfrac{du}{dx}$.

Rule 9. If $y = u^v$, where $u = f(x)$ and $v = g(x)$,

$$\frac{dy}{dx} = vu^{v-1}\frac{du}{dx} + u^v \ln u\,\frac{dv}{dx}$$

Note that Rule 8 is a special case of Rule 9.

● **Trigonometric Functions**

Rule 10. If $y = \sin u$, where $u = f(x)$,

$$\frac{dy}{dx} = \cos v \frac{du}{dx}$$

Using Rule 10, it can be shown that if $y = \cos u$, where $u = f(x)$,

$$\frac{dy}{dx} = -\sin u \frac{du}{dx}$$

and if $y = \tan u$, where $u = f(x)$,

$$\frac{dy}{dx} = \sec^2 u \frac{du}{dx}$$

● **Inverse Functions**

Rule 11. If $y = f(x)$ and $x = g(y)$ are inverse functions,

$$\frac{dy}{dx} = \frac{1}{\dfrac{dx}{dy}}$$

● **Composite Functions**

Rule 12. If $y = \emptyset(u)$ and $u = F(x)$,

$$\frac{dy}{dx} = \frac{dy}{du} \cdot \frac{du}{dx}$$

Note that Rules 6, 7, 8, 9, and 10 are special cases of Rule 12.

■ **2.6 DIFFERENTIALS**

In the preceding discussion of derivatives, $\dfrac{dy}{dx}$ is considered not as a fraction with numerator dy and denominator dx, but as a symbol denoting the limit of $\dfrac{\Delta y}{\Delta x}$ as Δx approaches zero as a limit. In some problems it is useful to interpret dx and dy separately. In this context dx is referred to as the *differential of x* and dy is referred to as the *differential of y*. Differentials are useful, for example, in applications of integral calculus and in approximating changes in the dependent variable associated with small changes in the independent variable.

If $f'(x)$ is the derivative of $f(x)$ for a particular value of x and Δx is an arbitrarily chosen increment of x, then the differential of $f(x)$, denoted by $df(x)$, is defined by the equation

$$df(x) = f'(x) \Delta x = \frac{dy}{dx} \Delta x$$

If $f(x) = x$, then $f'(x) = 1$ and

$$dx = \Delta x$$

Thus when x is the independent variable, the differential dx of x is equal to Δx.

If $y = f(x)$, then

$$dy = f'(x)\, dx = \frac{dy}{dx}\, dx$$

Thus the differential of a function or dependent variable equals its derivative multiplied by the differential of the independent variable.

Geometrically, consider the curve $y = f(x)$ (see Fig. 2.20) and let $f'(x)$ be the value of the derivative at P. Then $dx = PQ$ and

$$dy = f'(x) = (\tan \theta)(PQ) = \frac{QT}{PQ} PQ = QT$$

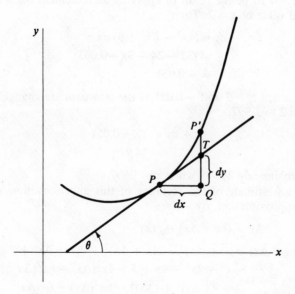

FIGURE 2.20

Therefore, dy or $df(x)$ is the increment (equal to QT) of the ordinate of the tangent corresponding to dx.

This geometrical argument provides the following interpretation of the derivative as a fraction. If an arbitrarily chosen increment of the independent variable x for a point $P(x, y)$ on the curve $y = f(x)$ is denoted by dx, then in the derivative

$$\frac{dy}{dx} = f'(x) = \tan \theta$$

dy denotes the corresponding increment of the ordinate of the tangent at P.

Note that the differential dy and the increment Δy of the function corresponding to the same value of $dx = \Delta x$ are not in general equal. In Fig. 2.20, $dy = QT$ but $\Delta y = QP'$.

☐ *APPROXIMATIONS*

It can be seen in Fig. 2.20 that $\Delta y = QP'$ and $dy = QT$ are approximately equal when $\Delta x = PQ$ is small. In fact, for sufficiently small changes in the independent variable, the differential of a function is as nearly equal to the increment of the function as desired. The value of the corresponding differential thus can be used as an approximation for the change in a function when the independent variable changes by a small amount.

Examples

If $y = x^4 - 2x^3 + 9x + 7$, use differentials to find an approximate value of y when $x = 1.997$.

Consider 1.997 to be the result of applying an increment $\Delta x = dx = -0.003$ to an original value of $x = 2$. Then

$$dy = (4x^3 - 6x^2 + 9)\, dx$$
$$= (32 - 24 + 9)(-0.003)$$
$$= -0.051$$

Since $y = 25$ when $x = 2$ and -0.051 is the approximate change in y when x changes from 2 to 1.997,

$$y + dy = 25 - 0.051$$
$$= 24.949$$

and y is approximately 24.949 when $x = 1.997$.

To obtain an estimate of the accuracy of this approximation, compute the error of the approximation, $\Delta y - dy$.

$$\Delta y = f(x + \Delta x) - f(x)$$

$$f(x + \Delta x) = (x + \Delta x)^4 - 2(x + \Delta x)^3 + 9(x + \Delta x) + 7$$
$$= x^4 - 2x^3 + 9x + 7 + 4x^3(\Delta x) + 6x^2(\Delta x)^2$$
$$+ 4x(\Delta x)^3 + (\Delta x)^4 - 6x^2(\Delta x) - 6x(\Delta x)^2$$
$$- 2(\Delta x)^3 + 9\,\Delta x$$

and thus

$$\Delta y = 4x^3(\Delta x) + 6x^2(\Delta x)^2 + 4x(\Delta x)^3 + (\Delta x)^4 - 6x^2(\Delta x)$$
$$- 6x(\Delta x)^2 - 2(\Delta x)^3 + 9(\Delta x)$$

Since $dy = (4x^3 - 6x^2 + 9)(\Delta x)$,

$$dy - \Delta y = 6x^2(\Delta x)^2 + 4x(\Delta x)^3 + (\Delta x)^4 - 6x(\Delta x)^2 - 2(\Delta x)^3$$

And, for $x = 2$,

$$dy - \Delta y = (24 - 12)(-0.003)^2 + (8 - 2)(-0.003)^3 + (-0.003)^4$$
$$= 0.000107838081$$

Thus $y + \Delta y = y + dy + (\Delta y - dy) = 24.949107838081$ and the approximation $y = 24.949$ is accurate to the three decimal places computed.

Using differentials, find an approximate value of $\sqrt{98}$.

The number 98 is close to the number 100, which is a perfect square. Thus the change in $y = \sqrt{x}$ corresponding to a change in x from 100 to 98 can be added to $y = \sqrt{100} = 10$ to obtain an approximate value for $\sqrt{98}$.

For $x = 100$ and $\Delta x = -2$,

$$dy = \frac{dx}{2\sqrt{x}}$$

$$= \frac{-2}{2\sqrt{100}}$$

$$= -0.1$$

and thus $\sqrt{98} = \sqrt{100} - 0.1 = 9.9$ approximately.

Using differentials, find an approximate value for $\tan 46°$ given $\tan 45° = 1$, $\sec 45° = \sqrt{2}$, and $1° = 0.0175$ radians.

If $y = \tan x$, $dy = \sec^2 x \, dx$. When x changes to dx, y changes to $y + dy$, approximately.

$$x = 45° = \frac{\pi}{4} \text{ radians}$$

$$\Delta x = 1° = 0.0175 \text{ radians}$$

$$dy = \sec^2 x \, dx$$

$$= (\sqrt{2})^2 (0.0175)$$

$$= 0.0350$$

Since $y = \tan 45° = 1$, $y + dy = 1.0350$ and $\tan 46° = 1.0350$ approximately.

Differentials can also be used to estimate small errors in calculation of a function which arise from lack of precision in the measurement of the independent variable or from other causes.

Example

Suppose $C = 5 + 0.6x + 0.2\sqrt{x}$, where C is total consumption (billions of dollars) and x is total disposable income (billions of dollars). If $x = 25$ with a maximum error of 0.3, find the approximate maximum error in consumption.

$$dC = 0.6 + \frac{0.1}{\sqrt{x}} \, dx$$

$$= \left(0.6 + \frac{0.1}{\sqrt{25}}\right)(0.3)$$

$$= \left(0.6 + \frac{0.1}{5}\right)(0.3)$$
$$= 0.18 + .006$$
$$= 0.186$$

If du is the error in u, then

$$\frac{du}{u} \text{ is the relative error in } u$$

and

$$100\,\frac{du}{u} \text{ is the percentage error in } u$$

For this example, the approximate maximum relative error is

$$\frac{dC}{C} = \frac{0.186}{25} = 0.00744$$

and the percentage error is 0.7440.

It is frequently convenient to find the relative error by logarithmic differentiation.

Example

For the demand function

$$x = \frac{16}{y^4}$$

where x is number of units demanded and y is price in dollars, assume y is 200 with a maximum error of 10 and determine the approximate maximum relative error in x.

$$\ln x = \ln 16 + 4 \ln y$$

$$\frac{dx}{x} = -4\frac{dy}{y}$$

and, for $y = 200$ and $dy = 10$, the relative error in x is

$$\frac{dx}{x} = \frac{40}{200} = \frac{1}{5}$$

and the percentage error is 20.

PROBLEMS

Use differentials to find the approximate value of each of the following.

1. $\sqrt[3]{1010}$

2. $\sqrt[4]{15}$

3. $\sqrt{66}$

4. $\sqrt[5]{34}$

Find dy and Δy for each of the following.

5. $y = x^4 - \dfrac{x^2}{2}$ for $x = 2$, $\Delta x = 0.1$

6. $y = \dfrac{12.8}{y}$ for $x = 10$, $\Delta x = 0.24$

7. $y = (x + 1)^3$ for $x = -3$, $\Delta x = -0.003$

8. $y = \sqrt{x}$ for $x = 4$, $\Delta x = 0.04$

9. A container is made in the form of a 10-cm cube to hold 1 liter (1000 cc). How accurately must the inner edge be made so that the volume will be correct to within 3 cc?

10. Using differentials, find the allowable percentage error in the diameter of a circle if the area is to be correct to within 4%.

11. Show that the relative error in the nth power of a measurement is approximately n times the relative error in the measurement.

12. Show that the relative error in the nth root of a measurement is approximately $1/n$ times the relative error in the measurement.

ANSWERS TO ODD-NUMBERED PROBLEMS

---

1. 10.033

3. 8.125

5. $dy = 3$; $\Delta y = 3.2431$

7. $dy = -0.036$; $\Delta y = -0.036027$

9. error must not exceed 0.01 cm

■ 2.7 HIGHER-ORDER DERIVATIVES

The derivative of $y = f(x)$ with respect to x is, in general, a function of x and may be differentiated with respect to x. The derivative of the first derivative is the *second derivative*; its derivative is the *third derivative*, and so on.

In general, the nth derivative of a function $y = f(x)$ is obtained by differentiating n times. The result of this differentiation—that is, the nth derivative—is denoted by

$$\frac{d^n y}{dx^n} \qquad f^{(n)}(x) \qquad y^{(n)} \qquad \frac{d^n}{dx}(y) \qquad D_x^n y \qquad D_x^n(y)$$

Examples

If $y = x^3 - 3x^2 + 2$,

$$\frac{dy}{dx} = 3x^2 - 6x$$

$$\frac{d^2 y}{dx^2} = 6x - 6$$

$$\frac{d^3 y}{dx^3} = 6$$

$$\frac{d^4 y}{dx^4} = 0$$

If $x = \sqrt{t^2 + 1}$,

$$\frac{dx}{dt} = \tfrac{1}{2}(t^2 + 1)^{-1/2}(2t)$$

$$= t(t^2 + 1)^{-1/2}$$

$$\frac{d^2 x}{dt^2} = (t^2 + 1)^{-1/2} + (-\tfrac{1}{2})t(t^2 + 1)^{-3/2}(2t)$$

$$= (t^2 + 1)^{-3/2}[t^2 + 1 - t^2]$$

$$= (t^2 + 1)^{-3/2}$$

$$\frac{d^3 x}{dt^3} = -\tfrac{3}{2}(t^2 + 1)^{-5/2}(2t)$$

$$= -3t(t^2 + 1)^{-5/2}$$

$$\frac{d^4 x}{dt^4} = -3(t^2 + 1)^{-5/2} - \tfrac{5}{2}(-3t)(t^2 + 1)^{-7/2}(2t)$$

$$= (t^2 + 1)^{-7/2}(-3t^2 - 3 + 15t^2)$$

$$= 3(4t^2 - 1)(t^2 + 1)^{-7/2}$$

and so forth for higher-order derivatives.

Just as the derivative of the function $y = f(x)$ with respect to x represents the rate of change in y as x changes, the second derivative of $y = f(x)$ with respect to x represents the rate of change in the first derivative $y' = f'(x)$ as x changes.

In general, the nth derivative with respect to x of a function $y = f(x)$ represents the rate of change in the $(n - 1)$st derivative of $y = f(x)$ as x changes.

Higher-order derivatives are very important in certain theoretical problems of mathematics and statistics; however, in most applied work derivatives of order higher than the second are not frequently encountered.

Second-order derivatives are useful in graphical representation of functions, as will be discussed in later sections, and are also useful whenever the rate of change of the quantity represented by the first derivative is of interest. For example, the rate of change of velocity is acceleration and the rate of change of marginal cost indicates whether marginal cost is increasing, decreasing, or constant under varying conditions of production.

Examples

If the position of a moving body at time t is represented by
$$s = (2t + 3)^2$$
find its velocity, $v = \dfrac{ds}{dt}$, and its acceleration, $a = \dfrac{dv}{dt} = \dfrac{d^2s}{dt^2}$.

$$v = \frac{ds}{dt} = 2(2t + 3)(2)$$

$$= 8t + 12$$

$$a = \frac{dv}{dt} = 8$$

An object projected vertically upward with a speed of 160 ft/sec reaches an elevation of
$$s = 160t - 16t^2$$
at the end of t sec. (a) How high does it rise? (b) How fast is it traveling when it reaches an elevation of 256 ft going up and again when it reaches this elevation coming down? (c) What is its acceleration?

(a) $v = \dfrac{ds}{dt} = 160 - 32t$ and $v = 0$ when $t = 5$. Thus its maximum height is

$$s = 160(5) - 16(5^2)$$

$$= 800 - 400$$

$$= 400 \text{ ft}$$

(b) If $s = 256$,

$$256 = 160t - 16t^2$$

$$t^2 - 10t + 16 = 0$$

$$(t - 8)(t - 2) = 0$$

$$t = 8, 2$$

The object is thus at an elevation of 256 ft going up after 2 sec and coming down after 8 sec.

$$\text{If } t = 2, v = \frac{ds}{dt} = 160 - 64 = 96 \text{ ft/sec}$$

$$\text{If } t = 8, v = \frac{ds}{dt} = 160 - 256 = -96 \text{ ft/sec}$$

(c) $a = \frac{dv}{dt} = -32 \text{ ft/sec.}$

Total cost (see Fig. 2.21) is represented by

$$y = 50 + 60x - 12x^2 + x^3$$

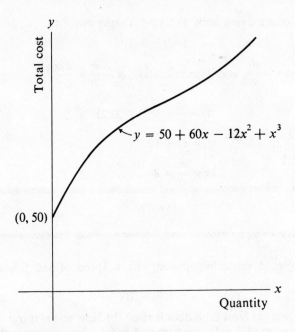

FIGURE 2.21

where y is total cost and x is output. Average cost is $\frac{y}{x} = \frac{50}{x} + 60 - 12x + x^2$ and marginal cost is $\frac{dy}{dx} = 60 - 24x + 3x^2$ (see Fig. 2.22).

$$\frac{d^2y}{dx^2} = -24 + 6x$$

$$= 0 \quad \text{when } x = 4$$

$$< 0 \quad \text{when } x < 4$$

$$> 0 \quad \text{when } x > 4$$

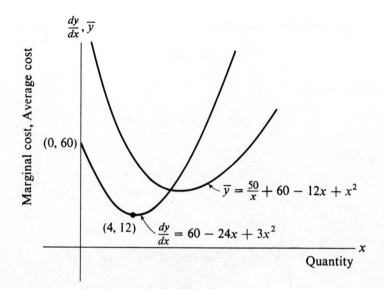

FIGURE 2.22

Thus marginal cost decreases for $x < 4$, increases for $x > 4$, and is constant for $x = 4$.

Total cost (see Fig. 2.23) is represented by

$$y = 200 + 1000x - 24x^2 + 4x^3 + x^4$$

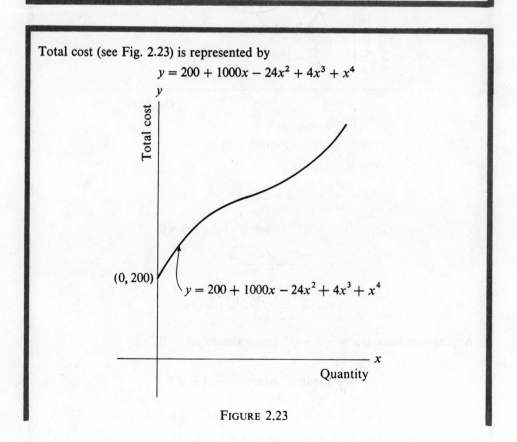

FIGURE 2.23

where y is total cost and x is output. Average cost is

$$\frac{y}{x} = \frac{200}{x} + 1000 - 24x + 4x^2 + x^3$$

and marginal cost is

$$\frac{dy}{dx} = 1000 - 48x + 12x^2 + 4x^3$$

(see Fig. 2.24).

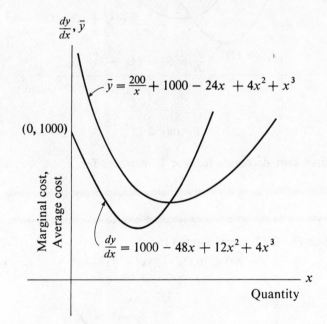

FIGURE 2.24

$$\frac{d^2y}{dx^2} = -48 + 24x + 12x^2$$

$$= 0 \quad \text{when } x^2 + 2x - 4 = 0$$

$$x = \frac{-2 \pm \sqrt{4 + 16}}{2}$$

$$= \frac{-2 \pm \sqrt{20}}{2} = -1 \pm \sqrt{5}$$

Appropriate value is $x = -1 + \sqrt{5}$ (approximately $x = 1.236$).

$$\frac{d^2y}{dx^2} = 0 \quad \text{when } x = -1 + \sqrt{5}$$

$$< 0 \quad \text{when } x < -1 + \sqrt{5}$$

$$> 0 \quad \text{when } x > -1 + \sqrt{5}$$

Thus marginal cost decreases for $x < -1 + \sqrt{5}$, increases for $x > -1 + \sqrt{5}$, and is constant for $x = -1 + \sqrt{5}$.

PROBLEMS

Find the first and second derivatives of each of the following functions.

1. $y = e^{3x}$

2. $y = x \ln x$

3. $y = \log\left(\dfrac{3}{x}\right)$

4. $y = x^2 e^x$

5. $y = e^{\ln(x^3 - 3)}$

6. $y = \left(\dfrac{x - 5}{x + 1}\right)^{-1}$

ANSWERS TO ODD-NUMBERED PROBLEMS

1. $3e^{3x}$, $9e^{3x}$

3. $-\dfrac{1}{x}\log e$, $\dfrac{1}{x^2}\log e$

5. $3x^2$, $6x$

■ 2.8 IMPLICIT DIFFERENTIATION

Functions of the form $y = f(x)$ express y explicitly in terms of x and can be differentiated according to the rules for the particular types of functions involved. However, as noted in preceding sections, some equations involving x and y, of the form $f(x, y) = 0$, do not give y explicitly in terms of x and cannot conveniently be written so that they do. Such equations define y as a function of x in the sense that for each value of x there is a corresponding value of y that satisfies the equation; therefore the equation is said to determine y as an implicit function of x. It is possible to calculate $\dfrac{dy}{dx}$ from such an equation by the method of *implicit differentiation*. In this method y is treated as an unknown but differentiable function of x and the rules for finding derivatives are applied. In general, this method gives an expression for $\dfrac{dy}{dx}$ in terms of both x and y. Higher-order derivatives can also be obtained by implicit differentiation.

● Procedure for Implicit Differentiation

When y is defined as an implicit function of x by an equation $f(x, y) = 0$, the derivative of y with respect to x is obtained by differentiating the equation $f(x, y) = 0$ term by term, regarding y as a function of x, and then solving the resulting equation for the derivative $\dfrac{dy}{dx}$.

Examples

$xy^2 - x^2 + y = 0$. Differentiating with respect to x,

$$2xy \frac{dy}{dx} + y^2 - 2x + \frac{dy}{dx} = 0$$

$$(2xy + 1)\frac{dy}{dx} = 2x - y^2$$

$$\frac{dy}{dx} = \frac{2x - y^2}{2xy + 1}$$

NOTE: $\frac{d}{dx}(y^2) = 2y\frac{dy}{dx}$ because y is a function of x. This is an application of Rule 6, which states that if $y = u^n$, where $u = f(x)$,

$$\frac{dy}{dx} = nu^{n-1}\frac{du}{dx}$$

$x^3 + y^3 - 3axy = 0$. Differentiating with respect to x,

$$3x^2 + 3y^2\frac{dy}{dx} - 3ax\frac{dy}{dx} - 3ay = 0$$

$$(y^2 - ax)\frac{dy}{dx} = ay - x^2$$

$$\frac{dy}{dx} = \frac{ay - x^2}{y^2 - ax}$$

$x^5 + 4xy^3 - 3y^5 = 2$. Differentiating with respect to x,

$$5x^4 + 4\left(3xy^2\frac{dy}{dx} + y^3\right) - 15y^4\frac{dy}{dx} = 0$$

$$(12xy^2 - 15y^4)\frac{dy}{dx} = -(5x^4 + 4y^3)$$

$$\frac{dy}{dx} = \frac{5x^4 + 4y^3}{15y^4 - 12xy^2}$$

$x^2 - y^2 = 1$. Differentiating with respect to x,

$$2x - 2y\frac{dy}{dx} = 0$$

$$\frac{dy}{dx} = \frac{x}{y}$$

Differentiating $\frac{dy}{dx}$ with respect to x,

$$\frac{d^2y}{dx^2} = \frac{y - x\dfrac{dy}{dx}}{y^2}$$

$$= \frac{y - x\dfrac{x}{y}}{y^2}$$

$$= \frac{y^2 - x^2}{y^3}$$

or, since $y^2 - x^2 = -1$,

$$\frac{d^2y}{dx^2} = -\frac{1}{y^3}$$

$x^2 + xy + y^2 = 1$. Differentiating with respect to x,

$$2x + x\frac{dy}{dx} + y + 2y\frac{dy}{dx} = 0$$

$$(x + 2y)\frac{dy}{dx} = -2x - y$$

$$\frac{dy}{dx} = -\frac{2x + y}{x + 2y}$$

Differentiating $\dfrac{dy}{dx}$ with respect to x,

$$\frac{d^2y}{dx^2} = -\frac{\left(2 + \dfrac{dy}{dx}\right)(x + 2y) - (2x + y)\left(1 + 2\dfrac{dy}{dx}\right)}{(x + 2y)^2}$$

$$= -\frac{(2x + 4y - 2x - y) + (x + 2y - 4x - 2y)\dfrac{dy}{dx}}{(x + 2y)^2}$$

$$= -\frac{3y + 3x\dfrac{dy}{dx}}{(x + 2y)^2}$$

$$= -3\left[\frac{y + x\left(\dfrac{2x + y}{x + 2y}\right)}{(x + 2y)^2}\right]$$

$$= -3\left[\frac{xy + 2y^2 + 2x^2 + xy}{(x + 2y)^3}\right]$$

or, since $x^2 + xy + y^2 = 1$,

$$\frac{d^2y}{dx^2} = \frac{-6}{(x + 2y)^3}$$

$x^{1/2} + y^{1/2} = a^{1/2}$. Differentiating with respect to x,

$$\tfrac{1}{2}x^{-1/2} + \tfrac{1}{2}y^{-1/2}\frac{dy}{dx} = 0$$

$$\frac{dy}{dx} = -\frac{y^{1/2}}{x^{1/2}}$$

Differentiating $\dfrac{dy}{dx}$ with respect to x,

$$\frac{d^2y}{dx^2} = \frac{\left(-\tfrac{1}{2}y^{-1/2}\dfrac{dy}{dx}\right)x^{1/2} + y^{1/2}(\tfrac{1}{2}x^{-1/2})}{x}$$

$$= \frac{\tfrac{1}{2} + \tfrac{1}{2}x^{-1/2}y^{1/2}}{x}$$

$$= \tfrac{1}{2}x^{-1} + \tfrac{1}{2}x^{-3/2}y^{1/2}$$

$$= \tfrac{1}{2}x^{-3/2}(x^{1/2} + y^{1/2})$$

$$= \tfrac{1}{2}a^{1/2}x^{-3/2}$$

PROBLEMS

Find (a) $\dfrac{dy}{dx}$ and (b) $\dfrac{d^2y}{dx^2}$ for each of the following functions by the method of implicit differentiation.

1. $x^2 + y^2 = 1$
2. $x^3 + y^3 = 1$
3. $x^{2/3} + y^{2/3} = 1$
4. $xy + y^2 = 1$
5. $y^2 = x^3$
6. $xy = a$
7. $x^2y^2 = b$
8. $x^2y^3 = c$
9. $x + y - xy = 2$
10. $x^2y^2 + xy = 1$
11. $x^3y^3 + x^2y^2 = a$
12. $x + y + xy + y^2 = b$
13. $x^3y^2 = a$
14. $x^2 + xy = a^2$
15. $xy^2 + y^2 = a$
16. $xy + y^3 = b$
17. $(x + y)^2 + (x + y)^3 = a^2$
18. $x^2 + y^2 = ab$

Find $\dfrac{dy}{dx}$ for each of the following functions by the method of implicit differentiation.

19. $y^2 = \dfrac{x - 1}{x + 1}$
20. $x^3 - xy + y^3 = 1$
21. $x^2 = \dfrac{x - y}{x + y}$
22. $y = x(x^2 + 1)^{-1/2}$

23. $y = x^{1/2} + x^{1/3} + x^{1/4}$

24. $y^2 = \dfrac{x^2 - 1}{x^2 + 1}$

25. $(x + y)^3 + (x - y)^3 = x^4 + y^4$

26. $y = (x + 5)^4(x^2 - 2)^3$

27. $\dfrac{1}{y} + \dfrac{1}{x} = 1$

28. $y = (x^2 + 3)^{1/3}x^{-1}$

ANSWERS TO ODD-NUMBERED PROBLEMS

1. (a) $-\dfrac{x}{y}$, (b) $-\dfrac{1}{y^3}$

3. (a) $-x^{-1/3}y^{1/3}$, (b) $\tfrac{1}{3}x^{-4/3}y^{-1/3}$

5. (a) $\dfrac{3x^2}{2y}$, (b) $\dfrac{3x}{4y}$

7. (a) $-\dfrac{y}{x}$, (b) $\dfrac{2y}{x^2}$

9. (a) $\dfrac{y - 1}{1 - x}$, (b) $\dfrac{2(y - 1)}{(1 - x)^2}$

11. (a) $-\dfrac{y}{x}$, (b) $\dfrac{2y}{x^2}$

13. (a) $-\dfrac{3y}{2x}$, (b) $\dfrac{15y}{4x^2}$

15. (a) $\dfrac{-y}{2(x + 1)}$, (b) $\dfrac{3y}{4(x + 1)^2}$

17. (a) -1, (b) 0

19. $\dfrac{1}{y(x + 1)^2}$

21. $\dfrac{y}{x} - (x + y)^2$

23. $\tfrac{1}{2}x^{-1/2} + \tfrac{1}{3}x^{-2/3} + \tfrac{1}{4}x^{-3/4}$

25. $\dfrac{2x^3 - 3x^2 - 3y^2}{6xy - 2y^3}$

27. $-\dfrac{y^2}{x^2}$

■ 2.9 DIFFERENTIABILITY AND CONTINUITY

It can be shown that if the function $y = f(x)$ has a finite derivative

$$f'(c) = \lim_{\Delta x \to 0} \frac{f(c + \Delta x) - f(c)}{\Delta x}$$

at $x = c$, then $f(x)$ is continuous at $x = c$.

Continuity at a point does not, however, imply the existence of a derivative at that point. Thus

$$\text{Differentiability} \rightleftharpoons \text{Continuity}$$

Examples

$f(x) = \sqrt{x^2}$ is continuous at $x = 0$, but does *not* have a derivative at $x = 0$, since

$$f'(x) = \quad 1 \qquad \text{for } x > 0$$
$$= -1 \qquad \text{for } x < 0$$

(see Fig. 2.25).

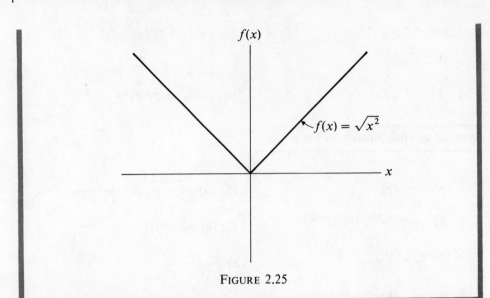

FIGURE 2.25

$f(x) = x^{1/3}$ is continuous at $x = 0$, but does *not* have a derivative at $x = 0$, since $f'(x) = \frac{1}{3}x^{-2/3}$ is not defined for $x = 0$ (see Fig. 2.26).

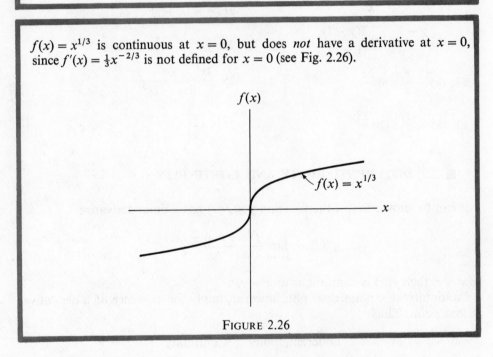

FIGURE 2.26

● **Smooth Functions**

A function $f(x)$ is said to be a *smooth function* if both $f(x)$ and its first derivative are continuous. The graph of a smooth function is said to be a smooth curve; such a curve is not only continuous and unbroken but also has a continuously turning tangent. As shown in the following sections, smooth functions have some useful properties not possessed by continuous curves whose first derivative is discontinuous at certain points.

Examples

$y = 1 - x^2$ is a smooth function throughout its entire extent, since y and its derivative $y' = -2x$ are everywhere continuous (see Fig. 2.27).

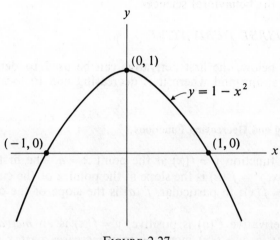

FIGURE 2.27

$y = (x - 1)^{2/3} + 1$ is *not* a smooth function at $x = 1$, since its derivative

$$\frac{dy}{dx} = \frac{2}{3\sqrt[3]{x - 1}}$$

is discontinuous (becomes infinite) at $x = 1$ (see Fig. 2.28).

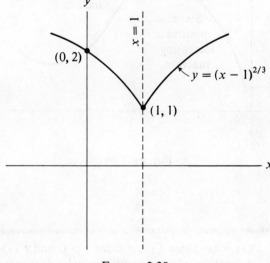

FIGURE 2.28

■ 2.10 APPLICATIONS OF DERIVATIVES

The following sections are concerned with the information about a function or curve which can be obtained from its first and second derivatives. Such information is useful not only for graphing but also for determining the appropriateness of equations for representing various relationships in business, economics, and the behavioral sciences.

□ THE FIRST DERIVATIVE

As discussed below, the first derivative can be used to determine where a function is increasing and where it is decreasing and to locate its stationary points (if any).

● Increasing and Decreasing Functions

Consider the function $y = f(x)$ at the point $x = a$. The first derivative of y with respect to x, $y' = f'(x)$ is the slope at the point x of the curve representing the function $y = f(x)$; in particular, $f'(a)$ is the slope of the curve $y = f(x)$ at the point $x = a$.

If the first derivative $f'(a)$ is positive, $y = f(x)$ is an *increasing function* of x at $x = a$ [that is, $y = f(x)$ increases as x increases past $x = a$]; if the first derivative $f'(a)$ is negative, $y = f(x)$ is a *decreasing function* of x at $x = a$ [that is, $y = f(x)$ decreases as x increases past $x = a$]. See Fig. 2.29.

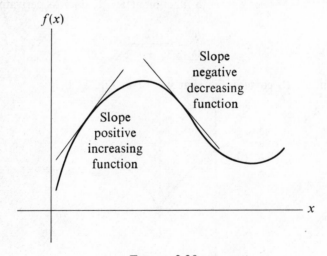

FIGURE 2.29

Examples

$f(x) = 2x^2 + 10$, $f'(x) = 4x$. Since $f'(x) > 0$ for $x > 0$ and $f'(x) < 0$ for $x < 0$, $f(x)$ is an increasing function of x for positive x and a decreasing function of x for negative x.

$f(x) = 3x^3$, $f'(x) = 9x^2$. Since $f'(x)$ is never negative, $f(x)$ is an increasing function of x for all values of x.

$f(x) = x^3 + 6x^2 + 15$, $f'(x) = 3x^2 + 12x = 3x(x + 4)$. Since $f'(x) > 0$ for $x > 0$ or $x < -4$ and $f'(x) < 0$ for $-4 < x < 0$, $f(x)$ is a decreasing function of x for the interval $-4 < x < 0$ and an increasing function of x for all $x < -4$ and $x > 0$.

In the examples above, the values of x for which $f'(x) = 0$ are not discussed; such values are of particular interest, as explained below.

● Relative (or Local) Maxima and Minima

A function $y = f(x)$ is said to have a *relative maximum* or local maximum at $x = a$ if $f(a)$ is greater than any value of $f(x)$ for x in an interval around a; a function $y = f(x)$ is said to have a *relative minimum* or local minimum at $x = a$ if $f(a)$ is smaller than any value of $f(x)$ for x in an interval around a. Note that a relative maximum or minimum of a function is its maximum or minimum for a given interval; the (absolute) maximum or minimum of the function over a larger interval can occur at an end point of the interval, rather than at any relative maximum or minimum. Also note that it is possible for a relative maximum value of a function to be less than a relative minimum value of the function (see Fig. 2.30).

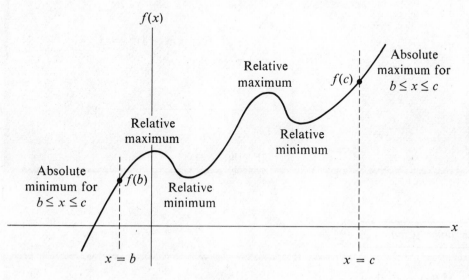

FIGURE 2.30

If a function $f(x)$ has a relative maximum or minimum at a value $x = a$ for which its first derivative is continuous, then $f'(a) = 0$. Values of x for which $f'(x)$ is discontinuous must be considered separately, as discussed below.

CAUTIONS

1. A relative maximum or minimum at $x = a$ implies $f'(a) = 0$ only if $f(x)$ and $f'(x)$ are continuous at $x = a$.

2. $f'(a) = 0$ does *not* imply a relative maximum or minimum at $x = a$ even if $f(x)$ and $f'(x)$ are continuous at $x = a$—that is, if $f(x)$ and $f'(x)$ are continuous at $x = a$, $f'(a) = 0$ is a necessary but not a sufficient condition for a relative maximum or minimum at $x = a$.

Example (Caution 1)

If $f(x) = (x - 1)^{2/3} + 1$, then

$$f'(x) = \frac{2}{3(x - 1)^{1/3}}$$

and $f'(x)$ is (infinitely) discontinuous at $x = 1$. Thus, although the function has a relative minimum at $x = 1$, $f'(1) \neq 0$ (see Fig. 2.31).

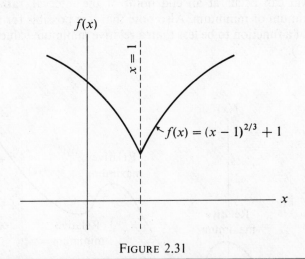

FIGURE 2.31

Example (Caution 2)

If $f(x) = x^3$, then

$$f'(x) = 3x^2$$

and $f'(x) = 0$ for $x = 0$. However, the function $f(x) = x^3$ does not have a relative maximum or minimum at $x = 0$ (see Fig. 2.32).

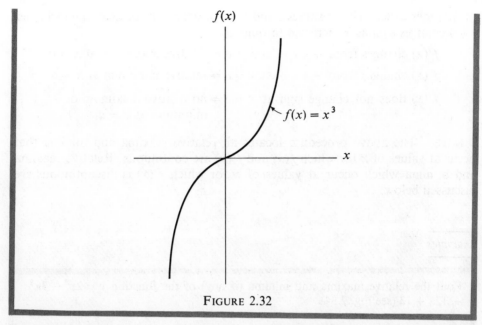

FIGURE 2.32

Consider a function $f(x)$ at a value $x = a$ for which $f(x)$ and $f'(x)$ are continuous. It is evident geometrically that if $f(a)$ is a relative maximum of $f(x)$, then the slope of $f(x)$ [that is, $f'(x)$] changes from positive to negative as x passes through the point $x = a$; similarly, if $f(a)$ is a relative minimum of $f(x)$, then the slope of $f(x)$ [that is, $f'(x)$] changes from negative to positive as x passes through the point $x = a$ (see Fig. 2.33). The corresponding algebraic argument is based on the fact that an increasing function has a positive slope and a decreasing function has a negative slope.

Thus, in order to determine the relative maximum and minimum values (if any) of a function $y = f(x)$, (1) solve the equation $f'(x) = 0$ to obtain its roots

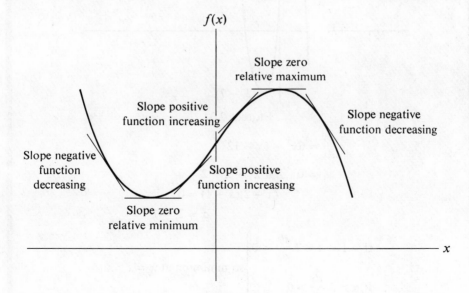

FIGURE 2.33

(sometimes called critical values), and (2) For each root a, determine whether $f'(x)$ changes sign as x increases through a:

$f'(x)$ changes from $+$ to $-$ at $x = a \Rightarrow$ relative maximum at $x = a$

$f'(x)$ changes from $-$ to $+$ at $x = a \Rightarrow$ relative minimum at $x = a$

$f'(x)$ does not change sign at $x = a \Rightarrow$ no relative maximum or minimum at $x = a$

NOTE: The above procedure locates all relative maxima and minima that occur at values of x for which $f(x)$ and $f'(x)$ are continuous. Relative maxima and minima which occur at values of x for which $f'(x)$ is discontinuous are discussed below.

Examples

Find the relative maxima and minima (if any) of the function $y = 2x^3 - 3x^2 - 12x + 13$ (see Fig. 2.34).

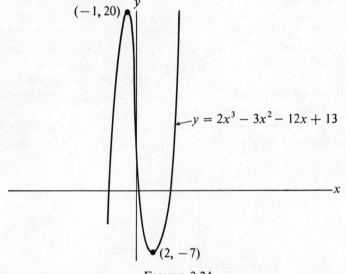

$(-1, 20)$

$-y = 2x^3 - 3x^2 - 12x + 13$

$(2, -7)$

FIGURE 2.34

$$\frac{dy}{dx} = 6x^2 - 6x - 12$$

$$= 0 \quad \text{if } x^2 - x - 2 = 0$$

$$(x - 2)(x + 1) = 0$$

$$x = 2, -1$$

If $-1 < x < 2, \dfrac{dy}{dx} < 0$

If $x > 2, \dfrac{dy}{dx} > 0$ $\Big\}$ so minimum at $x = 2$

$$\text{If } x < -1, \frac{dy}{dx} > 0$$

$$\text{If } -1 < x < 2, \frac{dy}{dx} < 0$$

so maximum at $x = -1$

Find the relative maxima and minima (if any) of the function $y = 3x^4 - 4x^3$ (see Fig. 2.35).

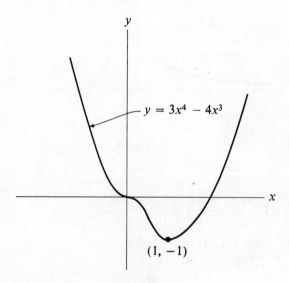

$$y = 3x^4 - 4x^3$$

$$(1, -1)$$

FIGURE 2.35

$$\frac{dy}{dx} = 12x^3 - 12x^2$$

$$= 0 \quad \text{if } x^3 - x^2 = 0$$

$$x^2(x - 1) = 0$$

$$x = 0, 1$$

$$\text{If } x < 0, \frac{dy}{dx} < 0$$

$$\text{If } 0 < x < 1, \frac{dy}{dx} < 0$$

so no maximum or minimum at $x = 0$

$$\text{If } 0 < x < 1, \frac{dy}{dx} < 0$$

$$\text{If } x > 1, \frac{dy}{dx} > 0$$

so minimum at $x = 1$

Find the relative maxima and minima (if any) of the function $y = \dfrac{x}{\sqrt{x^2 + 1}}$ (see Fig. 2.36).

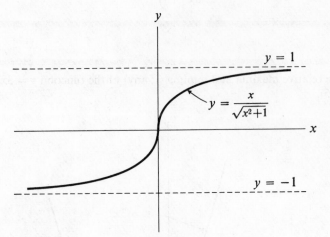

FIGURE 2.36

$$\frac{dy}{dx} = \frac{(x^2 + 1)^{1/2} - \frac{1}{2}x(x^2 + 1)^{-1/2}(2x)}{(x^2 + 1)}$$

$$= \frac{x^2 + 1 - x^2}{(x^2 + 1)^{3/2}}$$

$$= \frac{1}{(x^2 + 1)^{3/2}}$$

$\neq 0$ for all values of x, so no maximum or minimum

In each of the examples above, the first derivative is continuous for all values of x. Thus relative maxima and minima can occur only for values $x = a$ for which $f'(a) = 0$. As noted above, relative maxima or minima may also occur for values $x = a$ for which $f'(a)$ is discontinuous. That is, if $f(x)$ is continuous at $x = a$ but its first derivative is discontinuous (finitely or infinitely) at $x = a$, then $f(a)$ may be a relative maximum or minimum even though $f'(a) \neq 0$. Again, a change in the sign of the first derivative as x passes through a is necessary for the existence of a relative maximum or minimum at $x = a$.

Thus, in order to determine relative maximum and minimum values (if any) of a function $y = f(x)$ at points where $f(x)$ is continuous but $f'(x)$ is discontinuous, (1) determine the values of x for which $f'(x)$ is finitely or infinitely discontinuous and $f(x)$ is continuous, and (2) for each value a such that $f(x)$ is continuous at $x = a$ and $f'(x)$ is discontinuous at $x = a$, determine whether $f'(x)$ changes sign as x increases through a:

$f'(x)$ changes from $+$ to $-$ at $x = a \Rightarrow$ relative maximum at $x = a$

$f'(x)$ changes from $-$ to $+$ at $x = a \Rightarrow$ relative minimum at $x = a$

$f'(x)$ does not change sign at $x = a \Rightarrow$ no relative maximum or minimum at $x = a$

Examples

Find the relative maxima and minima (if any) of the function $y = x^{2/3}$ (see Fig. 2.37).

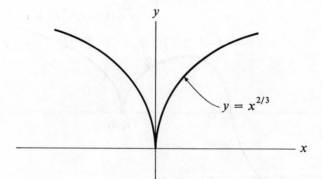

FIGURE 2.37

$$\frac{dy}{dx} = \tfrac{2}{3}x^{-1/3}$$

$$\neq 0 \qquad \text{for all values of } x$$

$\dfrac{dy}{dx} \to -\infty$ as $x \to 0^-$ and $\dfrac{dy}{dx} \to \infty$ as $x \to 0^+$,

so infinite discontinuity at $x = 0$

$$\left.\begin{array}{l} \text{If } x < 0, \dfrac{dy}{dx} < 0 \\[2mm] \text{If } x > 0, \dfrac{dy}{dx} > 0 \end{array}\right\} \text{so minimum at } x = 0$$

Find the relative maxima and minima (if any) of the function $y = (1 - x)^{2/3}(2 + x)^{1/3}$ (see Fig. 2.38).

$$\frac{dy}{dx} = -\tfrac{2}{3}(1-x)^{-1/3}(2+x)^{1/3} + (1-x)^{2/3}(\tfrac{1}{3})(2+x)^{-2/3}$$

$$= \frac{-2(2+x) + (1-x)}{3(1-x)^{1/3}(2+x)^{2/3}}$$

$$= \frac{-(x+1)}{(1-x)^{1/3}(2+x)^{2/3}}$$

$$= 0 \qquad \text{if } x = -1$$

$$\frac{dy}{dx} \to -\infty \text{ as } x \to 1^- \text{ and } \frac{dy}{dx} \to \infty \text{ as } x \to 1^+,$$

so infinite discontinuity at $x = 1$

$\dfrac{dy}{dx} \to \infty$ as $x \to -2$, so infinite discontinuity at $x = -2$

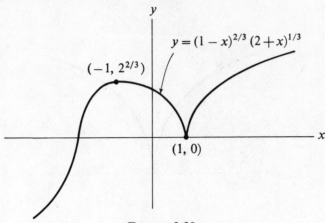

FIGURE 2.38

If $-2 < x < -1, \dfrac{dy}{dx} > 0$

If $-1 < x < 1, \dfrac{dy}{dx} < 0$ $\Bigg\}$ so maximum at $x = -1$

If $-1 < x < 1, \dfrac{dy}{dx} < 0$

If $x > 1, \dfrac{dy}{dx} > 0$ $\Bigg\}$ so minimum at $x = 1$

If $x < -2, \dfrac{dy}{dx} > 0$

If $-2 < x < -1, \dfrac{dy}{dx} > 0$ $\Bigg\}$ so no maximum or minimum at $x = -2$

Find the relative maxima and minima (if any) of the function $y = (x - 1)^{1/3}(x + 1)^{2/3}$ (see Fig. 2.39).

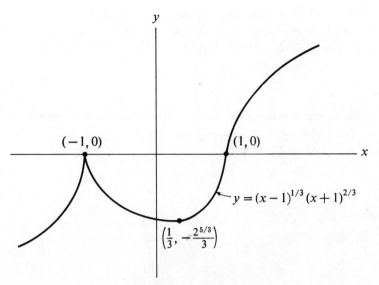

$(-1, 0)$

$(1, 0)$

$y = (x - 1)^{1/3} (x + 1)^{2/3}$

$\left(\frac{1}{3}, -\frac{2^{5/3}}{3} \right)$

FIGURE 2.39

$$\frac{dy}{dx} = \tfrac{1}{3}(x - 1)^{-2/3}(x + 1)^{2/3} + (x - 1)^{1/3}(\tfrac{2}{3})(x + 1)^{-1/3}$$

$$= \frac{(x + 1) + 2(x - 1)}{3(x - 1)^{2/3}(x + 1)^{1/3}}$$

$$= \frac{3x - 1}{3(x - 1)^{2/3}(x + 1)^{1/3}}$$

$$= 0 \qquad \text{if } x = \tfrac{1}{3}$$

$\dfrac{dy}{dx} \to \infty$ as $x \to 1$, so infinite discontinuity at $x = 1$

$\dfrac{dy}{dx} \to \infty$ as $x \to -1^-$ and $\dfrac{dy}{dx} \to -\infty$ as $x \to -1^+$,
so infinite discontinuity at $x = -1$

If $-1 < x < \tfrac{1}{3}, \dfrac{dy}{dx} < 0$

If $\tfrac{1}{3} < x < 1, \dfrac{dy}{dx} > 0$ } so minimum at $x = \tfrac{1}{3}$

If $\tfrac{1}{3} < x < 1, \dfrac{dy}{dx} > 0$

If $x > 1, \dfrac{dy}{dx} > 0$ } so no maximum or minimum at $x = 1$

If $x < -1, \dfrac{dy}{dx} > 0$

If $-1 < x < \tfrac{1}{3}, \dfrac{dy}{dx} < 0$ } so maximum at $x = -1$

NOTE: The least (or greatest) value of a function in an interval—that is, its absolute minimum or maximum in an interval—may occur at an end point of the interval rather than at a relative minimum or maximum value.

Examples

Find the maximum and minimum values of the function $y = x^2 - 2x$ in the interval $2 \leq x \leq 4$ (see Fig. 2.40).

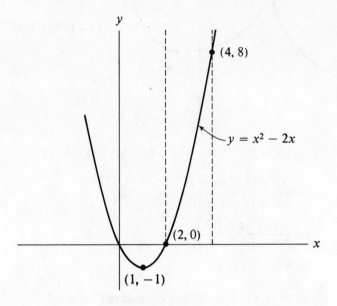

FIGURE 2.40

$$\frac{dy}{dx} = 2x - 2$$

$$= 0 \quad \text{if } x = 1$$

$$\left.\begin{array}{ll} < 0 & \text{if } x < 1 \\ > 0 & \text{if } x > 1 \end{array}\right\} \text{so minimum at } x = 1$$

But $x = 1$ is outside the interval $2 \leq x \leq 4$.

$$\text{If } x = 2, y = 0$$

$$\text{If } x = 4, y = 8$$

Thus in the interval $2 \leq x \leq 4$ the least value of y occurs at the end point $x = 2$, and the greatest value occurs at the end point $x = 4$; at neither of these points is $\frac{dy}{dx}$ equal to zero.

The total cost curve of a commodity is $y = 2x - 2x^2 + x^3$, where y represents total cost and x represents quantity. Suppose that market conditions indicate that between 3 and 10 units should be produced (that is, $3 \leq x \leq 10$). For what quantity in this interval is average cost a minimum (see Fig. 2.41)?

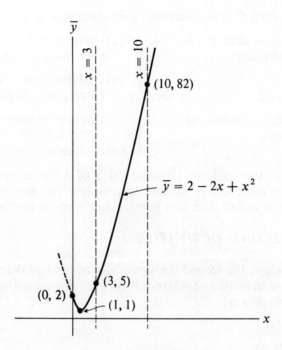

FIGURE 2.41

Average cost $= \dfrac{y}{x} = \bar{y} = 2 - 2x + x^2$.

$$\frac{d\bar{y}}{dx} = -2 + 2x$$

$$= 0 \quad \text{if } x = 1$$

$$\left. \begin{array}{ll} < 0 & \text{if } x < 1 \\ > 0 & \text{if } x > 1 \end{array} \right\} \text{so minimum at } x = 1$$

But $x = 1$ is outside the interval $3 \leq x \leq 10$.

$$\text{If } x = 3, \bar{y} = 5$$

$$\text{If } x = 10, \bar{y} = 82$$

Thus in the interval $3 \leq x \leq 10$ the least value of $\bar{y}$ occurs at $x = 3$ and the greatest value occurs at $x = 10$; at neither of these points is $\dfrac{d\bar{y}}{dx}$ equal to zero. Thus, for between 3 and 10 units, average cost is minimum for 3 units.

□ SUMMARY OF THE INFORMATION THAT CAN BE OBTAINED FROM THE FIRST DERIVATIVE

Consider the function $y = f(x)$ at the point $x = a$

$f'(a) > 0 \Rightarrow f(x)$ is an increasing function of x at $x = a$

$f'(a) < 0 \Rightarrow f(x)$ is a decreasing function of x at $x = a$

If $\begin{cases} f(x) \text{ is continuous at } x = a \\ \quad \text{and either} \\ f'(a) = 0 \\ \quad\quad \text{or} \\ f'(x) \text{ is discontinuous at} \\ \quad\quad x = a \end{cases}$ then $\begin{cases} f'(x) \text{ changes from } + \text{ to } - \text{ at} \\ x = a \Rightarrow \text{relative maximum at } x = a \\ f'(x) \text{ changes from } - \text{ to } + \text{ at} \\ x = a \Rightarrow \text{relative minimum at } x = a \\ f'(x) \text{ does not change sign at} \\ x = a \Rightarrow \text{no relative maximum} \\ \text{or minimum at } x = a \end{cases}$

As noted above, the least (or greatest) value of a function in an interval, that is, its absolute minimum or maximum in an interval, may occur at an end point of the interval rather than at a relative minimum or maximum value.

□ THE SECOND DERIVATIVE

As discussed below, the second derivative can be used to determine where a function is concave upward and where it is concave downward and to locate its points of inflection (if any).

● Concavity

Consider the function $y = f(x)$ at the point $x = a$. The second derivative of y with respect to x, $y'' = f''(x)$ is the slope at the point x of the curve representing the derivative $y' = f'(x)$ of the function $f(x)$; in particular, $f''(a)$ is the slope of the curve $y' = f'(x)$ at the point $x = a$.

If the second derivative $f''(a)$ of a function $y = f(x)$ is positive, $y' = f'(x)$ is an increasing function of x at $x = a$; the curve representing $y = f(x)$ is said to be *concave upward*, where $f''(x)$ is positive. If the second derivative $f''(a)$ of a function $y = f(x)$ is negative, $y' = f'(x)$ is a decreasing function of x at $x = a$; the curve representing $y = f(x)$ is said to be *concave downward* where $f''(x)$ is negative (see Fig. 2.42).

Consider a function $f(x)$ at a value $x = a$ for which $f(x)$ and $f'(x)$ are continuous. It is evident geometrically that if $f'(a) = 0$ and $f(x)$ is concave downward at $x = a$, then $f(x)$ has a maximum at a; similarly, if $f'(a) = 0$ and $f(x)$ is concave upward at $x = a$, then $f(x)$ has a minimum at a. The corresponding algebraic argument is based on the fact that a positive second derivative indicates an increasing slope and a negative second derivative indicates a decreasing slope.

CAUTION: The second derivative test is only sufficient, not necessary, for a relative maximum or minimum, since $f(x)$ may be concave upward or downward at $x = a$ if $f''(a) = 0$. That is, if $f'(a) = 0$, then

$$f''(a) > 0 \underset{\not\Leftarrow}{\Rightarrow} \text{ concave upward}$$

$$f''(a) < 0 \underset{\not\Leftarrow}{\Rightarrow} \text{ concave downward}$$

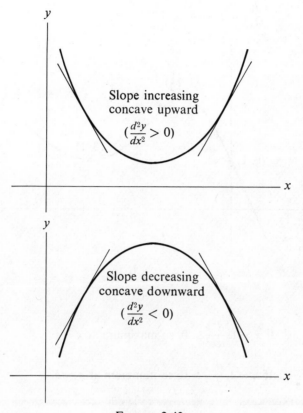

FIGURE 2.42

From this follows a very convenient, although not always applicable, test for relative maximum and minimum values:

$$
If \begin{cases} f(x) \text{ and } f'(x) \text{ are continuous} \\ \quad \text{at } x = a \\ \\ \text{and} \\ \\ f'(a) = 0 \end{cases}
\quad then \quad
\begin{cases} f''(a) > 0 \Rightarrow \text{relative minimum} \\ \quad \text{at } x = a \\ \\ f''(a) < 0 \Rightarrow \text{relative maximum} \\ \quad \text{at } x = a \\ \\ f''(a) = 0 \Rightarrow \text{test does not apply} \end{cases}
$$

Examples

Find the relative maxima and minima (if any) of the function $y = \frac{1}{3}x^3 - 2x^2 + 3x + 1$ (see Fig. 2.43).

$$\frac{dy}{dx} = x^2 - 4x + 3$$

$$= 0 \quad \text{if } x^2 - 4x + 3 = 0$$
$$(x - 3)(x - 1) = 0$$
$$x = 3, 1$$

$$\frac{dy^2}{dx^2} = 2x - 4$$

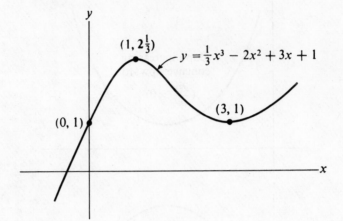

FIGURE 2.43

If $x = 1$, $\dfrac{d^2y}{dx^2} < 0$, so maximum at $x = 1$

If $x = 3$, $\dfrac{d^2y}{dx^2} > 0$, so minimum at $x = 3$

Find the relative maxima and minima (if any) of the function $y = x^4$ (see Fig. 2.44).

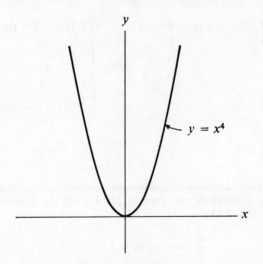

FIGURE 2.44

$$\frac{dy}{dx} = 4x^3$$

$$= 0 \quad \text{if } x = 0$$

$$\frac{d^2y}{dx^2} = 12x^2$$

If $x = 0$, $\frac{d^2y}{dx^2} = 0$, so there may or may not be a maximum or minimum at $x = 0$

If $x < 0$ $\frac{dy}{dx} < 0$ ⎫
⎬ so minimum at $x = 0$
If $x > 0$ $\frac{dy}{dx} > 0$ ⎭

Find the relative maxima and minima (if any) of the function $y = x^3$ (see Fig. 2.45).

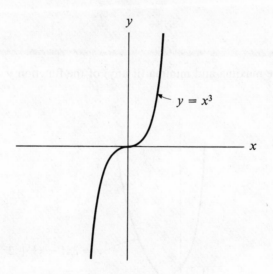

$y = x^3$

FIGURE 2.45

$$\frac{dy}{dx} = 3x^2$$

$$= 0 \quad \text{if } x = 0$$

$$\frac{d^2y}{dx^2} = 6x$$

If $x = 0$, $\frac{d^2y}{dx^2} = 0$, so there may or may not be a maximum or minimum at $x = 0$

$$\left. \begin{array}{l} \text{If } x < 0, \dfrac{dy}{dx} > 0 \\[2mm] \text{If } x > 0, \dfrac{dy}{dx} > 0 \end{array} \right\} \text{so no maximum or minimum at } x = 0$$

In the examples above, when $f''(a) = 0$—that is, when the second derivative test for a maximum or minimum does not apply—the first derivative is examined for change of sign as x passes through a. There is, however, an alternative procedure, involving derivatives of higher order, which is more convenient in some cases.

$$\text{If} \left\{ \begin{array}{l} f'(a) = f''(a) = \cdots = f^{(n-1)}(a) = 0 \\[2mm] \text{and} \\[2mm] f^{(n)}(a) \neq 0 \end{array} \right. \qquad \text{then} \left\{ \begin{array}{l} \text{for } n \text{ even} \left\{ \begin{array}{l} f^{(n)}(a) < 0 \Rightarrow \text{relative} \\ \quad \text{maximum at } x = a \\[2mm] f^{(n)}(a) > 0 \Rightarrow \text{relative} \\ \quad \text{minimum at } x = a \end{array} \right. \\[6mm] \text{for } n \text{ odd } f(a) \text{ is neither a} \\ \text{relative maximum or minimum} \end{array} \right.$$

Example

Find the relative maxima and minima (if any) of the function $y = 3x^4 - x^3 + 2$ (see Fig. 2.46).

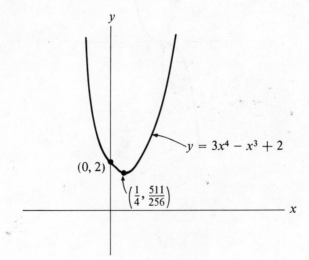

FIGURE 2.46

$$\frac{dy}{dx} = 12x^3 - 3x^2$$

$$= 0 \qquad \text{if } 12x^3 - 3x^2 = 0$$

$$3x^2(4x - 1) = 0$$

$$x = 0, \tfrac{1}{4}$$

$$\frac{d^2y}{dx^2} = 36x^2 - 6x$$

$$= 6x(6x - 1)$$

If $x = \tfrac{1}{4}$, $\dfrac{d^2y}{dx^2} > 0$, so minimum at $x = \tfrac{1}{4}$

If $x = 0$, $\dfrac{d^2y}{dx^2} = 0$, so there may or may not be a maximum or minimum at $x = 0$

$$\frac{d^3y}{dx^3} = 72x - 6$$

$$= 6(12x - 1)$$

If $x = 0$, $\dfrac{d^3y}{dx^3} < 0$, so no maximum or minimum at $x = 0$

Alternative procedure using change of sign of the first derivative:

$$\left. \begin{array}{l} \text{If } x < 0, \dfrac{dy}{dx} < 0 \\[3mm] \text{If } 0 < x < \tfrac{1}{4}, \dfrac{dy}{dx} < 0 \end{array} \right\} \text{so no maximum or minimum at } x = 0$$

$$\left. \begin{array}{l} \text{If } 0 < x < \tfrac{1}{4}, \dfrac{dy}{dx} < 0 \\[3mm] \text{If } x > \tfrac{1}{4}, \dfrac{dy}{dx} > 0 \end{array} \right\} \text{so minimum at } x = \tfrac{1}{4}$$

● **Points of Inflection**

A function $y = f(x)$ is said to have a *point of inflection* at a point where the concavity of the curve changes. Geometrically, at a point of inflection the tangent crosses the curve. Since the sign of the second derivative indicates the concavity of a curve, it follows that a change in the sign of the second derivative implies a change in concavity (and thus a point of inflection).

If a function $f(x)$ has a point of inflection at a value $x = a$ for which its second derivative is continuous, then $f''(a) = 0$. Values of x for which $f''(x)$ is discontinuous must be considered separately, as discussed below.

CAUTIONS

1. A point of inflection at $x = a$ implies $f''(a) = 0$ only if $f(x)$ and $f''(x)$ are continuous at $x = a$.
2. $f''(a) = 0$ does *not* imply a point of inflection at $x = a$ even if $f(x)$ and $f''(x)$ are continuous at $x = a$; that is, if $f(x)$ and $f''(x)$ are continuous at

$x = a$, $f''(a) = 0$ is a necessary but not a sufficient condition for a point of inflection at $x = a$.

Consider a function $f(x)$ at a value $x = a$ for which $f(x)$ and $f''(x)$ are continuous. If $f''(x)$ changes sign as x passes through the point $x = a$, then the curve representing $f(x)$ has a point of inflection at $x = a$. In this case $f''(a) = 0$.

A point of inflection may also occur at a value $x = a$ for which $f(x)$ is continuous but $f''(x)$ is discontinuous. Again, change in the sign of the second derivative as x passes through a is necessary for the existence of a point of inflection at $x = a$.

Thus, in order to determine the points of inflection (if any) of a function $y = f(x)$, (1) determine the values of x for which $f''(x)$ is either zero or discontinuous and $f(x)$ is continuous, and (2) for each value a such that $f(x)$ is continuous at $x = a$ and $f''(x)$ is either zero or discontinuous at $x = a$, determine whether $f''(x)$ changes sign as x increases through a:

$f''(x)$ changes sign at $x = a \Rightarrow$ point of inflection at $x = a$
$f''(x)$ does not change sign at $x = a \Rightarrow$ no point of inflection at $x = a$

NOTE: If $f(x)$ and $f''(x)$ are continuous at $x = a$ and $f''(a) = 0$, then $f'''(a) \neq 0$ implies a point of inflection at $x = a$; this may be used as an alternative to checking for change of sign of the second derivative at $x = a$.

Examples

Find the relative maxima and minima and the points of inflection (if any) of the function $y = x^{1/3}$ (see Fig. 2.47).

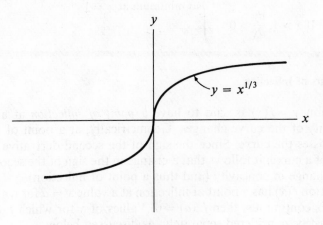

$y = x^{1/3}$

FIGURE 2.47

$$\frac{dy}{dx} = \tfrac{1}{3}x^{-2/3}$$

$$\neq 0 \qquad \text{for all } x$$

$$\frac{dy}{dx} \quad \text{discontinuous at } 0$$

$$\left.\begin{array}{l} \text{If } x < 0, \dfrac{dy}{dx} > 0 \\[2ex] \text{If } x > 0, \dfrac{dy}{dx} > 0 \end{array}\right\} \text{so no maximum or minimum at } x = 0$$

$$\frac{d^2y}{dx^2} = -\tfrac{2}{9}x^{-5/3}$$

$$\neq 0 \qquad \text{for all } x$$

$$\frac{d^2y}{dx^2} \quad \text{discontinuous at } 0$$

$$\left.\begin{array}{l} \text{If } x < 0, \dfrac{d^2y}{dx^2} > 0 \\[2ex] \text{If } x > 0, \dfrac{d^2y}{dx^2} < 0 \end{array}\right\} \text{so point of inflection at } x = 0$$

Find the relative maxima and minima and the points of inflection (if any) of the function $y = \tfrac{1}{6}(x^3 - 6x^2 + 9x + 6)$ (see Fig. 2.48).

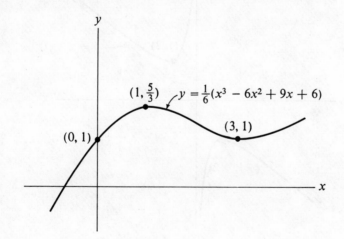

FIGURE 2.48

$$\frac{dy}{dx} = \tfrac{1}{6}(3x^2 - 12x + 9)$$

$$= \tfrac{1}{2}(x^2 - 4x + 3)$$

$$= \tfrac{1}{2}(x - 1)(x - 3)$$

$$= 0 \qquad \text{if } x = 1, 3$$

$$\frac{d^2y}{dx^2} = \tfrac{1}{2}(2x - 4)$$

$$= x - 2$$

If $x = 1$, $\dfrac{d^2y}{dx^2} < 0$, so maximum at $x = 1$

If $x = 3$, $\dfrac{d^2y}{dx^2} > 0$, so minimum at $x = 3$

$$\frac{d^2y}{dx^2} = 0 \qquad \text{if } x = 2$$

$$\frac{d^3y}{dx^3} = 1, \text{ so point of inflection at } x = 2$$

Find the relative maxima and minima and the points of inflection (if any) of the function $y = x + \dfrac{1}{x}$ (see Fig. 2.49).

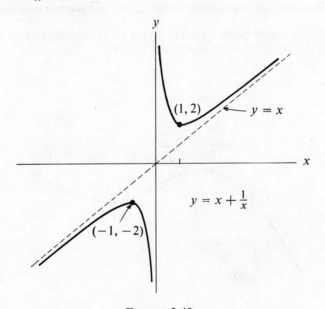

FIGURE 2.49

$$\frac{dy}{dx} = 1 - \frac{1}{x^2}$$

$$= \frac{x^2 - 1}{x^2}$$

$$= 0 \qquad \text{if } x = \pm 1$$

$$\frac{dy}{dx} \quad \text{discontinuous at } x = 0$$

$$\text{If } x < -1, \frac{dy}{dx} > 0$$

$$\text{If } -1 < x < 0, \frac{dy}{dx} < 0$$

so maximum at $x = -1$

$$\text{If } 0 < x < 1, \frac{dy}{dx} < 0$$

$$\text{If } x > 1, \frac{dy}{dx} > 0$$

so minimum at $x = 1$

$$\text{If } -1 < x < 0, \frac{dy}{dx} < 0$$

$$\text{If } 0 < x < 1, \frac{dy}{dx} < 0$$

so no maximum or minimum at $x = 0$

$$\frac{d^2y}{dx^2} = \frac{2}{x^3}$$

$$\neq 0 \qquad \text{for all } x$$

$\dfrac{d^2y}{dx^2}$ discontinuous at $x = 0$ but $\dfrac{dy}{dx}$ also discontinuous at $x = 0$, so no point of inflection at $x = 0$

☐ SUMMARY OF THE INFORMATION THAT CAN BE OBTAINED FROM THE SECOND DERIVATIVE

Consider the function $y = f(x)$ at the point $x = a$:

$$f''(a) > 0 \Rightarrow f(x) \text{ concave upward at } x = a$$

$$f''(a) < 0 \Rightarrow f(x) \text{ concave downward at } x = a$$

If $\begin{cases} f(x) \text{ and } f'(x) \text{ are continuous} \\ \quad \text{at } x = a \\ \text{and} \\ f'(a) = 0 \end{cases}$ then $\begin{cases} f''(a) > 0 \Rightarrow \text{relative minimum at} \\ \quad x = a \\ f''(a) < 0 \Rightarrow \text{relative maximum at} \\ \quad x = a \\ f''(a) = 0 \Rightarrow \text{test does not apply} \end{cases}$

If $\begin{cases} f(x) \text{ is continuous at } x = a \\ \quad \text{and either} \\ f''(a) = 0 \\ \quad \text{or} \\ f''(x) \text{ is discontinuous at } x = a \end{cases}$ then $\begin{cases} f''(x) \text{ changes sign at } x = a \\ \quad \Rightarrow \text{point of inflection at } x = a \\ \\ f''(x) \text{ does not change sign at } x = a \\ \quad \Rightarrow \text{no point of inflection at } x = a \end{cases}$

□ *SUMMARY OF PROCEDURE FOR SKETCHING THE GRAPH OF $y = f(x)$ USING INFORMATION PROVIDED BY FIRST AND SECOND DERIVATIVES*

1. Calculate $\dfrac{dy}{dx}$ and $\dfrac{d^2y}{dx^2}$.

2. Determine the ranges of values of x for which $\dfrac{dy}{dx}$ is positive and for which it is negative.

3. Calculate y and $\dfrac{d^2y}{dx^2}$ at the points where $\dfrac{dy}{dx} = 0$. Check these points for possible maxima or minima.

4. Check points where $\dfrac{dy}{dx}$ is discontinuous for possible maxima or minima.

5. Determine the ranges of values of x for which $\dfrac{d^2y}{dx^2}$ is positive and for which it is negative.

6. Calculate y and $\dfrac{dy}{dx}$ at the points where $\dfrac{d^2y}{dx^2} = 0$. Check these points for possible points of inflection.

7. Check points where $\dfrac{d^2y}{dx^2}$ is discontinuous for possible points of inflection.

8. Determine the intercepts.

9. Note the nature of the curve for large values of $|x|$.

10. Sketch the curve as indicated by the signs of $\dfrac{dy}{dx}$ (increasing or decreasing) and of $\dfrac{d^2y}{dx^2}$ (concave upward or downward), the intercepts, asymptotic properties, and discontinuities.

Examples

Sketch the curve represented by the function $y = 4 + 3x - x^3$ (see Fig. 2.50).

$$\frac{dy}{dx} = 3 - 3x^2$$

$$\frac{d^2y}{dx^2} = -6x$$

$$\frac{dy}{dx} = 0 \qquad \text{if } x = \pm 1$$

If $x < -1, \dfrac{dy}{dx} < 0$ \qquad (decreasing)

If $-1 < x < 1, \dfrac{dy}{dx} > 0$ \qquad (increasing)

If $x > 1, \dfrac{dy}{dx} < 0$ (decreasing)

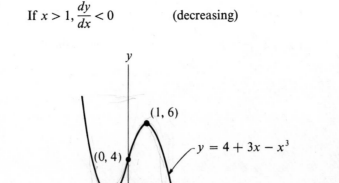

FIGURE 2.50

so minimum at $(-1, 2)$ and maximum at $(1, 6)$. $\left(\text{If } x = -1, \dfrac{d^2y}{dx^2} = 6, \text{ and if }\right.$

$x = 1, \dfrac{d^2y}{dx^2} = -6.\Big)$

$$\dfrac{d^2y}{dx^2} = 0 \qquad \text{if } x = 0$$

$$> 0 \qquad \text{if } x < 0 \qquad \text{(concave upward)}$$

$$< 0 \qquad \text{if } x > 0 \qquad \text{(concave downward)}$$

so point of inflection at $(0, 4)$. If $x = 0$, $y = 4$. As $x \to \infty$, $y \to -\infty$, and as $x \to -\infty$, $y \to \infty$.

Sketch the curve represented by the function $y = x + \dfrac{4}{x}$ (see Fig. 2.51).

$$\dfrac{dy}{dx} = 1 - \dfrac{4}{x^2}$$

$$\dfrac{d^2y}{dx^2} = \dfrac{8x}{x^4} = \dfrac{8}{x^3}$$

$$\dfrac{dy}{dx} = 0 \qquad \text{if } x = \pm 2$$

If $x < -2, \dfrac{dy}{dx} > 0$ (increasing)

If $-2 < x < 2$ and $x \neq 0$, $\dfrac{dy}{dx} < 0$ (decreasing)

If $x > 2$, $\dfrac{dy}{dx} > 0$ (increasing)

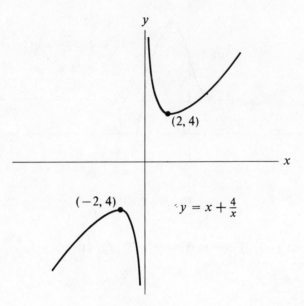

FIGURE 2.51

so minimum at $(2, 4)$ and maximum at $(-2, -4)$. y, $\dfrac{dy}{dx}$, and $\dfrac{d^2y}{dx^2}$ discontinuous at $x = 0$ $\left(\text{if } x = 2, \dfrac{d^2y}{dx^2} = 1, \text{ and if } x = -2, \dfrac{d^2y}{dx^2} = -1 \right)$.

$$\dfrac{d^2y}{dx^2} < 0 \quad \text{if } x < 0 \quad \text{(concave downward)}$$

$$> 0 \quad \text{if } x > 0 \quad \text{(concave upward)}$$

No point of inflection at $x = 0$ because of discontinuity of $y = x + \dfrac{4}{x}$. No x-intercepts or y-intercepts. As $x \to \infty$, $y \to \infty$, and as $x \to -\infty$, $y \to -\infty$.

Find the points at which the curve represented by the function $x = y^4 - 2y^2 + 2$ has vertical tangents and sketch the curve (see Fig. 2.52).

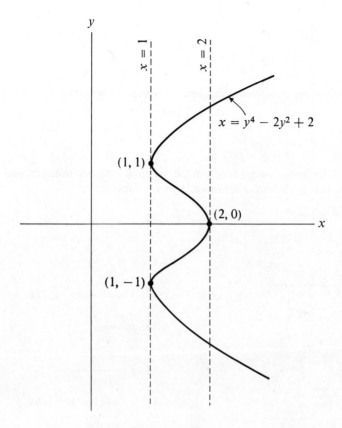

FIGURE 2.52

$$\frac{dx}{dx} = 1 = 4y^3 \frac{dy}{dx} - 4y \frac{dy}{dx}$$

$$\frac{dy}{dx} = \frac{1}{4y(y^2 - 1)}$$

so vertical tangents at $(2, 0)$, $(1, -1)$, and $(1, 1)$.

$$\frac{d^2y}{dx^2} = \frac{-(12y^2 - 4)\dfrac{dy}{dx}}{[4y(y^2 - 1)]^2} = \frac{-4(3y^2 - 1)}{[4y(y^2 - 1)]^3}$$

If $y < -1$, $\dfrac{d^2y}{dx^2} > 0$ (concave upward)

If $-1 < y < -\sqrt{\tfrac{1}{3}}$, $\dfrac{d^2y}{dx^2} < 0$ (concave downward)

If $-\sqrt{\tfrac{1}{3}} < y < 0$, $\dfrac{d^2y}{dx^2} > 0$ (concave upward)

If $0 < y < \sqrt{\tfrac{1}{3}}$, $\dfrac{d^2y}{dx^2} < 0$ (concave downward)

If $\sqrt{\frac{1}{3}} < y < 1$, $\dfrac{d^2y}{dx^2} > 0$ (concave upward)

If $y > 1$, $\dfrac{d^2y}{dx^2} < 0$ (concave downward)

PROBLEMS

For each of the following functions, determine maxima, minima, and points of inflection; sketch the curve representing each function.

1. $y = 12 - 12x + x^3$

2. $y = \dfrac{x}{x + 1}$

3. $y = \dfrac{x^3}{3} - \dfrac{x^2}{2} - 6x$

4. $y = x^4 - 32x + 48$

5. $y = \dfrac{x}{\sqrt{x^2 + 7}}$

6. $y = \dfrac{2x}{\sqrt{x^2 - 1}}$

7. $y = x^2 - 4x + 3$

8. $y = x\sqrt{1 - x^2}$

9. $y = x^3 - 3x^2 + 2$

10. $y = \dfrac{1}{x^2 + 4}$

11. $y = \dfrac{x^2}{\sqrt{x^2 - 8}}$

12. $y = x^4 - 4x^3 + 12$

13. $y = \dfrac{3x^2}{\sqrt{x^2 + 3}}$

14. $y = \dfrac{1}{16 - x^2}$

15. $y = \frac{2}{3}x^3 - 4x^2 + 6x + 2$

16. $y = \dfrac{8x}{x^2 + 4}$

17. $y = \dfrac{x + 3}{x^2}$

18. $y = x^5 + 6$

19. Show that a cubic curve whose equation is of the form
$$y = ax^3 + bx^2 + cx + d \qquad a, b, c, d \neq 0$$
has one (and only one) point of inflection.

20. Sketch a continuous curve $y = f(x)$ for $x > 0$ if $f(1) = 0$ and $f'(x) = \dfrac{1}{x}$ for $x > 0$. Is such a curve necessarily concave upward or downward?

21. Sketch a smooth curve $y = f(x)$ having (all) the following properties:

(a) $f(1) = 0$
$f'(x) < 0$ for $x < 1$
$f'(x) > 0$ for $x > 1$

(b) $f(1) = 0$
$f''(x) < 0$ for $x < 1$
$f''(x) > 0$ for $x > 1$

22. Sketch a smooth curve $y = f(x)$ having (all) the following properties:

$f(0) = 10$ $f'(6) = 0$ $f''(x) < 0$ for $x < 9$
$f(6) = 15$ $f'(10) = 0$ $f''(9) = 0$
$f(10) = 0$ $f''(x) > 0$ for $x > 9$

23. Sketch a continuous curve $y = f(x)$ having (all) the following properties:

$f(-2) = 8$ $f'(x) > 0$ for $|x| > 2$ $f''(x) < 0$ for $x < 0$
$f(0) = 4$ $f'(2) = f'(-2) = 0$ $f''(x) > 0$ for $x > 0$
$f(2) = 0$

24. Sketch a continuous curve $y = f(x)$ having the following properties:

$f'(x) > 0$ for $x < 2$ $f'(x) < 0$ for $x > 2$
(a) If $f'(x)$ is continuous at $x = 2$
(b) If $f'(x) \to 1$ as $x \to 2^-$ and $f'(x) \to -1$ as $x \to 2^+$
(c) If $f'(x) = 1$ for $x < 2$ and $f'(x) = -1$ for $x > 2$

25. Sketch a continuous curve $y = f(x)$ having the following properties:

(a) $f(2) = f'(2) = 0$ (b) $f(2) = f'(2) = 0$
    $f(0) = 2$ $f(0) = 2$
    $f''(x) < 0$ for $x < 1$ and $x > 3$ $f''(x) > 0$ for all x
    $f''(x) > 0$ for $1 < x < 3$

26. Sketch a continuous curve $y = f(x)$ having (all) the following properties:

$f(0) = 10$ $f'(x) > 0$ for $x < 0$ $f''(x) > 0$ for $x < 0$
$f(-3) = 0$ $f'(x) < 0$ for $x > 0$ $f''(x) > 0$ for $x > 0$
$f(3) = 0$

The curves representing the functions discussed on pages 226-235 were sketched without discussion of points of inflection; investigate points of inflection and sketch the curves accurately.

ANSWERS TO ODD-NUMBERED PROBLEMS

1. max $(-2, 28)$
   min $(2, -4)$
   pt. inf. $(0, 12)$

3. max $(-2, \frac{22}{3})$
   min $(3, -\frac{27}{2})$
   pt. inf. $(\frac{1}{2}, -\frac{37}{12})$

5. no max
   no min
   pt. inf. $(0, 0)$

7. no max
   min $(2, -1)$
   no pt. inf.

9. max $(0, 2)$
   min $(2, -2)$
   pt. inf. $(1, 0)$

11. no max
    min $(\pm 4, 4\sqrt{2})$
    no pt. inf.

13. no max
    min $(0, 0)$
    pt. inf. $(\pm\sqrt{6}, 6)$

15. max $(1, \frac{14}{3})$
    min $(3, 2)$
    pt. inf. $(2, \frac{10}{3})$

17. no max
    min $(-6, -\frac{1}{2})$
    pt. inf. $(-9, -\frac{2}{27})$

19. pt. inf. at $x = -\dfrac{b}{3a}$

■ 2.11 APPLICATIONS OF DERIVATIVES IN BUSINESS AND ECONOMICS

□ COST, AVERAGE COST, AND MARGINAL COST

If the total cost y of producing and marketing x units of a commodity is assumed to be a function of x only, then the total cost function can be represented by $y = f(x)$.

Functions of various types are used to represent total cost curves; in general, cost curves have the following properties:

1. When no units are produced, total cost is zero or positive—that is, $f(0) \geq 0$. If $f(0) > 0$, then $f(0)$ is amount of overhead or fixed costs of production.

2. Total cost increases as x increases, so $f'(x)$ is always positive.

3. The cost of producing an extremely large quantity of any commodity usually reaches a point at which it increases at an increasing rate. Thus usually the total cost curve eventually is concave upward, that is, $f''(x) > 0$; however, in a limited range the total cost curve is frequently concave downward, corresponding to decreasing marginal cost.

If the total cost function is represented by

$$y = f(x)$$

then the average or per unit cost is

$$\bar{y} = \frac{y}{x} = \frac{f(x)}{x}$$

and the marginal cost is

$$\frac{dy}{dx} = f'(x)$$

The first derivative of average cost (the marginal average cost) is

$$\frac{d\bar{y}}{dx} = \frac{xf'(x) - f(x)}{x^2}$$

$$= 0 \qquad \text{if and only if } xf'(x) - f(x) = 0$$

$$\text{that is, } f(x) = xf'(x),$$

$$\frac{f(x)}{x} = f'(x)$$

Thus average cost is minimum at the value of x for which average cost equals marginal cost; that is, the average and marginal cost curves intersect at the point of minimum average cost. Note that the value of x (if any) for which $\frac{d\bar{y}}{dx} = 0$ is assumed to be a minimum because of the third property of cost curves mentioned above; for a particular total cost curve the existence of this minimum can be checked in the usual way.

Examples

Linear cost functions:

Total cost: $y = ax + b$, where $a > 0$, $b \geq 0$

Average cost: $\bar{y} = \dfrac{y}{x} = a + \dfrac{b}{x}$

Marginal cost: $\dfrac{dy}{dx} = a$

Marginal average cost: $\dfrac{d\bar{y}}{dx} = -\dfrac{b}{x^2}$

Total cost and marginal cost are represented by straight lines and average cost is represented by the first quadrant branch of an equilateral hyperbola with horizontal asymptote $\bar{y} = a$. Average cost is thus a decreasing function of the number of units produced; it has no minimum value but approaches a, the marginal cost, as the number of units increases (see Fig. 2.53).

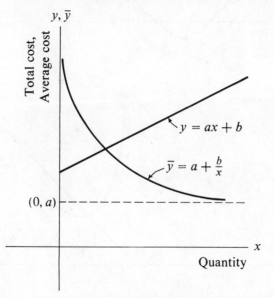

FIGURE 2.53

Quadratic cost functions:

Total cost: $y = ax^2 + bx + c$, where $a > 0$, $b \geq 0$, $c \geq 0$

Average cost: $\bar{y} = \dfrac{y}{x} = ax + b + \dfrac{c}{x}$

Marginal cost: $\dfrac{dy}{dx} = 2ax + b$

Marginal average cost: $\dfrac{d\bar{y}}{dx} = a - \dfrac{c}{x^2}$

Total cost is represented by the first quadrant part of a parabola, average cost is represented by the first quadrant branch of a hyperbola, and marginal cost is represented by a straight line (see Fig. 2.54).

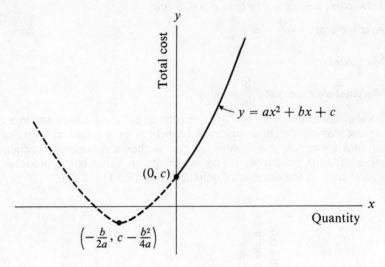

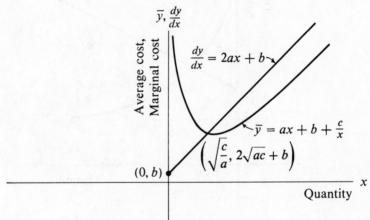

FIGURE 2.54

$$\frac{d\bar{y}}{dx} = 0 \qquad \text{if } ax^2 = c$$

$$x = \pm\sqrt{\frac{c}{a}}, \text{ but only } x = \sqrt{\frac{c}{a}} \text{ is of interest}$$

$$\frac{d\bar{y}^2}{dx^2} = -\frac{-2cx}{x^4} = \frac{2c}{x^3} > 0 \text{ for } x > 0, \text{ so minimum at } x = \sqrt{\frac{c}{a}}$$

Note that average and marginal cost are equal if $x = \sqrt{\frac{c}{a}}$, since

$$\bar{y} = a\sqrt{\frac{c}{a}} + b + c\sqrt{\frac{a}{c}}$$

and

$$= 2\sqrt{ac} + b$$

$$\frac{dy}{dx} = 2a\sqrt{\frac{c}{a}} + b$$

$$= 2\sqrt{ac} + b$$

Cubic cost functions:

Total cost: $y = ax^3 + bx^2 + cx + d$, where $a > 0, b \leq 0, c \geq 0, d \geq 0, b^2 \leq 3ac$

Average cost: $\bar{y} = \dfrac{y}{x} = ax^2 + bx + c + \dfrac{d}{x}$

Marginal cost: $\dfrac{dy}{dx} = 3ax^2 + 2bx + c$

Marginal average cost: $\dfrac{d\bar{y}}{dx} = 2ax + b - \dfrac{d}{x^2}$

Total cost is represented by the first quadrant part of a cubic curve, average cost is represented by the first quadrant branch of a hyperbola, and marginal cost is represented by the first quadrant part of a parabola (see Fig. 2.55).

Cubic cost functions are frequently appropriate when the concavity of the cost function changes in a specified interval; however, such a function must have no relative maximum or minimum in the first quadrant:

$$\frac{dy}{dx} = 3ax^2 + 2bx + c$$

$$= 0 \quad \text{if } 3ax^2 + 2bx + c = 0$$

$$x = \frac{-2b \pm \sqrt{4b^2 - 12ac}}{6a} = \frac{-b \pm \sqrt{b^2 - 3ac}}{3a}$$

If $b^2 - 3ac < 0$, $y = ax^3 + bx^2 + cx + d$ has no relative maximum or minimum.

If $b^2 - 3ac = 0$, $x = -\dfrac{b}{3a}$ and

$$y = a\left(\frac{-b^3}{27a^3}\right) + b\left(\frac{b^2}{9a^2}\right) + c\left(\frac{-b}{3a}\right) + d$$

$$= \frac{2b^3}{27a^2} - \frac{bc}{3a} + d$$

$$= \frac{b(2b^2 - 9ac)}{27a^2} + d$$

$2b^2 - 9ac < 0$, since $b^2 - 3ac < 0$ and thus, since $a > 0$ and $b < 0$, $\dfrac{b(2b^2 - 9ac)}{27a^2} \geq 0$ and $\left(\dfrac{-b}{3a}, \dfrac{b(2b^2 - 9ac)}{27a^2} + d\right)$ lies in the first quadrant.

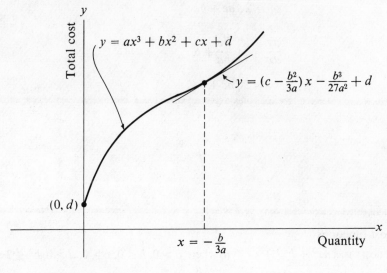

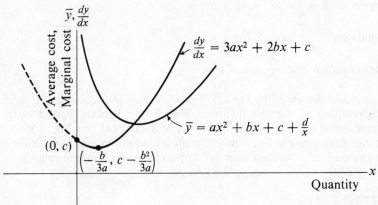

FIGURE 2.55

$$\frac{dy^2}{dx^2} = 6ax + 2b$$

$$\left.\frac{d^2y}{dx^2}\right|_{x=-b/3a} = 0$$

$$\frac{d^3y}{dx^3} = 6a \neq 0$$

So no relative maximum or minimum at $x = -\dfrac{b}{3a}$ but a point of inflection at $x = -\dfrac{b}{3a}$. Thus, if $b^2 - 3ac \leq 0$, then $y = ax^3 + bx^2 + cx + d$ has no relative maximum or minimum in the first quadrant; a point of inflection occurs at $x = -\dfrac{b}{3a}, y = \dfrac{b(2b^2 - 9ac)}{27a^2} + d$.

NOTE: $b^2 - 3ac \leq 0$ is a sufficient but not a necessary condition for

$$y = ax^3 + bx^2 + cx + d$$

to have no relative maximum or minimum in the first quadrant. If $b^2 - 3ac > 0$, then $\dfrac{dy}{dx} = 0$ if $x = \dfrac{-b \pm \sqrt{b^2 - 3ac}}{3a}$.

$$x = \frac{-b \pm \sqrt{b^2 - 3ac}}{3a} > 0, \text{ since } a > 0, b < 0 \text{ and } |b^2 - 3ac| < |b|$$

(note that $b^2 - 3ac > 0 \Rightarrow b \neq 0$).

$$y = a\left(\frac{-b \pm \sqrt{b^2 - 3ac}}{3a}\right)^3 + b\left(\frac{-b \pm \sqrt{b^2 - 3ac}}{3a}\right)^2 + c\left(\frac{-b \pm \sqrt{b^2 - 3ac}}{3a}\right) + d$$

Since $a > 0$, $b < 0$, $c \geq 0$, $d \geq 0$ and $\dfrac{-b \pm \sqrt{b^2 - 3ac}}{3a} > 0$, the first term in the expression for y is positive, the second term is negative, and the third and fourth terms are positive or zero. Thus y may be positive or negative depending on the relative value of the coefficients a, b, c, and d, and (x, y) may lie in either the first or second quadrant. Since

$$\left.\frac{d^2y}{dx^2}\right|_{x=[-b\pm\sqrt{b^2-3ac}]/3a} = 2(-b \pm \sqrt{b^2 - 3ac} + b) = \pm 2\sqrt{b^2 - 3ac}$$

and $b^2 - 3ac > 0$, $\left.\dfrac{d^2y}{dx^2}\right|_{x=[-b\pm\sqrt{b^2-3ac}]/3a} \neq 0$ and $y = ax^3 + bx^2 + cx + d$ has a

relative maximum or minimum at the point for which $\dfrac{dy}{dx} = 0$. Thus, if $b^2 - 3ac > 0$, $y = ax^3 + bx^2 + cx + d$ has a relative maximum or minimum in the first quadrant only for certain values of the coefficients. For simplicity, only equations for which $b^2 - 3ac \leq 0$ are considered.

Frequently the tangent at the point of inflection provides a good linear approximation of a cubic cost function for a limited range. The tangent at the point of inflection $x = -\dfrac{b}{3a}$ has slope

$$\frac{dy}{dx} = 3ax^2 + 2bx + c$$

$$\left.\frac{dy}{dx}\right|_{x=-b/3a} = \frac{b^2}{3a} - \frac{2b^2}{3a} + c$$

$$= c - \frac{b^2}{3a}, \text{ which is } \geq 0, \text{ since } b^2 \leq 3ac$$

If $x = -\dfrac{b}{3a}$,

$$y = a\left(-\frac{b^3}{27a^3}\right) + b\left(\frac{b^2}{9a^2}\right) + c\left(-\frac{b}{3a}\right) + d$$

$$= \frac{2b^3}{27a^2} - \frac{bc}{3a} + d$$

The line through the point $\left(-\dfrac{b}{3a}, \dfrac{2b^3}{27a^2} - \dfrac{bc}{3a} + d\right)$ and having slope $c - \dfrac{b^2}{3a}$

is given by

$$y - y_1 = m(x - x_1)$$

$$y - \left(\frac{2b^3}{27a^2} - \frac{bc}{3a} + d\right) = \left(c - \frac{b^2}{3a}\right)\left(x + \frac{b}{3a}\right)$$

$$y = \left(c - \frac{b^2}{3a}\right)x + \frac{bc}{3a} - \frac{b^3}{9a^2} + \frac{2b^3}{27a^2} - \frac{bc}{3a} + d$$

$$= \left(c - \frac{b^2}{3a}\right)x - \frac{b^3}{27a^2} + d$$

Examples

Higher-order polynomial cost functions:

Total cost: $y = ax^b + c$, where $a > 0$, $b > 1$, $c \geq 0$

Average cost: $\bar{y} = \dfrac{y}{x} = ax^{b-1} + \dfrac{c}{x}$

Marginal cost: $\dfrac{dy}{dx} = abx^{b-1}$

Marginal average cost: $\dfrac{d\bar{y}}{dx} = a(b-1)x^{b-2} - \dfrac{c}{x^2}$

Total cost is represented by the first quadrant part of an algebraic curve, average cost is represented by the first quadrant branch of a hyperbola, and marginal cost is represented by the first quadrant part of an algebraic curve (see Fig. 2.56).

This type of simple polynomial curve is always concave upward for $x \geq 0$ and thus in practice is usually appropriate only for limited ranges of x.

$$\frac{d\bar{y}}{dx} = 0 \text{ if } a(b-1)x^b = c$$

$$\text{that is, } x = \left[\frac{c}{a(b-1)}\right]^{1/b}$$

$$\frac{d\bar{y}^2}{dx^2} = a(b-1)(b-2)x^{b-3} + \frac{2c}{x^3}$$

$$= x^{-3}[a(b-1)(b-2)x^b + 2c]$$

If $x = \left[\dfrac{x}{a(b-1)}\right]^{1/b}$, then

$$\frac{d\bar{y}^2}{dx^2} = \left[\frac{c}{a(b-1)}\right]^{-3/b}\left[a(b-1)(b-2)\frac{c}{a(b-1)} + 2c\right]$$

$$> 0, \text{ so minimum at } x = \left[\frac{c}{a(b-1)}\right]^{1/b}$$

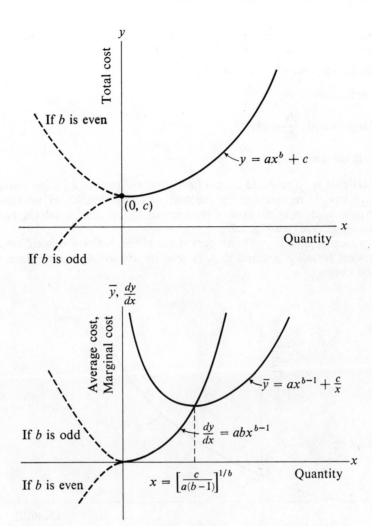

FIGURE 2.56

Note that average cost and marginal cost are equal if $x = \left(\dfrac{c}{a(b-1)}\right)^{1/b}$, since

$$\bar{y} = a\left(\frac{c}{a(b-1)}\right)^{(b-1)/b} + c\left(\frac{c}{a(b-1)}\right)^{-1/b}$$

$$= \left(\frac{c}{a(b-1)}\right)^{(b-1)/b}\left[a + c\left(\frac{c}{a(b-1)}\right)^{-1}\right]$$

$$= \left(\frac{c}{a(b-1)}\right)^{(b-1)/b}[a + a(b-1)]$$

$$= ab\left(\frac{c}{a(b-1)}\right)^{(b-1)/b}$$

and

$$\frac{dy}{dx} = ab\left(\frac{c}{a(b-1)}\right)^{(b-1)/b}$$

Exponential cost functions:

Total cost: $y = ae^{bx}$, where $a > 0$, $b > 0$

Average cost: $\bar{y} = \dfrac{y}{x} = \dfrac{ae^{bx}}{x}$

Marginal cost: $\dfrac{dy}{dx} = abe^{bx}$

Marginal average cost: $\dfrac{d\bar{y}}{dx} = \dfrac{abxe^{bx} - ae^{bx}}{x^2}$

Total cost is represented by the first quadrant part of an exponential curve, average cost is represented by the first quadrant branch of an exponential hyperbola, and marginal cost is represented by the first quadrant part of an exponential curve (see Fig. 2.57).

Exponential and logarithmic curves are either concave upward or concave downward for all $x \geq 0$ and thus in practice are usually appropriate only for limited ranges of x.

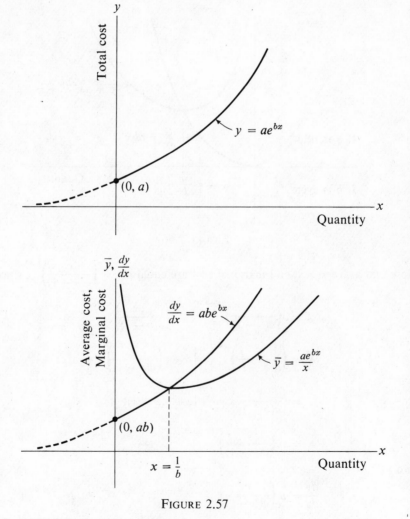

FIGURE 2.57

$$\frac{d\bar{y}}{dx} = 0 \text{ if } ae^{bx}(bx - 1) = 0$$

$$\text{that is, } x = \frac{1}{b}$$

$$\frac{d\bar{y}^2}{dx^2} = \frac{(abe^{bx} + ab^2xe^{bx} - abe^{bx})x^2 - (abxe^{bx} - ae^{bx})(2x)}{x^4}$$

$$= \frac{axe^{bx}(b^2x^2 - 2bx + 2)}{x^4}$$

If $x = \frac{1}{b}$, then

$$\frac{d\bar{y}^2}{dx^2} = \frac{\frac{a}{b}e(1 - 2 + 2)}{\frac{1}{b^4}}$$

$$= ab^3e > 0 \text{ so minimum at } x = \frac{1}{b}$$

Note that average cost and marginal cost are equal if $x = \frac{1}{b}$, since

$$\bar{y} = abe \text{ and } \frac{dy}{dx} = abe$$

PROBLEMS

1. For each of the following average cost functions find the minimum average cost and show that at the minimum average cost, marginal cost and average cost are equal.
   (a) $\bar{y}_c = 25 - 8x + x^2$ (b) $\bar{y}_c = 2 + x \ln x$
   (c) $\bar{y}_c = 2e^x + e^{-x}$ (d) $\bar{y}_c = 3x + 5 + \dfrac{6}{x}$
   (e) $\bar{y}_c = 2x + 5 + \dfrac{18}{x}$ (f) $\bar{y}_c = 20 + 2x^2 + 4x^4$
   (g) $\bar{y}_c = 10 - 4x^3 + 3x^4$ (h) $\bar{y}_c = 6x + 7 + \dfrac{36}{x}$

2. For each of the following total cost functions, find marginal cost and determine the nature of marginal cost (increasing, decreasing).
   (a) $y_c = 1000x - 180x^2 + 3x^3$ (b) $y_c = 220 + 55x - 2x^3 + x^4$

3. Determine the nature of the marginal and average cost functions for each of the following total cost functions:
   (a) $y_c = \sqrt{x} + 25, \ 0 \leq x \leq 10$ (b) $y_c = 9x + 5xe^{-2x}$

4. For the following total cost function find the equation of the tangent at the point of inflection as an approximation of the function near that point.

$$y_c = x^3 - 6x^2 + 14x + 6$$

5. The Precision Machine Tool Manufacturing Company has a total cost function represented by the equation $y_c = 2x^3 - 3x^2 - 12x$.
   (a) What equation represents the marginal cost function?
   (b) What is the equation for the average cost function? At what point is average cost at its minimum?
   (c) Is this a set of equations one might realistically expect to find in a business? Why?

6. The Minute Man Colonial Furniture Company total revenue function is expressed by the equation $R = 24x - 3x^2$.
   (a) What is the maximum revenue the company can expect, assuming this equation is valid?
   (b) What is the equation that represents the average revenue function for this company?
   (c) What is the equation that represents the marginal revenue function for this company?
   (d) On one graph, plot the three functions above.

7. Arto Company manufactures cabinets for TV sets, and the total cost of producing a certain model is represented by the equation $y_c = 4x - x^2 + 2x^3$, where y_c represents total cost and x represents quantity, in thousands of units. The sales department has indicated that between 2 and 6 units (in thousands) should be produced. At what quantity is marginal cost a minimum? Explain your answer, and graph the marginal cost curve.

8. If the general formula for the total cost function is

$$TC = f(x) = ax^3 + bx^2 + cx + d$$

   (a) What is the corresponding equation for the marginal cost function?
   (b) What is the corresponding equation for the average cost function?

9. An important generalization is often made about the relationships between the total revenue (TR), average revenue (AR), and marginal revenue (MR) functions:

> When $MR = 0$, TR is at a maximum point
> When $MR > AR$, AR is increasing
> When $MR < AR$, AR is decreasing
> When $MR = AR$, AR is unchanging

   (a) Illustrate this with an example from your reading or an example from the text.
   (b) Work out the analogous relationships for the total cost (TC), average cost (AC), and marginal cost (MC) functions.

10. Henderson and Quandt in their book *Microeconomic Theory* state the following[†]:
    "A monopolist is free to select any price-quantity combination which lies on his negatively sloped demand curve. Since an expansion of his output results in a reduction of his price, his MR is less than his price. His first-order condition for profit maximization requires the equality of MR and MC. His second-order condition requires that MC be increasing more

† J. M. Henderson and R. E. Quandt, *Microeconomic Theory, a Mathematical Approach*, McGraw-Hill, New York, 1958, p. 198.

rapidly than *MR*." (Note that increasing more rapidly is logically equivalent to decreasing less rapidly.)

Which, if any, of the three diagrams in Fig. 2.58 satisfies both conditions?

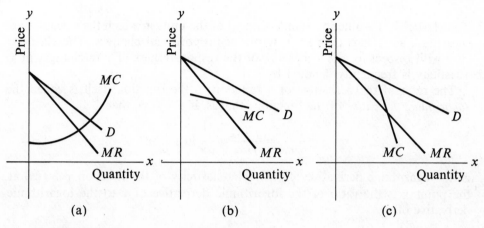

FIGURE 2.58

ANSWERS TO ODD-NUMBERED PROBLEMS

---

1. (a) $\bar{y}_{min} = 9$ (b) $\bar{y}_{min} = 2 - \dfrac{1}{e}$

  (c) $\bar{y}_{min} = 2^{3/2}$ (d) $\bar{y}_{min} = 5 + 6\sqrt{2}$

  (e) $\bar{y}_{min} = 17$ (f) $\bar{y}_{min} = 20$

  (g) $\bar{y}_{min} = 9$ (h) $\bar{y}_{min} = 7 + 12\sqrt{6}$

3. (a) for $0 \leq x \leq 10$, marginal and average cost always decreasing
   (b) marginal cost decreasing for $x < 1$ and increasing for $x > 1$; average cost always decreasing; $\bar{y}_c \to 9$ as $x \to \infty$

5. (a) $MC = 6x^2 - 6x - 12$
   (b) $AC = 2x^2 - 3x - 12$, min at $x = \frac{3}{4}$

   (c) no, TC not in first quadrant for $x < \dfrac{3 + \sqrt{105}}{4}$

7. in interval $2 \leq x \leq 6$, MC is minimum for $x = 2$

9. (b) when $MC = 0$, TC is maximum
   when $MC > AC$, AC is increasing
   when $MC < AC$, AC is decreasing
   when $MC = AC$, AC is unchanging

□ *ELASTICITY*

The *point elasticity* of the function $y = f(x)$ at the point x is the ratio of the proportional change in y to the proportional change in x at the point in question:

$$\frac{Ey}{Ex} = \frac{\frac{dy}{y}}{\frac{dx}{x}} = \frac{x}{y} \cdot \frac{dy}{dx}$$

The elasticity of a function is independent of the units in which the variables are measured, since it is defined in terms of proportional changes. The elasticity of y with respect to x is a measure of the responsiveness of y to changes in x. Elasticity is frequently denoted by η.

The ratio of the derivative of a function to the function itself is called the *logarithmic derivative* of the function; that is, if $y = f(x)$, then

$$\frac{1}{y}\frac{dy}{dx} = \frac{f'(x)}{f(x)} = \frac{d}{dx}\ln y$$

is the logarithmic derivative of $f(x)$. The elasticity of the function $y = f(x)$ at the point x is the ratio of the logarithmic derivative of y to the logarithmic derivative of x:

$$\frac{Ey}{Ex} = \frac{\frac{d}{dx}\ln y}{\frac{d}{dx}\ln x} = \frac{\frac{1}{y}\frac{dy}{dx}}{\frac{1}{x}\frac{dx}{dx}} = \frac{x}{y} \cdot \frac{dy}{dx}$$

Elasticity is defined as a property of any differentiable function; however, in economic theory elasticity is most frequently considered for demand, supply, price, cost, and revenue functions. Elasticity is used, for example, as a measure of the responsiveness of demand or supply to changes in price or income, and the responsiveness of price, total cost, or total revenue to changes in quantity.

Point elasticity is unambiguous and is easily measured when the function is specified. But frequently the economist or businessman is less interested in the elasticity at a point than in elasticity between two points, that is, over an arc. Unfortunately, there is no one unambigous way of measuring elasticity over an arc and the value obtained depends somewhat on the formula used.

The following formulas are frequently used for measuring arc elasticity between the points (x_1, y_1) and (x_2, y_2).

$$\frac{Ey}{Ex} = \frac{x_1}{y_1} \cdot \frac{y_2 - y_1}{x_2 - x_1} = \frac{x_1}{y_1} \cdot \frac{\Delta y}{\Delta x}$$

$$\frac{Ey}{Ex} = \frac{x_2}{y_2} \cdot \frac{y_2 - y_1}{x_2 - x_1} = \frac{x_2}{y_2} \cdot \frac{\Delta y}{\Delta x}$$

$$\frac{Ey}{Ex} = \frac{x_1 + x_2}{y_1 + y_2} \cdot \frac{y_2 - y_1}{x_2 - x_1} = \frac{x_1 + x_2}{y_1 + y_2} \cdot \frac{\Delta y}{\Delta x}$$

The first formula is an approximation of the point elasticity at (x_1, y_1). The second formula is an approximation of the point elasticity at (x_2, y_2). The third formula is the average of the first two and is probably the most commonly used.

The concept of *cross elasticity* is useful as a measure of the relationship between the demands for two or more commodities. Cross elasticity measures the responsiveness of demand for one commodity to changes in price of another commodity. The elasticity of demand for x_1 with respect to price of x_2 is defined as

$$\frac{Eq_{x_1}}{Ep_{x_2}} = \frac{\dfrac{dq}{q}}{\dfrac{dp}{p}} = \frac{p}{q} \cdot \frac{dq}{dp}$$

and *arc cross elasticity* as p changes from p_1 to p_2 and q changes from q_1 to q_2 is given by

$$\frac{Eq_{x_1}}{Ep_{x_2}} = \frac{p_1 + p_2}{q_1 + q_2} \cdot \frac{q_2 - q_1}{p_2 - p_1}$$

where the q's are the quantities of x_1, the p's are the prices of x_2, and the price of x_1 is assumed to be constant. The elasticity of demand for x_2 with respect to price of x_1 is similarly defined.

When commodities are substitutes for each other, their cross elasticities are positive. For example, when the price of butter increases, the consumption of margarine also increases, assuming that the price of margarine and other relevant factors remain constant. When commodities are complementary to each other, their cross elasticities are negative. For example, when the price of lettuce increases, the consumption of salad dressing decreases, assuming that other relevant factors remain constant.

NOTE: In the following examples x represents quantity demanded and y represents price per unit. Thus, when quantity is considered to be a function of price, the convention of using y for the dependent variable and x for the independent variable is violated. This should be noted also in the graphical representations.

Examples

The demand function for a particular commodity is given by $x = 20 - 2y^2$ for $0 \leq y \leq \sqrt{10}$, where y is price per unit and x is number of units demanded. Consider the point $y = 2$, $x = 12$. If the price decreases by 6%, determine the corresponding increase in demand and an approximation to the elasticity of demand at the point $y = 2$, $x = 12$; compare this with the exact elasticity of demand at the point $y = 2$, $x = 12$. Then compute an approximation to the elasticity of demand and the exact elasticity of demand at the point representing the changed price and quantity; also compute the arc elasticity based on average price and quantity (see Figs. 2.59 and 2.60).

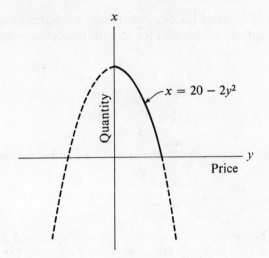

FIGURE 2.59

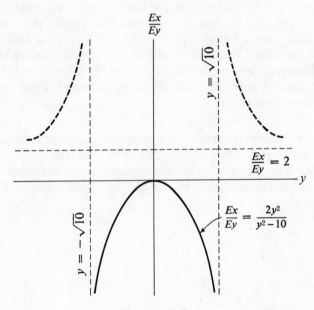

FIGURE 2.60

$$y_1 = 2 \qquad y_2 = 2 - (0.06)(2) = 1.88 \qquad \Delta y = -0.12$$

$$x_1 = 12 \qquad x_2 = 20 - 2(1.88)^2 = 12.94 \qquad \Delta x = 0.94$$

For the point $y_1 = 2$, $x_1 = 12$,

$$\frac{Ex}{Ey} = \frac{y_1}{x_1} \cdot \frac{\Delta x}{\Delta y}$$

$$= \tfrac{2}{12}\left(-\frac{0.94}{0.12}\right)$$

$$= -1.31, \text{ approximate elasticity of demand at } y = 2, x = 12$$

$$\frac{Ex}{Ey} = \frac{y}{x} \cdot \frac{dx}{dy}$$

$$= \frac{-4y^2}{20 - 2y^2}$$

$$= \frac{2y^2}{y^2 - 10}$$

$$\left.\frac{Ex}{Ey}\right|_{y=2} = -\frac{8}{6} = -1.33, \text{ exact elasticity of demand at } y = 2, x = 12$$

For the point $y_2 = 1.88$, $x_2 = 12.94$,

$$\frac{Ex}{Ey} = \frac{y_2}{x_2} \cdot \frac{\Delta x}{\Delta y}$$

$$= \frac{1.88}{12.94}\left(-\frac{0.94}{0.12}\right)$$

$$= -1.14, \text{ approximate elasticity of demand at } y_2 = 1.88, x_2 = 12.94$$

$$\frac{Ex}{Ey} = \frac{2y^2}{y^2 - 10}$$

$$\left.\frac{Ex}{Ey}\right|_{y=1.88} = -1.09, \text{ exact elasticity of demand at } y_2 = 1.88, x_2 = 12.9$$

The arc elasticity based on average price and quantity is given by

$$\frac{Ex}{Ey} = \frac{y_1 + y_2}{x_1 + x_2} \cdot \frac{x_2 - x_1}{y_2 - y_1} = \frac{3.88}{24.94}\left(\frac{0.94}{0.12}\right)$$

$$= -1.22$$

The demand for margarine is related to the price of butter as follows:

$$q = 5 + 2\sqrt{p}$$

where q is the demand for margarine (hundreds of pounds) and p is the price of butter (dollars per pound). Find the equation for cross elasticity of demand for margarine with respect to price of butter. What is the demand for margarine when butter is 81 cents per pound? What is the demand for margarine when butter is \$1.00 per pound? What is the cross elasticity of demand for margarine as butter goes from 81 cents to \$1.00 per pound? (See Figs. 2.61 and 2.62.)

The elasticity of demand for margarine with respect to price of butter is

$$\frac{Eq}{Ep} = \frac{dq}{dp} \cdot \frac{p}{q} = \frac{1}{\sqrt{p}} \cdot \frac{p}{5 + 2\sqrt{p}}$$

$$= \frac{\sqrt{p}}{5 + 2\sqrt{p}}$$

When $p = 0.81$, $q = 5 + 2\sqrt{.81}$ or 680 pounds.
When $p = 1.00$, $q = 5 + 2\sqrt{1.00}$ or 700 pounds.

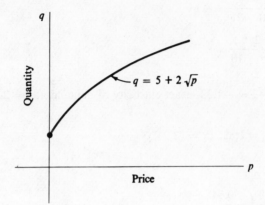

FIGURE 2.61

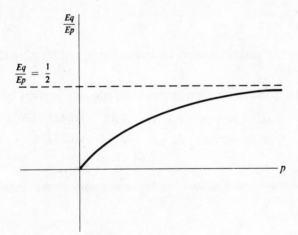

FIGURE 2.62

Cross elasticity is

for $p = 0.81$,

$$\left.\frac{Eq}{Ep}\right|_{p=0.81} = \frac{0.9}{5 + 2(0.9)} = \frac{0.9}{6.8} = 0.13$$

for $p = 1.00$,

$$\left.\frac{Eq}{Ep}\right|_{p=1.00} = \frac{1}{5 + 2} = \frac{1}{7} = 0.14$$

● **Constant Elasticity of Demand**

If the demand function is given by the generalized equilateral hyperbola

$$x = \frac{a}{y^m}$$

then

$$\frac{dx}{dy} = -amy^{-m-1}$$

$$\frac{Ex}{Ey} = \frac{y}{x} \cdot \frac{dx}{dy}$$

$$= y \left(\frac{y^m}{a}\right)(-amy^{-m-1})$$

$$= -m$$

That is, elasticity of demand is the constant $-m$. In terms of approximate changes in price and quantity demanded, an increase of 1% in price results in a decrease of $m\%$ in demand at any level of price and quantity. Only a rectangular hyperbola has constant elasticity over its range. For any other type of function, elasticity varies for different values of x and y, that is, for different points on the curve. (See previous examples).

Example

The demand function is given by

$$x = \frac{25}{y^4} \qquad \text{for } 1 \le y \le 5$$

Determine the elasticity of demand. Consider the point $y = 2$, $x = \frac{25}{16}$; if the price increases by 5%, determine an approximation to the elasticity at the point $y = 2$, $x = \frac{25}{16}$, and at the point representing the changed price and quantity (see Figs. 2.63 and 2.64).

$$\frac{dx}{dy} = \frac{-100y^3}{y^8}$$

$$= \frac{-100}{y^5}$$

$$\frac{Ex}{Ey} = \frac{y}{x} \cdot \frac{dx}{dy}$$

$$= \frac{y}{\frac{25}{y^4}} \left(\frac{-100}{y^5}\right)$$

$$= -4, \text{ as could be obtained from the derivation for the general case given above.}$$

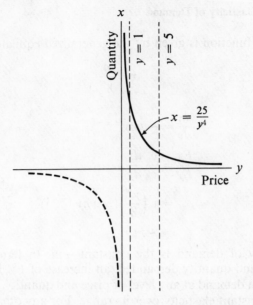

FIGURE 2.63

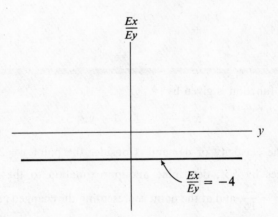

FIGURE 2.64

$$y_1 = 2 \qquad y_2 = 2 + (0.05)(2) = 2.1 \qquad \Delta y = 0.1$$

$$x_1 = 1.56 \qquad x_2 = \frac{25}{(2.1)^4} = 1.29 \qquad \Delta x = -0.27$$

For the point $y_1 = 2$, $x_1 = 1.56$, approximate elasticity of demand is

$$\frac{Ex}{Ey} = \frac{y_1}{x_1} \cdot \frac{\Delta x}{\Delta y}$$

$$= \frac{2}{1.56} \left(\frac{-0.27}{0.1} \right)$$

$$= -3.46$$

For the point $y_2 = 2.1$, $x_2 = 1.29$, approximate elasticity of demand is

$$\frac{Ex}{Ey} = \frac{y_2}{x_2} \cdot \frac{\Delta x}{\Delta y}$$

$$= \frac{2.1}{1.29} \left(\frac{-0.27}{0.1} \right)$$

$$= -4.40$$

☐ *REVENUE, MARGINAL REVENUE,*
  AND ELASTICITY OF DEMAND

For any given demand function $y = f(x)$, the total revenue $R = F(x)$ is the product of x, the number of units demanded, and y, the price per unit quantity demanded,

$$R = F(x) = xy = x \cdot f(x)$$

and the marginal revenue with respect to demand is

$$\frac{dR}{dx} = x \frac{dy}{dx} + y$$

Elasticity of demand with respect to price is

$$\frac{Ex}{Ey} = \frac{y}{x} \cdot \frac{dx}{dy}$$

and, since $\dfrac{dx}{dy} = \dfrac{1}{\dfrac{dy}{dx}}$,

$$\frac{Ex}{Ey} = \frac{y}{x} \left(\frac{1}{\dfrac{dy}{dx}} \right)$$

$$\frac{dy}{dx} = \frac{y}{x \left(\dfrac{Ex}{Ey} \right)}$$

Thus

$$\frac{dR}{dx} = \frac{y}{\dfrac{Ex}{Ey}} + y$$

$$= y \left(1 + \frac{1}{\dfrac{Ex}{Ey}} \right)$$

Alternatively, $\qquad \dfrac{dR}{dx} = x \dfrac{dy}{dx} + y$

$$= y\left(\frac{x}{y}\frac{dy}{dx} + 1\right)$$

$$= y\left(1 + \frac{Ey}{Ex}\right)$$

$$= y\left(1 + \frac{1}{\frac{Ex}{Ey}}\right)$$

That is, marginal revenue is the product of the price per unit quantity demanded and one plus the reciprocal of the elasticity of demand.

Since both x and y are either zero or positive, the total revenue, $R = xy$, is also either zero or positive; however, the marginal revenue may be either positive or negative.

NOTE: Logically, R could also be considered a function of price

$$R = F(x) = xy = y \cdot g(y) = G(y)$$

and marginal revenue with respect to price defined as

$$\frac{dR}{dy} = y\frac{dx}{dy} + x$$

This would perhaps be simpler for cases when the demand function is in the form $x = g(y)$ and it is not easy to solve for y in terms of x. However, to keep the geometrical representation consistent (that is, to use x as the independent variable), it is preferable to use implicit differentiation and the chain rule to obtain $\frac{dR}{dx}$ and $\frac{d^2R}{dx^2}$ when the demand function is in the form $x = g(y)$.

Examples

The demand relation for a particular commodity is given by

$$y = (12 - x)^{1/2} \qquad \text{for } 0 \le x \le 12$$

where x is quantity demanded and y is price per unit.

Determine the price and quantity for which revenue is maximum. Show for this demand function that the relationship between marginal revenue and elasticity of demand holds (see Fig. 2.65).

Demand: $y = (12 - x)^{1/2} \qquad \text{for } 0 \le x \le 12$

Revenue: $R = x(12 - x)^{1/2}$

$$\frac{dR}{dx} = (12 - x)^{1/2} - \tfrac{1}{2}x(12 - x)^{-1/2}$$

$$= (12 - x)^{-1/2}[12 - x - \tfrac{1}{2}x]$$

$$= \frac{3(8 - x)}{2(12 - x)^{1/2}}$$

$$= 0 \qquad \text{if } x = 8, y = 16$$

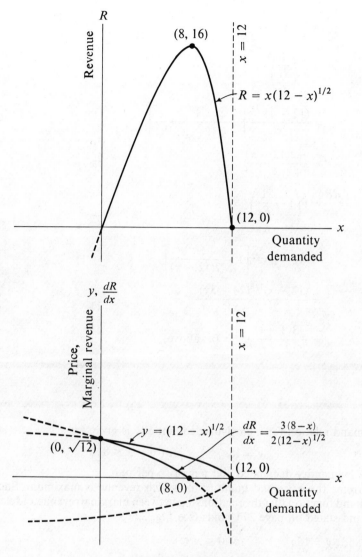

FIGURE 2.65

$$\frac{d^2R}{dx^2} = \tfrac{3}{2}\left[\frac{-(12-x)^{1/2} - (8-x)(-\tfrac{1}{2})(12-x)^{-1/2}}{12-x}\right]$$

$$= \tfrac{3}{2}\left[\frac{(12-x)^{-1/2}[-12 + x + \tfrac{1}{2}(8-x)]}{12-x}\right]$$

$$= \tfrac{3}{4}\left[\frac{x-16}{(12-x)^{3/2}}\right]$$

< 0 if $x = 8$, so maximum at $x = 8$, $y = 16$

< 0 for $0 \le x < 12$, so no point of inflection

thus $R = x(12 - x)^{1/2}$ is concave downward for $0 \le x \le 12$.

$$\frac{Ex}{Ey} = \frac{y}{x} \cdot \frac{dx}{dy}$$

$$= \frac{y}{x}\left(\frac{1}{\dfrac{dy}{dx}}\right)$$

$$= \frac{(12-x)^{1/2}}{x}\left[\frac{1}{-\frac{1}{2}(12-x)^{-1/2}}\right]$$

$$= \frac{-2(12-x)}{x}$$

$$\frac{dR}{dx} = y\left(1 + \frac{1}{\dfrac{Ex}{Ey}}\right)$$

$$= (12-x)^{1/2}\left[1 - \frac{x}{2(12-x)}\right]$$

$$= \frac{(12-x)^{1/2}(24-3x)}{2(12-x)}$$

$$= \frac{3(8-x)}{2(12-x)^{1/2}} \qquad \text{(as above)}$$

The demand relation for a particular commodity is given by

$$y = 15e^{-x/3} \qquad \text{for } 0 \le x \le 8$$

where x is quantity demanded and y is price per unit.

Determine the price and quantity for which revenue is maximum. Show for this demand function that the relationship between marginal revenue and elasticity of demand stated on page 271 holds (see Fig. 2.66).

Demand: $y = 15e^{-x/3} \qquad$ for $0 \le x \le 8$

Revenue: $R = 15xe^{-x/3}$

$$\frac{dR}{dx} = -5xe^{-x/3} + 15e^{-x/3}$$

$$= 5e^{-x/3}(3 - x)$$

$$= 0 \text{ if } x = 3, \ R = \frac{45}{e}$$

$$\frac{d^2R}{dx^2} = -\tfrac{5}{3}e^{-x/3}(3 - x) - 5e^{-x/3}$$

$$= 5e^{-x/3}(\tfrac{1}{3}x - 2)$$

$$< 0 \qquad \text{if } x = 3, \text{ so maximum at } x = 3, \ R = \frac{45}{e} \approx 16.7$$

$$= 0 \qquad \text{if } x = 6$$

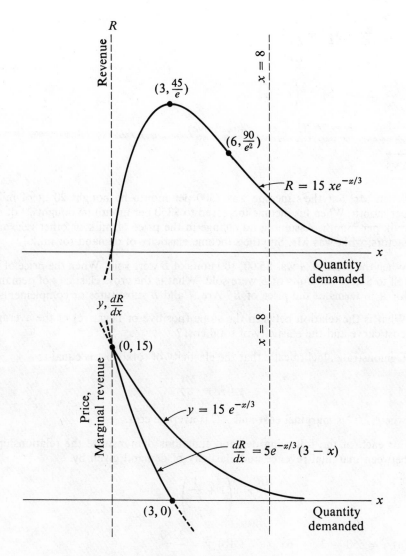

FIGURE 2.66

$$\frac{d^3R}{dx^3} = -\tfrac{5}{3}e^{-x/3}(\tfrac{1}{3}x - 2) + \tfrac{5}{3}e^{-x/3}$$

$$= 5e^{-x/3}(1 - \tfrac{1}{6}x) > 0 \qquad \text{if } x = 6, \text{ so point of inflection at}$$

$$x = 6, R = \frac{90}{e^2} \approx 12.3.$$

$$\frac{Ex}{Ey} = \frac{y}{x} \cdot \frac{dx}{dy}$$

$$= \frac{y}{x}\left(\frac{1}{\dfrac{dy}{dx}}\right)$$

$$= \frac{15e^{-x/3}}{x}\left(\frac{1}{-5e^{-x/3}}\right)$$

$$= -\frac{3}{x}$$

$$\frac{dR}{dx} = y\left(1 + \frac{1}{\frac{Ex}{Ey}}\right)$$

$$= 15e^{-x/3}\left(1 - \frac{x}{3}\right)$$

$$= 5e^{-x/3}(3 - x) \qquad \text{(as above)}$$

PROBLEMS

1. When Mr. Smythe's income was $300 per month he bought 20 qt of milk per month. When his income increased to $350 per month he bought 24 qt of milk per month. Assuming no change in the price of milk or other relevant factors, what was Mr. Smythe's income elasticity of demand for milk?

2. When the price of A was $5.00, 100 units of B were sold. When the price of A fell to $4.00, 120 units of B were sold. What is the cross elasticity of demand for A in terms of the price of B? Are A and B substitutes or complements?

3. What is the relation between the slope (positive or negative) of the average cost curve and the elasticity of total cost?

4. Demonstrate algebraically that the elasticity of total cost is equal to

$$E_{TC} = \frac{MC}{AC}$$

where MC is marginal cost and AC is average cost.

5. For each of the following demand functions demonstrate the relationship between marginal revenue and elasticity of demand given by

$$\frac{dR}{dx} = y\left(1 + \frac{1}{\frac{Ex}{Ey}}\right)$$

(a) $y = 550 - 3x - 6x^2$ (b) $y = \dfrac{3250}{x^3}$

(c) $y = 17 - 6x$ (d) $y = 86 - 25x$

(e) $y = 100 - 6x^2$

6. Find elasticity of demand with respect to price for each of the following functions.

(a) $y = \dfrac{3}{1 + 2x^2}$ (b) $y = (x - 8)^2,\ 0 \le x \le 8$

(c) $y = ae^{-kx}$ (d) $y = 13e^{-5/4x}$

(e) $x = \dfrac{10}{y^{5/4}}$

7. For each of the following demand functions, (i) determine approximate elasticity at the point specified, (ii) determine approximate elasticity at the point corresponding to the specified change in price or demand, (iii) deter-

mine exact elasticity at the two points, (iv) determine arc elasticity based on average quantities and prices, and (v) show that $\dfrac{dy}{dx}$ and $\dfrac{dx}{dy}$ are reciprocals of each other.

(a) $x = 60 - 2y^2$; $x = 10$, $y = 5$; price decrease 8%
(b) $x + 2y = 15$; $x = 7$, $y = 4$; price increase 5%
(c) $x = 25 - 5y^2$; $x = 5$, $y = 2$; price increase 5%
(d) $x = 10 - 5y^2$; $x = 5$, $y = 1$; price increase 10%
(e) $y = (x - 10)^2$, $0 \le x \le 10$; $x = 8$, $y = 4$; demand decrease 5%
(f) $x = 19 - 4y^2$; $x = 3$, $y = 2$; price decrease 5%
(g) $x = 36 - 4y^2$; $x = 20$, $y = 2$; price increase 5%
(h) $y = (x - 4)^2$; $x = 1$, $y = 9$; demand increase 30%

8. Show that if demand is linear and negatively sloped the elasticity of total revenue is always less than 1, but to the left of its maximum value the elasticity of total revenue is positive and to the right of the maximum value the elasticity of total revenue is negative.

ANSWERS TO ODD-NUMBERED PROBLEMS

---

1. 13/11

3. when slope of AC is negative, E_{TC} is less than 1
   when slope of AC is zero, E_{TC} is equal to 1
   when slope of AC is positive, E_{TC} is greater than 1

7. (a) -9.6, -5.00, -10, -4.79, -6.73
   (b) -1.14, -1.27, -1.14, -1.27, -1.21
   (c) -8.2, -14.59, -8, -14.95, -10.57
   (d) -2.1, -2.92, -2, -3.06, -2.46
   (e) -0.11, -0.17, -0.13, -0.17, -0.14
   (f) -10.4, -6.5, -10.67, -6.33, -8.05
   (g) -1.64, -1.88, -1.6, -1.92, -1.75
   (h) -1.58, $-.98$, -1.50, -1.04, -1.24

☐ *REVENUE FROM TAXATION*

If the government imposes a tax on a given commodity, it is assumed that the price to the consumer will increase and correspondingly the quantity demanded will decrease. The discussion in this section concerns the effect of taxation on market equilibrium under the following conditions: (1) pure competition in which the consumer's demand depends only on price—the demand function does not change, (2) the producers adjust the supply curve to the new price which includes the tax, and (3) a tax of t monetary units is imposed on each unit of quantity produced.

The supply function can be represented by

$$y = g(x)$$

where x is the number of units of the commodity supplied and y is the price per unit. If a tax of t per unit quantity is imposed, the supply function after taxation is

$$y_t = g(x) + t$$

If the demand function is

$$y = f(x)$$

then the equilibrium point before taxation, $E(x, y)$, is the solution of the equations

Demand: $y = f(x)$

Supply: $y = g(x)$

and the equilibrium point after taxation, $E(x_t, y_t)$, is the solution of the equations

Demand: $y = f(x)$

Supply: $y_t = g(x) + t$

See Fig. 2.67.

NOTE: If the supply function before taxation is in the form

$$x = G(y)$$

it may be possible to solve for y in a convenient form. If not, the supply function after taxation,

$$y_t - t = g(x)$$

shows that the quantity supplied is

$$x = G(y_t - t)$$

and equilibrium after taxation occurs at the solution of the equations

Demand: $y = f(x)$

Supply: $x = G(y_t - t)$

Geometrically, this is equivalent to moving the original supply curve upward t units. Except for the case of constant price, where price does not depend on quantity produced, the increase in equilibrium price is less than the amount of the tax. Note that a subsidy may be considered a negative tax. The supply curve is moved downward the amount of the subsidy, price to the consumer decreases, and demand increases.

The total tax revenue T received by the government from a tax of t per unit quantity is

$$T = tx_t$$

where x_t is the equilibrium quantity after taxation. This total may be represented by the area of a rectangle of dimensions t and x_t, which, if the supply function is linear, is equivalent to the parallelogram in Fig. 2.67. As this diagram indicates,

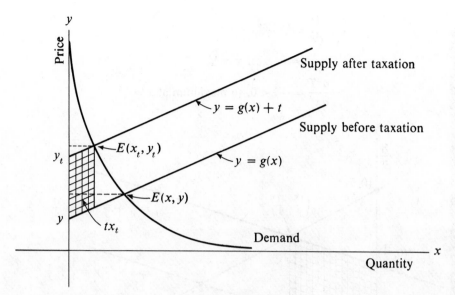

FIGURE 2.67

the tax may be large enough to reduce demand to the vanishing point. If the government is interested in taxation for revenue purposes, the question is what tax will maximize revenue—if the tax t is considered as a variable, then there is no revenue if $t = 0$ and there is also no revenue if t is large enough so that demand is zero; for some intermediate value of t the tax revenue $T = tx_t$ is maximum. Since T may be considered a function of either t or x, maximum revenue possible from taxation can be determined by considering marginal tax revenue with respect to either t or x. It is usually more convenient to consider T as a function of x, since t occurs linearly in the relation between t and x.

Examples

The demand and supply functions for a particular commodity are

$$\text{Demand: } 2y + x = 14$$

$$\text{Supply: } y = \tfrac{3}{4} + \frac{x}{3}$$

Determine the maximum possible revenue from taxation which can be obtained from a tax of t per unit quantity and the corresponding tax rate (see Fig. 2.68).

The supply function after taxation is $y = \tfrac{3}{4} + \dfrac{x}{3} + t$. Thus, after taxation, at equilibrium,

$$y = 7 - \frac{x}{2} = \tfrac{3}{4} + \frac{x}{3} + t$$

$$t = \tfrac{25}{4} - \tfrac{5}{6}x$$

$$T = tx = \tfrac{25}{4}x - \tfrac{5}{6}x^2$$

$$\frac{dT}{dx} = \frac{25}{4} - \frac{5}{3}x$$

$$= 0 \qquad \text{if } x = \frac{15}{4}$$

$$\frac{d^2T}{dx^2} = -\frac{5}{3} < 0, \text{ so maximum at } x = \frac{15}{4}$$

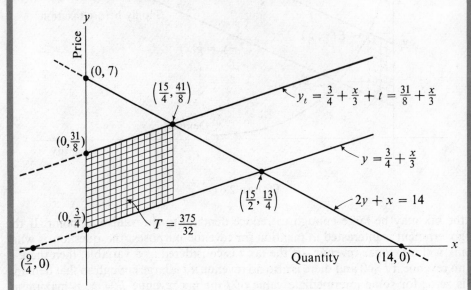

FIGURE 2.68

If $x = \frac{15}{4}$, $t = \frac{25}{4} - \frac{5}{6}(\frac{15}{4}) = \frac{25}{8}$, and $T_{max} = \frac{375}{32}$. So the maximum possible revenue from taxation is $T_{max} = \frac{375}{32}$ obtained from a tax of $t = \frac{25}{8}$ per unit quantity. Alternatively,

$$x = \frac{15}{2} - \frac{6}{5}t$$

$$T = \frac{15}{2}t - \frac{6}{5}t^2$$

$$\frac{dT}{dt} = \frac{15}{2} - \frac{12}{5}t$$

$$= 0 \qquad \text{if } t = \frac{25}{8}$$

$$\frac{d^2T}{dt^2} = -\frac{12}{5} < 0, \text{ so maximum at } t = \frac{25}{8}$$

$$T_{max} = (\frac{15}{2})(\frac{25}{8}) - \frac{6}{5}(\frac{25}{8})^2 = \frac{375}{32}$$

The demand and supply functions for a particular commodity are

Demand: $y = 30 - 2x^2$

Supply: $y = 3 + x^2$

Determine the maximum possible revenue from taxation which can be obtained from a tax of t per unit quantity and the corresponding tax rate (see Fig. 2.69).

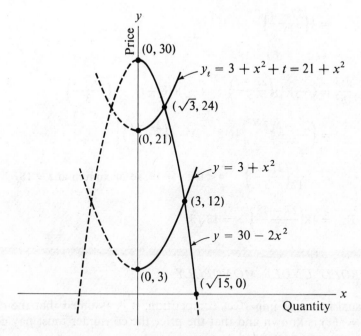

FIGURE 2.69

The supply function after taxation is $y = 3 + x^2 + t$. Thus, after taxation, at equilibrium,

$$y = 30 - 2x^2 = 3 + x^2 + t$$

$$t = 27 - 3x^2$$

$$T = tx = 27x - 3x^3$$

$$\frac{dT}{dx} = 27 - 9x^2$$

$$= 0 \quad \text{if } x = \sqrt{3}$$

$$\frac{d^2T}{dx^2} = -18x < 0 \text{ if } x = \sqrt{3}, \text{ so maximum at } x = \sqrt{3}$$

If $x = \sqrt{3}$, $t = 27 - 9 = 18$, and $T_{max} = 18\sqrt{3}$. So the maximum possible revenue from taxation is $T_{max} = 18\sqrt{3}$, obtained from a tax of $t = 18$ per unit quantity. Alternatively,

$$x = \sqrt{\frac{27 - t}{3}}$$

$$T = t\left(\frac{27 - t}{3}\right)^{1/2} = \left(\frac{27t^2 - t^3}{3}\right)^{1/2}$$

$$\frac{dT}{dt} = \frac{1}{2}\left(\frac{27t^2 - t^3}{3}\right)^{-1/2}\left(\frac{54t - 3t^2}{3}\right)$$

$$= \frac{1}{2}\left(\frac{27 - t}{3}\right)^{-1/2}(18 - t)$$

$$= 0 \quad \text{if } t = 18$$

$$\frac{d^2T}{dt^2} = (-\tfrac{1}{2})(\tfrac{1}{2})\left(\frac{27 - t}{3}\right)^{-3/2}(-1)(18 - t) - \tfrac{1}{2}\left(\frac{27 - t}{3}\right)^{-1/2}$$

$$= \left(\frac{27 - t}{3}\right)^{-3/2}\left[\tfrac{1}{4}(18 - t) - \tfrac{1}{2}\left(\frac{27 - t}{3}\right)\right]$$

$$= -\frac{t}{12}\left(\frac{27 - t}{3}\right)^{-3/2} < 0 \text{ if } t = 18, \text{ so maximum at } t = 18$$

$$T_{\text{max}} = 18\left(\frac{27 - 18}{3}\right)^{1/2} = 18\sqrt{3}$$

□ *PROFIT UNDER MONOPOLY*

In the usual forms of imperfect competition, it is assumed that the demand function $y = f(x)$ is known and that the price the consumer must pay depends only on the quantity demanded.

In a monopolistic situation, the monopolist controls the price by regulating the supply of the commodity—when supply is limited, price is relatively high, and when supply increases, price decreases.

If $\bar{y}_c$ is the average cost of producing a unit of commodity (as a function of the quantity produced), then the total cost y_c of producing x units is

$$y_c = x\bar{y}_c$$

(Note that in previous sections y has been used to denote price in some contexts and cost in others; the subscript c is used here to differentiate cost from price.)

Presumably the monopolist will control the supply x and thus the price y (determined by the demand function) so as to maximize his profit. The total revenue he receives is

$$R = xy$$

where $y = f(x)$; the total profit P is the difference between total revenue and total cost

$$P = R - y_c = xy - x\bar{y}_c$$

P has a relative maximum if and only if

$$\frac{dP}{dx} = 0; \quad \text{that is,} \quad \frac{dR}{dx} = \frac{dy_c}{dx}$$

and

$$\frac{d^2P}{dx^2} < 0; \quad \text{that is,} \quad \frac{d^2R}{dx^2} < \frac{d^2y_c}{dx^2}$$

In order to be meaningful this maximum must occur in the interval for which the cost and demand functions have economic significance.

NOTE: If the demand function is in the form

$$x = F(y)$$

and it is not possible or convenient to solve for y in terms of x, profit may be expressed as a function of y and the problem solved with y as the independent variable.

Examples

The demand function for a particular commodity is

$$y = 26 - 2x - 4x^2$$

and the average cost to the monopolist of producing and marketing the commodity is

$$\bar{y}_c = x + 8$$

Determine the maximum profit obtainable by the monopolist.

Revenue: $R = 26x - 2x^2 - 4x^3$

Total cost: $y_c = x^2 + 8x$

Profit: $\qquad P = 26x - 2x^2 - 4x^3 - x^2 - 8x$

$$= 18x - 3x^2 - 4x^3$$

$$\frac{dP}{dx} = 18 - 6x - 12x^2$$

$$= 0 \qquad \text{if } 2x^2 + x - 3 = 0$$

$$(2x + 3)(x - 1) = 0$$

$$x = 1$$

$$\frac{d^2P}{dx^2} = -6 - 24x$$

$$< 0 \text{ if } x = 1, \text{ so maximum at } x = 1$$

$$P_{\text{max}} = 11$$

Alternatively,

$$\frac{dR}{dx} = 26 - 4x - 12x^2$$

$$\frac{dy_c}{dx} = 2x + 8$$

$$\frac{dR}{dx} = \frac{dy_c}{dx} \qquad \text{if } 26 - 4x - 12x^2 = 2x + 8$$

$$2x^2 + x - 3 = 0$$
$$(2x + 3)(x - 1) = 0$$
$$x = 1$$

$$\left. \begin{array}{l} \dfrac{d^2R}{dx^2} = -4 - 24x \\[2ex] \dfrac{d^2y_c}{dx^2} = 2 \end{array} \right\} \quad \dfrac{d^2R}{dx^2} < \dfrac{d^2y_c}{dx^2} \quad \text{if } x = 1, \text{ so maximum at } x = 1$$

$$P_{\max} = 11$$

The demand function for a particular commodity is

$$y = 28 - 5x$$

and the total cost to the monopolist of producing and marketing the commodity is

$$y_c = x^2 + 4x$$

Determine the maximum profit obtainable by the monopolist.

Revenue: $R = 28x - 5x^2$

Total cost: $y_c = x^2 + 4x$

Profit:
$$P = 28x - 5x^2 - x^2 - 4x$$
$$= 24x - 6x^2$$

$$\frac{dP}{dx} = 24 - 12x$$

$$\frac{dP}{dx} = 0 \quad \text{if } 2 - x = 0$$

$$x = 2$$

$$\frac{d^2P}{dx^2} = -12 < 0, \text{ so maximum at } x = 2$$

$$P_{\max} = 24$$

Alternatively,

$$\frac{dR}{dx} = 28 - 10x$$

$$\frac{dy_c}{dx} = 2x + 4$$

$$\frac{dR}{dx} = \frac{dy_c}{dx} \quad \text{if } 28 - 10x = 2x + 4$$

$$x = 2$$

$$\left.\begin{aligned} \frac{d^2R}{dx^2} &= -10 \\[2mm] \frac{d^2y_c}{dx^2} &= 2 \end{aligned}\right\} \frac{d^2R}{dx^2} < \frac{d^2y_c}{dx^2}, \text{ so maximum at } x = 2$$

$$P_{max} = 24$$

or alternatively,

$$x = \tfrac{1}{5}(28 - y)$$

$$R = \tfrac{1}{5}y(28 - y)$$

$$y_c = \tfrac{1}{25}(28 - y)^2 + \tfrac{4}{5}(28 - y)$$

$$\quad = \tfrac{1}{25}(28 - y)(48 - y)$$

$$\frac{dR}{dy} = \tfrac{28}{5} - \tfrac{2}{5}y$$

$$\frac{dy_c}{dy} = \tfrac{2}{25}y - \tfrac{76}{25}$$

$$\frac{dR}{dy} = \frac{dy_c}{dy} \quad \text{if } \tfrac{28}{5} - \tfrac{2}{5}y = \tfrac{2}{25}y - \tfrac{76}{25}$$

$$y = 18$$

$$\left.\begin{aligned} \frac{d^2R}{dy^2} &= -\tfrac{2}{5} \\[2mm] \frac{d^2y_c}{dy^2} &= \tfrac{2}{25} \end{aligned}\right\} \frac{d^2R}{dy^2} < \frac{d^2y_c}{dy^2}, \text{ so maximum at } y = 18$$

$$P_{max} = R - y_c = 36 - 12 = 24$$

The following two geometric representations of profit under monopoly illustrate the economic relationships involved and also provide a method for determining approximate maximum profit in cases for which algebraic solution is difficult or impossible.

1. If the revenue and total cost curves are drawn on the same diagram, then the vertical distance between them at any given value of x measures the profit corresponding to production of x units of the commodity. The maximum vertical distance corresponds to maximum profit and this occurs for the value of x where the slopes of the curves are equal, that is, where $\dfrac{dR}{dx} = \dfrac{dy_c}{dx}$ (see Fig. 2.70).

2. If the marginal revenue and marginal cost curves are drawn on the same diagram, they intersect at a point which gives the value of x corresponding to maximum profit. If the demand curve $y = f(x)$ and the average cost curve $\bar{y}_c = g(x)$

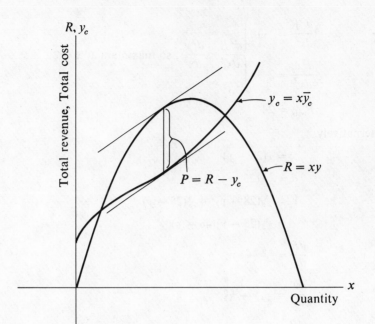

FIGURE 2.70

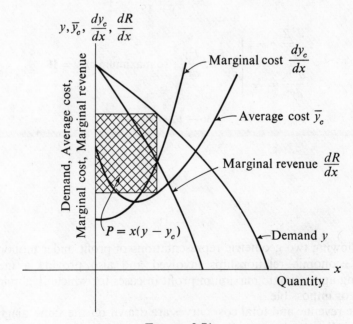

FIGURE 2.71

are drawn on the same diagram, then the vertical distance between them is $y - \bar{y}_c$. For any given value of x, the area of the rectangle of height $y - \bar{y}_c$ and width x represents profit; this area is greatest for the value of x where the marginal revenue and marginal cost curves intersect (see Fig. 2.71).

□ *EFFECT OF TAXATION ON MONOPOLY*

The imposition of a tax t per unit quantity on a commodity produced by a monopolist increases the average cost by t and the total cost by tx. The equilibrium price and quantity for which the monopolist's profit is maximum after taxation are thus obtained by maximizing profit using the cost function after taxation,

$$y_{c_t} = y_c + tx$$

Profit after taxation is

$$P = R - y_{c_t} = R - y_c - tx$$

P has a relative maximum if and only if

$$\frac{dP}{dx} = 0; \quad \text{that is,} \quad \frac{dR}{dx} = \frac{dy_{c_t}}{dx}$$

and

$$\frac{d^2P}{dx^2} < 0; \quad \text{that is,} \quad \frac{d^2R}{dx^2} < \frac{d^2y_{c_t}}{dx}$$

Since the marginal cost curve after taxation is the marginal cost curve before taxation translated upward a distance t, the amount produced for maximum profit will be decreased and the price increased after taxation.

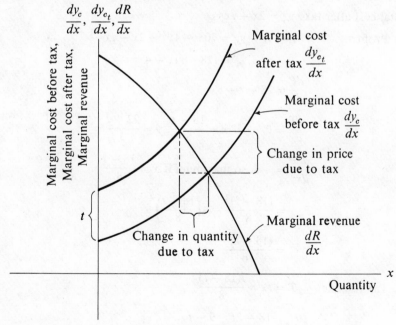

FIGURE 2.72

The total revenue received by the government is

$$T = tx$$

where x is the amount produced after the tax is imposed. T is again a function of t and is zero if t is either zero or large enough to tax the product out of the market. Thus T has a maximum value obtainable in the usual way. As before, a subsidy may be considered a negative tax and the general analysis is unchanged (see Fig. 2.72).

Examples

The demand function for a particular commodity is

$$y = 20 - 4x$$

and the average cost to the monopolist is

$$\bar{y}_c = 2$$

(a) If a tax of t per unit quantity is imposed on the monopolist, determine his maximum possible profit and the value of t for which tax revenue is maximized.
(b) Determine the monopolist's maximum possible profit if a $33\frac{1}{3}\%$ sales tax is imposed.

Demand: $y = 20 - 4x$

Revenue: $R = x(20 - 4x)$

Average cost: $\bar{y}_c = 2$

Total cost: $y_c = 2x$

Total cost after tax: $y_{c_t} = 2x + tx$

(a) Profit:

$$P = R - y_{c_t} = 20x - 4x^2 - 2x - tx$$
$$= (18 - t)x - 4x^2$$

$$\frac{dP}{dx} = 18 - t - 8x$$

$$\frac{dP}{dx} = 0 \quad \text{if } x = \frac{18 - t}{8}, \, y = \frac{22 + t}{2}$$

$$\frac{d^2P}{dx^2} = -8, \text{ so maximum if } x = \frac{18 - t}{8}$$

$$P_{\max} = \frac{(18 - t)^2}{8} - 4\left(\frac{18 - t}{8}\right)^2$$
$$= \frac{(18 - t)^2}{16}$$

Tax revenue:

$$T = tx = \frac{t(18 - t)}{8}$$

$$\frac{dT}{dt} = \frac{18 - 2t}{8} = \frac{9 - t}{4}$$

$$= 0 \quad \text{if } t = 9$$

$$\frac{d^2T}{dt^2} = -\frac{1}{4} < 0, \text{ so maximum if } t = 9$$

If $t = 9$,

$$P_{\text{max}} = \tfrac{81}{16}$$
$$T_{\text{max}} = \tfrac{81}{8}$$

See Fig. 2.73

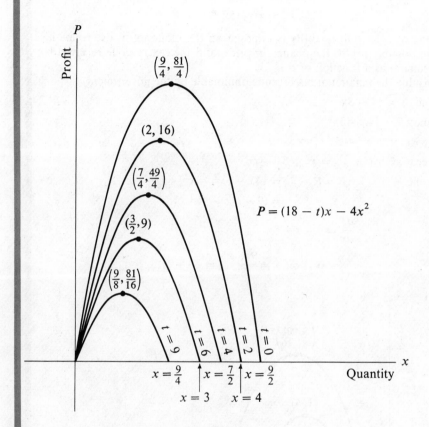

$$P = (18 - t)x - 4x^2$$

FIGURE 2.73

(b) Demand function: $y = 20 - 4x$. So the price paid by the monopolist after allowing for $33\tfrac{1}{3}\%$ sales tax is

$$y_t = \tfrac{3}{4}(20 - 4x)$$

Profit: $P = \tfrac{3}{4}x(20 - 4x) - 2x$

$$= 13x - 3x^2$$

$$\frac{dP}{dx} = 13 - 6x$$

$$= 0 \quad \text{if } x = \tfrac{13}{16}$$

$$\frac{d^2P}{dx^2} = -6, \text{ so maximum if } x = \tfrac{11}{16}$$

$$P_{\text{max}} = \tfrac{121}{12}$$

The demand function for a particular commodity is
$$y = 14 - 3x$$
and the total cost to the monopolist is
$$y_c = x^2 + 5x$$

(a) If a tax of t per unit quantity is imposed on the monopolist, determine his maximum possible profit, the change in price, and the tax revenue received by the government as a function of t.

(b) Determine the maximum tax revenue obtainable by the government.

Demand: $y = 14 - 3x$

Revenue: $R = 14x - 3x^2$

Total cost: $y_c = x^2 + 5x$

Total cost after tax: $y_{c_t} = x^2 + 5x + tx$

(a) Profit: $\quad\quad P = R - y_{c_t} = 14x - 3x^2 - x^2 - 5x - tx$
$$= (9 - t)x - 4x^2$$

$$\frac{dP}{dx} = 9 - t - 8x$$

$$= 0 \quad \text{if } x = \frac{9 - t}{8}, y = \tfrac{85}{8} + \tfrac{3}{8}t$$

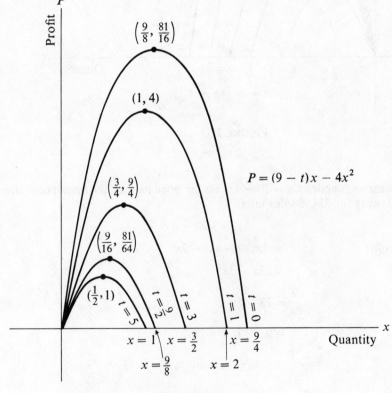

FIGURE 2.74

$$\frac{d^2P}{dx^2} = -8, \text{ so maximum if } x = \frac{9-t}{8}$$

$$P_{max} = \frac{(9-t)^2}{8} - 4\left(\frac{9-t}{8}\right)^2$$

$$= \frac{(9-t)^2}{16}$$

If $x = \frac{9-t}{8}$, $y = \frac{8.5}{8} + \frac{3}{8}t$, which is a change in price of $\frac{3}{8}t$, since if $t = 0$ the monopolist's profit is maximized if $x = \frac{9}{8}$, $y = \frac{8.5}{8}$ (see Fig. 2.74).

Tax revenue: $T = tx = \frac{t(9-t)}{8}$

(b)

$$\frac{dT}{dt} = \frac{9}{8} - \frac{t}{4}$$

$$= 0 \quad \text{if } t = \frac{9}{2}$$

$$\frac{d^2T}{dt^2} = -\frac{1}{4}, \text{ so maximum if } t = \frac{9}{2}$$

$$T_{max} = \frac{\frac{9}{2}(9 - \frac{9}{2})}{8} = \frac{81}{32}$$

PROBLEMS

1. Plot the demand curve $y = 120 - x$ and the supply curve $y = x - 10$, where x is quantity demanded and y is price per unit, and indicate the equilibrium price and quantity. (a) Assume that a tax of \$15 per unit is imposed on the seller; draw the new supply curve and indicate the new equilibrium. (b) Assume that instead of a tax a subsidy of \$10 is paid to the producers; draw the appropriate supply curve and indicate the corresponding equilibrium.

2. For each of the following pairs of demand and supply functions find the maximum revenue that can be obtained by imposing a tax of t per unit and illustrate graphically (by sketching the demand curve, the supply curves before and after taxation, and the revenue curve).
   (a) Demand: $y = 14 - 3x$ (b) Demand: $y = 25 - 2x^2$
        Supply: $y = 4 + 2x$ Supply: $y = 5 + x$
   (c) Demand: $y = 50 - 4x^2$ (d) Demand: $y = 28 - x^2$
        Supply: $y = 5 + x^2$ Supply: $y = 4 + x^2$
   (e) Demand: $y = 45 - x^2$ (f) Demand: $y = 30 - 2x^2$
        Supply: $y = 6 + 2x$ Supply: $y = 3 + x^2$

3. For each of the following pairs of demand and (average or total) cost functions find the maximum profit obtainable by a monopolist.
   (a) $y = 24 - 7x$ (b) $y = 26 - 3x^2$
       $\bar{y}_c = 6 - x$ $y_c = 3x^2 + 2x + 14$
   (c) $y = 12 - 4x$ (d) $y = 12 - 5x$
       $y_c = 8x - x^2$ $\bar{y}_c = 4x + 6$
   (e) $y = 26 - 2x - 4x^2$
       $\bar{y}_c = x + 8$

4. For each of the following pairs of demand and cost functions find (i) change in price, maximum profit, and maximum revenue from taxation as functions of t if an additive tax of t per unit is imposed on a monopolist and determine the maximum revenue that can be obtained by such taxation, and (ii) find the maximum revenue that can be obtained by the specified sales tax.

(a) $y = 50 - 6x$
$y_c = x^2 + 9x$
Sales tax 20%

(b) $y = 25 - 2x^2$
$y_c = 3x$
Sales tax 25%

(c) $y = 12 - 4x$
$\bar{y}_c = 2x$
Sales tax $33\frac{1}{3}$%

(d) $y = 33 - 5x^2$
$\bar{y}_c = 3x^2$
Sales tax 10%

(e) $y = 20 - 4x$
$\bar{y}_c = 2$
Sales tax $33\frac{1}{3}$%

(f) $y = 72 - 7x^2$
$\bar{y}_c = x^2$
Sales tax 40%

ANSWERS TO ODD-NUMBERED PROBLEMS

---

3. (a) $P_{max} = \frac{27}{2}$
(b) $P_{max} = \frac{50}{9}$
(c) $P_{max} = \frac{4}{3}$
(d) $P_{max} = 1$
(e) $P_{max} = 11$

□ INVENTORY MODELS

The objective of inventory control is to minimize total inventory cost. Inventory costs are of three types: (1) cost of placing an order or starting a production run (setup cost); (2) cost of holding inventory, including cost of capital or interest and storage cost (carrying cost); and (3) cost of going short, including loss of goodwill (shortage cost). Inventory control attempts to balance the economies of large orders or large production runs against the cost of holding inventory and, in some models, against the cost of going short.

In practice, various situations occur with regard to the nature of demand, the procedures involved in ordering or production, the ease of storage, the seriousness of shortages, and so forth. All the inventory models discussed in this book (including two in this section and one in Chapter 3) assume that demand is known and uniform. Although this assumption may be appropriate, at least as an approximation, in many situations involving demand for an input of production, it is entirely unrealistic in many situations involving retail demand. For these situations a model assuming probabilistic demand is more appropriate.

The models in this book also assume that the setup cost, the per unit carrying cost, and the per unit shortage cost do not depend on the number of items involved.

Neither of the two models discussed in this section permits shortages; each of them can be derived as a special case of a model that does permit shortages by letting the shortage cost become very large. The first model assumes that items enter inventory in batches; the second model assumes that items enter inventory continuously during the period of ordering or production.

Model A: uniform demand, no shortages, batch arrival

D = demand per period
c_1 = setup cost
c_2 = carrying cost per item per period
q = number of items that should be placed in inventory at one time in order to minimize the total cost of inventory

(See Fig. 2.75.)

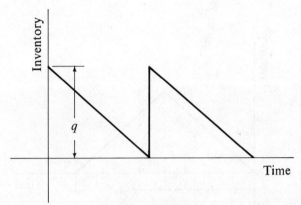

FIGURE 2.75

There are $\dfrac{D}{q}$ batches per period for which the total setup cost is $\dfrac{c_1 D}{q}$. The average inventory is $\dfrac{q}{2}$ and the carrying cost per period is $\dfrac{c_2 q}{2}$. The total cost of inventory per period is thus

$$K = \frac{c_2 q}{2} + \frac{c_1 D}{q}$$

$$\frac{dK}{dq} = \frac{c_2}{2} - \frac{c_1 D}{q^2}$$

If $\dfrac{dK}{dq} = 0$, $q = \sqrt{\dfrac{2c_1 D}{c_2}}$.

$$\frac{d^2 K}{dq} = \frac{2c_1 D}{q^3}$$

> 0, so K is minimum if $q = \sqrt{\dfrac{2c_1 D}{c_2}}$

Thus $\sqrt{\dfrac{2c_1 D}{c_2}}$ items should be placed in inventory every $\dfrac{q}{D}$ periods.

Model B: uniform demand, no shortages, continuous arrival

D = demand per period
k = number of items that arrive per period (at a uniform rate) during buildup of inventory

c_1 = setup cost

c_2 = carrying cost per item per period

q = number of items that should be placed in inventory during buildup of inventory in order to minimize the total cost of inventory

t_1 = time during which items are placed in inventory

t_2 = time during which items are not placed in inventory

$t = t_1 + t_2$ = time required by one inventory cycle

(See Fig. 2.76).

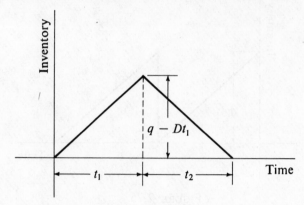

FIGURE 2.76

Note that $t_1 = \dfrac{q}{k}$ and $t = \dfrac{D}{q}$. The carrying cost per period is

$$\frac{c_2(q - Dt_1)}{2} = \frac{c_2 q\left(1 - \dfrac{D}{k}\right)}{2}$$

and the setup cost is c_1. So the total inventory cost per period is

$$K = \tfrac{1}{2} c_2 q\left(1 - \frac{D}{k}\right) + \frac{c_1 D}{q}$$

$$\frac{dK}{dq} = \tfrac{1}{2} c_2 \left(1 - \frac{D}{k}\right) - \frac{c_1 D}{q^2}$$

$$= 0 \quad \text{if } q = \sqrt{\frac{2c_1 D}{c_2\left(1 - \dfrac{D}{k}\right)}}$$

$$\frac{d^2 K}{dq^2} = \frac{2c_1 D}{q^3} > 0, \text{ so } K \text{ is minimum if } q = \sqrt{\frac{2c_1 D}{c_2\left(1 - \dfrac{D}{k}\right)}}$$

Thus $\sqrt{\dfrac{2c_1 D}{c_2\left(1 - \dfrac{D}{k}\right)}}$ items should be produced every $\dfrac{q}{D}$ periods.

Example

Alicor needs 2500 widgets per quarter. It costs $3.00 a month to store a widget. The cost of ordering a supply of widgets (any number of widgets not exceeding 2500) is $0.50. Alicor has two alternatives: (1) purchase the widgets periodically in lots and allow no shortages to occur and (2) purchase the widgets periodically from a supplier who sends them at the rate of 1500 per month until an order is filled and allow no shortages to occur. Determine the quarterly cost of the optimal policy for each of these alternatives. In order to minimize total quarterly cost of inventory, what policy should Alicor adopt?

Considering demand and costs on a quarterly basis,

$$D = 2500$$
$$c_1 = 0.50$$
$$c_2 = 9.00$$
$$k = 4500$$

The optimal order quantity for alternative 1 is given by

$$q = \sqrt{\frac{2c_1 D}{c_2}} = \sqrt{\frac{(2)(0.50)(2500)}{9}} = \frac{50}{3}$$

and the associated quarterly cost is

$$K = \frac{c_2 q}{2} + \frac{c_1 D}{q} = \frac{9(\frac{50}{3})}{2} + \frac{(\frac{1}{2})(2500)}{\frac{50}{3}} = 150$$

The optimal order quantity for alternative 2 is given by

$$q = \sqrt{\frac{2c_1 D}{c_2 \left(1 - \frac{D}{k}\right)}} = \sqrt{\frac{(2)(0.50)(2500)}{9(1 - \frac{2500}{4500})}} = 25$$

and the associated quarterly cost is

$$K = \tfrac{1}{2}c_2 q \left(1 - \frac{D}{k}\right) + \frac{c_1 D}{q} = \tfrac{1}{2}(9)(25)(1 - \tfrac{5}{9}) + \frac{\frac{1}{2}(2500)}{25} = 100$$

Alternative 2 is preferable. As can be observed by comparing the cost formulas, this is always the case if the costs of ordering and carrying are the same for the two models.

For this problem demand, supply, and costs could be considered on a monthly basis. Since demand and supply are assumed to be uniform, any convenient common time base can be used for computation.

PROBLEMS

1. The Ace Manufacturing Company has a contract to supply 4000 refrigerators a year at a uniform monthly rate. The annual storage cost per refrigerator is $50 and the setup cost for a production run is $160. If production is instantaneous and shortages are not permitted, determine the number of refrigerators which should be produced in each run to minimize the total annual cost of inventory.

2. The Harvest Company has a contract to supply 500 tractors a month at a uniform daily rate. The monthly storage cost per tractor is $10 and the setup cost for a production run is $200. Production is at a constant rate of 1000 tractors per month. If shortages are not permitted, determine the number of tractors which should be produced in each run to minimize the total monthly inventory cost.

3. Profitco Electronics requires 25 transistors per month to make color TV sets. The monthly storage cost is $2.00 per transistor and every time an order is placed it costs Profitco $4.00. (a) If orders are filled immediately and no shortages are permitted, how many orders of what size should be placed every month? What is the monthly total cost of this inventory policy? (b) Suppose Profitco can order so that delivery is at the rate of 45 per month (in a uniform flow, not a block) and that no shortages are permitted. How much inventory should be accumulated before stopping the flow and how many times per month will the flow be stopped? What is the total monthly cost of this inventory policy?

4. Fabric Corporation owns a machine which can produce 25 bolts of a particular type of cloth per day and another machine which can make 10 bolts of this cloth into slipcovers per day. It costs $1.50 to hold a bolt of cloth in inventory for a day and it costs $2.00 every time the machine producing the cloth must be stopped. (a) What amount of inventory should be built up before the machine producing the cloth is stopped in order to minimize total inventory cost? (b) How many times will the machine be shut down in a period of 90 days? (c) What is the total amount of cloth that will be produced in a period of 90 days? (d) If the demand and cost conditions remain the same, except that the cost of stopping the machine is interpreted as the cost of ordering, and the cloth must be ordered in batches from another company, how many orders of what size will be placed in 90 days (assume no shortages)?

5. The yearly demand for a large cable bolt produced by Lanier Corporation is 9000. It costs Lanier $1000 to put the production line for this cable into production. The monthly cost of carrying this item in inventory is $6000. Assuming that Lanier does not permit shortages to occur, how many cable bolts should be produced per production run and how frequently should production be stopped?

6. Bookworms Cooperative stocks a very popular gourmet cookbook for which there is a demand of 1500 copies per month. The publisher pays postage, but the cooperative pays $2.50 for each order in secretarial and administrative costs. Carrying cost is $0.50 per copy per month. In order to minimize total inventory costs, how many books should be ordered at one time? How frequently should orders be placed?

ANSWERS TO ODD-NUMBERED PROBLEMS

1. 160

3. (a) 10 transistors $2\frac{1}{2}$ times per month
   cost $20
   (b) accumulate 20/3 transistors and stop 5/3 times per month
   cost $40/3

5. 500 cable bolts and stop 18 times per year

■ 2.12 INDETERMINATE FORMS

In previous sections concerning limits, the evaluation of

$$\lim_{x \to a} f(x) \quad \text{when } f(a) = \frac{0}{0} \quad \text{or} \quad \frac{\infty}{\infty}$$

is discussed for certain particular types of functions $f(x)$. In this section more general procedures for evaluating these and other indeterminate forms are discussed. These procedures are based on *L'Hospital's rule*:

$$If \begin{cases} f(a) = g(a) = 0 \\ \qquad \text{or} \\ f(a) = g(a) = \infty \qquad then \lim_{x \to a} \frac{f(x)}{g(x)} = \lim_{x \to a} \frac{f'(x)}{g'(x)} \\ \qquad \text{and} \\ \lim_{x \to a} \frac{f'(x)}{g'(x)} \text{ exists} \end{cases}$$

(this rule holds for finite or infinite a). If $\lim_{x \to a} \dfrac{f'(x)}{g'(x)}$ is itself an indeterminate form $\dfrac{0}{0}$ or $\dfrac{\infty}{\infty}$, then L'Hospital's rule is applied again and $\lim_{x \to a} \dfrac{f'(x)}{g'(x)} = \lim_{x \to a} \dfrac{f''(x)}{g''(x)}$, and so forth.

CAUTIONS

1. $\lim_{x \to a} \dfrac{f'(x)}{g'(x)} \neq \lim_{x \to a} \dfrac{d}{dx}\left(\dfrac{f(x)}{g(x)}\right)$—that is, the quotient of the derivatives is *not* in general equal to the derivative of the quotient.

2. $\lim_{x \to a} \dfrac{f'(x)}{g'(x)} = \lim_{x \to a} \dfrac{f''(x)}{g''(x)}$ if and *only* if $\lim_{x \to a} \dfrac{f'(x)}{g'(x)}$ is the indeterminate form $\dfrac{0}{0}$ or $\dfrac{\infty}{\infty}$—that is, L'Hospital's rule applies only to indeterminate forms; thus when the rule is applied successively the first determinate answer is correct and in general further applications give incorrect answers.

L'Hospital's rule is applicable to other types of indeterminate forms, if they are first put into the form $\dfrac{0}{0}$ or $\dfrac{\infty}{\infty}$, as follows.

Type $\infty \cdot 0$:

If $\lim_{x \to a} f(x)g(x) = \infty \cdot 0$, where $\lim_{x \to a} f(x) = \infty$, $\lim_{x \to a} g(x) = 0$, then $\lim_{x \to a} \dfrac{f(x)}{\dfrac{1}{g(x)}}$ is of type $\dfrac{\infty}{\infty}$.

Type 1^∞:

If $\lim\limits_{x \to a} f(x)^{g(x)} = 1^\infty$, where $\lim\limits_{x \to a} f(x) = 1$, $\lim\limits_{x \to a} g(x) = \infty$, then $\lim\limits_{x \to a} \log f(x)^{g(x)}$
$= \lim\limits_{x \to a} g(x)\log f(x) = \infty \cdot 0$ and

$$\lim_{x \to a} \left(\frac{\log f(x)}{\dfrac{1}{g(x)}} \right) \text{ is of type } \frac{0}{0}$$

or

$$\lim_{x \to a} \left(\frac{g(x)}{\dfrac{1}{\log f(x)}} \right) \text{ is of type } \frac{\infty}{\infty}$$

Type 0^0:

If $\lim\limits_{x \to a} f(x)^{g(x)} = 0^0$, where $\lim\limits_{x \to a} f(x) = 0$, $\lim\limits_{x \to a} g(x) = 0$, then

$$\lim_{x \to a} \left(\frac{g(x)}{\dfrac{1}{\log f(x)}} \right) \text{ is of type } \frac{0}{0}$$

Type ∞^0:

If $\lim\limits_{x \to a} f(x)^{g(x)} = \infty^0$, where $\lim\limits_{x \to a} f(x) = \infty$, $\lim\limits_{x \to a} g(x) = 0$, then

$$\lim_{x \to a} \left(\frac{g(x)}{\dfrac{1}{\log f(x)}} \right) \text{ is of type } \frac{0}{0}$$

Type $\infty - \infty$:

If $\lim\limits_{x \to a} [f(x) - g(x)] = \infty - \infty$, where $\lim\limits_{x \to a} f(x) = \infty$, $\lim\limits_{x \to a} g(x) = \infty$, then

$$\lim_{x \to a} \left(\frac{1}{\dfrac{1}{f(x)}} - \frac{1}{\dfrac{1}{g(x)}} \right) = \lim_{x \to a} \left(\frac{\dfrac{1}{g(x)} - \dfrac{1}{f(x)}}{\dfrac{1}{g(x)} \cdot \dfrac{1}{f(x)}} \right) \text{ is of type } \frac{0}{0}$$

Table 2.1

SUMMARY OF APPLICATION OF L'HOSPITAL'S RULE

Type of indeterminate form	Apply L'Hospital's rule to
1. $\lim \dfrac{f(x)}{g(x)} = \dfrac{0}{0}$	$\lim \dfrac{f(x)}{g(x)}$
2. $\lim \dfrac{f(x)}{g(x)} = \dfrac{\infty}{\infty}$	
3. $\lim f(x)g(x) = \infty \cdot 0$	$\lim \left(\dfrac{f(x)}{\dfrac{1}{g(x)}} \right)$ or to $\lim \left(\dfrac{g(x)}{\dfrac{1}{f(x)}} \right)$
4. $\lim f(x)^{g(x)} = 1^{\infty}$	$\lim \left(\dfrac{\ln f(x)}{\dfrac{1}{g(x)}} \right)$ or to $\lim \left(\dfrac{g(x)}{\dfrac{1}{\ln f(x)}} \right)$
5. $\lim f(x)^{g(x)} = 0^{0}$	If L'Hospital's rule applied to one of these gives a constant b for the limit, then the original limit is e^{b}
6. $\lim f(x)^{g(x)} = \infty^{0}$	
7. $\lim [f(x) - g(x)] = \infty - \infty$	$\lim \left(\dfrac{\dfrac{1}{g(x)} - \dfrac{1}{f(x)}}{\dfrac{1}{g(x)} \cdot \dfrac{1}{f(x)}} \right)$

Examples

Evaluate $\lim\limits_{h \to 0} \dfrac{\sqrt{4 + h} - 2}{h}$

type $\dfrac{0}{0}$, so $\lim\limits_{h \to 0} \dfrac{\sqrt{4 + h} - 2}{h} = \lim\limits_{h \to 0} \dfrac{\frac{1}{2}(4 + h)^{-1/2}}{1} = \frac{1}{4}$

Evaluate $\lim\limits_{x \to 0} \dfrac{e^{x} - (1 + x)}{x^{2}}$

type $\dfrac{0}{0}$, so $\displaystyle\lim_{x\to 0}\dfrac{e^x-(1+x)}{x^2}=\lim_{x\to 0}\dfrac{e^x-1}{2x}$

$$=\lim_{x\to 0}\dfrac{e^x}{2}=\tfrac{1}{2}$$

Evaluate $\displaystyle\lim_{x\to\infty}\dfrac{\ln x}{x}$

type $\dfrac{\infty}{\infty}$, so $\displaystyle\lim_{x\to\infty}\dfrac{\ln x}{x}=\lim_{x\to\infty}\dfrac{\dfrac{1}{x}}{1}=0$

Evaluate $\displaystyle\lim_{x\to\infty}\dfrac{x^n}{e^x}$

type $\dfrac{\infty}{\infty}$, so $\displaystyle\lim_{x\to\infty}\dfrac{x^n}{e^x}=\lim_{x\to\infty}\dfrac{nx^{n-1}}{e^x}$

$$=\lim_{x\to\infty}\dfrac{n(n-1)x^{n-2}}{e^x}$$

$$=\cdots=\lim_{x\to\infty}\dfrac{n!}{e^x}=0$$

Evaluate $\displaystyle\lim_{x\to 0}x\ln x$

type $0\cdot\infty$, so $\displaystyle\lim_{x\to 0}x\ln x=\lim_{x\to 0}\dfrac{\ln x}{\dfrac{1}{x}}$

$$=\lim_{x\to 0}\dfrac{\dfrac{1}{x}}{-\dfrac{1}{x^2}}=0$$

Evaluate $\displaystyle\lim_{x\to\infty}x(e^{1/x}-1)$

type $\infty\cdot 0$, so $\displaystyle\lim_{x\to\infty}x(e^{1/x}-1)=\lim_{x\to\infty}\dfrac{e^{1/x}-1}{\dfrac{1}{x}}$

$$=\lim_{x\to\infty}\dfrac{-\dfrac{1}{x^2}\cdot e^{1/x}}{-\dfrac{1}{x^2}}=1$$

Evaluate $\lim\limits_{x\to 0}(1-2x)^{3/x}$

type 1^{∞}, so $\lim\limits_{x\to 0}(1-2x)^{3/x} = \exp\lim\limits_{x\to 0}\dfrac{\ln(1-2x)}{\dfrac{x}{3}}$

$$\lim_{x\to 0}\frac{\ln(1-2x)}{\dfrac{x}{3}} = \lim_{x\to 0}\frac{\dfrac{-2}{1-2x}}{\frac{1}{3}} = -6$$

$$\lim_{x\to 0}(1-2x)^{3/x} = e^{-6}$$

NOTE: Notation $\exp f(x)$ means $e^{f(x)}$.

Evaluate $\lim\limits_{x\to\infty}\left(1+\dfrac{2}{x}\right)^{x}$

type 1^{∞}, so $\lim\limits_{x\to\infty}\left(1+\dfrac{2}{x}\right)^{x} = \exp\lim\limits_{x\to\infty}\dfrac{\ln\left(1+\dfrac{2}{x}\right)}{\dfrac{1}{x}}$

$$\lim_{x\to\infty}\frac{\ln\left(1+\dfrac{2}{x}\right)}{\dfrac{1}{x}} = \lim_{x\to\infty}\frac{\dfrac{-2/x^{2}}{(1+2/x)}}{-\dfrac{1}{x^{2}}} = 2$$

$$\lim_{x\to\infty}\left(1+\frac{2}{x}\right)^{x} = e^{2}$$

Evaluate $\lim\limits_{x\to 0^{+}} x^{x}$

type 0^{0}, so $\lim\limits_{x\to 0^{+}} x^{x} = \exp\lim\limits_{x\to 0^{+}}\dfrac{\ln x}{\dfrac{1}{x}}$

$$\lim_{x\to 0^{+}}\frac{\ln x}{\dfrac{1}{x}} = \lim_{x\to 0^{+}}\frac{\dfrac{1}{x}}{-\dfrac{1}{x^{2}}} = 0$$

$$\lim_{x\to 0^{+}} x^{x} = e^{0} = 1$$

Evaluate $\lim\limits_{x \to 1^-} (\sqrt{2 - x^2} - 1)^{x-1}$

type 0^0, so $\lim\limits_{x \to 1^-} (\sqrt{2 - x^2} - 1)^{x-1} = \exp \lim\limits_{x \to 1^-} \dfrac{\ln(\sqrt{2 - x^2} - 1)}{\dfrac{1}{x - 1}}$

$$\lim_{x \to 1^-} \frac{\ln(\sqrt{2 - x^2} - 1)}{\dfrac{1}{x - 1}} = \lim_{x \to 1^-} \frac{\dfrac{\frac{1}{2}(2 - x^2)^{-1/2}(-2x)}{\sqrt{2 - x^2} - 1}}{\dfrac{-1}{(x - 1)^2}}$$

$$= \lim_{x \to 1^-} \frac{x(x - 1)^2}{(2 - x^2) - (2 - x^2)^{1/2}}$$

$$= \lim_{x \to 1^-} \frac{(x - 1)^2 + 2x(x - 1)}{-2x - 1/2(2 - x^2)^{-1/2}(-2x)}$$

$$= \lim_{x \to 1^-} \frac{3x^2 - 4x + 1}{-2x + x(2 - x^2)^{-1/2}} = \frac{0}{1} = 0$$

$$\lim_{x \to 1^-} (\sqrt{2 - x^2} - 1)^{x-1} = e^0 = 1$$

Evaluate $\lim\limits_{x \to \infty} (x + e^x)^{2/x}$

type ∞^0, so $\lim\limits_{x \to \infty} (x + e^x)^{2/x} = \exp \lim\limits_{x \to \infty} \dfrac{\ln(x + e^x)}{\dfrac{x}{2}}$

$$\lim_{x \to \infty} \frac{\ln(x + e^x)}{\dfrac{x}{2}} = \lim_{x \to \infty} \frac{\dfrac{1 + e^x}{x + e^x}}{\dfrac{1}{2}}$$

$$= \lim_{x \to \infty} \frac{2(1 + e^x)}{x + e^x}$$

$$= \lim_{x \to \infty} \frac{2e^x}{1 + e^x}$$

$$= \lim_{x \to \infty} \frac{2e^x}{e^x} = 2$$

$$\lim_{x \to \infty} (x + e^x)^{2/x} = e^2$$

Evaluate $\lim\limits_{x \to \infty} x^{1/x}$

type ∞^0, so $\lim\limits_{x \to \infty} x^{1/x} = \exp \lim\limits_{x \to \infty} \dfrac{\ln x}{x}$

$$\lim_{x\to\infty}\frac{\ln x}{x} = \lim_{x\to\infty}\frac{\frac{1}{x}}{1} = 0$$

$$\lim_{x\to\infty} x^{1/x} = e^0 = 1$$

Evaluate $\lim_{x\to 1}\left(\frac{1}{\ln x} - \frac{1}{x-1}\right)$

type $\infty - \infty$, so $\lim_{x\to 1}\left(\frac{1}{\ln x} - \frac{1}{x-1}\right) = \lim_{x\to 1}\frac{x-1-\ln x}{(x-1)\ln x}$

$$= \lim_{x\to 1}\frac{1 - \frac{1}{x}}{\ln x + \frac{(x-1)}{x}}$$

$$= \lim_{x\to 1}\frac{\frac{1}{x^2}}{\frac{1}{x} + \frac{x-(x-1)}{x^2}} = \tfrac{1}{2}$$

Evaluate $\lim_{x\to 0}\left(\frac{1}{x} - \frac{1}{e^x - 1}\right)$

type $\infty - \infty$, so $\lim_{x\to 0}\left(\frac{1}{x} - \frac{1}{e^x - 1}\right) = \lim_{x\to 0}\frac{e^x - 1 - x}{x(e^x - 1)}$

$$= \lim_{x\to 0}\frac{e^x - 1}{e^x + xe^x - 1}$$

$$= \lim_{x\to 0}\frac{e^x}{e^x + e^x + xe^x} = \tfrac{1}{2}$$

PROBLEMS

Evaluate the following limits.

1. $\lim\limits_{x \to 1^-} x^{\frac{1}{1-x^2}}$

2. $\lim\limits_{x \to 0} \dfrac{x}{e^x}$

3. $\lim\limits_{x \to \infty} \dfrac{\ln x}{x^k} \quad (k > 0)$

4. $\lim\limits_{z \to \infty} z^{1/z}$

5. $\lim\limits_{x \to 0} \dfrac{e^x - \ln(x+1) - 1}{x^2}$

6. $\lim\limits_{x \to 0} (1 + x^2)^{1/x^2}$

7. $\lim\limits_{x \to \infty} \dfrac{x^2 + x - 1}{e^x + e^{-x}}$

8. $\lim\limits_{x \to 0} \dfrac{e^x + e^{-x} - 2}{x^2}$

9. $\lim\limits_{x \to \infty} \dfrac{x^k}{e^x} \quad (k > 0)$

10. $\lim\limits_{x \to 1} \dfrac{\ln x}{x^2 - 1}$

11. $\lim\limits_{x \to \infty} x e^{-x}$

12. $\lim\limits_{x \to 1} \dfrac{2x^3 + 5x^2 - 4x - 3}{x^3 + x^2 - 10x + 8}$

13. $\lim\limits_{x \to \infty} (1 + x)^{1/x}$ 0

14. $\lim\limits_{x \to 0} x^n \ln x \quad (n > 0)$

15. $\lim\limits_{x \to 0} (e^x + x)^{1/x}$

16. $\lim\limits_{x \to \infty} (1 + ax)^{b/x}$

17. $\lim\limits_{x \to 1^+} \left(\dfrac{1}{x - 1} - \dfrac{1}{\sqrt{x - 1}} \right)$

18. $\lim\limits_{x \to 1} \left(\dfrac{1}{\ln x} - \dfrac{x}{\ln x} \right)$

19. $\lim\limits_{x \to 1} \left(\dfrac{1}{\ln x} - \dfrac{x}{x - 1} \right)$

20. $\lim\limits_{x \to \infty} (x - 1) e^{-x^2}$

21. $\lim\limits_{x \to -\infty} x^2 e^x$

22. $\lim\limits_{x \to \infty} \dfrac{x^k}{\ln x}$

23. $\lim\limits_{x \to \infty} \dfrac{e^x}{x^k}$

24. $\lim\limits_{x \to \infty} (1 + e^{-x})^{e^x}$

25. $\lim\limits_{x \to 0^+} x e^{1/x}$

26. $\lim\limits_{x \to \infty} (x - \sqrt{x^2 + x})$

27. $\lim\limits_{x \to 0} (e^x + 2x)^{1/x}$

28. $\lim\limits_{x \to 1^-} x^{1/(1 - x^2)}$

29. $\lim\limits_{x \to 0} \dfrac{\sqrt{1 - x} - \sqrt{1 + x}}{x}$

30. $\lim\limits_{x \to 0} \dfrac{1 - \sqrt{x + 1}}{x}$

31. $\lim\limits_{y \to \infty} \dfrac{e^y}{y^2}$

32. $\lim\limits_{x \to \infty} (x - 2) e^{-x^2}$

33. $\lim\limits_{x \to 0} x^2 e^{-3x}$

34. $\lim\limits_{x \to 0} \dfrac{2 - 3e^{-x} - e^{-2x}}{2x^2}$

35. $\lim\limits_{x \to \infty} \dfrac{e^x}{x^3}$

36. $\lim\limits_{x \to 4} (x - 4)^{x^2 - 16}$

37. $\lim\limits_{x \to \infty} \dfrac{\ln x}{x - 1}$

38. $\displaystyle\lim_{x\to 2} \frac{x^4 - 4x^3 + 16}{x^3 - 8}$

39. $\displaystyle\lim_{x\to\infty} (x^2 + a)^{1/x}$

40. $\displaystyle\lim_{x\to\infty} \frac{4x^2 + 3x - 6}{8x + 2}$

41. $\displaystyle\lim_{y\to 0} \frac{4y^3 + 6y}{3y^3 + 2y}$

42. $\displaystyle\lim_{x\to\infty} x^2 e^{-x}$

43. $\displaystyle\lim_{t\to 0} (1 + ct^2)^{c/t}$

44. $\displaystyle\lim_{x\to\infty} \frac{e^x}{x}$

45. $\displaystyle\lim_{x\to 1} x^{1/x^2 - 1}$

46. $\displaystyle\lim_{y\to\infty} (e^y - 1)^{1/y}$

47. $\displaystyle\lim_{x\to 0} \frac{e^x - 1}{x^2 - x}$

48. $\displaystyle\lim_{x\to -3} \frac{x^3 + 27}{x + 3}$

49. $\displaystyle\lim_{x\to\infty} \frac{x^2}{e^x - 1}$

50. $\displaystyle\lim_{x\to\infty} (1 + x^2)^{1/x}$

51. $\displaystyle\lim_{x\to 0} \frac{4 - 3e^x - e^{-3x}}{4x^2}$

52. $\displaystyle\lim_{x\to 2} \frac{x^3 - 4x}{x^2 - 2x}$

53. $\displaystyle\lim_{x\to 0} x^2 \ln x$

54. $\displaystyle\lim_{x\to\infty} \frac{x^3}{e^x + x^2 - 2}$

ANSWERS TO ODD-NUMBERED PROBLEMS

1. $e^{-1/2}$

3. 0

5. 1

7. 0

9. 0

11. 0

13. 1

15. e^2

17. ∞

19. $-\frac{1}{2}$

21. 0

23. ∞

25. 0

27. e^3

29. -1

31. ∞

33. 0

35. ∞

37. 0

39. 1

41. 3

43. 1

45. $e^{1/2}$

47. -1

49. 0

51. $-\frac{3}{2}$

53. 0

■ **2.13 SEQUENCES AND SERIES**

A *sequence* is a succession of terms formed according to some fixed rule; a *series* is the indicated sum of the terms of a sequence. The general term, or *n*th term, indicates the rule of formation of the terms. A finite sequence or a finite series is one having a specified (limited) number of terms; an infinite sequence or an infinite series is one whose number of terms is not specified or limited.

Example

$1, \frac{1}{2}, \frac{1}{3}, \frac{1}{4}, \frac{1}{5}, \ldots$ is an infinite sequence. $1 + \frac{1}{2} + \frac{1}{3} + \frac{1}{4} + \frac{1}{5} + \cdots$ is an infinite series. The general term is $\dfrac{1}{n}$.

Although a finite sequence must have a finite sum, the limit of the sum of an infinite sequence may be finite or infinite.

Let S_n represent the sum of the first n terms of an infinite sequence $u_1, u_2, \ldots, u_n, \ldots,$

$$S_n = u_1 + u_2 + \cdots + u_n = \sum_{i=1}^{n} u_i$$

and let S represent the limit of S_n as $n \to \infty$,

$$S = \lim_{n \to \infty} S_n = \sum_{i=1}^{\infty} u_n$$

If the limit S exists finitely, the infinite series is *convergent* and is said to converge to the value S; if the limit does not exist finitely, the infinite series is *divergent*. Divergence may occur because S_n becomes infinite as $n \to \infty$ or because S_n oscillates without approaching a limit.

Example

For the geometric series of n terms,

$$S_n = a + ar + ar^2 + \cdots + ar^{n-1}$$

it can be shown that

$$S_n = \frac{a(1 - r^n)}{1 - r} = \frac{a(r^n - 1)}{r - 1}$$

The first form is generally used if $|r| < 1$; the second form is generally used if $|r| > 1$.

If $|r| < 1$, then $\lim\limits_{n \to \infty} r^n = 0$ and $\lim\limits_{n \to \infty} S_n = \dfrac{a}{1 - r}$ and the series is convergent.

If $|r| \geq 1$, then $\lim\limits_{n \to \infty} r^n = \infty$ and $\lim\limits_{n \to \infty} S_n = \infty$ and the series is divergent.

NOTE: If $r = -1$, the geometric series is

$$a - a + a - a + a - a + \cdots$$

and if n is odd, $S_n = a$; if n is even, $S_n = 0$. Such a series has no limit and is thus divergent; it is referred to as an *oscillating series*.

Establishing convergence or divergence is clearly more difficult if an expression for S_n is not known. In such cases, the following tests are used.

1. *Necessary condition for convergence.* If an infinite series $\sum\limits_{n=1}^{\infty} u_n$ is convergent, then $\lim\limits_{n \to \infty} u_n = 0$. That is, if the nth term of a series does not approach 0 as n becomes infinite, the series is divergent. Note that $\lim\limits_{n \to \infty} u_n = 0$ is a necessary but *not* a sufficient condition for convergence.

2. *Alternating-series test.* An alternating series is a series whose terms are alternately positive and negative. Such a series is convergent if $\lim\limits_{n \to \infty} u_n = 0$ and each term is less in absolute value than the term which precedes it—that is, if $|u_{n+1}| < |u_n|$ for all $n = 1, 2, \ldots.$

NOTE: It can be shown that the error involved in breaking a convergent alternating series at any term does not exceed in absolute value the first of the terms discarded. That is, if $u_1 - u_2 + u_3 - u_4 + \cdots$ is a convergent alternating series, then for any k,

$$\left| \sum_{n=k+1}^{\infty} u_n \right| \le \left| u_k \right|$$

3. *Absolute convergence.* A series of some positive and some negative terms is said to be *absolutely convergent* if the series formed from it by making all its terms positive is convergent. Other convergent series of some positive and some negative terms are said to be *conditionally convergent*. If a series of some positive and some negative terms is absolutely convergent, it is conditionally convergent, but the converse is not necessarily true.

4. *Cauchy's test-ratio test.* Let

$$u_1 + u_2 + u_3 + \cdots + u_{n+1} + \cdots$$

be an infinite series of positive terms. Using consecutive general terms u_n and u_{n+1}, form the test ratio

$$\frac{u_{n+1}}{u_n}$$

and let

$$\rho = \lim_{n \to \infty} \frac{u_{n+1}}{u_n}$$

Then

If $\rho < 1$, the series is convergent

If $\rho > 1$, the series is divergent

If $\rho = 1$, the test fails

5. *Comparison tests.* In many cases it is possible to determine whether a given series is convergent or divergent by comparing it term by term with a series known to be convergent or divergent. A series of positive terms is convergent if each of its terms is equal to or less than the corresponding term of a known convergent series. A series of positive terms is divergent if each of its terms is equal to or greater than the corresponding term of a known divergent series. The geometric

series discussed above and the "p-series" are frequently useful in applying the comparison test. The "p-series" is given by

$$1 + \frac{1}{2^p} + \frac{1}{3^p} + \cdots + \frac{1}{n^p} + \cdots$$

This series is convergent if $p > 1$ and divergent if $p \leq 1$.

NOTE: Since convergence or divergence of a series cannot be affected by the omission of a finite number of terms, comparison tests may be applied to the terms $u_k, u_{k+1}, u_{k+2}, \ldots$ rather than to the terms $u_1, u_2, u_3, \ldots$.

□ *SUMMARY OF PROCEDURE FOR TESTING CONVERGENCE OR DIVERGENCE OF AN INFINITE SERIES*

In determining convergence or divergence of an infinite series, the tests should generally be applied in the order in which they are given above; thus the procedure is:

1. Determine whether $\lim_{n \to \infty} u_n$ is zero.

    If $\lim_{n \to \infty} u_n \neq 0$, the series is divergent

    If $\lim_{n \to \infty} u_n = 0$, further testing is necessary

Assuming $\lim_{n \to \infty} u_n = 0$,

2. Apply the alternating-series test (if appropriate): An alternating series whose terms decrease in numerical value and for which $\lim_{n \to \infty} u_n = 0$ is convergent.

3. Apply the ratio test: If $\lim_{n \to \infty} \frac{u_{n+1}}{u_n} = \rho$, then

    $|\rho_n| < 1 \Rightarrow$ series convergent (absolutely)

    $|\rho| > 1 \Rightarrow$ series divergent

    $|\rho| = 1 \Rightarrow$ test fails

4. Apply the comparison test: Compare the series with a series known to be convergent or divergent, such as the geometric series or the p-series.

Geometric series: $\quad a + ar + ar^2 + \cdots + ar^{n-1} + \cdots$

Convergent if $|r| < 1$

Divergent if $|r| \geq 1$

p-series: $\quad 1 + \frac{1}{2^p} + \frac{1}{3^p} + \cdots + \frac{1}{n^p} + \cdots$

Convergent if $p > 1$

Divergent if $p \leq 1$

Examples

Determine the convergence or divergence of the infinite series

$$\frac{1}{2} - \frac{3}{2^2} + \frac{5}{2^3} - \frac{7}{2^4} + \cdots$$

General term:

$$u_n = (-1)^{n+1} \frac{2n - 1}{2^n}$$

$$\lim_{n \to \infty} u_n = 0$$

$$\rho = \lim_{n \to \infty} \frac{u_{n+1}}{u_n} = \lim_{n \to \infty} \left(\frac{-\dfrac{2(n+1) - 1}{2^{n+1}}}{\dfrac{2n - 1}{2^n}} \right)$$

$$= \lim_{n \to \infty} \left(-\frac{2n + 1}{2(2n - 1)} \right) = \lim_{n \to \infty} (-\tfrac{2}{4}) = -\tfrac{1}{2}$$

$|\rho| = |-\tfrac{1}{2}| < 1$, so series absolutely convergent

Determine the convergence or divergence of the infinite series

$$\tfrac{2}{3} - \tfrac{3}{5} + \tfrac{4}{7} - \tfrac{5}{9} + \cdots$$

General term:

$$u_n = (-1)^{n+1} \frac{n + 1}{2n + 1}$$

$\lim_{n \to \infty} u_n = \tfrac{1}{2}$, so series divergent

Determine the convergence or divergence of the infinite series

$$1 - \frac{1}{\sqrt{3}} + \frac{1}{\sqrt{5}} - \frac{1}{\sqrt{7}} + \cdots$$

General term:

$$u_n = (-1)^{n+1} \frac{1}{\sqrt{2n - 1}}$$

$$\lim_{n \to \infty} u_n = 0$$

$|u_{n+1}| < |u_n|$ for all n, so alternating series is conditionally convergent

$|\rho| = 1$, so ratio test for absolute convergence fails

$\dfrac{1}{(2n-1)^{1/2}} > \dfrac{1}{n}$ (p-series, $p = 1$), so divergent as a positive series

Thus the series is conditionally convergent.

Determine the convergence or divergence of the infinite series

$$\frac{1}{9} + \frac{2!}{9^2} + \frac{3!}{9^3} + \frac{4!}{9^4} + \cdots$$

General term:

$$u_n = \frac{n!}{9^n}$$

$\lim\limits_{n \to \infty} u_n = \infty$, so series divergent

---

Determine the convergence or divergence of the infinite series

$$\tfrac{3}{4} + 2(\tfrac{3}{4})^2 + 3(\tfrac{3}{4})^3 + 4(\tfrac{3}{4})^4 + \cdots$$

General term:

$$u_n = n(\tfrac{3}{4})^n$$

$$\lim\limits_{n \to \infty} u_n = 0$$

$$\rho = \lim\limits_{n \to \infty} \frac{u_{n+1}}{u_n} = \lim\limits_{n \to \infty}\left(\frac{(n+1)(\tfrac{3}{4})^{n+1}}{n(\tfrac{3}{4})^n}\right)$$

$$= \lim\limits_{n \to \infty} \tfrac{3}{4}\left(\frac{n+1}{n}\right) = \tfrac{3}{4}$$

$|\rho| = |\tfrac{3}{4}| < 1$, so series convergent

Determine the convergence or divergence of the infinite series

$$5 + \frac{5^2}{2!} + \frac{5^3}{3!} + \frac{5^4}{4!} + \cdots$$

General term:

$$u_n = \frac{5^n}{n!}$$

$$\lim\limits_{n \to \infty} u_n = 0$$

$$\rho = \lim_{n \to \infty} \left(\frac{\dfrac{5^{n+1}}{(n+1)!}}{\dfrac{5^n}{n!}} \right) = \lim_{n \to \infty} \frac{5}{n+1} = 0$$

$|\rho| = 0 < 1$, so series convergent

☐ *POWER SERIES*

An infinite series of the form

$$a_0 + a_1 x + a_2 x^2 + \cdots + a_n x^n + \cdots = \sum_{n=0}^{\infty} a_n x^n$$

where the coefficients a_0, a_1, a_2, . . . are independent of x, is called a *power series in x*. More generally, an infinite series of the form

$$b_0 + b_1(x - a) + b_2(x - a)^2 + \cdots + b_n(x - a)^n + \cdots = \sum_{n=0}^{\infty} b_n(x - a)^n$$

where the coefficients b_0, b_1, b_2, . . . are independent of x, is called a *power series in x − a*.

A power series in x (or in $x - a$) may converge for all values of x, or for no values of x other than $x = 0$ (or $x = a$); or it may converge for some values of x and diverge for others. The interval of convergence is determined by the following procedure, derived from the Cauchy test-ratio test.

Power series in x:

If $\lim\limits_{n \to \infty} \dfrac{a_{n+1}}{a_n} = L,$ *then*

$\begin{cases} L = 0 \Rightarrow \text{series converges for all } x \\ L \neq 0 \Rightarrow \text{series converges for the interval} \\ \quad -\dfrac{1}{|L|} < x < \dfrac{1}{|L|} \text{ and diverges outside} \\ \quad \text{this interval; the end points of the} \\ \quad \text{interval of convergence must be} \\ \quad \text{examined separately} \end{cases}$

Power series in x-a:

If $\lim\limits_{n \to \infty} \dfrac{b_{n+1}}{b_n} = M,$ *then*

$\begin{cases} M = 0 \Rightarrow \text{series converges for all } x \\ M \neq 0 \Rightarrow \text{series converges for the interval} \\ \quad a - \dfrac{1}{|M|} < x < a + \dfrac{1}{|M|} \text{ and di-} \\ \quad \text{verges outside this interval; the} \\ \quad \text{end points of the interval of} \\ \quad \text{convergence must be examined} \\ \quad \text{separately} \end{cases}$

Examples

Find the interval of convergence for the power series

$$1 + 2x + 3x^2 + 4x^3 + \cdots$$

General term:

$$u_n = nx^{n-1}$$

$$L = \lim_{n \to \infty} \frac{n+1}{n} = 1,$$

so the interval of convergence is $-1 < x < 1$ and the end points must be tested.

If $x = -1$, series is $1 - 2 + 3 - 4 + \cdots$

$$u_n = (-1)^{n-1}n$$

$$\lim_{n \to \infty} u_n \neq 0, \text{ so series divergent}$$

If $x = 1$, series is $1 + 2 + 3 + 4 + \cdots$

$$u_n = n$$

$$\lim_{n \to \infty} u_n \neq 0, \text{ so series divergent}$$

Thus the original series converges for $-1 < x < 1$.

Find the interval of convergence for the power series

$$1 - \frac{x}{2} + \frac{x^2}{3 \cdot 2^2} - \frac{x^3}{5 \cdot 2^3} + \frac{x^4}{7 \cdot 2^4} - \cdots$$

General term:

$$u_n = \frac{(-1)^{n+1}x^{n-1}}{(2n-3)2^{n-1}}$$

$$L = \lim_{n \to \infty}\left(-\frac{(2n-3)2^{n-1}}{[2(n+1)-3]2^n}\right) = \lim_{n \to \infty}\left(-\frac{2n-3}{4n-2}\right) = -\tfrac{1}{2}$$

so the interval of convergence is $-2 < x < 2$ and the end points must be tested.

If $x = -2$, series is $1 + \dfrac{2}{2} + \dfrac{2^2}{3 \cdot 2^2} + \dfrac{2^3}{5 \cdot 2^3} + \dfrac{2^4}{7 \cdot 2^4} + \cdots$ or $1 + 1 + \tfrac{1}{3} + \tfrac{1}{5}$

$$+ \tfrac{1}{7} + \cdots.$$

$$u_n = \frac{1}{2n-1} \text{ (omitting first term)}$$

$$\lim_{n \to \infty} u_n = 0$$

$$\lim_{n \to \infty} \frac{u_{n+1}}{u_n} = 1, \text{ so test-ratio test fails}$$

$$u_n = \frac{1}{2n-1} > \frac{1}{2n} \ (p\text{-series}, \ p = 1), \text{ so series divergent}$$

NOTE: Multiplying a series by a constant does *not* affect convergence.

If $x = 2$, series is $1 - \dfrac{2}{2} + \dfrac{2^2}{3 \cdot 2^2} - \dfrac{2^3}{5 \cdot 2^3} + \dfrac{2^4}{7 \cdot 2^4} - \cdots$ or $1 - 1 + \frac{1}{3} - \frac{1}{5} + \frac{1}{7}$

$$- \cdots.$$

$$u_n = (-1)^n \frac{1}{2n-1} \text{ (omitting first term)}$$

$$\lim_{n \to \infty} u_n = 0$$

$$|u_{n+1}| < |u_n|, \text{ so alternating series convergent}$$

Thus the original series converges for $-2 < x \leq 2$.

Find the interval of convergence for the power series

$$1 + x + 2!x^2 + 3!x^3 + \cdots$$

General term:

$$u_n = (n-1)!x^{n-1}$$

$$L = \lim_{n \to \infty} \frac{n!}{(n-1)!} = \lim_{n \to \infty} n = \infty$$

Thus the series converges only for $x = 0$.

Find the interval of convergence for the power series

$$(x-1) - \tfrac{1}{2}(x-1)^2 + \tfrac{1}{3}(x-1)^3 - \tfrac{1}{4}(x-1)^4 + \cdots$$

General term:

$$u_n = (-1)^{n+1} \frac{(x-1)^n}{n}$$

$M = \lim\limits_{n \to \infty} \left(-\dfrac{n}{n+1} \right) = -1$, so the interval of convergence is $0 < x < 2$ and the end points must be tested.

If $x = 0$, series is $-1 - \frac{1}{2} - \frac{1}{3} - \frac{1}{4} - \cdots$.

$$u_n = -\frac{1}{n}$$

$$\lim_{n \to \infty} u_n = 0$$

$$\lim_{n \to \infty} \frac{u_{n+1}}{u_n} = 1, \text{ so test-ratio test fails}$$

$$u_n = \frac{1}{n} \ (p\text{-series}, \ p = 1), \text{ so series divergent}$$

If $x = 2$, series is $1 - \frac{1}{2} + \frac{1}{3} - \frac{1}{4} + \cdots$.

$$u_n = (-1)^{n+1} \frac{1}{n}$$

$$\lim_{n \to \infty} u_n = 0$$

$|u_{n+1}| < |u_n|$, so alternating series convergent

Thus the original series converges for $0 < x \le 2$.

Find the interval of convergence for the power series

$$(x - 1) - \tfrac{1}{4}(x - 1)^2 + \tfrac{1}{9}(x - 1)^3 - \tfrac{1}{16}(x - 1)^4 + \cdots$$

General term:

$$u_n = (-1)^{n+1} \frac{(x - 1)^n}{n^2}$$

$M = \lim\limits_{n \to \infty} \left(-\dfrac{n^2}{(n + 1)^2} \right) = -1$, so the interval of convergence is $0 < x < 2$ and the end points must be tested.

If $x = 0$, series is $-1 - \frac{1}{4} - \frac{1}{9} - \frac{1}{16} - \cdots$.

$$u_n = -\frac{1}{n^2}$$

$$\lim_{n \to \infty} u_n = 0$$

$$\lim_{n \to \infty} \frac{u_{n+1}}{u_n} = 1, \text{ so test-ratio test fails}$$

$$|u_n| = \frac{1}{n^2} \ (p\text{-series}, \ p = 2), \text{ so series convergent}$$

If $x = 2$, series is $1 - \frac{1}{4} + \frac{1}{9} - \frac{1}{16} + \cdots$.

$$u_n = (-1)^{n+1} \frac{1}{n^2}, \text{ so series absolutely convergent (by procedure above)}$$

Thus the original series converges for $0 \le x \le 2$.

Find the interval of convergence for the power series

$$2(x - 2) + \frac{3(x - 2)^2}{2!} + \frac{4(x - 2)^3}{3!} + \frac{5(x - 2)^4}{4!} + \cdots.$$

General term:

$$u_n = \frac{(n+1)(x-2)^n}{n!}$$

$$M = \lim_{n \to \infty} \left(\frac{\frac{n+2}{(n+1)!}}{\frac{n+1}{n!}} \right) = \lim_{n \to \infty} \frac{n+2}{(n+1)^2} = 0$$

Thus the series converges for all x.

□ TAYLOR'S THEOREM

For either theoretical or computational purposes, it is frequently convenient to represent a function of x by a power series; Taylor's theorem provides appropriate power series for representing many functions.

It should be noted that any differentiable function can be expanded in a Taylor's series: A function that can be differentiated only a finite number of times can be expanded in a series having a finite number of terms; a function that can be differentiated indefinitely can be expanded in an infinite series. However, to be a valid representation of a function the series must converge for values of x in the range of interest; in addition, to be useful for computational purposes, the series must converge fairly rapidly, so a reasonably accurate approximation can be obtained using a manageable number of terms. Thus, before using a Taylor's series expansion to represent a function, its convergence properties should be investigated.

TAYLOR'S THEOREM: The infinite series

$$f(a) + f'(a)\frac{x-a}{1!} + f''(a)\frac{(x-a)^2}{2!} + \cdots + f^{(n-1)}(a)\frac{(x-a)^{n-1}}{(n-1)!} + R_n$$

converges and represents the function $f(x)$ for those values of x for which all the derivatives of $f(x)$ exist and for which $R_n \to 0$ as $n \to \infty$. In this case $f(x)$ is said to be expanded in a *Taylor's series about* $x = a$. For the special case $a = 0$, the expansion is a *Maclaurin's series*.

R_n is called the *remainder after n terms* and it can be shown that

$$R_n = f^{(n)}(\xi)\frac{(x-a)^n}{n!} \qquad \text{where } a < \xi < x$$

This formula may be used to determine a bound for the error involved in using only the first n terms of the series.

NOTE: There are some functions for which Taylor's series converges for values of x for which the remainder does not approach 0 as $n \to \infty$; for such values of x, the series does not represent the function. However, in most cases the interval of convergence of the series is the same as the interval for which $R_n \to 0$ as $n \to \infty$, and the former interval is usually easier to obtain.

A Taylor's series about $x = a$ is useful for calculating the function it represents for values of x near a. Similarly, a Maclaurin series is useful for calculating the function it represents for values of x near zero.

A rigorous proof of Taylor's theorem is not simple and will not be given. However, the result can be made plausible by the argument presented in Technical Note II.

Examples

Expand the function $f(x) = x^{-1/3}$ in powers of $(x - 1)$ and determine the interval of convergence of the series.

$$f(x) = x^{-1/3}$$

$$f'(x) = -\tfrac{1}{3}x^{-4/3}$$

$$f''(x) = \frac{1 \cdot 4}{3^2} x^{-7/3}$$

$$f'''(x) = -\frac{1 \cdot 4 \cdot 7}{3^3} x^{-10/3}$$

$$f^{(IV)}(x) = \frac{1 \cdot 4 \cdot 7 \cdot 10}{3^4} x^{-13/3}$$

$$f^{(V)}(x) = -\frac{1 \cdot 4 \cdot 7 \cdot 10 \cdot 13}{3^5} x^{-16/3}$$

$$\vdots$$

$$f^n(x) = (-1)^n \frac{(3n - 2)(3n - 5) \cdots 1}{3^n} x^{-(3n+1)/3}$$

$$f(x) = f(a) + \frac{f'(a)}{1!}(x - a) + \frac{f''(a)}{2!}(x - a)^2 + \cdots + \frac{f^{(n)}(a)}{n!}(x - a)^n + \cdots$$

$$= 1 - \frac{1}{3 \cdot 1!}(x - 1) + \frac{1 \cdot 4}{3^2 \cdot 2!}(x - 1)^2 - \frac{1 \cdot 4 \cdot 7}{3^3 \cdot 3!}(x - 1)^3 + \cdots$$

$$+ (-1)^n \frac{(3n - 2)(3n - 5) \cdots 1}{3^n \cdot n!}(x - 1)^n + \cdots$$

$$\frac{b_{n+1}}{b_n} = -\frac{\dfrac{(3n + 1)(3n - 2) \cdots 1}{3^{n+1}(n + 1)!}}{\dfrac{(3n - 2)(3n - 5) \cdots 1}{3^n n!}} = -\frac{3n + 1}{3(n + 1)}$$

$\lim\limits_{n \to \infty} \dfrac{b_{n+1}}{b_n} = -1$, so the interval of convergence is $0 < x < 2$ and the end points must be tested.

If $x = 0$, $u_n = (-1)^n \dfrac{(3n - 2)(3n - 5) \cdots 1}{3^n \cdot n!}$.

$\lim\limits_{n \to \infty} u_n = 1 \neq 0$, so series divergent

If $x = 2$, $u_n = \dfrac{(3n-2)(3n-5) \cdots 1}{3^n n!}$.

$$\lim_{n \to \infty} u_n = 1 \neq 0, \text{ so series divergent}$$

Thus the power series expansion converges for $0 < x < 2$.

Expand the function $f(x) = \dfrac{1}{(1+x)^2}$ in powers of $(x - 2)$ and determine the interval of convergence of the series.

$$f(x) = (1 + x)^{-2}$$

$$f'(x) = -2(1 + x)^{-3}$$

$$f''(x) = 2 \cdot 3(1 + x)^{-4}$$

$$f'''(x) = -2 \cdot 3 \cdot 4(1 + x)^{-5}$$

$$f^{(IV)}(x) = 2 \cdot 3 \cdot 4 \cdot 5(1 + x)^{-6}$$

$$f^{(V)}(x) = -2 \cdot 3 \cdot 4 \cdot 5 \cdot 6(1 + x)^{-7}$$

$$\vdots$$

$$f^n(x) = (-1)^n (n + 1)!(1 + x)^{-(n+2)}$$

$$f(x) = f(a) + \frac{f'(a)}{1!}(x - a) + \frac{f''(a)}{2!}(x - a)^2 + \cdots + \frac{f^{(n)}(a)}{n!}(x - a)^n + \cdots$$

$$= \frac{1}{3^2} - \frac{2}{3^3}(x - 2) + \frac{3}{3^4}(x - 2)^2 - \frac{4}{3^5}(x - 2)^3 + \cdots$$

$$+ (-1)^n \frac{n + 1}{3^{n+2}}(x - 2)^n + \cdots$$

$$\frac{b_{n+1}}{b_n} = -\frac{\dfrac{n + 2}{3^{n+3}}}{\dfrac{n + 1}{3^{n+2}}} = -\frac{n + 2}{3(n + 1)}$$

$\lim\limits_{n \to \infty} \dfrac{b_{n+1}}{b_n} = -\frac{1}{3}$ so the interval of convergence is $-1 < x < 5$ and the end points must be tested.

If $x = -1$, $u_n = \dfrac{n}{3^2}$.

$$\lim_{n \to \infty} u_n = \infty \neq 0, \text{ so series divergent}$$

If $x = 5$, $u_n = (-1)^{n+1} \dfrac{n}{3^2}$.

$$\lim_{n \to \infty} u_n = \infty \neq 0, \text{ so series divergent}$$

Thus the power series expansion converges for $-1 < x < 5$.

Expand the function $f(x) = (1 + x)^m$, where m is any real number, in powers of x and determine the interval of convergence of the series. This is known as the *binomial expansion*.

$$f(x) = (1 + x)^m$$

$$f'(x) = m(1 + x)^{m-1}$$

$$f''(x) = m(m - 1)(1 + x)^{m-2}$$

$$f'''(x) = m(m - 1)(m - 2)(1 + x)^{m-3}$$

$$f^{(IV)}(x) = m(m - 1)(m - 2)(m - 3)(1 + x)^{m-4}$$

$$f^{(V)}(x) = m(m - 1)(m - 2)(m - 3)(m - 4)(1 + x)^{m-5}$$

$$\vdots$$

$$f^n(x) = \frac{m!}{(m - n)!}(1 + x)^{m-n}$$

$$f(x) = f(a) + \frac{f'(a)}{1!}x + \frac{f''(a)}{2!}x^2 + \cdots + \frac{f^{(n)}(a)}{n!}x^n + \cdots$$

$$= 1 + \frac{m}{1!}x + \frac{m(m - 1)}{2!}x^2 + \frac{m(m - 1)(m - 2)}{3!}x^3 + \cdots$$

$$+ \frac{m(m - 1)(m - 2) \cdots (m - n + 1)}{n!}x^n + \cdots$$

$$\frac{b_{n+1}}{b_n} = \frac{\dfrac{m(m - 1)(m - 2) \cdots (m - n)}{(n + 1)!}}{\dfrac{m(m - 1)(m - 2) \cdots (m - n + 1)}{n!}} = \frac{m - n}{n + 1}$$

$\lim\limits_{n \to \infty} \dfrac{b_{n+1}}{b_n} = -1$, so the interval of convergence is $-1 < x < 1$ and the end points must be tested.

If $x = -1$, $u_n = (-1)^n \dfrac{m(m - 1)(m - 2) \cdots (m - n + 1)}{n!}$.

$$\lim_{n \to \infty} u_n = 0$$

If $x = 1$, $u_n = \dfrac{m(m - 1)(m - 2) \cdots (m - n + 1)}{n!}$.

$$\lim_{n \to \infty} u_n = 0$$

If $x = \pm 1$, $\left|\dfrac{u_{n+1}}{u_n}\right| = \left|\dfrac{n - m}{n + 1}\right|$, so $|u_{n+1}| < |u_n|$ does not hold for unrestricted m.

Thus the power series expansion converges for $-1 < x < 1$.

Expand $\ln x$ in a Taylor's series about $x = 1$ and determine the interval of convergence; use this series to evaluate $\ln 1.04$ correct to five decimal places.

$$f(x) = \ln x$$

$$f'(x) = -\frac{1}{x}$$

$$f''(x) = -\frac{1}{x^2}$$

$$f'''(x) = \frac{2}{x^3}$$

$$f^{(IV)}(x) = -\frac{6}{x^4}$$

$$f^{(V)}(x) = \frac{24}{x^5}$$

$$\vdots$$

$$f^n(x) = (-1)^{n+1} \frac{(n-1)!}{x^n}$$

$$\ln x = f(1) + \frac{f'(1)}{1!}(x-1) + \frac{f''(1)}{2!}(x-1)^2 + \cdots + \frac{f^{(n-1)}(1)}{(n-1)!}(x-1)^{n-1} + R_n$$

$$= 0 + (x-1) - \tfrac{1}{2}(x-1)^2 + \tfrac{1}{3}(x-1)^3 - \cdots$$

$$+ (-1)^{n+1} \frac{1}{n-1}(x-1)^{n-1} + R_n$$

$$\frac{b_{n+1}}{b_n} = -\frac{n+1}{n}$$

$\lim\limits_{n \to \infty} \dfrac{b_{n+1}}{b_n} = -1$, so the interval of convergence is $0 < x < 2$ and the end points must be tested.

If $x = 0$, $u_n = -\dfrac{1}{n}$.

$$\lim_{n \to \infty} u_n = 0$$

$$\lim_{n \to \infty} \frac{u_{n+1}}{u_n} = 1, \text{ so test-ratio test fails}$$

but

$$u_n = \frac{1}{n} \ (p\text{-series, } p = 1), \text{ so series divergent}$$

If $x = 2$, $u_n = (-1)^{n+1} \dfrac{1}{n}$.

$$\lim_{n \to \infty} u_n = 0$$

$|u_{n+1}| < |u_n|$, so series conditionally convergent

Thus the power series expansion converges for $0 < x \le 2$.

$$\ln(1.04) = 0 + 0.04 - \tfrac{1}{2}(0.04)^2 + \tfrac{1}{3}(0.04)^3 + R_4$$

$$= 0.04 - 0.0008 + 0.000021 + R_4$$

$$= 0.039221 + R_4$$

$$R_n = f^n(\xi) \frac{(x-a)^n}{n} \qquad a < \xi < x$$

$$R_4 = (-1)^5 \frac{3!}{\xi^4} \frac{(0.04)^4}{4!} \qquad 1 < \xi < 1.04$$

$$= (-1)^5 \frac{(0.04)^4}{4\xi^4}$$

$$|R_4| < \tfrac{1}{4}(0.04)^4 = 0.00000064$$

so $\ln 1.04 = 0.03922$, correct to five decimal places.

NOTE: Since the series is alternating, the error in truncating is less in absolute value than the next term, which for this example gives the same bound on the error as above.

Expand e^x in a Maclaurin's series about $x = 0$ and determine the interval of convergence; use this series to evaluate $e^{1/2}$ correct to four decimal places.

$$f(x) = e^x$$

$$f'(x) = e^x$$

$$f''(x) = e^x$$

$$\vdots$$

$$f^n(x) = e^x$$

$$e^x = f(0) + \frac{f'(0)}{1!}x + \frac{f''(0)}{2!}x^2 + \cdots + \frac{f^{(n-1)}(0)}{(n-1)!}x^{n-1} + R_n$$

$$= 1 + x + \frac{x^2}{2!} + \frac{x^3}{3!} + \cdots + \frac{x^{n-1}}{(n-1)!} + R_n$$

$$\frac{b_{n+1}}{b_n} = \frac{1}{n+1}$$

$$\lim_{n \to \infty} \frac{b_{n+1}}{b_n} = 0$$

Thus the power series expansion converges for all x.

$$e^{1/2} = 1 + \tfrac{1}{2} + \frac{(\tfrac{1}{2})^2}{2!} + \frac{(\tfrac{1}{2})^3}{3!} + \frac{(\tfrac{1}{2})^4}{4!} + \frac{(\tfrac{1}{2})^5}{5!} + R_6$$

$$= 1 + 0.5 + 0.125 + 0.02083333 + 0.00260417 + 0.000260417 + R_6$$

$$= 1.648697917 + R_6$$

$$R_n = f^n(\xi) \frac{(x - a)^n}{n!} \qquad a < \xi < x$$

$$R_6 = e^\xi \frac{(\tfrac{1}{2})^6}{6!} \qquad 0 < \xi < \tfrac{1}{2}$$

$$|R_6| < \frac{(\tfrac{1}{2})^6}{6!} e^{1/2}$$

and, since $e^{1/2} < 2$, $|R^6| < 0.00004$, so $e^{1/2} = 1.6487$, correct to four decimal places.

Expand $(1 + x)^{1/2}$ in a Maclaurin's series about $x = 0$ and determine the interval of convergence; use this series to evaluate $\sqrt{1.10}$ correct to six decimal places.

$$f(x) = (1 + x)^{1/2}$$

$$f'(x) = \tfrac{1}{2}(1 + x)^{-1/2}$$

$$f''(x) = -\frac{1}{2^2} (1 + x)^{-3/2}$$

$$f'''(x) = \frac{3}{2^3} (1 + x)^{-5/2}$$

$$f^{(IV)}(x) = -\frac{3 \cdot 5}{2^4} (1 + x)^{-7/2}$$

$$f^{(V)}(x) = \frac{3 \cdot 5 \cdot 7}{2^5} (1 + x)^{-9/2}$$

$$\vdots$$

$$f^n(x) = (-1)^{n+1} \frac{(2n - 3)(2n - 5) \cdots 1}{2^n} (1 + x)^{-\frac{2n-1}{2}}$$

$$(1 + x)^{1/2} = f(0) + \frac{f'(0)}{1!} x - \frac{f''(0)}{2!} x^2 + \cdots + (-1)^{n+1} \frac{f^{(n-1)}(0)}{(n - 1)!} x^{n-1} + R_n$$

$$= 1 + \frac{1}{2 \cdot 1!} x - \frac{1}{2^2 \cdot 2!} x^2 + \frac{3}{2^2 \cdot 3!} x^3 - \cdots$$

$$+ (-1)^{n+1} \frac{(2n - 5)(2n - 7) \cdots 1}{2^{n-1}(n - 1)!} x^{n-1} + R_n$$

$$\frac{b_{n+1}}{b_n} = -\frac{2n - 3}{2n}$$

$\lim\limits_{n \to \infty} \dfrac{b_{n+1}}{b_n} = -1$, so the interval of convergence is $-1 < x < 1$ and the end points must be tested.

If $x = -1, f(x) = 0$, so expansion unnecessary.

If $x = 1, u_n = (-1)^{n+1} \dfrac{(2n - 3)(2n - 5) \cdots 1}{2^n \cdot n!}$.

$\lim\limits_{n \to \infty} u_n = 0$

$\left| \dfrac{u_{n+1}}{u_n} \right| = \dfrac{2n - 1}{2n + 2} < 1$, so alternating series conditionally convergent.

Thus the power series expansion converges for $-1 < x \le 1$.

$$(1.10)^{1/2} = 1 + \frac{1}{2 \cdot 1!}\left(\tfrac{1}{10}\right) - \frac{1}{2^2 \cdot 2!}\left(\tfrac{1}{10}\right)^2 + \frac{3}{2^3 \cdot 3!}\left(\tfrac{1}{10}\right)^3 - \frac{3 \cdot 5}{2^4 \cdot 4!}\left(\tfrac{1}{10}\right)^4$$

$$+ \frac{3 \cdot 5 \cdot 7}{2^5 \cdot 5!}\left(\tfrac{1}{10}\right)^5 + R_6$$

$$= 1 + 0.05 - 0.00125 + 0.0000625 - 0.000003906 + 0.000000273 + R_6$$

$$= 1.048808867 + R_6$$

Alternating series, so the error is less than the absolute value of next term,

$$\frac{3 \cdot 5 \cdot 7 \cdot 9}{2^6 \cdot 6!}\left(\tfrac{1}{10}\right)^6 = 0.0000000205$$

so correct to six decimal places, $(1.10)^{1/2} = 1.048809$.

NOTE: Alternatively, a bound on the error can be obtained using R_6:

$$R_n = f^n(\xi)\frac{(x - a)^n}{n!} \qquad a < \xi < x$$

$$R_6 = -\frac{9 \cdot 7 \cdot 5 \cdot 3 \cdot 1}{2^6 \cdot 6!}(1 + \xi)^{-11/2}\left(\tfrac{1}{10}\right)^6 \qquad 0 < \xi < \tfrac{1}{10}$$

$$|R_6| < \frac{9 \cdot 7 \cdot 5 \cdot 3 \cdot 1}{2^6 \cdot 6!}\left(\tfrac{1}{10}\right)^6$$

$$|R_6| < 0.0000000205$$

PROBLEMS

For each of the following series, write out the first few terms and determine whether the series is divergent or convergent (conditionally or absolutely).

1. $\displaystyle\sum_{n=1}^{\infty} (-1)^{n+1}\frac{1}{n^2 + 1}$

2. $\displaystyle\sum_{n=1}^{\infty} \frac{\sqrt{n}}{n^2 + 1}$

3. $\displaystyle\sum_{n=1}^{\infty} \frac{n}{n + 2}$

4. $\displaystyle\sum_{n=1}^{\infty} \frac{1}{1 + \ln n}$

5. $\sum_{n=0}^{\infty} (-1)^{n+1} \dfrac{1}{(2n+1)!}$

6. $\sum_{n=1}^{\infty} \dfrac{(n+1)(n+2)}{n!}$

7. $\sum_{n=1}^{\infty} (-1)^{n+1} \dfrac{n^2}{2^n}$

8. $\sum_{n=0}^{\infty} \dfrac{(n+3)!}{3!\,n!\,3^n}$

9. $\sum_{n=1}^{\infty} (-1)^{n+1} \dfrac{2^n}{n^3+1}$

10. $\sum_{n=1}^{\infty} \dfrac{10^n}{n!}$

11. $\sum_{n=1}^{\infty} \dfrac{n!}{9^n}$

12. $\sum_{n=1}^{\infty} \dfrac{n^2}{10(2n-1)}$

13. $\sum_{n=1}^{\infty} e^{1/n}$

14. $\sum_{n=1}^{\infty} (-1)^{n+1} \dfrac{3^n}{n2^n}$

15. $\sum_{n=0}^{\infty} (-1)^{n+1} \dfrac{3n-1}{4^n}$

16. $\sum_{n=0}^{\infty} (-1)^{n+1} \dfrac{3n^{2/3}-1}{4^n}$

17. $\sum_{n=0}^{\infty} (-1)^{n+1} \dfrac{10}{(5n-2)^{1/4}}$

18. $\sum_{n=0}^{\infty} (-1)^{n+1} \dfrac{(n-3)!}{3^{n-1}}$

19. $\sum_{n=1}^{\infty} (-1)^{n+1} \dfrac{n+2}{n+1}$

20. $\sum_{n=1}^{\infty} \dfrac{n^3}{n!}$

21. $\sum_{n=1}^{\infty} \dfrac{3^{2n-1}}{n^2+1}$

22. $\sum_{n=1}^{\infty} (-1)^{n+1} \dfrac{1}{\sqrt{n}}$

For each of the following power series, determine the general term and the interval of convergence.

23. $x - \dfrac{x^3}{3!} + \dfrac{x^5}{5!} - \dfrac{x^7}{7!} + \cdots$

24. $2x + 4x^2 + 8x^3 + 16x^4 + \cdots$

25. $1 + \dfrac{x}{\sqrt{2}} + \dfrac{x^2}{\sqrt{3}} + \dfrac{x^3}{\sqrt{4}} + \cdots$

26. $\dfrac{x}{1\cdot 2} + \dfrac{x^2}{2^2 \cdot 2^2} + \dfrac{x^3}{3^2 \cdot 2^3} + \dfrac{x^4}{4^2 \cdot 2^4} + \cdots$

27. $1 - \dfrac{3x}{2} + \dfrac{5x^2}{4} - \dfrac{7x^3}{8} + \dfrac{9x^4}{16} - \cdots$

28. $1 + \dfrac{(x+3)}{2^2} + \dfrac{(x+3)^2}{3^2} + \dfrac{(x+3)^3}{4^2} + \cdots$

29. $\dfrac{1}{2!} x + \dfrac{2}{3!} x^3 + \dfrac{3}{4!} x^5 + \dfrac{4}{5!} x^7 + \cdots$

30. $\dfrac{x+4}{\sqrt[3]{2}} - \dfrac{(x+4)^2}{\sqrt[3]{3}} + \dfrac{(x+4)^3}{\sqrt[3]{4}} - \dfrac{(x+4)^4}{\sqrt[3]{5}} + \cdots$

31. $\frac{1}{2} x - \dfrac{2^2}{5} x^2 + \dfrac{3^2}{8} x^3 - \dfrac{4^2}{11} x^4 + \dfrac{5^2}{14} x^5 + \cdots$

32. $\dfrac{6}{2}(x-5) + \dfrac{6^2}{5}(x-5)^2 + \dfrac{6^3}{10}(x-5)^3 + \dfrac{6^4}{17}(x-5)^4 + \dfrac{6^5}{26}(x-5)^5 + \cdots$

Expand the following functions in power series, determine the interval of convergence, and choose some appropriate value of x for which to estimate the function.

33. $f(x) = x^{1/2}$ in powers of $(x-1)$

34. $f(x) = \dfrac{1}{1+x^2}$ in powers of x

35. $f(x) = e^{-1/2x}$ in powers of $(x-2)$

36. $f(x) - \frac{1}{2}(e^x + e^{-x})$ in powers of x

37. $f(x) = \ln(a-x)$ in powers of x

38. $f(x) = \ln(a+x)$ in powers of x

ANSWERS TO ODD-NUMBERED PROBLEMS

1. absolutely convergent

3. divergent

5. absolutely convergent

7. absolutely convergent

9. divergent

11. divergent

13. divergent

15. absolutely convergent

17. conditionally convergent

19. divergent

21. divergent

23. $(-1)^{n+1}\dfrac{x^{2n-1}}{(2n-1)!}$, conv. all x

25. $\dfrac{x^{n-1}}{\sqrt{n}}$, conv. $-1 \le x < 1$

27. $(-1)^{n-1}\dfrac{(2n-1)x^{n-1}}{2^{n-1}}$, conv. $-2 < x < 2$

29. $\dfrac{n}{(n+1)!}x^{2n-1}$, conv. all x

31. $(-1)^{n+1}\dfrac{n^2}{3n-1}x^n$, conv. $-1 < x < 1$

33. $f(x) = 1 + \dfrac{1}{2 \cdot 1!}(x-1) - \dfrac{1}{2^2 \cdot 2!}(x-1)^2 + \dfrac{1 \cdot 3}{2^3 \cdot 3!}(x-1)^3$

$\qquad - \dfrac{1 \cdot 3 \cdot 5}{2^4 \cdot 4!}(x-1)^4 + \dfrac{1 \cdot 3 \cdot 5 \cdot 7}{2^5 \cdot 5!}(x-1)^5 + \cdots$

$\qquad\qquad + (-1)^{n+1}\dfrac{(2n-3)(2n-5)\cdots 1}{2^n \cdot n!}(x-1)^n + \cdots,$

$\qquad\qquad\qquad\qquad\qquad\qquad\qquad \text{conv. } 0 < x \le 2$

35. $f(x) = 1 - \dfrac{e^{-1}}{2 \cdot 1!}(x - 2) + \dfrac{e^{-1}}{2^2 \cdot 2!}(x - 2)^2 - \dfrac{e^{-1}}{2^3 \cdot 3!}(x - 2)^3$

$$+ \dfrac{e^{-1}}{2^4 \cdot 4!}(x - 2)^4 - \dfrac{e^{-1}}{2^5 \cdot 5!}(x - 2)^5 + \cdots$$

$$+ (-1)^n \dfrac{e^{-1}}{2^n \cdot n!}(x - 2)^n + \cdots, \text{ conv. all } x$$

37. $f(x) = \ln a - \dfrac{1}{a}x - \dfrac{1}{2a^2}x^2 - \dfrac{1}{3a^3}x^3 - \dfrac{1}{4a^4}x^4 - \cdots - \dfrac{1}{na^n}x^n - \cdots,$

$$\text{conv. } -a \le x < a$$

Technical Note I   Derivation of Rules for Differentiation

NOTE: For mathematical convenience, the rules for differentiation are not derived in the same order as they are given in the text.

● **Polynomial Functions**

Rule 1. If $y = c$,

$$\Delta y = 0$$

$$\dfrac{\Delta y}{\Delta x} = 0$$

$$\dfrac{dy}{dx} = \lim_{\Delta x \to 0} \dfrac{\Delta y}{\Delta x} = 0$$

If $y = cu$, where $u = f(x)$ is a differentiable function of x,

$$y + \Delta y = c(u + \Delta u)$$

$$\Delta y = c \, \Delta u$$

$$\dfrac{\Delta y}{\Delta x} = c \, \dfrac{\Delta u}{\Delta x}$$

$$\dfrac{dy}{dx} = \lim_{\Delta x \to 0} \dfrac{\Delta y}{\Delta x} = c \, \dfrac{du}{dx}$$

Rule 2. If $y = x^n$, where n is a positive integer,

$$y + \Delta y = (x + \Delta x)^n$$

$$= x^n + nx^{n-1}\Delta x + \dfrac{n(n - 1)}{2!}x^{n-2}(\Delta x)^2 + \cdots + (\Delta x)^n$$

$$\Delta y = nx^{n-1}\Delta x + \dfrac{n(n - 1)}{2!}x^{n-2}(\Delta x)^2 + \cdots + (\Delta x)^n$$

$$\frac{\Delta y}{\Delta x} = nx^{n-1} + \frac{n(n-1)}{2!} x^{n-2}(\Delta x) + \cdots + (\Delta x)^{n-1}$$

$$\frac{dy}{dx} = \lim_{\Delta x \to 0} \frac{\Delta y}{\Delta x} = nx^{n-1}$$

Rule 3. If $y = u + v$, where $u = f(x)$ and $v = g(x)$ are differentiable functions of x,

$$y + \Delta y = u + \Delta u + v + \Delta v$$

$$\Delta y = \Delta u + \Delta v$$

$$\frac{\Delta y}{\Delta x} = \frac{\Delta u}{\Delta x} + \frac{\Delta v}{\Delta x}$$

$$\frac{dy}{dx} = \lim_{\Delta x \to 0} \frac{\Delta y}{\Delta x} = \frac{du}{dx} + \frac{dv}{dx}$$

● **Algebraic Functions**

Rule 4. If $y = uv$, where $u = f(x)$ and $v = g(x)$ are differentiable functions of x,

$$y + \Delta y = (u + \Delta u)(v + \Delta v)$$

$$= uv + u(\Delta v) + v(\Delta u) + (\Delta u)(\Delta v)$$

$$\Delta y = u(\Delta v) + v(\Delta u) + (\Delta u)(\Delta v)$$

$$\frac{\Delta y}{\Delta x} = u \frac{\Delta v}{\Delta x} + v \frac{\Delta u}{\Delta x} + \frac{(\Delta u)(\Delta v)}{\Delta x}$$

$$\frac{dy}{dx} = \lim_{\Delta x \to 0} \frac{\Delta y}{\Delta x} = u \frac{dv}{dx} + v \frac{du}{dx}$$

Rule 5. If $y = \dfrac{u}{v}$, where $u = f(x)$ and $v = g(x)$ are differentiable functions of x,

$$y + \Delta y = \frac{u + \Delta u}{v + \Delta v}$$

$$\Delta y = \frac{v(u + \Delta u) - u(v + \Delta v)}{v(v + \Delta v)}$$

$$= \frac{v(\Delta u) - u(\Delta v)}{v(v + \Delta v)}$$

$$\frac{\Delta y}{\Delta x} = \frac{v \dfrac{\Delta u}{\Delta x} - u \dfrac{\Delta v}{\Delta x}}{v(v + \Delta v)}$$

$$\frac{dy}{dx} = \lim_{\Delta x \to 0} \frac{\Delta y}{\Delta x} = \frac{v \dfrac{du}{dx} - u \dfrac{dv}{dx}}{v^2}$$

● Logarithmic Functions

Rule 7. If $y = \log_a u$, where $u = f(x)$ is a differentiable function of x,

$$y + \Delta y = \log_a(u + \Delta u)$$

$$\Delta y = \log_a(u + \Delta u) - \log_a u$$

$$= \log_a\left(\frac{u + \Delta u}{u}\right)$$

$$= \log_a\left(1 + \frac{\Delta u}{u}\right)$$

$$\frac{\Delta y}{\Delta u} = \frac{1}{\Delta u} \log_a\left(1 + \frac{\Delta u}{u}\right)$$

$$= \frac{1}{u} \cdot \frac{u}{\Delta u} \log_a\left(1 + \frac{\Delta u}{u}\right)$$

$$= \frac{1}{u} \log_a\left(1 + \frac{\Delta u}{u}\right)^{u/\Delta u}$$

Let $\dfrac{\Delta u}{u} = h$; then $\dfrac{u}{\Delta u} = \dfrac{1}{h}$ and $h \to 0$ as $\Delta u \to 0$. Thus $\dfrac{\Delta y}{\Delta u} = \dfrac{1}{u} \log_a(1 + h)^{1/h}$
and, since (by definition) $(1 + h)^{1/h} \to e$ as $h \to 0$,

$$\lim_{\Delta u \to 0} \frac{\Delta y}{\Delta u} = \frac{1}{u} \log_a\left[\lim_{h \to 0}(1 + h)^{1/h}\right]$$

$$\frac{dy}{du} = \frac{1}{u} \log_a e.$$

If $u = f(x)$,

$$\frac{dy}{dx} = \frac{1}{u} \log_a e \frac{du}{dx}$$

● Exponential Functions

Rule 8. If $y = a^u$, where $u = f(x)$ is a differentiable function of x,

$$\ln y = \ln a^u$$

$$= u \ln a$$

$$\frac{1}{y}\frac{dy}{dx} = \frac{du}{dx} \ln a$$

$$\frac{dy}{dx} = y \frac{du}{dx} \ln a$$

$$= a^u \ln a \frac{du}{dx}$$

Rule 9. If $y = u^v$, where $u = f(x)$ and $v = g(x)$ are differentiable functions of x,

$$\ln y = v \ln u$$

$$\frac{1}{y}\frac{dy}{dx} = v\frac{1}{u}\frac{du}{dx} + \ln u \frac{dv}{dx}$$

$$\frac{dy}{dx} = vu^{v-1}\frac{du}{dx} + u^v \ln u \frac{dv}{dx}$$

Rule 6. If $y = u^n$, where $u = f(x)$ is a differentiable function of x and n is any real number,

$$\ln y = n \ln u$$

$$\frac{1}{y}\frac{dy}{dx} = n\frac{1}{u}\frac{du}{dx}$$

$$\frac{dy}{dx} = nu^{n-1}\frac{du}{dx}$$

● Trigonometric Functions

Rule 10. If $y = \sin u$, where $u = f(x)$ is a differentiable function of x,

$$y + \Delta y = \sin(u + \Delta u)$$
$$y = \sin(u + \Delta u) - \sin u$$

$$= 2 \cos\left(u + \frac{\Delta u}{2}\right) \sin\frac{\Delta u}{2}$$

$$\text{since } \sin x - \sin y = 2 \cos \tfrac{1}{2}(x + y) \sin \tfrac{1}{2}(x - y)$$

$$\frac{\Delta y}{\Delta u} = 2 \cos\left(u + \frac{\Delta u}{2}\right) \frac{\sin(\Delta u/2)}{\Delta u}$$

$$= \cos\left(u + \frac{\Delta u}{2}\right) \frac{\sin(\Delta u/2)}{\Delta u/2}$$

$$\frac{dy}{du} = \lim_{\Delta u \to 0} \frac{\Delta y}{\Delta u} = \lim_{\Delta u \to 0} \cos\left(u + \frac{\Delta u}{2}\right) \frac{\sin(\Delta u/2)}{\Delta u/2}$$

$$= \cos u, \quad \text{since } \lim_{\Delta u \to 0} \frac{\sin(\Delta u/2)}{\Delta u/2} = 1$$

If $u = f(x)$,

$$\frac{dy}{dx} = \cos u \frac{du}{dx}$$

● Inverse Functions

Rule 11. If $y = f(x)$ and $x = g(y)$ are inverse differentiable functions,

$$\frac{g(y + \Delta y) - g(y)}{\Delta y} = \frac{h}{\Delta y} \qquad \text{where } x = g(y)$$
$$x + h = g(y + \Delta y)$$

$$y + \Delta y = f(x + h) \qquad \text{since } f[g(x)] = x$$

and thus

$$\Delta y = f(x + h) - f(x)$$

$$\frac{g(y + \Delta y) - g(y)}{\Delta y} = \frac{\Delta x}{f(x + h) - f(x)}$$

As $\Delta y \to 0$, $\Delta x \to 0$ and

$$\lim_{\Delta y \to 0} \frac{g(y + \Delta y) - g(y)}{\Delta y} = g'(y) = \lim_{\Delta x \to 0} \frac{\Delta x}{f(x + h) - f(x)} = \frac{1}{f'(x)}$$

That is,

$$\frac{dx}{dy} = \frac{1}{\dfrac{dy}{dx}}$$

● Composite Functions

Rule 12. If $y = \phi(u)$ and $u = F(x)$

$$\frac{\Delta y}{\Delta x} = \frac{\Delta y}{\Delta u} \cdot \frac{\Delta u}{\Delta x}$$

$$\lim_{\Delta x \to 0} \frac{\Delta y}{\Delta x} = \frac{dy}{du} \cdot \frac{du}{dx}$$

TECHNICAL NOTE II   TAYLOR'S THEOREM

Assume that the function $f(x)$ has a power series expansion and that the power series can be differentiated term by term.

$$f(x) = a_0 + a_1(x - a) + a_2(x - a)^2 + \cdots + a_n(x - a)^n + \cdots$$

If $x = a, f(a) = a_0$.

$$f'(x) = a_1 + 2a_2(x - a) + \cdots + na_n(x - a)^{n-1} + \cdots$$

If $x = a, f'(a) = a_1$.

$$f''(x) = 2a_2 + 3 \cdot 2a_3(x - a) + \cdots + n(n - 1)a_n(x - a)^{n-2} + \cdots$$

If $x = a, f''(a) = 2a_2$.

$$f'''(x) = 3 \cdot 2a_3 + 4 \cdot 3 \cdot 2a_4(x - a) + \cdots + n(n - 1)(n - 2)a_n(x - a)^{n-3} + \cdots$$

If $x = a, f'''(a) = 3 \cdot 2a_3$.

$$\vdots$$

$$f^k(x) = k(k - 1)a_k + (k + 1)(k)(k - 1)a_{k+1}(x - a) + \cdots$$

$$+ n(n - 1) \cdots (n - k + 1)a_n(x - a)^{n-k} + \cdots$$

If $x = a$, $f^k(a) = k!a_k$.

Thus

$$a_n = \frac{f^n(a)}{n!} \quad \text{for } n = 1, 2, \ldots ; a_0 = f(a)$$

$$f(x) = f(a) + \frac{f'(a)}{1!}(x - a) + \frac{f''(a)}{2!}(x - a)^2 + \cdots + \frac{f^n(a)}{n!}(x - a)^n + \cdots$$

3

DIFFERENTIAL CALCULUS: FUNCTIONS OF MORE THAN ONE VARIABLE

■ 3.1 **INTRODUCTION**

Chapter 2 is concerned with functions of one variable—that is, functions of the explicit form $y = f(x)$ or the implicit form $f(x, y) = 0$. Such functions express a relationship between two variables (x and y) and implicitly assume that the processes being studied can be represented adequately in terms of only two variables. Although in many cases this type of representation provides a reasonably accurate first approximation to reality, there are clearly many cases in which such a representation is so inadequate as to be virtually useless and it is necessary to express a relationship in terms of several variables or to express one variable as a function of more than one other variable. For example, in economic theory supply and demand of a commodity frequently depend not only on its price but also on the prices of related commodities, on income level, on time, and on various other factors.

Relations and functions of several variables can be defined by appropriate extensions of the corresponding definitions for two variables. Geometric representation is not possible for functions involving more than three variables, but, with this exception, the following discussion and definitions are appropriate for any finite number of variables.

Just as a point in two-dimensional space is represented by an ordered pair of real numbers, a point in three-dimensional space is represented by an ordered triple of real numbers and a point in n-dimensional space is represented by an ordered n-tuple of real numbers $(x_1, x_2, \ldots, x_n)$. Thus a point in n-dimensional

331

space is an ordered arrangement of n real numbers. The set of all points in n-dimensional space is denoted by U_n. For convenience, a point in n-dimensional space is sometimes denoted by a single letter, say X.

A set of ordered pairs $\{(X, z)\}$, where $X \in U_n$, is a relation. If $(X_1, z_1) \in F$ and $(X_1, z_2) \in F$ implies that $z_1 = z_2$, then $\{(X, z)\}$ is a function of n variables. The domain of the function is the set of points $\{X\}$ in the space U_n and the range is the set of values $\{z\}$ appearing in the set of pairs in F. Note that the set of ordered pairs is a relation and, if to each point of the domain there corresponds only one point of the range, the relation is a function.

When $X \in U_2$, the pair (X, z) is an ordered triple, say (x, y, z), which may be interpreted as a point in three-dimensional space. Functions whose domain is U_k, where $k > 2$, cannot be represented geometrically.

A function of several variables is frequently described by an equation expressing the correspondence between the coordinates of the point X and the functional value z. For this purpose, the functional notation $y = f(x)$ can be extended for functions defined on U_n. For example, if $X \in U_n$, $z = F(X)$ indicates that F is a function of n variables. If the domain is in U_2,

$$z = F(x, y) \quad \text{or} \quad z = F(X)$$

and z is a function of two variables. In general, if $X \in U_n$,

$$z = F(x_1, x_2, \ldots, x_n) \quad \text{or} \quad z = F(X)$$

and z is a function of n variables. The coordinates of X are called *independent variables* and z is called a *dependent variable*. Implicit functions of several variables can be written, for example, as $f(x, y, z) = 0$ or, more generally, as $f(x_1, x_2, \ldots, x_n, z) = 0$.

● Continuity

A function $f(x, y)$ is said to be *continuous at* $x = a, y = b$, if the following three conditions are satisfied:

1. $f(a, b)$ exists.
2. $\lim\limits_{\substack{x \to a \\ y \to b}} f(x, y)$ exists.
3. $\lim\limits_{\substack{x \to a \\ y \to b}} f(x, y) = f(a, b)$, no matter in what manner $x \to a, y \to b$.

A function of x and y is said to be *continuous in a region* of the xy-plane if it is continuous at every point of the region. Analogous definitions are appropriate for functions of n variables.

■ 3.2 PARTIAL DIFFERENTIATION

Consider the function z of two independent variables x and y,

$$z = f(x, y)$$

If y is held constant, z is a function only of x and the derivative of z with respect to x can be computed. The derivative obtained in this way is the *partial derivative* of z with respect to x and is denoted by

$$\frac{\partial z}{\partial x} \quad \frac{\partial f}{\partial x} \quad \frac{\partial}{\partial x} f(x, y) \quad f_x(x, y) \quad f_x \quad z_x$$

Similarly, if x is held constant the partial derivative with respect to y can be computed and is denoted by

$$\frac{\partial z}{\partial y} \quad \frac{\partial f}{\partial y} \quad \frac{\partial}{\partial y} f(x, y) \quad f_y(x, y) \quad f_y \quad z_y$$

The partial derivative of z with respect to x is defined as

$$\frac{\partial z}{\partial x} = \lim_{\Delta x \to 0} \frac{\Delta z}{\Delta x} = \lim_{\Delta x \to 0} \frac{f(x + \Delta x, y) - f(x, y)}{\Delta x}$$

and the partial derivative of z with respect to y is defined as

$$\frac{\partial z}{\partial y} = \lim_{y \to 0} \frac{\Delta z}{\Delta y} = \lim_{\Delta y \to 0} \frac{f(x, y + \Delta y) - f(x, y)}{\Delta y}$$

NOTE: In general, a function of any number of variables may have a partial derivative with respect to each of its variables.

Examples

$$z = 2x^2 + 3xy - 6y^2$$

$$\frac{\partial z}{\partial x} = 4x + 3y$$

$$\frac{\partial z}{\partial y} = 3x - 12y$$

$$z = xy + \ln x$$

$$\frac{\partial z}{\partial x} = y + \frac{1}{x}$$

$$\frac{\partial z}{\partial y} = x$$

If $z = \dfrac{x^3 - y^3}{xy}$, show that $x \dfrac{\partial z}{\partial x} + y \dfrac{\partial z}{\partial y} = z$.

$$z = x^2 y^{-1} - x^{-1} y^2$$

$$\frac{\partial z}{\partial x} = 2xy^{-1} + x^{-2} y^2$$

$$\frac{\partial z}{\partial y} = -x^2 y^{-2} - 2x^{-1}y$$

$$x\frac{\partial z}{\partial x} + y\frac{\partial z}{\partial y} = 2x^2 y^{-1} + x^{-1}y^2 - x^2 y^{-1} - 2x^{-1}y^2$$

$$= x^2 y^{-1} - x^{-1}y^2 = z$$

Just as a function of one variable can be represented by a curve in a plane, a function of two variables can be represented by a surface in space. In Fig. 3.1 consider the surface represented by $z = f(x, y)$. If a plane is passed through any point of P of the surface parallel to the yz-plane, it cuts the curve APB, along which x remains constant, and the slope of the tangent line to APB at P represents the rate at which z changes with respect to y. Similar statements hold for a plane parallel to the xz-plane. Thus the partial derivatives have the following geometrical significance:

$$\frac{\partial z}{\partial y} = \tan \alpha = \text{slope of } APB \text{ at } P$$

$$\frac{\partial z}{\partial x} = \tan \beta = \text{slope of } CPD \text{ at } P$$

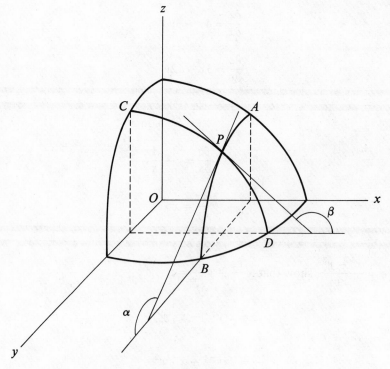

FIGURE 3.1

Since, in general, the partial derivatives of a function $z = f(x, y)$ are functions of x and y, they may be differentiated with respect to either x or y; these derivatives, if they exist, are called the *second partial derivatives* of z and are denoted, respectively, by

$$\frac{\partial}{\partial x}\left(\frac{\partial z}{\partial x}\right) = \frac{\partial^2 z}{\partial x^2} = z_{xx} = \frac{\partial^2 f}{\partial x^2} = f_{xx}$$

$$\frac{\partial}{\partial x}\left(\frac{\partial z}{\partial y}\right) = \frac{\partial^2 z}{\partial x \, \partial y} = z_{yx} = \frac{\partial^2 f}{\partial x \, \partial y} = f_{yx}$$

$$\frac{\partial}{\partial y}\left(\frac{\partial z}{\partial x}\right) = \frac{\partial^2 z}{\partial y \, \partial x} = z_{xy} = \frac{\partial^2 f}{\partial y \, \partial x} = f_{xy}$$

$$\frac{\partial}{\partial y}\left(\frac{\partial z}{\partial y}\right) = \frac{\partial^2 z}{\partial y^2} = z_{yy} = \frac{\partial^2 f}{\partial y^2} = f_{yy}$$

Of these four derivatives, only three are generally distinct, since $f_{yx} = f_{xy}$ for all values of x and y for which f_{yx} and f_{xy} are continuous. Because of this property, it follows that a mixed partial derivative of second (or higher) order may be obtained by differentiating with respect to the variables in any order, provided only that the derivatives are continuous. (A second- or higher-order partial derivative which is obtained by differentiating with respect to more than one variable is referred to as a *mixed partial derivative*.)

Similar definitions and equalities hold for higher-order partial derivatives of functions of two variables and for partial derivatives of functions of more than two variables.

Examples

$$z = (x^2 + y^2)^{3/2}$$

$$\frac{\partial z}{\partial x} = \tfrac{3}{2}(x^2 + y^2)^{1/2}(2x)$$

$$= 3x(x^2 + y^2)^{1/2}$$

$$\frac{\partial^2 z}{\partial y \, \partial x} = \tfrac{3}{2}x(x^2 + y^2)^{-1/2}(2y)$$

$$= 3xy(x^2 + y^2)^{-1/2}$$

$$\frac{\partial z}{\partial y} = \tfrac{3}{2}(x^2 + y^2)^{1/2}(2y)$$

$$= 3y(x^2 + y^2)^{1/2}$$

$$\frac{\partial^2 z}{\partial x \, \partial y} = \tfrac{3}{2}y(x^2 + y^2)^{-1/2}(2x)$$

$$= 3xy(x^2 + y^2)^{-1/2}$$

$$\frac{\partial^2 z}{\partial y \, \partial x} = \frac{\partial^2 z}{\partial x \, \partial y} = 3xy(x^2 + y^2)^{-1/2}$$

If $u = Ax^4 + Bx^3y + Cx^2y^2 + Dxy^3 + Ey^4$, find $\dfrac{\partial^3 u}{\partial x^3}$, $\dfrac{\partial^3 u}{\partial x\,\partial y^2}$, $\dfrac{\partial^3 u}{\partial x^2\,\partial y}$, and $\dfrac{\partial^3 u}{\partial y^3}$

$$\frac{\partial u}{\partial x} = 4Ax^3 + 3Bx^2y + 2Cxy^2 + Dy^3$$

$$\frac{\partial^2 u}{\partial x^2} = 12Ax^2 + 6Bxy + 2Cy^2$$

$$\frac{\partial^3 u}{\partial x^3} = 24Ax + 6By$$

$$\frac{\partial^3 u}{\partial x^2\,\partial y} = 6Bx + 4Cy$$

$$\frac{\partial u}{\partial y} = Bx^3 + 2Cx^2y + 3Dxy^2 + 4Ey^3$$

$$\frac{\partial^2 u}{\partial y^2} = 2Cx^2 + 6Dxy + 12Ey^2$$

$$\frac{\partial^3 u}{\partial y^3} = 6Dx + 24Ey$$

$$\frac{\partial^3 u}{\partial y^2\,\partial x} = 4Cx + 6Dy$$

PROBLEMS

1. If $u = xy - \ln xy$, find u_x and u_y.

2. If $z = (x - y)/(x + y)$, find z_x and z_y.

3. If $z = ye^{x/y}$, find z_x and z_y.

4. If $z = \ln\!\left(\dfrac{x^2 - y^2}{x^2 + y^2}\right)$, find z_x and z_y.

5. If $u = \sin xy$, find u_x and u_y.

6. If $z = \sqrt{xy}$, find z_x and z_y.

7. If $z = e^{au + bv^2 + cw^3}$, find z_u, z_v, and z_w.

8. If $u = x^2y + y^2z + z^2x$, show that $u_x + u_y + u_z = (x + y + z)^2$.

9. If $z = x^2 \sin(y/x) + y^2 \cos(y/x)$, find $xz_x + yz_y$.

10. If $a = \cos xu \sin yu$, find z_x, z_y, and z_u.

11. If $z = xy + y \ln xy$, show that $x\dfrac{\partial^2 z}{\partial x^2} + y\dfrac{\partial^2 z}{\partial x\,\partial y} = y^2 \dfrac{\partial^2 z}{\partial y^2}$.

12. If $u = \sqrt{x - y^2}$, show that $\dfrac{\partial u}{\partial x} \cdot \dfrac{\partial^2 u}{\partial x\,\partial y} = \dfrac{\partial u}{\partial y} \cdot \dfrac{\partial^2 u}{\partial x^2}$.

13. If $z = xy + xe^{1/y}$, show that $\dfrac{\partial^2 z}{\partial x\,\partial y} = \dfrac{\partial^2 z}{\partial y\,\partial x}$.

14. If $v = \dfrac{x + y}{x - y}$, show that $\dfrac{\partial^2 v}{\partial x\,\partial y} = \dfrac{\partial^2 v}{\partial y\,\partial x}$.

15. If $z = 2x^2 - 2y^2 - 3x - 4xy^2$, show that $\dfrac{\partial^2 z}{\partial x\,\partial y} = \dfrac{\partial^2 z}{\partial y\,\partial x}$.

16. If $z = \ln(x^2 + y^2)$, show that $\dfrac{\partial^2 z}{\partial x^2} + \dfrac{\partial^2 z}{\partial y^2} = 0$.

17. If $f(x, y) = x^3 e^{x^2 + y}$, find f_x, f_y, and f_{xy}.

18. If $f(x, y) = Ax + By + Ce^{xy}$, find f_{xx}, f_{yy}, and f_{xy}.

19. If $f(x, y) = x^2 \cos y + y^2 \sin x$, find f_{xx}, f_{yy}, and f_{xy}.

20. If $f(x, y) = x^3 + 3x^2 y + 6xy^2 - y^3$, find $f_{xx}(2, 3), f_{yy}(2, 3)$, and $f_{xy}(2, 3)$.

21. If $f(x, y) = x^4 - 4x^3 y + 8xy^3 - y^4$, find $f_{xx}(0, 1), f_{yy}(0, 1)$, and $f_{xy}(0, 1)$.

22. If $f(x, y) = 2x^2 - 3xy + 4y^2$, find $f_x(1, -1)$ and $f_y(1, -1)$.

23. If $f(x, y) = \dfrac{2x}{x - y}$, find $f_x(3, 1)$ and $f_y(3, 1)$.

24. If $f(x, y) = e^{-x} \sin(x + 2y)$, find $f_x\left(0, \dfrac{\pi}{4}\right)$ and $f_y\left(0, \dfrac{\pi}{4}\right)$.

25. If $u = \dfrac{x^2 y^2}{x + y}$, show that $xu_x + yu_y = 3u$.

26. If $u = \ln(x + y + z)$, show that $\ln u_x + \ln u_y + \ln u_z = -3u$.

27. If $u = \dfrac{Ax^n + By^n}{Cx^2 + Dy^2}$, show that $xu_x + yu_y = (n - 2)u$.

28. If $u = f(x, y), v = g(x, y), u_x = v_y$, and $u_y = -v_x$, show that if $x = r \cos \theta$ and $y = r \sin \theta$, then $u_r = \dfrac{1}{r} v_\theta$ and $v_r = \dfrac{1}{r} u_\theta$.

29. If $u = f(x, y), x = r \cos \theta$, and $y = r \sin \theta$, find $u_r^2 + \dfrac{1}{r} u_\theta^2$ in terms of x and y.

30. If $z = f(x, y), x = g(u, v)$, and $y = h(u, v)$, find z_{uu}.

31. If $u = \ln \sqrt{x^2 + y^2}$, show that $u_{xx} = -u_{yy}$.

32. If $u = \dfrac{1}{r}$ and $r = \sqrt{x^2 + y^2 + z^2}$, show that $u_{xx} + u_{yy} + u_{zz} = \dfrac{1}{r^4}$.

Answers to Odd-Numbered Problems

1. $u_x = y - \dfrac{1}{x}$; $u_y = x - \dfrac{1}{y}$

3. $z_x = e^{x/y}$; $z_y = e^{x/y}\left(1 - \dfrac{x}{y}\right)$

5. $u_x = y \cos xy; u_y = x \cos xy$

7. $z_u = ae^{au+bv2+cw3}; z_v = 2bve^{au+bv2+cw3}; z_w = 3cw^2 e^{au+bv2+cw3}$

9. $2z$

17. $f_x = x^2 e^{x^2+y}(3 + 2x^2); f_y = x^3 e^{x^2+y}; f_{xy} = x^2 e^{x^2+y}(3 + 2x^2)$

19. $f_{xx} = 2\cos y - y^2 \sin x; f_{yy} = -x^2 \cos y + 2\sin x;$
    $f_{xy} = -2x \sin y + 2y \cos x$

21. $f_{xx}(0, 1) = 0 ; f_{yy}(0, 1) = -12; f_{xy}(0, 1) = 24$

23. $f_x(3, 1) = -\frac{1}{2}; f_y(3, 1) = \frac{3}{2}$

29. $u_x^2 + u_y^2$

□ THE TOTAL DIFFERENTIAL

The total differential of a function

$$w = f(x, y, z)$$

is defined by

$$dw = \frac{\partial w}{\partial x} dx + \frac{\partial w}{\partial y} dy + \frac{\partial w}{\partial z} dz$$

The separate terms $\frac{\partial w}{\partial x} dx$, $\frac{\partial w}{\partial y} dy$, and $\frac{\partial w}{\partial z} dz$ are sometimes called partial differentials of w with respect to x, y, and z, respectively. The sum of the partial differentials of a function is its total differential.

In general, the total differential of a function

$$w = f(x_1, x_2, \ldots, x_n)$$

is the sum of all its partial differentials

$$dw = \sum_{i=1}^{n} \frac{\partial f}{\partial x_i} dx_i$$

If the x's are differentiable functions of another variable, say t, then

$$dx_i = \frac{dx_i}{dt} dt$$

and if the x's are differentiable functions of two variables, say r and s, then

$$dx_i = \frac{\partial x_i}{\partial r} dr + \frac{\partial x_i}{\partial s} ds$$

Examples

If $w = x^2 + y^2 + z^2$, where $x = r \cos t$, $y = r \sin t$, and $z = r$, then

$$dw = \frac{\partial w}{\partial x} dx + \frac{\partial w}{\partial y} dy + \frac{\partial w}{\partial z} dz$$

$$= 2x \, dx + 2y \, dy + 2z \, dz$$

$$= 2x(\cos t \, dr - r \sin t \, dt) + 2y(\sin t \, dr + r \cos t \, dt) + 2z \, dr$$
$$= 2(r \cos^2 t \, dr - r^2 \sin t \cos t \, dt + r \sin^2 t \, dr + r^2 \sin t \cos t \, dt + r \, dr)$$
$$= 2(r + r)$$
$$= 4r$$

If $u = (x + y)\sqrt{x - y}$, compute du when $x = 6$, $y = 2$, $dx = \frac{1}{2}$, and $dy = -1$.

$$du = \frac{\partial u}{\partial x} \, dx + \frac{\partial u}{\partial y} \, dy$$
$$= [\sqrt{x - y} + (x + y)(\tfrac{1}{2})(x - y)^{-1/2}] dx$$
$$\qquad\qquad + [\sqrt{x - y} + (x + y)(-\tfrac{1}{2})(x - y)^{-1/2}] \, dy$$
$$= [2 + (8)(\tfrac{1}{2})(\tfrac{1}{2})](\tfrac{1}{2}) + [2 + (8)(-\tfrac{1}{2})(\tfrac{1}{2})](-1)$$
$$= 2 + 0$$
$$= 2$$

□ THE TOTAL DERIVATIVE

If $w = f(x, y, z)$ has continuous partial derivatives $\dfrac{\partial w}{\partial x}$, $\dfrac{\partial w}{\partial y}$, and $\dfrac{\partial w}{\partial z}$ in some region and x, y, and z are functions of another variable t, then

$$\frac{dw}{dt} = \frac{\partial w}{\partial x} \frac{\partial x}{\partial t} + \frac{\partial w}{\partial y} \frac{\partial y}{\partial t} + \frac{\partial w}{\partial z} \frac{\partial z}{\partial t}$$

and $\dfrac{dw}{dt}$ is said to be the *total derivative* of w with respect to t. Thus $\dfrac{dw}{dt}$ represents the rate of change in w as t changes. Heuristically, the total derivative can be obtained by dividing the total differential by Δt and letting Δt approach zero as a limit. Note that w is actually a function only of t.

Example

If $w = x^2 + y^2 + z^2$, where $x = e^t \cos t$, $y = e^t \sin t$, and $z = e^t$, find $\dfrac{dw}{dt}$.

$$\frac{dw}{dt} = \frac{\partial w}{\partial x} \frac{\partial x}{\partial t} + \frac{\partial w}{\partial y} \frac{\partial y}{\partial t} + \frac{\partial w}{\partial z} \frac{\partial z}{\partial t}$$

$$\frac{dw}{dt} = 2x(e^t \cos t + e^t \sin t) + 2y(e^t \sin t + e^t \cos t) + 2te^t$$

$$= 2[e^{2t} \cos^2 t - e^{2t} \sin t \cos t + e^{2t} \sin^2 t + e^{2t} \sin t \cos t + e^{2t}]$$
$$= 2[e^{2t}(\cos^2 t + \sin^2 t)] + 2e^{2t}$$
$$= 4e^{2t}$$

Alternatively,

$$w = e^{2t} \cos^2 t + e^{2t} \sin^2 t + e^{2t}$$

$$\frac{dw}{dt} = 2e^{2t} \cos^2 t - 2e^{2t} \sin t \cos t + 2e^{2t} \sin^2 t + 2e^{2t} \sin^2 t + 2e^{2t}$$

$$= 2e^{2t}(\cos^2 t + \sin^2 t) + 2e^{2t}$$

$$= 4e^{2t}$$

Similarly, if $w = f(x, y, z)$ and x, y, and z are differentiable functions of r and s, then $\dfrac{\partial w}{\partial r}$ and $\dfrac{\partial w}{\partial s}$ can be obtained as follows:·

$$\frac{\partial w}{\partial r} = \frac{\partial w}{\partial x} \frac{\partial x}{\partial r} + \frac{\partial w}{\partial y} \frac{\partial y}{\partial r} + \frac{\partial w}{\partial z} \frac{dz}{\partial r}$$

$$\frac{\partial w}{\partial s} = \frac{\partial w}{\partial x} \frac{\partial x}{\partial s} + \frac{\partial w}{\partial y} \frac{\partial y}{\partial s} + \frac{\partial w}{\partial z} \frac{\partial z}{\partial s}$$

In general, if w is a differentiable function of $x_1, x_2, \ldots, x_n$ and the x's are differentiable functions of a second set of variables $u_1, u_2, \ldots, u_m$, then the partial derivative of w with respect to a variable in the second set, say u_j, is given by

$$\frac{\partial w}{\partial u_j} = \frac{\partial w}{\partial x_1} \frac{\partial x_1}{\partial u_j} + \frac{\partial w}{\partial x_2} \frac{\partial x_2}{\partial u_j} + \cdots + \frac{\partial w}{\partial x_n} \frac{\partial x_u}{\partial u_j}$$

Example

If $w = \ln(x^2 + y^2 + 2z)$, where $x = r + s$, $y = r - s$, and $z = 2rs$,

$$\frac{\partial w}{\partial r} = \frac{\partial w}{\partial x} \frac{\partial x}{\partial r} + \frac{\partial w}{\partial y} \frac{\partial y}{\partial r} + \frac{\partial w}{\partial z} \frac{\partial z}{\partial r}$$

$$= \frac{2x}{x^2 + y^2 + 2z} (1) + \frac{2y}{x^2 + y^2 + 2z} (1) + \frac{2}{x^2 + y^2 + 2z} (2s)$$

$$= \frac{2(r + s) + 2(r - s) + 4s}{r^2 + 2rs + s^2 + r^2 - 2rs + s^2 + 4rs}$$

$$= \frac{4(r + s)}{2(r + s)^2}$$

$$= \frac{2}{r + s}$$

and

$$\frac{\partial w}{\partial s} = \frac{\partial w}{\partial x} \frac{\partial x}{\partial s} + \frac{\partial w}{\partial y} \frac{\partial y}{\partial s} + \frac{\partial w}{\partial z} \frac{\partial z}{\partial s}$$

$$= \frac{2x}{x^2 + y^2 + 2z} (1) + \frac{2y}{x^2 + y^2 + 2z} (-1) + \frac{2}{x^2 + y^2 + 2z} (2r)$$

$$= \frac{2(r + s) - 2(r - s) + 4r}{2(r + s)^2}$$

$$= \frac{4(r+s)}{2(r+s)^2}$$

$$= \frac{2}{r+s}$$

The composite function rule, which is valid also for partial derivatives, can be used to obtain the total derivatives of functions whose independent variables are related in various ways.

For example, if $u = f(x, y, z)$, where $x = t$, $y = y(t)$, and $z = z(t)$, then

$$\frac{du}{dt} = \frac{\partial u}{\partial x}\frac{\partial x}{\partial t} + \frac{\partial u}{\partial y}\frac{\partial y}{\partial t} + \frac{\partial u}{\partial z}\frac{\partial z}{\partial t}$$

$$= \frac{\partial u}{\partial x} + \frac{\partial u}{\partial y}\frac{\partial y}{\partial t} + \frac{\partial u}{\partial z}\frac{\partial z}{\partial t}$$

since $\dfrac{\partial x}{\partial t} = 1$.

If $u = f(x, y, z)$, where $x = x(t)$, $y = y(x)$, and $z = z(t)$, then

$$\frac{du}{dt} = \frac{\partial u}{\partial x}\frac{\partial x}{\partial t} + \frac{\partial u}{\partial y}\frac{\partial y}{\partial x}\frac{\partial x}{\partial t} + \frac{\partial u}{\partial z}\frac{\partial z}{\partial t}$$

using the composite function rule.

If $u = f(x, y, z)$, where $x = x(r, s)$, $y = y(r)$, and $z = z(y)$, then

$$\frac{\partial u}{\partial r} = \frac{\partial u}{\partial x}\frac{\partial x}{\partial r} + \frac{\partial u}{\partial y}\frac{\partial y}{\partial r} + \frac{\partial u}{\partial z}\frac{\partial z}{\partial y}\frac{\partial y}{\partial r}$$

using the composite function rule, and

$$\frac{\partial u}{\partial s} = \frac{\partial u}{\partial x}\frac{\partial x}{\partial s}$$

since $\dfrac{\partial y}{\partial s} = 0$.

If $u = f(x, y, z)$, where $x = x(t)$, $y = y(x)$, and $z = z(y)$, then

$$\frac{du}{dt} = \frac{\partial u}{\partial x}\frac{\partial x}{\partial t} + \frac{\partial u}{\partial y}\frac{\partial y}{\partial x}\frac{\partial x}{\partial t} + \frac{\partial u}{\partial z}\frac{\partial z}{\partial y}\frac{\partial y}{\partial x}\frac{\partial x}{\partial t}$$

using the composite function rule.

□ *DIFFERENTIATION OF IMPLICIT FUNCTIONS*

The equation $f(x, y) = 0$ defines x and y as implicit functions of each other. Let

$$u = f(x, y)$$

Then

$$\frac{\partial u}{\partial x} = \frac{\partial f}{\partial x} + \frac{\partial f}{\partial y}\frac{dy}{dx}$$

But if $u = 0$, $\frac{\partial u}{\partial x} = 0$ and

$$\frac{\partial f}{\partial x} + \frac{\partial f}{\partial y}\frac{dy}{dx} = 0$$

Thus

$$\frac{dy}{dx} = -\frac{\dfrac{\partial f}{\partial x}}{\dfrac{\partial f}{\partial y}}$$

and $\frac{dx}{dy}$ can be obtained as the reciprocal of $\frac{dy}{dx}$.

Examples

If $e^x \sin y + e^y \cos x = 1$, find $\frac{dy}{dx}$.

$$F(x, y) = e^x \sin y + e^y \cos x - 1 = 0$$

$$\frac{dy}{dx} = -\frac{\dfrac{\partial F}{\partial x}}{\dfrac{\partial F}{\partial y}}$$

$$= -\frac{e^x \sin y - e^y \sin x}{e^x \cos y + e^y \cos x}$$

If $x = f(u, v)$ and $y = g(u, v)$ are considered to define u and v implicitly as functions of x and y,

   (a) express dx and dy in terms of du and dv and solve these equations for du and dv in terms of dx and dy.

   (b) Show that

$$\frac{\partial u}{\partial x} = \frac{g_v}{f_u g_v - f_v g_u}$$

provided $f_u g_v - f_v g_u \neq 0$.

   (a)

$$dx = \frac{\partial x}{\partial u} du + \frac{\partial x}{\partial v} dv = f_u \, du + f_v \, dv$$

$$dy = \frac{\partial y}{\partial u} du + \frac{\partial y}{\partial v} dv = g_u du + g_v dv$$

$$g_v dx = g_v f_u du + g_v f_v dv$$

$$f_v dy = f_v g_u du + f_v g_v dv$$

$$du = \frac{g_v dx - f_v dy}{g_v f_u - f_v g_u}$$

Similarly,

$$dv = \frac{f_u dy - g_u dx}{g_v f_u - f_v g_u}$$

(b)

$$\frac{\partial x}{\partial u} = \frac{\partial f}{\partial u} + \frac{\partial f}{\partial v} \frac{\partial v}{\partial u}$$

but

$$\frac{\partial v}{\partial u} = \frac{\dfrac{\partial g}{\partial u}}{\dfrac{\partial g}{\partial v}}$$

$$\frac{\partial x}{\partial u} = f_u + f_v \frac{g_u}{g_v}$$

$$= \frac{f_u g_v + f_v g_u}{g_v}$$

and

$$\frac{\partial u}{\partial x} = \frac{1}{\dfrac{\partial x}{\partial u}} = \frac{g_v}{f_u g_v + f_v g_u}$$

If z is defined as an implicit function of x and y by the equation $F(x, y, z) = 0$, then

$$\frac{\partial z}{\partial x} = - \frac{\dfrac{\partial F}{\partial x}}{\dfrac{\partial F}{\partial z}} \qquad \text{for } \frac{\partial F}{\partial z} \neq 0$$

$$\frac{\partial z}{\partial y} = - \frac{\dfrac{\partial F}{\partial y}}{\dfrac{\partial F}{\partial z}} \qquad \text{for } \frac{\partial F}{\partial z} \neq 0$$

provided the derivatives are defined. Similar formulas are appropriate for obtaining the partial derivatives of implicit functions of any finite number of variables.

Example

Find $\dfrac{\partial z}{\partial x}$ and $\dfrac{\partial z}{\partial y}$ for the function $ze^x + e^y - ye^z = 0$.

$$\frac{\partial F}{\partial x} = ze^x = -e^y + ye^z$$

$$\frac{\partial F}{\partial y} = e^y - e^z$$

$$\frac{\partial F}{\partial z} = e^x - ye^z$$

$$\frac{\partial z}{\partial x} = -\frac{\dfrac{\partial F}{\partial x}}{\dfrac{\partial F}{\partial z}} = \frac{e^y - ye^z}{e^x - ye^z}$$

$$\frac{\partial z}{\partial y} = -\frac{\dfrac{\partial F}{\partial y}}{\dfrac{\partial F}{\partial z}} = \frac{e^z - e^y}{e^x - ye^z}$$

PROBLEMS

1. If $z = x^3 + x^2y - y^3$, find dz.
2. If $u = \ln(x^2 + y^2 + z^2)^{1/2}$, find du.
3. If $u = e^{xyz}$, find du.
4. If $u = e^z \sin(x - y)z$, find du.
5. If $z = 2x^3 - 4xy^2 + 3y^3$, find dz.
6. If $u = xy^2z^3$, find du.
7. If $x^2 + y^2 + z^2 = a^2$, find dz.
8. If $u = x + 4x^{1/2}y^{1/2} - 3y$, $x = t^3$, and $y = \dfrac{1}{t}$, find $\dfrac{du}{dt}$.
9. If $x^3 + y^3 - 3bxy = 0$, find $\dfrac{dy}{dx}$.
10. If $x^2 + 2xy + 2y = 15$, find $\dfrac{dy}{dx}$ if $x = 2$, $y = 3$.
11. If $x^3 - y^3 - 4xy = -\frac{1}{2}$, find $\dfrac{dy}{dx}$ if $x = 2$, $y = -2$.
12. If $Ax + By + Ce^{xy} = D$, find $\dfrac{dy}{dx}$ if $x = y = 0$.
13. If $Ax^2 + By^2 + Cz^2 = D$, find z_x and z_y.

14. If $xy + yz + zx = 9xyz$, find z_x and z_y.

15. If $xz = \cos yz + a$, find z_x and z_y.

16. If $e^x + e^y + e^z = axyz$, find y_x.

17. If $F(x, y, z) = 0$, show that $x_y y_z z_x = -1$.

18. If $u = x^3 - 3xy + y^3$, $x = r^2 + s$, and $y = rs^2$, find $\dfrac{\partial u}{\partial r}$.

19. If $u = xy + yz$, $x = e^t/t$, $y = e^{-t}/t$, and $z = t^2$, find $\dfrac{du}{dt}$.

20. If $z = x \ln y + y \ln x$, $x = e^{u+v}$, and $y = e^{u-v}$, find $\dfrac{\partial z}{\partial u}$ and $\dfrac{\partial z}{\partial v}$.

21. If $z = \ln(x^2 + y^2) + \sqrt{x^2 + y^2}$, $x = e^u \cos v$, and $y = e^u \sin v$, find $\dfrac{\partial z}{\partial u}$.

22. If $u = xy + yz + zx$, $x = r^s$, $y = sr$, and $z = r + s$, find u_r.

23. If $x \ln yz - y \ln xz = 0$, find z_x and z_y.

24. If $e^{xyz} = e^x + e^y + e^z$, find z_x and z_y.

25. If $e^x + e^y + e^z = e^{x+y+z}$, find z_x and z_y.

26. If $u \ln \dfrac{v}{w} - w \ln uv = 0$, find u_v and u_w.

Answers to Odd-Numbered Problems

1. $dz = (3x^2 + 2xy)\, dx + (x^2 - 3y^2)\, dy$

3. $du = e^{xyz}(yz\, dx + xz\, dy + xy\, dz)$

5. $dz = (6x^2 - 4y^2)\, dx + (9y^2 - 8xy)\, dy$

7. $dz = -(x\, dx + y\, dy)/z$

9. $\dfrac{dy}{dx} = \dfrac{by - x^2}{y^2 - bx}$

11. $\dfrac{dy}{dx} = 1$

13. $z_x = -\dfrac{Ax}{Cz}$; $z_y = -\dfrac{By}{Cz}$

15. $z_x = -z/(x + y \sin yz)$; $z_y = -(z \sin yz)/(x + y \sin yz)$

19. $\dfrac{du}{dt} = e^{-t}(1 - t) - \dfrac{2}{t^3}$

21. $\dfrac{\partial z}{\partial u} = 2 + e^u$

23. $\dfrac{\partial z}{\partial x} = \dfrac{yz(1 - \ln xz)}{x(x - y)}$

  $\dfrac{\partial z}{\partial y} = \dfrac{-xz(1 - \ln yz)}{y(x - y)}$

25. $\dfrac{\partial z}{\partial x} = -\dfrac{e^y + e^z}{e^x + e^y}$

  $\dfrac{\partial z}{\partial y} = -\dfrac{e^x + e^z}{e^x + e^y}$

■ 3.3 APPLICATIONS OF PARTIAL DERIVATIVES IN BUSINESS AND ECONOMICS

□ MARGINAL COST

If the joint-cost function of producing the quantities x and y of two commodities is given by

$$C = Q(x, y)$$

then the partial derivatives of C are the *marginal cost functions*:

$\dfrac{\partial C}{\partial x}$ is the (partial) marginal cost with respect to x

$\dfrac{\partial C}{\partial y}$ is the (partial) marginal cost with respect to y

In most economic situations marginal costs are positive.

Example

If the joint-cost function of producing quantities x and y of two commodities is

$$C = x \ln(5 + y)$$

then

$\dfrac{\partial C}{dx} = \ln(5 + y)$ is the marginal cost with respect to x

$\dfrac{\partial C}{\partial y} = \dfrac{x}{5 + y}$ is the marginal cost with respect to y

□ DEMAND SURFACES

If there are two related commodities for which the quantities demanded are x and y and the respective prices are p and q, then the demand functions can be represented by

$$x = f(p, q) \qquad \text{and} \qquad y = g(p, q)$$

assuming that the quantities demanded, x and y, depend only on the prices, p and q, of the two commodities. If a demand function of two independent variables is continuous, it can be represented by a surface, referred to as a *demand surface*.

NOTE: The notation p_x and p_y is frequently used for the prices of the two commodities. It is not used in this section to avoid possible confusion with the subscript notation for partial derivatives.

In the usual economic situations, the demand functions $x = f(p, q)$ and $y = g(p, q)$ have the following properties:
1. All the variables, x, y, p, and q, are zero or positive.
2. If q is constant, then x is a monotonically decreasing function of p; similarly, if p is constant, then y is a monotonically decreasing function of q.
3. The functions $f(x, y)$ and $g(x, y)$ and the region for which they are defined are such that it is possible to obtain their inverse functions $p = F(x, y)$ and $q = G(x, y)$.

For a constant price p, as q increases y decreases, but x may either increase or decrease; if x increases, the two commodities are said to be *competitive*, since an increase in the demand for one corresponds to a decrease in the demand for the other. For a constant price p, as q decreases, y increases; if x also increases, the commodities are said to be *complementary*, since an increase in the demand for one corresponds to an increase in the demand for the other. Corresponding relationships hold for changes in p for a constant q.

NOTE: Usually, it is assumed that related commodities which are either competitive or complementary at one set of prices have the same relationship at other prices; however, in some cases the relationship between commodities may differ for different prices and is thus defined for a particular set of prices.

● **Marginal Demand**

If the demand functions for two related commodities are

$$x = f(p, q) \qquad y = g(p, q)$$

then the partial derivatives of x and y are the *marginal demand functions*:

$\dfrac{\partial x}{\partial p}$ is the (partial) marginal demand of x with respect to p

$\dfrac{\partial x}{\partial q}$ is the (partial) marginal demand of x with respect to q

$\dfrac{\partial y}{\partial p}$ is the (partial) marginal demand of y with respect to p

$\dfrac{\partial y}{\partial q}$ is the (partial) marginal demand of y with respect to q

Since, for the usual demand functions, x increases if its corresponding price

p decreases and y increases if its corresponding price q decreases, $\dfrac{\partial x}{\partial p}$ and $\dfrac{\partial y}{\partial q}$ are negative for all economically meaningful values of p and q.

If $\dfrac{\partial x}{\partial q}$ and $\dfrac{\partial y}{\partial p}$ are both negative for given (p, q), the commodities are complementary, since then a decrease in either price corresponds to increases in both demands. If $\dfrac{\partial x}{\partial q}$ and $\dfrac{\partial y}{\partial p}$ are both positive for given (p, q), the goods are competitive, since then a decrease in either price corresponds to an increase in one demand and a decrease in the other. If $\dfrac{\partial x}{\partial q}$ and $\dfrac{\partial y}{\partial p}$ have opposite signs, the commodities are neither complementary nor competitive; in this case, a decrease in the price of one of the commodities corresponds to increases in both demands while a decrease in the price of the other commodity corresponds to an increase in one demand and a decrease in the other. Such a situation might occur, for example, if two different grades of a material could be used and the better grade material could be obtained only by processing the lower grade material.

NOTE: Complementary and competitive commodities are defined in terms of the signs of their cross elasticities in Chapter 2. Those definitions and the definitions above are equivalent, since the signs of the cross elasticities are the same as the signs of the appropriate partial derivatives.

Examples

If the demand surfaces are linear functions of p and q,

$$x = a_1 + b_1 p + c_1 q \qquad y = a_2 + b_2 p + c_2 q$$

then the marginal demand functions are

$$\frac{\partial x}{\partial p} = b_1 \qquad \frac{\partial y}{\partial p} = b_2$$

$$\frac{\partial x}{\partial q} = c_1 \qquad \frac{\partial y}{\partial q} = c_2$$

Thus, for the usual economic situations, $b_1 < 0$ and $c_2 < 0$. If c_1 and b_2 are both positive, the commodities are competitive; if c_1 and b_2 are both negative, the commodities are complementary.

If the demand functions for two related commodities are given by

$$x = \frac{a}{p^2 q} \qquad y = \frac{a}{pq} \qquad a > 0$$

then the marginal demand functions are

$$\frac{\partial x}{\partial p} = -\frac{2a}{p^3 q} \qquad \frac{\partial y}{\partial p} = -\frac{a}{p^2 q}$$

$$\frac{\partial x}{\partial q} = -\frac{a}{p^2 q^2} \qquad \frac{\partial y}{\partial q} = -\frac{a}{pq^2}$$

Since $\dfrac{\partial x}{\partial q} < 0$ and $\dfrac{\partial y}{\partial q} < 0$, the commodities are complementary.

If the demand functions for two related commodities are given by

$$x = ae^{q-p} \qquad y = be^{p-q} \qquad a > 0 \quad b > 0$$

then the marginal demand functions are

$$\frac{\partial x}{\partial p} = -ae^{q-p} \qquad \frac{\partial y}{\partial p} = be^{p-q}$$

$$\frac{\partial x}{\partial q} = ae^{q-p} \qquad \frac{\partial y}{\partial q} = -be^{p-q}$$

Since $\dfrac{\partial x}{\partial q} > 0$ and $\dfrac{\partial y}{\partial p} > 0$, the commodities are competitive.

If the demand functions for two related commodities are given by

$$x = a_1 q^2 - b_1 pq \qquad y = a_2 p^2 - b_2 pq \qquad a_1 > 0 \quad a_2 > 0 \quad b_1 > 0 \quad b_2 > 0$$

then the marginal demand functions are

$$\frac{\partial x}{\partial p} = -b_1 q \qquad \frac{\partial y}{\partial p} = 2a_2 p - b_2 q$$

$$\frac{\partial x}{\partial q} = 2a_1 q - b_1 p \qquad \frac{\partial y}{\partial q} = -b_2 p$$

$$\frac{\partial x}{\partial q} > 0 \qquad \text{if } \frac{q}{p} > \frac{b_1}{2a_1} \qquad \frac{\partial y}{\partial p} > 0 \qquad \text{if } \frac{q}{p} < \frac{2a_2}{b_2}$$

$$\frac{\partial x}{\partial q} < 0 \qquad \text{if } \frac{q}{p} < \frac{b_1}{2a_1} \qquad \frac{\partial y}{\partial p} < 0 \qquad \text{if } \frac{q}{p} > \frac{2a_2}{b_2}$$

$$x > 0 \qquad \text{if } \frac{q}{p} > \frac{b_1}{a_1} \qquad y > 0 \qquad \text{if } \frac{q}{p} < \frac{a_2}{b_2}$$

Thus the demand functions are appropriate for values of p and q such that

$$\frac{b_1}{a_1} < \frac{q}{p} < \frac{a_2}{b_2}$$

The commodities are competitive for values of p and q such that the demand functions are appropriate $\left(\text{since } \dfrac{b_1}{a_1} < \dfrac{q}{p} < \dfrac{a_2}{b_2} \Rightarrow \dfrac{b_1}{2a} < \dfrac{q}{p} < \dfrac{2a_2}{b_2}\right)$.

If the demand functions for two related commodities are given by

$$x = ae^{-pq} \qquad y = be^{p-q} \qquad a > 0 \quad b > 0$$

then the marginal demand functions are

$$\frac{\partial x}{\partial p} = -aqe^{-pq} \qquad \frac{\partial y}{\partial p} = be^{p-q}$$

$$\frac{\partial x}{\partial q} = -ape^{-pq} \qquad \frac{\partial y}{\partial q} = -be^{p-q}$$

Since $\frac{\partial x}{\partial q} < 0$ and $\frac{\partial y}{\partial p} > 0$, the commodities are neither competitive nor complementary.

● **Partial Elasticities of Demand**

If the demand functions for two related commodities are

$$x = f(p, q) \qquad y = g(p, q)$$

then the partial elasticities of demand are given by

$$\frac{Ex}{Ep}\bigg|_{q=c_1} = \frac{p}{x} \cdot \frac{\partial x}{\partial p} = \frac{\frac{\partial}{\partial x}\ln x}{\frac{\partial}{\partial x}\ln p} \qquad \text{the partial elasticity of demand } x \text{ with respect to price } p, \text{ for a constant price } q = c_1$$

$$\frac{Ex}{Eq}\bigg|_{p=c_2} = \frac{q}{x} \cdot \frac{\partial x}{\partial q} = \frac{\frac{\partial}{\partial x}\ln x}{\frac{\partial}{\partial x}\ln q} \qquad \text{the partial elasticity of demand } x \text{ with respect to price } q, \text{ for a constant price } p = c_2$$

$$\frac{Ey}{Ep}\bigg|_{q=c_3} = \frac{p}{y} \cdot \frac{\partial y}{\partial p} = \frac{\frac{\partial}{\partial y}\ln y}{\frac{\partial}{\partial y}\ln p} \qquad \text{the partial elasticity of demand } y \text{ with respect to price } p, \text{ for a constant price } q = c_3$$

$$\frac{Ey}{Eq}\bigg|_{p=c_4} = \frac{q}{y} \cdot \frac{\partial y}{\partial q} = \frac{\frac{\partial}{\partial y}\ln y}{\frac{\partial}{\partial y}\ln q} \qquad \text{the partial elasticity of demand } y \text{ with respect to price } q, \text{ for a constant price } p = c_4$$

Note that a partial elasticity of demand is the ratio of the proportional change in quantity demanded of one commodity to the proportional change in price of one commodity, with the price of the other commodity constant. Partial elasticities of price are similarly defined.

Examples

If the demand functions for two related commodities are given by

$$x = ae^{q-p} \qquad y = be^{p-q}$$

then the partial elasticities of demand are

$$\frac{Ex}{Ep} = \frac{p}{x} \cdot \frac{\partial x}{\partial p} = \frac{p}{ae^{q-p}}(-ae^{q-p}) = -p$$

$$\frac{Ex}{Eq} = \frac{q}{x} \cdot \frac{\partial x}{\partial q} = \frac{q}{ae^{q-p}}(ae^{q-p}) = q$$

$$\frac{Ey}{Ep} = \frac{p}{y} \cdot \frac{\partial y}{\partial p} = \frac{p}{be^{p-q}}(be^{p-q}) = p$$

$$\frac{Ey}{Eq} = \frac{q}{y} \cdot \frac{\partial y}{\partial q} = \frac{q}{be^{p-q}}(-be^{p-q}) = -q$$

If the demand functions for two related commodities are given by

$$x = a_1 q^2 - b_1 pq \qquad y = a_2 p^2 - b_2 pq \qquad a_1 > 0 \quad a_2 > 0 \quad b_1 > 0 \quad b_2 > 0$$

then the partial elasticities of demand are

$$\frac{Ex}{Ep} = \frac{p}{x} \cdot \frac{\partial x}{\partial p} = \frac{p}{a_1 q^2 - b_1 pq}(-b_1 q) = \frac{b_1 p}{b_1 p - a_1 q}$$

$$\frac{Ex}{Eq} = \frac{q}{x} \cdot \frac{\partial x}{\partial q} = \frac{q}{a_1 q^2 - b_1 pq}(2a_1 q - b_1 p) = \frac{2a_1 q - b_1 p}{a_1 q - b_1 p}$$

$$\frac{Ey}{Ep} = \frac{p}{y} \cdot \frac{\partial y}{\partial p} = \frac{p}{a_2 p^2 - b_2 pq}(2a_2 p - b_2 q) = \frac{2a_2 p - b_2 q}{a_2 p - b_2 q}$$

$$\frac{Ey}{Eq} = \frac{q}{y} \cdot \frac{\partial y}{\partial q} = \frac{q}{a_2 p^2 - b_2 pq}(-b_2 p) = \frac{b_2 q}{b_2 q - a_2 p}$$

☐ PRODUCTION FUNCTIONS

The production of most commodities requires the use of at least two factors of production—for example, labor, land, capital, materials, or machines. If the quantity z of a commodity is produced using the amounts x and y, respectively, of two factors of production, then the *production function*

$$z = f(x, y)$$

gives the amount of *output z* when the amounts x and y, respectively, of the *inputs* are used simultaneously.

For such a representation to be economically meaningful, it is assumed that the amounts of the inputs can be varied without restriction, at least in the range of interest, and that the production function is continuous.

● Marginal Productivity

If the production function is given by $z = f(x, y)$, then the partial derivative $\frac{\partial z}{\partial x}$ of z with respect to x (with y held constant) is the *marginal productivity of x* or the *marginal product of x*; the partial derivative $\frac{\partial z}{\partial y}$ of z with respect to y (with x held constant) is the *marginal productivity of y* or the *marginal product of y*. Note that the marginal productivity of either input is the rate of increase of the total product as that input is increased, assuming that the amount of the other input remains constant.

Usually, for a considerable range marginal productivity is positive—that is, as the amount of one input increases (with the amount of the other input held constant) the output also increases. However, as the input of one factor increases, the output usually increases at a decreasing rate until the point is reached at which there is no further increase in output but, in fact, a decrease in total output occurs with additional inputs of the particular factor under analysis. This characteristic behavior of production functions is known as the *law of eventually diminishing marginal productivity*.

Examples

If the production function is given by
$$z = 4x^{3/4}y^{1/4}$$
then the marginal productivity of x is
$$\frac{\partial z}{\partial x} = 3x^{-1/4}y^{1/4}$$
and the marginal productivity of y is
$$\frac{\partial z}{\partial y} = x^{3/4}y^{-3/4}$$

Note that $\frac{\partial z}{\partial x}$ is always positive, but decreases as x increases; similarly, $\frac{\partial z}{\partial y}$ is always positive, but decreases as y increases. This can be verified immediately from the signs of the second derivatives when x and y are positive.

If the production function is given by
$$z = 4xy - x^2 - 3y^2$$
then the marginal productivity of x is
$$\frac{\partial z}{\partial x} = 4y - 2x$$
and the marginal productivity of y is
$$\frac{\partial z}{\partial y} = 4x - 6y$$

Note that $\frac{\partial z}{\partial x} > 0$ for $x < 2y$, $\frac{\partial z}{\partial x} = 0$ for $x = 2y$, and $\frac{\partial z}{\partial x} < 0$ for $x > 2y$ (where

y is held constant); similarly, $\dfrac{\partial z}{\partial y} > 0$ for $y < \frac{2}{3}x$, and $\dfrac{\partial z}{\partial y} = 0$ for $y = \frac{2}{3}x$,

and $\dfrac{\partial z}{\partial y} > 0$ for $y > \frac{2}{3}x$.

If a production function is given by

$$z^2 + 4x^2 + 5y^2 - 12xy = 0$$

where z is the amount of output and x and y are the amounts of the inputs, find the marginal productivities.

$$\frac{\partial F}{\partial x} = 8x - 12y$$

$$\frac{\partial F}{\partial y} = 10y - 12x$$

$$\frac{\partial F}{\partial z} = 2z$$

The marginal productivity of x is

$$\frac{\partial z}{\partial x} = -\frac{\dfrac{\partial F}{\partial x}}{\dfrac{\partial F}{\partial z}} = \frac{6y - 4x}{z}$$

and the marginal productivity of y is

$$\frac{\partial z}{\partial y} = -\frac{\dfrac{\partial F}{\partial y}}{\dfrac{\partial F}{\partial z}} = \frac{6x - 5y}{z}$$

☐ EULER'S THEOREM

If the function $z = f(x, y)$ has the property that, for any constant λ,

$$f(\lambda x, \lambda y) = \lambda^n f(x, y)$$

then z is said to be *homogeneous of degree n*. If $n > 0$, the function is said to be *positively homogeneous*; if $n = 1$, the function is said to be *linear homogeneous*.

If $z = f(x, y)$ is positively homogeneous of degree n and the first-order partial derivatives exist, then it can be shown that

$$x \frac{\partial z}{\partial x} + y \frac{\partial z}{\partial y} = nf(x, y)$$

This relationship is known as *Euler's theorem*.

Examples

The function $z = f(x, y) = 3x^4 + 2x^2y^2 + 7y^4$ is homogeneous of degree 4, since

$$f(\lambda x, \lambda y) = 3\lambda^4 x^4 + 2\lambda^4 x^2 y^2 + 7\lambda^4 y^4$$

$$= \lambda^4 f(x, y)$$

Thus, according to Euler's theorem,

$$x \frac{\partial z}{\partial x} + y \frac{\partial z}{\partial y} = 4f(x, y)$$

which can be verified as follows:

$$x \frac{\partial z}{\partial x} + y \frac{\partial z}{\partial y} = x(12x^3 + 4xy^2) + y(4x^2y + 28y^3)$$

$$= 12x^4 + 8x^2y^2 + 28y^4$$

$$= 4f(x, y)$$

The function $z = f(x, y) = \dfrac{xy}{x^2 + y^2}$ is homogeneous of degree zero, since

$$f(\lambda x, \lambda y) = \frac{\lambda^2 xy}{\lambda^2 (x^2 + y^2)}$$

$$= \lambda^0 f(x, y)$$

Thus, according to Euler's theorem,

$$x \frac{\partial z}{\partial x} + y \frac{\partial z}{\partial y} = 0$$

which can be verified as follows:

$$x \frac{\partial z}{\partial x} + y \frac{\partial z}{\partial y} = x \frac{y(x^2 + y^2) - xy(2x)}{(x^2 + y^2)^2} + y \frac{x(x^2 + y^2) - xy(2y)}{(x^2 + y^2)^2}$$

$$= \frac{2xy(x^2 + y^2) - 2x^3y - 2xy^3}{(x^2 + y^2)^2}$$

$$= 0$$

In addition to the property known as Euler's theorem, linear homogeneous functions have the following properties: If $z = f(x, y)$ is a linear homogeneous function, then

(1)
$$\begin{cases} \dfrac{z}{x} = g_1\left(\dfrac{y}{x}\right), & \text{that is, } \dfrac{z}{x} \text{ is a function of } \dfrac{y}{x} \\[2em] \dfrac{z}{y} = g_2\left(\dfrac{x}{y}\right), & \text{that is, } \dfrac{z}{y} \text{ is a function of } \dfrac{x}{y} \end{cases}$$

(2)
$$\begin{cases} \dfrac{\partial z}{\partial x} = h_1\left(\dfrac{y}{x}\right), & \text{that is, } \dfrac{\partial z}{\partial x} \text{ is a function of } \dfrac{y}{x} \\[2em] \dfrac{\partial z}{\partial y} = h_2\left(\dfrac{x}{y}\right), & \text{that is, } \dfrac{\partial z}{\partial y} \text{ is a function of } \dfrac{x}{y} \end{cases}$$

(3)
$$\begin{cases} \dfrac{\partial^2 z}{\partial x^2} = -\dfrac{y}{x} \cdot \dfrac{\partial^2 z}{\partial x\, \partial y} \\[2em] \dfrac{\partial^2 z}{\partial y^2} = -\dfrac{x}{y} \cdot \dfrac{\partial^2 z}{\partial x\, \partial y} \end{cases}$$

Example

The function $z = \dfrac{xy}{x+y}$ is linear homogeneous, since

$$f(\lambda x, \lambda y) = \frac{\lambda^2 xy}{\lambda(x+y)}$$
$$= \lambda f(x, y)$$

Thus, according to Euler's theorem,

$$x\frac{\partial z}{\partial x} + y\frac{\partial z}{\partial y} = f(x, y)$$

which can be verified as follows:

$$x\frac{\partial z}{\partial x} + y\frac{\partial z}{\partial y} = x\frac{y(x+y) - xy}{(x+y)^2} + y\frac{x(x+y) - xy}{(x+y)^2}$$

$$= \frac{xy^2 + x^2 y}{(x+y)^2}$$

$$= \frac{xy(x+y)}{(x+y)^2}$$

$$= f(x, y)$$

According to property (1),

$$\frac{z}{x} = g_1\left(\frac{y}{x}\right)$$

$$\frac{z}{y} = g_2\left(\frac{x}{y}\right)$$

which can be verified as follows:

$$\frac{z}{x} = \frac{y}{x+y} = \frac{y}{x}\left(1 + \frac{y}{x}\right)^{-1} = g_1\left(\frac{y}{x}\right)$$

$$\frac{z}{y} = \frac{x}{x+y} = \frac{x}{y}\left(1 + \frac{x}{y}\right)^{-1} = g_2\left(\frac{x}{y}\right)$$

According to property (2),

$$\frac{\partial z}{\partial x} = h_1\left(\frac{y}{x}\right)$$

$$\frac{\partial z}{\partial y} = h_2\left(\frac{x}{y}\right)$$

which can be verified as follows:

$$\frac{\partial z}{\partial x} = \frac{y^2}{(x+y)^2} = \left(\frac{y}{x}\right)^2\left(1 + \frac{y}{x}\right)^{-2} = h_1\left(\frac{y}{x}\right)$$

$$\frac{\partial z}{\partial y} = \frac{x^2}{(x+y)^2} = \left(\frac{x}{y}\right)^2\left(1 + \frac{x}{y}\right)^{-2} = h_2\left(\frac{y}{x}\right)$$

According to property (3),

$$\frac{\partial^2 z}{\partial x^2} = -\frac{y}{x} \cdot \frac{\partial^2 z}{\partial x\,\partial y}$$

$$\frac{\partial^2 z}{\partial y^2} = -\frac{x}{y} \cdot \frac{\partial^2 z}{\partial x\,\partial y}$$

which can be verified as follows:

$$\frac{\partial^2 z}{\partial x^2} = \frac{-2y^2}{(x+y)^3}$$

$$\frac{\partial^2 z}{\partial x\,\partial y} = \frac{2y(x+y)^2 - y^2(2)(x+y)}{(x+y)^4}$$

$$= \frac{2xy}{(x+y)^3}$$

And thus

$$\frac{\partial^2 z}{\partial x^2} = -\frac{y}{x} \cdot \frac{\partial^2 z}{\partial x\,\partial y} = \frac{-2y^2}{(x+y)^3}$$

Similarly,

$$\frac{\partial^2 z}{\partial y^2} = \frac{-2x^2}{(x+y)^3}$$

$$= -\frac{x}{y} \cdot \frac{\partial^2 z}{\partial x\, \partial y} = \frac{-2x^2}{(x+y)^3}$$

● Linear Homogeneous Production Functions

If a production function $z = f(x, y)$ is linear homogeneous, then according to Euler's theorem,

$$\underbrace{x\frac{\partial z}{\partial x}} + \underbrace{y\frac{\partial z}{\partial y}} = f(x, y)$$

Total due   Total due
to   to
factor x factor y

That is, total production or output is equal to the product of the amount of one input and its marginal productivity plus the product of the amount of the other input and its marginal productivity. The total product is thus allocated to the two factors on the basis of their marginal productivities. Euler's theorem plays an important part in the development of the marginal-productivity theory of distribution. The basic assumptions of this theory are (1) each input is paid the value of its marginal productivity, and (2) total output is just exhausted. As shown by Euler's theorem, these conditions are satisfied by linear homogeneous production functions; thus in the development of the theory production functions were generally assumed to be of this type. Note that if the production function is homogeneous of degree n and each input is paid the value of its marginal productivity, then total output would exceed payments for $n > 1$ and would be less than payments for $n < 1$.

☐ CONSTANT PRODUCT CURVES

The production function $z = f(x, y)$ is frequently studied by considering the family of curves

$$f(x, y) = \text{constant}$$

in the xy-plane. These curves, no two of which intersect, are called *constant product curves*, *equal product curves*, or *isoquants*. Each curve shows the combinations of factors x and y which result in a specified output. As discussed below, constant product curves are such that a decrease in the input of one factor is compensated for by an increase in the input of the other factor. The slope $\dfrac{dy}{dx}$ of the tangent at a point on an isoquant is the rate at which x must be substituted for y to maintain the level of output. The negative of this derivative $-\dfrac{dy}{dx}$ is defined as the *rate of technical substitution.*

Equal product curves are of various shapes, depending on the nature of the production function, but in general they have negative slopes and are convex to the origin in the area of interest.

Actually, there are some economic situations in which portions of the equal product curves have positive slopes—that is, there are some situations in which additional amounts of a factor of input result in decreased production. For example, if the two factors of production are land and labor, so many men might be employed (for a fixed amount of land) that they would interfere with each other and production would decrease. However, assuming the objective of profit maximization, portions of equal product curves having positive slopes would not be used in practice, since the given output could be obtained at less cost by a factor combination on a portion of the curve having negative slope. Thus, as shown in Fig. 3.2, only the portions of the equal product curves lying between their respective vertical and horizontal tangents are relevant; the lines through these points of tangency are known as *ridge lines.* The firm would never operate above the upper ridge line or to the right of the lower ridge line, since this would require more input than necessary to produce a specified output.

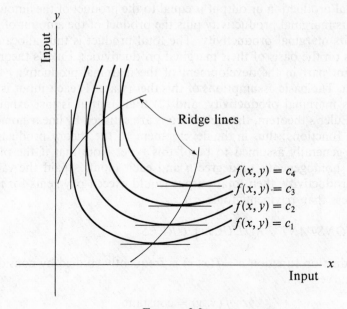

FIGURE 3.2

The assumption that equal product curves are convex to the origin implies that the marginal significance of one factor with respect to the other factor decreases along an equal product curve—that is, as the amount of factor x that is used increases, the amount of factor y that can be given up in exchange for a further unit of factor x decreases, if the product remains constant; similarly, as the amount of factor y that is used increases, the amount of factor x that can be given up in exchange for a further unit of factor y decreases, if the product remains constant. If the marginal significance of a factor increased as the amount used increased, as would be the case for a concave equal product curve, then only that one factor should be used, since each unit of the factor would be progressively more worth purchasing. Thus, in practice, any portions of equal product curves for which marginal significance of the factors is not decreasing are not relevant.

If factors x and y are purchased in a perfectly competitive market at constant unit prices, then the total cost of production is given by

$$C = p_x x + p_y y + b$$

where p_x and p_y are the respective prices of x and y and b is the cost of the fixed inputs. *Isocost curves* give the combinations of input factors that can be purchased for a specified total cost and in this case are represented by the family of lines

$$p_x x + p_y y + b = \text{constant}$$

The slopes of the isocost lines are equal to the negative of the input price ratio, since

$$y = -\frac{p_x}{p_y} x - \frac{b}{p_y} + \frac{\text{constant}}{p_y}$$

The greatest total output than can be produced for a specified total cost is given by the point of tangency of the relevant isocost curve and an isoquant. Similarly, the lowest possible cost of producing a specified output is given by the

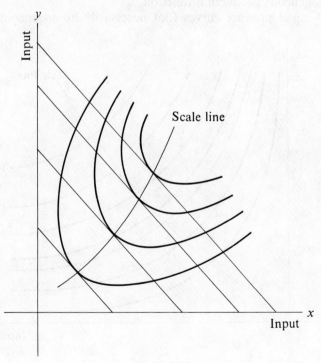

FIGURE 3.3

point of tangency of the relevant isoquant and an isocost curve. The curve connecting the points of tangency of the isocost curves and isoquants is known as the *expansion path* or *scale line*. This line gives the lowest-cost combinations of factors as output increases; the firm will thus always produce at some point on the scale line (see Fig. 3.3).

□ RETURNS TO SCALE

Returns to scale describes the change in output with a proportionate increase in all inputs. If output increases by the same proportion as the inputs increase, then returns to scale are constant; if output increases by a greater proportion than inputs, returns to scale are increasing; if output increases by a smaller proportion than inputs, returns to scale are decreasing. Very frequently, there are increasing returns to scale for relatively small inputs (economies of scale), returns to scale are then constant for a range of inputs, and finally there are decreasing returns to scale for large inputs (diseconomies of scale).

Returns to scale are easily determined for homogeneous production functions. If a production function is homogeneous of degree n, returns to scale are increasing if $n > 1$, constant if $n = 1$, and decreasing if $n < 1$. In practice, a degree of homogeneity other than 1 is seldom assumed for production functions. The expansion path (at all points of which the rate of technical substitution equals the fixed input-price ratio) is a straight line if the production function is homogeneous of any degree. A straight-line expansion path does not, however, imply a homogeneous production function.

If a set of equal product curves (not necessarily homogeneous) represents

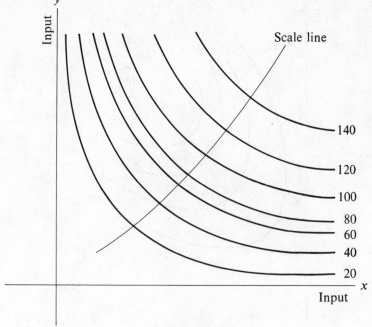

FIGURE 3.4

successive increases in production of a given amount, then returns to scale increase as output increases if the distance along the scale line between successive curves decreases; similarly, returns to scale decrease as output increases if the distance along the scale line between successive curves increases. Thus, in Fig. 3.4, returns to scale increase from 20 to 80 units of production and decrease from 80 to 140 units of production.

Note that if the proportions of the amounts of the two factors of production vary, it is necessary to refer to *returns to outlay* rather than returns to scale, since the factors are not increased by the same scale.

□ *UTILITY FUNCTIONS*

In the theory of consumer behavior the consumer is assumed to choose among the alternatives available to him in such a way that the satisfaction derived from consuming commodities is maximized. This implies that the consumer is aware of his alternatives and is capable of evaluating them. All information concerning the satisfaction a consumer derives from various quantities of commodities is contained in his utility function.

The concept of utility is based not on some type of psychological satisfaction on the part of the consumer, but only on his choice behavior. The assertion that a consumer derives more satisfaction or utility from A than from B means that he would choose A rather than B if A and B were presented as alternatives. In addition, the consumer is assumed to make consistent choices so that if A is preferred to B and B is preferred to C, then A is preferred to C.

Modern utility theory assumes only an ordinal utility scale; that is, for all pairs of alternatives A and B, the consumer is assumed to know whether he prefers A to B, prefers B to A, or is indifferent between them, but he is not assumed capable of assigning numbers representing amounts of utility to alternatives.

A consumer's ranking (preference order) of commodities is expressed mathematically by his utility function. The utility function associates certain numbers (utility) with various quantities of commodities consumed, but these numbers represent only a ranking or ordering of preferences. Thus if the utility of alternative A is 20 and the utility of alternative B is 5, then A is preferred to B but it is incorrect (and meaningless) to say that A is preferred 4 times as strongly as B.

Consider the simple case in which the consumer's purchases are limited to two commodities and his utility function is

$$U = f(q_1, q_2)$$

where q_1 and q_2 are the quantities of the two commodities Q_1 and Q_2 which he consumes. It is assumed that $f(q_1, q_2)$ is continuous and has continuous first-order and second-order partial derivatives.

The utility function is with respect to consumption during a specified period of time, a period long enough for the desire for variety to be satisfied but not so long that tastes change. Utility is derived from the consumption of commodities. By definition, a commodity is something of which the consumer would rather have more than less; otherwise a discommodity is involved. In reality, a commodity consumed in sufficiently large amounts may become a discommodity (for example, too much candy); the following discussion assumes that such a point of satiation has not been reached. Thus the partial derivatives of U with respect to q_1 and q_2, denoted f_1 and f_2, are positive.

Since the utility function is continuous, a given level of utility can be derived from an infinite number of combinations of q_1 and q_2. The locus of all combinations of quantities of commodities from which the consumer derives the same utility is an *indifference curve*. A collection of indifference curves corresponding to different levels of utility is an *indifference map*. (See Fig. 3.5.) One indifference curve passes through every point of the first quadrant; indifference curves corresponding to increasing levels of utility are farther from the origin. Indifference curves cannot intersect because this would imply that the same combination of q_1 and q_2 has different utilities.

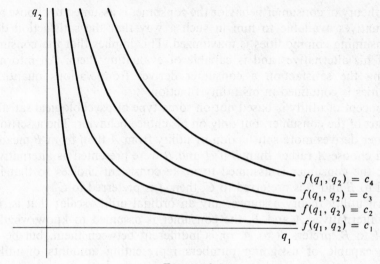

FIGURE 3.5

Note that $U = f(q_1, q_2)$ can be represented by a utility surface in three dimensions. Each indifference curve represents the intersection of that surface and a plane parallel to the $q_1 q_2$-plane at a certain value of U. The points on an indifference curve represent the various combinations of quantities of the commodities that have the same utility for the consumer and among which, therefore, he is indifferent.

The total differential of the utility function is

$$dU = f_1 \, dq_1 + f_2 \, dq_2$$

where f_1 and f_2 are the partial derivatives of U with respect to q_1 and q_2, respectively. Since the change in utility along any indifference curve is zero by definition, $dU = 0$ and

$$f_1 \, dq_1 + f_2 \, dq_2 = 0$$

$$-\frac{dq_2}{dq_1} = \frac{f_1}{f_2}$$

The slope of an indifference curve dq_2/dq_1 is the rate at which a consumer would be willing to substitute Q_1 for Q_2 or Q_2 for Q_1 to maintain a given level of utility. The negative of the slope $-dq_2/dq_1$ is the *rate of commodity substitution or marginal rate of substitution* of Q_1 for Q_2 or Q_2 for Q_1 and equals the ratio of the partial derivatives of the utility function.

The partial derivatives f_1 and f_2 are said to be the marginal utilities of the commodities Q_1 and Q_2. The magnitudes of the marginal utilities are without meaning when the utility function is ordinal, but their signs and ratios are meaningful. Note that if the marginal utilities are positive, an increase in the quantity consumed of one commodity with no change in the quantity consumed of the other commodity will move the consumer to a higher indifference curve.

PROBLEMS

1. For each of the following pairs of demand functions for two related commodities find the partial elasticities of demand.

   (a) $x = \dfrac{a}{p^2 q}$ and $y = \dfrac{a}{pq}$, $a > 0$

   (b) $x = ae^{-pq}$ and $y = be^{p-q}$, $a > 0$, $b > 0$

2. For each of the following pairs of demand functions determine the four partial marginal demands, the nature of the relationship between the two commodities, and the four partial elasticities of demand.

   (a) $x = 20 - 2p - q$ (b) $x = 15 - 2p + q$
   $\quad\ y = 9 - p - 2q$ $\quad\ y = 16 + p - q$

   (c) $x = 5 - 2p + q$ (d) $x = \dfrac{q}{p}$
   $\quad\ y = 8 - 2p - 3q$

   $\qquad\qquad\qquad\qquad\qquad\ \ y = \dfrac{p^2}{q}$

   (e) $x = \dfrac{4}{p^2 q}$ (f) $x = \dfrac{4}{pq}$

   $\quad\ y = \dfrac{16}{pq^2}$ $\quad\ y = \dfrac{16}{pq}$

3. For each of the following production functions find the marginal productivities.

   (a) $z = 25 - \dfrac{1}{x} - \dfrac{1}{y}$ at $x = 1$, $y = 1$
   (b) $z = 5xy - 2x^2 - 2y^2$ at $x = 1$, $y = 1$
   (c) $16z^2 - z - 80 + 4(x - 5)^2 + 2(y - 4)^2 = 0$
   (d) $6z^3 - z^2 - 6x - 24y + x^2 + 4y^2 + 50 = 0$

4. The Cobb-Douglas production function for the economy as a whole is given by

$$z = ax^b y^c$$

where z is total product, x is quantity of labor, y is quantity of capital, and a, b, and c are constants. It is frequently assumed that $b + c = 1$. Is this function homogeneous and, if so, of what degree?

5. For each of the following production functions, determine the degree of homogeneity and the nature of the returns to scale.

(a) $z = 3x^3 + 5xy^2 + y^3$ (b) $z = \dfrac{14}{x} - \dfrac{20}{y}$

(c) $z = 25y^6 - x^2y^4$ (d) $z = \dfrac{3}{x^2} + \dfrac{25}{xy} + \dfrac{6}{y^2}$

6. Determine whether each of the following functions is homogeneous; for homogeneous functions, determine the degree and demonstrate Euler's theorem; for linear homogeneous functions, also demonstrate the other three properties given in the text.

(a) $z = 3x^2 + 4xy + 15y^3$ (b) $z = 4x^3 + x^2y - 3xy^2 - 7y^3$

(c) $z = 3e^x + 3e^y$ (d) $z = 6 \ln 3^{-2x} - \ln 4^{-5y}$

(e) $z = \dfrac{x^4 + 3x^2y^2 + xy^3 + 6y^4}{x^3}$ (f) $z = 3x \ln 5^{x/y} - 9y \ln 8^{y/x}$

(g) $z = \dfrac{x^2y + y^3}{x^6}$ (h) $z = \dfrac{x^2 + 3xy + y^2}{y^2}$

(i) $z = 4x^2e^y + 3y^2e^x$ (j) $z = 3x^2 \ln a^{1/y^2} - 5y^3 \ln b^{1/y^3}$

(k) $z = \dfrac{x^2 + xy}{3y}$ (l) $z = 3x^2y + 4xy^2 + y^3 + 10$

7. If a consumer's utility function is given by $U = q_1q_2^2$ and the consumer purchases 4 units of Q_1 and 5 units of Q_2, (a) what quantity of Q_1 must he purchase to maintain the same level of utility if his purchase of Q_2 increases to 6 units? (b) What quantity of Q_2 must he purchase to maintain the same level of utility if his purchase of Q_1 increases to 6 units? (c) What quantity of Q_1 must he purchase to maintain the same level of utility if his purchase of Q_2 decreases to 4 units? (d) What quantity of Q_2 must he purchase to maintain the same level of utility if his purchase of Q_1 decreases to 2 units?

8. Find the marginal utilities for each of the following utility functions.

(a) $U = q_1^3q_2$

(b) $U = q_1q_2 + q_1^2$

ANSWERS TO ODD-NUMBERED PROBLEMS

1. (a) $\dfrac{Ex}{Ep} = -2$ (b) $\dfrac{Ex}{Ep} = -pq$

$\dfrac{Ex}{Eq} = -1$ $\dfrac{Ex}{Eq} = -pq$

$\dfrac{Ey}{Ep} = -1$ $\dfrac{Ey}{Ep} = p$

$\dfrac{Ey}{Eq} = -1$ $\dfrac{Ey}{Eq} = -q$

3. (a) $\dfrac{\partial z}{\partial x} = 1$, $\dfrac{\partial z}{\partial y} = 1$

   (b) $\dfrac{\partial z}{\partial x} = 1$, $\dfrac{\partial z}{\partial y} = 1$

   (c) $\dfrac{\partial z}{\partial x} = -\dfrac{8(x-5)}{32z-1}$

   $\dfrac{\partial z}{\partial y} = -\dfrac{4(y-4)}{32z-1}$

   (d) $\dfrac{\partial z}{\partial x} = -\dfrac{x-3}{z(9z-1)}$

   $\dfrac{\partial z}{\partial y} = -\dfrac{4(y-3)}{z(9z-1)}$

5. (a) degree 3, increasing returns to scale
   (b) degree -1, decreasing returns to scale
   (c) degree 6, increasing returns to scale
   (d) degree -2, decreasing returns to scale

7. (a) $q_1 = 25/9$

   (b) $q_2 = \dfrac{5\sqrt{6}}{3}$

   (c) $q_1 = 25/4$

   (d) $q_2 = 5\sqrt{2}$

■ 3.4 MAXIMA AND MINIMA OF FUNCTIONS OF TWO VARIABLES

A function $f(x, y)$ of two independent variables is said to have a local maximum value (or minimum value) for $x = a$, $y = b$, if $f(a, b)$ is greater (or less) than $f(x, y)$ for all values of x and y close to $x = a$, $y = b$.

If $f(x, y)$ has a maximum (or minimum) value at $x = a$, $y = b$, it follows that the function $f(x, b)$ has a maximum (or minimum) at $x = a$ and the function $f(a, y)$ has a maximum (or minimum) at $y = b$. Thus, for the function $f(x, y)$ to have a maximum (or minimum) at $x = a$, $y = b$, it is necessary that

$$\frac{\partial}{\partial x} f(x, y)\bigg|_{x=a,\, y=b} = 0$$

$$\frac{\partial}{\partial y} f(x, y)\bigg|_{x=a,\, y=b} = 0$$

These two conditions are used to determine the critical points; the procedure below is then used to determine whether the critical points are in fact local maxima or minima.

$$\text{If } \begin{cases} \dfrac{\partial}{\partial x} f(x, y)\bigg|_{x=a,\, y=b} = 0 \\[2ex] \dfrac{\partial}{\partial y} f(x, y)\bigg|_{x=a,\, y=b} = 0 \end{cases}$$

$$\text{and } \Delta = \left(\frac{\partial^2}{\partial x^2} f(x, y)\bigg|_{x=a,\, y=b}\right)\left(\frac{\partial^2}{\partial y^2} f(x, y)\bigg|_{x=a,\, y=b}\right) - \left(\frac{\partial^2}{\partial x\, \partial y} f(x, y)\bigg|_{x=a,\, y=b}\right)^2$$

$$then \begin{cases} \Delta > 0 \Rightarrow \begin{cases} \text{maximum at } x = a, y = b, \text{ if } \dfrac{\partial^2}{\partial x^2} f(x, y) < 0 \text{ and } \dfrac{\partial^2}{\partial y^2} f(x, y) < 0 \\[3mm] \text{minimum at } x = a, y = b, \text{ if } \dfrac{\partial^2}{\partial x^2} f(x, y) > 0 \text{ and } \dfrac{\partial^2}{\partial y^2} f(x, y) > 0 \end{cases} \\[6mm] \Delta < 0 \Rightarrow \text{neither maximum nor minimum at } x = a, y = b, \text{ but a saddle} \\ \qquad \text{point at } x = a, y = b \\[3mm] \Delta = 0 \Rightarrow \text{test fails, function must be investigated near } x = a, y = b \end{cases}$$

These conditions can be stated more concisely as follows:

necessary condition for a critical point: $f_x = 0, f_y = 0$

determination of local maxima or minima:

$$f_{xx}f_{yy} - f_{xy}^2 > 0 \Rightarrow \begin{cases} \text{maximum if} \\ f_{xx} < 0, f_{yy} < 0 \\ \text{minimum if} \\ f_{xx} > 0, f_{yy} > 0 \end{cases}$$

$$f_{xx}f_{yy} - f_{xy}^2 < 0 \Rightarrow \text{saddle point}$$

$$f_{xx}f_{yy} - f_{xy}^2 = 0 \Rightarrow \text{test fails and the function must be investigated near the critical point}$$

where the partial derivatives are evaluated for the critical point.

Note that this procedure is used to identify local maxima and minima. In order to determine global maxima or minima it is necessary not only to compare the values of the local maxima or minima, but also to determine the values of the function at the limits of its range, if its range is limited. The procedure for determining global maxima and minima for functions of two variables is thus analogous to the procedure for functions of one variable.

Examples of functions having at the origin (a) a minimum, (b) a maximum and (c) a saddle point are illustrated in Fig. 3.6. Note that at a saddle point a

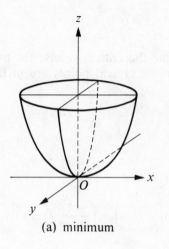

(a) minimum

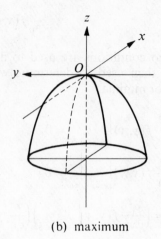

(b) maximum

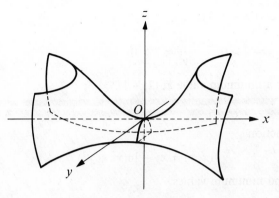

(c) saddle point

FIGURE 3.6

function has a minimum with respect to one variable and a maximum with respect to the other variable. For example, in Fig. 3.6(c) the origin looks like a minimum to a person traveling along the surface in the yz-plane, but to a person traveling in the xz-plane the origin looks like a maximum.

Examples

Examine the function

$$f(x, y) = x^2 + xy + y^2 - 3x + 2$$

for maximum and minimum values.

$$\frac{\partial f}{\partial x} = 2x + y - 3$$

$$\frac{\partial f}{\partial y} = x + 2y$$

$$2x + y = 3$$

$$x + 2y = 0$$

$$3y = -3$$

$$y = -1, x = 2, \text{ so } (2, -1) \text{ may be a maximum or minimum}$$

$$\frac{\partial^2 f}{\partial x^2} = 2$$

$$\frac{\partial^2 f}{\partial y^2} = 2$$

$$\frac{\partial^2 f}{\partial x \, \partial y} = 1$$

$$\Delta = 4 - 1 > 0$$

$$\frac{\partial^2 f}{\partial x^2} = 2 > 0 \qquad \frac{\partial^2 f}{\partial y^2} = 2 > 0$$

Thus $f(x, y)$ has a minimum value at $(2, -1)$.

Examine the function

$$f(x, y) = xy - \ln(x^2 + y^2)$$

for maximum and minimum values.

$$\frac{\partial f}{\partial x} = y - \frac{2x}{x^2 + y^2}$$

$$\frac{\partial f}{\partial y} = x - \frac{2y}{x^2 + y^2}$$

$$x^2 y + y^3 - 2x = 0$$
$$x^3 + xy^2 - 2y = 0$$
$$-2x^2 + 2y^2 = 0$$
$$x^2 = y^2$$

Thus $y^3 = x$ and $x^3 = y$ and $(1,1)$ and $(-1,-1)$ may be a maximum or minimum.

$$\frac{\partial^2 f}{\partial x^2} = -\frac{2(x^2 + y^2) - 2x(2x)}{(x^2 + y^2)^2} = -\frac{2(y^2 - x^2)}{(x^2 + y^2)^2} = 0$$

$$\frac{\partial^2 f}{\partial y^2} = -\frac{2(x^2 + y^2) - 2y(2y)}{(x^2 + y^2)^2} = -\frac{2(x^2 - y^2)}{(x^2 + y^2)^2} = 0$$

$$\frac{\partial f}{\partial x \, \partial y} = 1 + \frac{4xy}{(x^2 + y^2)^2} = 2$$

$$\Delta = 0 - 2 < 0$$

Thus $f(x,y)$ has no maximum or minimum, but does have saddle points at $(1,1)$ and $(-1,-1)$.

Examine the function

$$f(x, y) = 1 + x^2 - y^2$$

for maximum and minimum values.

$$\frac{\partial f}{\partial x} = 2x$$

$$\frac{\partial f}{\partial y} = -2y$$

$$\begin{array}{ll} 2x = 0 & \text{if } x = 0 \\ -2y = 0 & \text{if } y = 0 \end{array} \Bigg\} \text{so } (0,0) \text{ may be a maximum or minimum}$$

$$\frac{\partial^2 f}{\partial x^2} = 2$$

$$\frac{\partial^2 f}{\partial y^2} = -2$$

$$\frac{\partial^2 f}{\partial x \, \partial y} = 0$$

$$\Delta = -4 - 0 < 0$$

Thus $f(x, y)$ has neither a maximum nor a minimum at $(0, 0)$, but does have a saddle point at $(0, 0)$.

Examine the function

$$f(x, y) = 25 + (x - y)^4 + (y - 1)^4$$

for maximum and minimum values.

$$\frac{\partial f}{\partial x} = 4(x - y)^3$$

$$\frac{\partial f}{\partial y} = -4(x - y)^3 + 4(y - 1)^3$$

$$\begin{array}{ll} (x - y)^3 = 0 & \text{if } x = y \\ (x - y)^3 = (y - 1)^3 & \text{if } x = y = 1 \end{array} \Bigg\} \begin{array}{l} \text{so } (1, 1) \text{ may be a maximum} \\ \text{or minimum} \end{array}$$

$$\frac{\partial^2 f}{\partial x^2} = 12(x - y)^2$$

$$\frac{\partial^2 f}{\partial y^2} = 12(x - y)^2 + 12(y - 1)^2$$

$$\frac{\partial^2 f}{\partial x \, \partial y} = -12(x - y)^2$$

$$\frac{\partial^2 f}{\partial x^2}\bigg|_{x=y=1} = 0$$

$$\frac{\partial^2 f}{\partial y^2}\bigg|_{x=y=1} = 0$$

$$\frac{\partial^2 f}{\partial x \, \partial y}\bigg|_{x=y=1} = 0$$

so $\Delta = 0$ and $f(x, y)$ must be examined further for maximum or minimum values. Suppose h and k are arbitrarily small positive or negative numbers; then

$$f(1 + h, 1 + k) - f(1, 1) = 25 + [(1 + h) - (1 + k)]^4 + (1 + k - 1)^4 - 25$$
$$= (h - k)^4 + k^4$$

But $(h - k)^4 + k^4 > 0$ for all h and k, so $f(1 + h, 1 + k) > f(1, 1)$ for all h and k, and thus there is a minimum at $(1, 1)$.

Examine the function

$$f(x, y) = x^2 - 6xy + 9y^2 + 3x - 10$$

for maximum and minimum values.

$$\frac{\partial f}{\partial x} = 2x - 6y + 3$$

$$\frac{\partial f}{\partial y} = -6x + 18y$$

$\left. \begin{array}{l} 2x - 6y = -3 \\ -2x + 6y = 0 \end{array} \right\}$ no simultaneous solution, so no maximum or minimum

---

If the demand functions are

$$p = 36 - 3x \qquad q = 40 - 5y$$

and the joint-cost function is

$$C = x^2 + 2xy + 3y^2$$

determine the quantities and prices that maximize profit for the monopolist and find the maximum profit.

$$P = px + qy - C$$
$$= 36x - 3x^2 + 40y - 5y^2 - x^2 - 2xy - 3y^2$$
$$= -4x^2 - 8y^2 - 2xy + 36x + 40y$$

$$\frac{\partial P}{\partial x} = -8x - 2y + 36$$

$$\frac{\partial P}{\partial y} = -16y - 2x + 40$$

$$4x + y = 18$$
$$x + 8y = 20$$
$$31y = 62$$
$\left. \begin{array}{l} y = 2 \\ x = 4 \end{array} \right\}$ so P may have a maximum or minimum at $(4, 2)$

$$\frac{\partial^2 P}{\partial x^2} = -8$$

MAXIMA AND MINIMA OF FUNCTIONS OF TWO VARIABLES | 371

$$\frac{\partial^2 P}{\partial y^2} = -16$$

$$\frac{\partial^2 P}{\partial x\, \partial y} = -2$$

$\Delta = 128 - (-2)^2 = 124 > 0$, so P has a maximum value for $x = 4$, $y = 2$

If $x = 4$, $y = 2$, $\qquad p = 24 \qquad q = 30 \qquad P_{max} = 112$.

Suppose the production function is

$$16z = 65 - 2(x - 5)^2 - 4(y - 4)^2$$

The unit prices of the inputs x and y (under pure competition) are 8 and 4, respectively, and the unit price of the output is 32; determine the maximum profit.

$P = 32z - 8x - 4y$

$\quad = 130 - 4(x - 5)^2 - 8(y - 4)^2 - 8x - 4y$

$\dfrac{\partial P}{\partial x} = -8(x - 5) - 8 = -8x + 32$

$\dfrac{\partial P}{\partial y} = -16(y - 4) - 4 = -16y + 60$

$\left.\begin{array}{l} 8x = 32 \\[4pt] x = 4 \\[4pt] 16y = 60 \\[4pt] y = \frac{15}{4} \end{array}\right\}$ so P may have a maximum or minimum at $(4, \frac{15}{4})$

$\dfrac{\partial^2 P}{\partial x^2} = -8$

$\dfrac{\partial^2 P}{\partial y^2} = -16$

$\dfrac{\partial^2 P}{\partial x\, \partial y} = 0$

$\Delta = (-8)(-16) - 0 = 128 > 0$, so P has a maximum value for $x = 4$, $y = \frac{15}{4}$

$P_{max} = 78\frac{1}{2}$

A manufacturer has a demand of D units per period T. The storage cost per period per unit is c_2 dollars, the shortage cost is c_3 dollars per unit short per period, and it costs c_1 dollars each time a production run is started (setup cost). Assuming that production orders are filled with no delay and demand is at a uniform rate, determine the frequency with which production should be scheduled, and the quantity which should be produced in each run to minimize the total per period inventory cost K. See Fig. 3.7, where $t = $ interval between production orders,

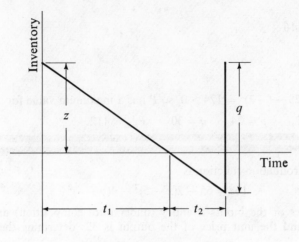

FIGURE 3.7

q = production quantity, z = planned inventory at completion of a production run, t_1 = time (during cycle) when stock is on hand, and t_2 = time (during cycle) when no stock is on hand. Note that shortages are assumed to be backlogged and not lost.

Note that $\dfrac{t_1}{t} = \dfrac{z}{q}$, $\dfrac{t_2}{t} = \dfrac{q-z}{q}$, and $\dfrac{t}{T} = \dfrac{q}{D}$.

setup cost: c_1

carrying cost per run: $\dfrac{c_2 t_1 z}{2} = \dfrac{c_2 t z^2}{2q} = \dfrac{c_2 T z^2}{2D}$

shortage cost per run: $\dfrac{c_3 t_2 (q-z)}{2} = \dfrac{c_3 t (q-z)^2}{2q} = \dfrac{c_3 T (q-z)^2}{2D}$

since the number of runs per period is $\dfrac{D}{q}$, the total inventory cost per period is

$$K = \frac{c_1 D}{q} + \frac{c_2 T z^2}{2q} + \frac{c_3 T (q-z)^2}{2q}$$

and, since K is a function of both q and z, partial derivatives must be obtained and set equal to zero to determine a minimum

$$\frac{\partial K}{\partial z} = \frac{c_2 T z}{q} - \frac{c_3 T (q-z)}{q}$$

If $\dfrac{\partial K}{\partial z} = 0$,

$$c_2 T z = c_3 T (q-z)$$

$$z = \frac{c_3 q}{c_2 + c_3}$$

$$\frac{\partial K}{\partial q} = -\frac{c_1 D}{q^2} - \frac{c_2 T z^2}{2q^2} + \frac{c_3 T}{2} - \frac{c_3 T z^2}{2q^2}$$

$$= -\frac{c_1 D}{q^2} - \frac{c_2 Tz^2}{2q^2} + \frac{c_3 T(q^2 - z^2)}{2q^2}$$

If $\dfrac{\partial K}{\partial q} = 0$,

$$c_3 T(q^2 - z^2) = 2c_1 D + c_2 Tz^2$$

$$q^2 = \frac{2c_1 D + c_2 Tz^2 + c_3 Tz^2}{c_3 T}$$

$$= \frac{2c_1 D}{c_3 T} + \frac{c_2 + c_3}{c_3} z^2$$

$$= \frac{2c_1 D}{c_3 T} + \frac{c_3}{c_2 + c_3} q^2$$

since $\quad z = \dfrac{c_3 q}{c_2 + c_3}$

thus

$$q^2 = \frac{2c_1 D}{\left(1 - \dfrac{c_3}{c_2 + c_3}\right) c_3 T}$$

$$q = \sqrt{\frac{2c_1 (c_2 + c_3) D}{c_2 c_3 T}}$$

$$z = \frac{c_3}{c_2 + c_3} q = \sqrt{\frac{2c_1 c_3 D}{c_2 (c_2 + c_3) T}}$$

$$t = \frac{Tq}{D} = \sqrt{\frac{2c_1 (c_2 + c_3) T}{c_2 c_3 D}}$$

The manufacturer should produce q units at intervals of time t, where q and t are determined by the formulas above.

PROBLEMS

Determine the maxima, minima, and saddle points (if any) for each of the following functions.

1. $g(x, y) = 2x^2 - 2xy + y^2 + 5x - 3y$
2. $h(x, y) = 3 + 2x + 2y - 2x^2 - 2xy - y^2$
3. $z(x, y) = xy + x - y$
4. $f(x, y) = x^2 + xy + y^2 - 6x + 2$
5. $u(x, y) = 4x + 2y - x^2 + xy - y^2$
6. $v(x, y) = x^2 + y^2 - 2x + 4y + 6$
7. $z(x, y) = x^3 - 3bxy + y^3$

8. $w(x, y) = x^2 - 2xy + 2y^2 - 2x + 2y + 1$

9. $g(x, y) = x^2 - y^2 - 2x + 4y + 6$

10. $h(x, y) = x^2 + 2xy$

11. $z(x, y) = xy - 2y^2$

12. $f(x, y) = axy$

Find the quantities and prices that maximize profit and the maximum profit for each of the following sets of demand functions and joint-cost functions for two commodities.

13. $x = 1 - p + 2q$
$y = 11 + p - 3q$
$C = 4x + y$

17. $p = 26 - x$
$q = 40 - 4y$
$C = x^2 + 2xy + y^2$

14. $x = 11 - 2p - 2q$
$y = 16 - 2p - 3q$
$C = 3x + y$

18. $p = 35 - 2x^2$
$q = 20 - y$
$C = 16 - 2x^3 + xy + 30x$
$\qquad + 12y + \frac{1}{2}x^2$

15. $p = 40 - 2x^2$
$q = 12 - 3y$
$C = 8 + 4x + 3y$

19. $p = 40 - 5x$
$q = 30 - 3y$
$C = x^2 + 2xy + 3y^2$

16. $p = 16 - x^2$
$q = 9 - y^2$
$C = x^2 + 3y^2$

20. $p = 28 - 3x^2$
$q = 56 - y^2$
$C = 2x^2 + y^2$

21. Determine the maximum profit if the production function is $z = 20 - x^2 + 10x - 2y^2 + 5y$, the prices of the inputs x and y are 2 and 1, respectively, and the price of the output is 5.

22. Determine the maximum profit if the production function is $z = 10 - 2x^2 + xy - y^2 + 5y$, the prices of the inputs x and y are each 3, and the price of the output is 6.

23. The Portland Company has a contract to furnish 1350 cement mixers annually. The yearly storage cost is \$40 per cement mixer, the shortage cost is \$50 per cement mixer short per year, and it costs \$150 to start a production run. If production orders are filled without delay and demand is at a constant rate, determine the frequency with which production should be scheduled and the quantity which should be produced in each run to minimize the total average annual cost.

24. The Filaway Company has a contract to supply 600 filing cabinets at a uniform rate during a 9-month period. The storage cost during this period is \$30 per cabinet, the shortage cost is \$60 per cabinet, and it costs \$20 to start a production run. If production occurs at a constant rate of 2400 cabinets per 9-month period, determine the frequency with which production should be scheduled and the quantity which should be produced in each run to minimize the total average annual cost.

Answers to Odd-Numbered Problems

1. minimum $(-1, \frac{1}{2})$

3. saddle point $(1, -1)$

5. maximum $(10/3, 8/3)$

7. minimum (b, b)

9. saddle point $(1, 2)$

11. saddle point $(0, 0)$

13. $p = 14$
    $q = 8$
    $x = 3$
    $y = 1$
    $P_{max} = 37$

15. $p = 28$
    $q = \frac{15}{2}$
    $x = \sqrt{6}$
    $y = \frac{3}{2}$
    $P_{max} = 24\sqrt{6} - \frac{5}{4}$
    (approximately 57.53)

17. $p = 21$
    $q = 28$
    $x = 5$
    $y = 3$
    $P_{max} = 125$

19. $p = 25$
    $q = 24$
    $x = 3$
    $y = 2$
    $P_{max} = 90$

21. $P_{max} = 229\frac{3}{5}$ for $x = \frac{24}{5}$ and $y = \frac{6}{5}$

23. Schedule production 10 times a year, producing 135 cement mixers each run

■ 3.5 MAXIMA AND MINIMA SUBJECT TO CONSTRAINTS

In many practical applications of maximization and minimization, the problem is to maximize or minimize a given function subject to certain side conditions or constraints on the variables involved. These constraints may be stated as equalities or inequalities.

For example, if a manufacturer produces two outputs, he may want to minimize the joint cost, while producing a specified minimum total amount; a company may want to maximize sales resulting from use of two advertising media, while keeping total advertising costs within a specified budget constraint; an engineer may want to minimize frequency of breakdowns, while keeping total cost of two types of preventive repairs from exceeding a specified amount; a consumer may want to maximize utility derived from the consumption of commodities, subject to his budget constraint; a chemist may want to minimize total sedimentation in a two-stage process, while keeping the temperatures in the two stages equal.

In some cases equations obtained from the constraints can be substituted into the function to be maximized or minimized; the problem is thus reduced to one involving unconstrained maxima or minima and can be solved by the methods of the preceding section. However, this procedure is not always feasible, particularly if the function to be maximized or minimized involves more than two variables and several constraints. The methods discussed in the following sections are appropriate for those cases.

□ LAGRANGE MULTIPLIERS

The most widely used method of obtaining maxima or minima of functions subject to equality constraints is that of *Lagrange multipliers*. Suppose $f(x, y)$ is to be maximized or minimized subject to the constraint $g(x, y) = 0$. Form the *objective function*

$$F(x, y, \lambda) = f(x, y) - \lambda g(x, y)$$

where λ, the Lagrange multiplier, is an unknown. Differentiate $F(x, y, \lambda)$ partially with respect to x, with respect to y, and with respect to λ, and set the results equal to zero; then the three equations

$$\frac{\partial F}{\partial x} = \frac{\partial f}{\partial x} - \lambda \frac{\partial g}{\partial x} = 0$$

$$\frac{\partial F}{\partial y} = \frac{\partial f}{\partial y} - \lambda \frac{\partial g}{\partial y} = 0$$

$$\frac{\partial F}{\partial \lambda} = g(x, y) = 0$$

can be solved for the three unknowns x, y, and λ. Note that $\frac{\partial F}{\partial \lambda} = g(x, y) = 0$ is the constraint, so $F(x, y, \lambda)$ really need be differentiated partially only with respect to x and with respect to·y. In many cases the values of the λ's (Lagrange multipliers) are not of interest and are not found; for this reason they are sometimes referred to as "undetermined multipliers." The Lagrange multiplier may be preceded by a plus sign rather than by a minus sign and this form is used by some authors. The only resulting change in the solution is a change in the sign of λ. The value of λ represents the amount of change in the objective function per unit of change in the constraint limit.

Solution of the above equations provides the critical points of the function to be maximized or minimized. These critical points must be tested as maxima or minima of the function by a procedure similar to that for unconstrained maxima or minima.

For a critical point $x = a$, $y = b$,

$$If \begin{cases} \frac{\partial F}{\partial x} \Big|_{x=a,\, y=b} = 0 \\[2mm] \frac{\partial F}{\partial y} \Big|_{x=a,\, y=b} = 0 \end{cases}$$

$$\text{and } \Delta^* = \left(\frac{\partial^2 F}{\partial x^2}\Big|_{x=a,\, y=b}\right)\left(\frac{\partial^2 F}{\partial y^2}\Big|_{x=a,\, y=b}\right) - \left(\frac{\partial^2 F}{\partial x\, \partial y}\Big|_{x=a,\, y=b}\right)^2$$

$$then \begin{cases} \Delta^* > 0 \Rightarrow \begin{cases} \text{maximum at } x = a,\, y = b, \text{ if } \dfrac{\partial^2 F}{\partial x^2} < 0 \text{ and } \dfrac{\partial^2 F}{\partial y^2} < 0 \\[4mm] \text{minimum at } x = a,\, y = b, \text{ if } \dfrac{\partial^2 F}{\partial x^2} > 0 \text{ and } \dfrac{\partial^2 F}{\partial y^2} > 0 \end{cases} \\[8mm] \Delta^* \leq 0 \Rightarrow \text{test fails, function must be investigated near } x = a,\, y = b \end{cases}$$

Note that for unconstrained maxima and minima, if $\Delta < 0$, the critical point is neither a maximum nor a minimum; however, for constrained maxima and minima, if $\Delta < 0$, the critical point may in fact be a maximum or minimum. This corresponds to the fact that a point may be a maximum or minimum of the constrained function, although it is not a maximum or minimum of the unconstrained function.

These conditions can be stated more concisely as follows.

necessary condition for a critical point: $\qquad f_x = 0, f_y = 0$

determination of constrained maxima or minima:

$$f_{xx}f_{yy} - f_{xy}^2 > 0 \Rightarrow \begin{cases} \text{maximum if} \\ f_{xx} < 0, f_{yy} < 0 \\ \text{minimum if} \\ f_{xx} > 0, f_{yy} > 0 \end{cases}$$

$f_{xx}f_{yy} - f_{xy}^2 \leq 0 \Rightarrow$ test fails and the function must be investigated near the critical point

where the partial derivatives are evaluated for the critical point.

NOTE: The method of Lagrange multipliers can be extended to a function of k variables, $f(x_1, x_2, \ldots, x_k)$, subject to the n constraints $g_j(x_1, x_2, \ldots, x_k) = 0$, $j = 1, 2, \ldots, n$, where $n \leq k$. Then

$$F(x_1, \ldots, x_k; \lambda_1, \ldots, \lambda_n) = f(x_1, \ldots, x_k) - \sum_{j=1}^{n} \lambda_j g_j(x_1, \ldots, x_k)$$

and partial differentiation results in $n + k$ equations to be solved for $n + k$ unknowns. The method of testing critical points as maxima or minima can also be extended for the general case.

Examples

Find the maxima and minima (if any) of $f(x, y) = 5x^2 + 6y^2 - xy$ subject to the constraint $x + 2y = 24$.

$$F(x, y, \lambda) \doteq 5x^2 + 6y^2 - xy - \lambda(x + 2y - 24)$$

$$\frac{\partial F}{\partial x} = 10x - y - \lambda$$

$$\frac{\partial F}{\partial y} = 12y - x - 2\lambda$$

$$20x - 2y - 2\lambda = 0$$

$$-x + 12y - 2\lambda = 0$$

$$21x - 14y = 0$$

$$3x - 2y = 0$$

$$x + 2y = 24$$

$$4x = 24$$

$$x = 6$$

Critical point: $(6, 9)$; $\lambda = 51$.

$$\frac{\partial^2 F}{\partial x^2} = 10$$

$$\frac{\partial^2 F}{\partial y^2} = 12$$

$$\frac{\partial^2 F}{\partial x \, \partial y} = -1$$

$$\Delta^* = (10)(12) - (-1)^2 = 119$$

so $(6, 9)$ is a minimum

Alternative method: $f(x, y) = 5x^2 + 6y^2 - xy$, $x + 2y = 24$.

$$G(y) = 5(24 - 2y)^2 + 6y^2 - y(24 - 2y)$$

$$= 2880 - 480y + 20y^2 + 6y^2 - 24y + 2y^2$$

$$= 2880 - 504y + 28y^2$$

$$\frac{dG}{dy} = -504 + 56y$$

$$= 0 \quad \text{if } 56y = 540$$

$$y = 9$$

$$x = 6$$

$$\frac{d^2 G}{dy^2} = 56 > 0, \text{ so } (6, 9) \text{ is a minimum}$$

Find the maxima and minima (if any) of $f(x, y) = 3xy$ subject to the constraint $x^2 + y^2 = 9$.

$$F(x, y, \lambda) = 3xy - \lambda(x^2 + y^2 - 9)$$

$$\frac{\partial F}{\partial x} = 3y - 2\lambda x$$

$$\frac{\partial F}{\partial y} = 3x - 2\lambda y$$

$$3y^2 - 2\lambda xy = 0$$

$$3x^2 - 2\lambda xy = 0$$

$$x^2 - y^2 = 0$$

$$x^2 + y^2 = 9$$

$$x = \pm\sqrt{\tfrac{9}{2}}$$

$$y = \pm\sqrt{\tfrac{9}{2}}$$

Critical points: $(\pm\sqrt{\frac{9}{2}}, \pm\sqrt{\frac{9}{2}}); \lambda = \frac{3}{2}$

$\qquad\qquad (\pm\sqrt{\frac{9}{2}}, \mp\sqrt{\frac{9}{2}}); \lambda = -\frac{3}{2}$

$$\frac{\partial^2 F}{\partial x^2} = 2\lambda$$

$$\frac{\partial^2 F}{\partial y^2} = 2\lambda$$

$$\frac{\partial^2 F}{\partial x\, \partial y} = 3$$

$\Delta^* = 4\lambda^2 - 9 \le 0$, so we must investigate the function near the points $(\pm\sqrt{\frac{9}{2}}, \pm\sqrt{\frac{9}{2}})$ and $(\pm\sqrt{\frac{9}{2}}, \mp\sqrt{\frac{9}{2}})$

$$(x + h)^2 + (y + k)^2 = 9$$

$$(\sqrt{\tfrac{9}{2}} + h)^2 + (\sqrt{\tfrac{9}{2}} + k)^2 = 9$$

$$2\sqrt{\tfrac{9}{2}}\, h + h^2 + 2\sqrt{\tfrac{9}{2}}\, k + k^2 = 0$$

$$k = \frac{-2\sqrt{\frac{9}{2}} \pm \sqrt{18 - 18\sqrt{\frac{9}{2}}\, h - 4h^2}}{2}$$

$$f(\sqrt{\tfrac{9}{2}} + h, \sqrt{\tfrac{9}{2}} + k) - f(\sqrt{\tfrac{9}{2}}, \sqrt{\tfrac{9}{2}})$$

$$= 3(\sqrt{\tfrac{9}{2}} + h)\left(\sqrt{\tfrac{9}{2}} + \frac{-2\sqrt{\frac{9}{2}} + \sqrt{18 - 8\sqrt{\frac{9}{2}}\, h - 4h^2}}{2}\right) - 3(\tfrac{9}{2})$$

$$= 3(\sqrt{\tfrac{9}{2}} + h)(\sqrt{\tfrac{9}{2} - 2\sqrt{\tfrac{9}{2}}\, h - h^2}) - 3(\tfrac{9}{2})$$

But $(\sqrt{\frac{9}{2}} - h) > \sqrt{\frac{9}{2} - 2\sqrt{\frac{9}{2}}\, h - h^2}$, and thus $f(\sqrt{\frac{9}{2}} + h, \sqrt{\frac{9}{2}} + k) - f(\sqrt{\frac{9}{2}}, \sqrt{\frac{9}{2}})$ $< 3(\sqrt{\frac{9}{2}} + h)(\sqrt{\frac{9}{2}} - h) - 3(\frac{9}{2}) = -3h^2$ and thus $(\sqrt{\frac{9}{2}}, \sqrt{\frac{9}{2}})$ is a maximum; similarly, $(-\sqrt{\frac{9}{2}}, -\sqrt{\frac{9}{2}})$ is a maximum.

$$(x + h)^2 + (y + k)^2 = 9$$

$$(\sqrt{\tfrac{9}{2}} + h)^2 + (-\sqrt{\tfrac{9}{2}} + k)^2 = 9$$

$$2\sqrt{\tfrac{9}{2}}\, h + h^2 - 2\sqrt{\tfrac{9}{2}}\, k + k^2 = 0$$

$$k = \frac{2\sqrt{\frac{9}{2}} \pm \sqrt{18 - 18\sqrt{\frac{9}{2}}\, h - 4h^2}}{2}$$

$$f(\sqrt{\tfrac{9}{2}} + h, -\sqrt{\tfrac{9}{2}} + k) - f(\sqrt{\tfrac{9}{2}}, -\sqrt{\tfrac{9}{2}})$$

$$= 3(\sqrt{\tfrac{9}{2}} + h)\left(-\sqrt{\tfrac{9}{2}} + \frac{2\sqrt{\frac{9}{2}} - \sqrt{18 - 18\sqrt{\frac{9}{2}} h - 4h^2}}{2}\right) - 3(\tfrac{9}{2})$$

$$= 3(\sqrt{\tfrac{9}{2}} + h)(-\sqrt{\tfrac{9}{2} - 2\sqrt{\tfrac{9}{2}}\, h - 4h^2}) - 3(\tfrac{9}{2})$$

But $-\sqrt{\frac{9}{2}} + h < -\sqrt{\frac{9}{2} - 2\sqrt{\frac{9}{2}}h - 4h^2}$, and thus $f(\sqrt{\frac{9}{2}} + h, -\sqrt{\frac{9}{2}} + k) - f(\sqrt{\frac{9}{2}}, -\sqrt{\frac{9}{2}}) > 3(\sqrt{\frac{9}{2}} + h)(-\sqrt{\frac{9}{2}} + h) - 3 \left(\frac{9}{2}\right) = 3h^2$ and thus $(\sqrt{\frac{9}{2}}, -\sqrt{\frac{9}{2}})$ is a minimum; similarly, $(-\sqrt{\frac{9}{2}}, \sqrt{\frac{9}{2}})$ is a minimum.

Alternative method: $f(x, y) = 3xy$, $x^2 + y^2 = 9$.

$$G(y) = \pm 3y(9 - y^2)^{1/2}$$

$$\frac{dG}{dy} = \pm 3(9 - y^2)^{1/2} \pm 3y(\tfrac{1}{2})(9 - y^2)^{-1/2}(-2y)$$

$$= \pm(9 - y^2)^{-1/2}(27 - 3y^2 - 3y^2)$$

$$= \pm(9 - y^2)^{-1/2}(27 - 6y^2)$$

$$= 0 \quad \text{if } 6y^2 = 27$$

$$y = \pm\sqrt{\tfrac{9}{2}}$$

$$x = \pm\sqrt{\tfrac{9}{2}}$$

$$\frac{d^2G}{dy^2} = \pm(-\tfrac{1}{2})(9 - y^2)^{-3/2}(-2y)(27 - 6y^2) \pm (9 - y^2)^{-1/2}(-12y)$$

$$= \pm(9 - y^2)^{-3/2}(27y - 6y^3 - 108y + 12y^3)$$

$$= \pm(9 - y^2)^{-3/2}(6y^3 - 81y)$$

$$\left.\frac{d^2G}{dy^2}\right|_{x=\sqrt{9/2},\, y=\sqrt{9/2}} < 0, \text{ so maximum at } (\sqrt{\tfrac{9}{2}}, \sqrt{\tfrac{9}{2}})$$

$$\left.\frac{d^2G}{dy^2}\right|_{x=-\sqrt{9/2},\, y=-\sqrt{9/2}} < 0, \text{ so maximum at } (-\sqrt{\tfrac{9}{2}}, -\sqrt{\tfrac{9}{2}})$$

$$\left.\frac{d^2G}{dy^2}\right|_{x=\sqrt{9/2},\, y=-\sqrt{9/2}} > 0, \text{ so minimum at } (\sqrt{\tfrac{9}{2}}, -\sqrt{\tfrac{9}{2}})$$

$$\left.\frac{d^2G}{dy^2}\right|_{x=-\sqrt{9/2},\, y=\sqrt{9/2}} > 0, \text{ so minimum at } (-\sqrt{\tfrac{9}{2}}, \sqrt{\tfrac{9}{2}})$$

Find the maxima and minima (if any) of $f(x, y) = 12xy - 3y^2 - x^2$ subject to the constraint $x + y = 16$.

$$F(\lambda, x, y) = 12xy - 3y^2 - x^2 - \lambda(x + y - 16)$$

$$\frac{\partial F}{\partial x} = 12y - 2x - \lambda$$

$$\frac{\partial F}{\partial y} = 12x - 6y - \lambda$$

$$14x - 18y = 0$$

$$7x - 9y = 0$$

$$7x + 7y = 112$$

$$16y = 112$$

$$y = 7$$

$$x = 9$$

Critical point: $(9, 7)$; $\lambda = 66$.

$$\frac{\partial^2 F}{\partial x^2} = -2$$

$$\frac{\partial^2 F}{\partial y^2} = -6$$

$$\frac{\partial^2 F}{\partial x \, \partial y} = 12$$

$$\Delta^* = (-2)(-6) - (12)^2 = -132 < 0, \text{ so we must}$$
investigate the function near $(9, 7)$

$$(x + h) + (y + k) = 16$$

$$9 + h + 7 + k = 16$$

$$k = -h$$

$$f(9 + h, 7 - h) - f(9, 7) = 12(9 + h)(7 - h) - 3(7 - n)^2 - (9 + h)^2$$

$$- 12(9)(7) - 3(7)^2 - 9^2$$

$$= -24h - 12h^2 + 42h - 3h^2 - 18h - h^2$$

$$= -16h^2 < 0, \text{ so maximum at } (9, 7)$$

Alternative method: $f(x, y) = 12xy - 3y^2 - x^2$, $x + y = 16$.

$$G(y) = 12y(16 - y) - 3y^2 - (16 - y)^2$$

$$= 192y - 12y^2 - 3y^2 - 256 + 32y - y^2$$

$$= -16y^2 + 224y - 256$$

$$\frac{dG}{dy} = -32y + 224$$

$$\frac{dG}{dy} = 0 \qquad \text{if } 32y = 224$$

$$y = 7$$

$$x = 9$$

$$\frac{d^2G}{dy^2} = -32, \text{ so maximum at } (9, 7)$$

A factory manufactures two types of heavy-duty machines, x and y. The joint-cost function is given by

$$f(x, y) = x^2 + 2y^2 - xy$$

To minimize cost, how many machines of each type should be produced if there must be a total of 8 machines?

$$F(x, y, \lambda) = x^2 + 2y^2 - xy - \lambda(x + y - 8)$$

$$\frac{\partial F}{\partial x} = 2x - y - \lambda = 0$$

$$\frac{\partial F}{\partial y} = 4y - x - \lambda = 0$$

$$3x - 5y = 0$$

$$3x + 3y = 24$$

$$8y = 3$$

$$y = 3$$

$$x = 5$$

$$\lambda = 7$$

$$\frac{\partial^2 F}{\partial x^2} = 2$$

$$\frac{\partial^2 F}{\partial y^2} = 4$$

$$\frac{\partial^2 F}{\partial x\, \partial y} = -1$$

$$\Delta = (2)(4) - (-1)^2 > 0$$

$$\frac{\partial^2 F}{\partial x^2} > 0, \frac{\partial^2 F}{\partial y^2} > 0, \text{ so } (5,3) \text{ is a minimum}$$

NOTE: The unconstrained minimum of the function $f(x, y) = x^2 + 2y^2 - xy$ occurs at $(0, 0)$.

Alternative method: $f(x, y) = x^2 + 2y^2 - xy$, $x + y = 8$.

$$G(x) = x^2 + 2(8 - x)^2 - x(8 - x)$$

$$= x^2 + 128 - 32x + 2x^2 - 8x + x^2$$

$$= 4x^2 - 40x + 128$$

$$\frac{dG}{dx} = 8x - 40 = 0$$

$$x = 5$$

$$y = 3$$

$$\frac{d^2G}{dx^2} = 8 > 0, \text{ so } (5,3) \text{ is a minimum}$$

The relationship between sales S and the amounts x and y spent on two advertising media is given by

$$S = \frac{200x}{5 + x} + \frac{100y}{10 + y}$$

Net profit is $\frac{1}{5}$ of sales minus the cost of advertising. The advertising budget is 25; determine how it should be allocated between the two media in order to maximize net profit.

$$F(x, y, \lambda) = \frac{1}{5}\left[\frac{200x}{5 + x} + \frac{100y}{10 + y}\right] - x - y - \lambda(x + y - 25)$$

$$= \frac{40x}{5 + x} + \frac{20y}{10 + y} - x - y - \lambda(x + y - 25)$$

$$\frac{\partial F}{\partial x} = \frac{40(5 + x) - 40x}{(5 + x)^2} - 1 - \lambda = 0$$

$$\frac{\partial F}{\partial y} = \frac{20(10 + y) - 20y}{(10 + y)^2} - 1 - \lambda = 0$$

$$\frac{200}{(5 + x)^2} = \frac{200}{(10 + y)^2}$$

$$(5 + x)^2 = (10 + y)^2$$

$$x + y = 25$$

so

$$(5 + 25 - y)^2 = (10 + y)^2$$

$$30 - y = 10 + y$$

$$y = 10$$

$$x = 15$$

$$\lambda = -\tfrac{1}{2}$$

$$\frac{\partial^2 F}{\partial x^2} = 200(-2)(5 + x)^{-3}$$

$$\frac{\partial^2 F}{\partial y^2} = 200(-2)(10 + y)^{-3}$$

$$\frac{\partial^2 F}{\partial x\,\partial y} = 0$$

$$\Delta = \left(\frac{-400}{(5+x)^3}\right)\left(\frac{-400}{(10+y)^3}\right) - 0 > 0$$

$\dfrac{\partial^2 F}{\partial x^2} < 0, \dfrac{\partial^2 F}{\partial y^2} < 0$, so (10,15) is a maximum

NOTE: The unconstrained maximum of the function

$$P(x, y) = \tfrac{1}{5}\left[\frac{200x}{5+x} + \frac{100y}{10+y}\right] - x - y \text{ occurs at } (10\sqrt{2} - 5, 10\sqrt{2} - 10).$$

Alternative method: $P(x, y) = \dfrac{40x}{5+x} + \dfrac{20y}{10+y} - x - y, \; x + y = 25.$

$$P(x) = \frac{40x}{5+x} + \frac{500 - 20x}{35 - x} - 25$$

$$\frac{dP}{dx} = \frac{40(5+x) - 40x}{(5+x)^2} + \frac{-20(35-x) + (500 - 20x)}{(35-x)^2}$$

$$\frac{200}{(5+x)^2} = \frac{200}{(35-x)^2}$$

$$5 + x = 35 - x$$

$$x = 10$$

$$y = 15$$

$\dfrac{d^2P}{dx^2} = 200(-2)(5+x)^{-3} + 200(-2)(30-x)^{-3} < 0$, so (10,15) is a maximum

---

Maximum profit for a given production function and given prices of the inputs and output can be determined using Lagrange multipliers. Suppose the production function is

$$16z = 65 - 2(x - 5)^2 - 4(y - 4)^2$$

and the unit prices of the inputs x and y are 8 and 4, respectively, and the unit price of the output is 32. (See the example on page 371.) Profit is maximized if the net revenue function $32z - 8x - 4y$ is maximized subject to the production function constraint $16z - 65 + 2(x - 5)^2 + 4(y - 4)^2 = 0$.

$$F = 32z - 8x - 4y - \lambda[16z - 65 + 2(x - 5)^2 + 4(y - 4)^2]$$

$$\frac{\partial F}{\partial z} = 32 - 16\lambda = 0$$

$$\lambda = 2$$

$$\frac{\partial F}{\partial x} = -8 - 4(x - 5)\lambda = 0$$

$$x = 4$$

$$\frac{\partial F}{\partial y} = -4 - 8\lambda(y - 4) = 0$$

$$y = 15/4$$

As shown previously, profit is maximized when $x = 4$, $y = 15/4$. F is a function of three variables x, y, and z. The second-order conditions for maximization of functions of more than two variables, which are somewhat more complex than the conditions for functions of two variables, are discussed in Chapter 8.

☐ CONSTRAINED UTILITY MAXIMIZATION

If his purchases are limited to two commodities Q_1 and Q_2, the rational consumer wishes to purchase that combination of Q_1 and Q_2 which will maximize his utility, subject to his budget constraint. Since his purchases are limited to the two commodities, the consumer's budget constraint can be written

$$y^\circ = p_1 q_1 + p_2 q_2$$

where y° is his fixed income and p_1, p_2, q_1, and q_2 are the prices and quantities of Q_1 and Q_2, respectively.

The budget line $y^\circ = p_1 q_1 + p_2 q_2$ shows all possible combinations of q_1 and q_2 which the consumer can purchase, given his budget constraint. In order to maximize his utility, the consumer will choose to purchase a combination of q_1 and q_2 lying on the highest possible indifference curve. As shown in Fig. 3.5, this maximizing point is the point at which the budget line is tangent to an indifference curve. Any movement from this point along the budget constraint puts the consumer on a lower indifference curve and results in diminished utility.

Mathematically, the problem is one of obtaining a constrained maximum.

$$\text{maximize } U(q_1, q_2)$$
$$\text{subject to } y^\circ = p_1 q_1 + p_2 q_2$$

The budget constraint can be written

$$\frac{y^\circ - p_1 q_1}{p_2} = q_2$$

and the utility function, as a function only of q_1, is

$$U = f\left(q_1, \frac{y^\circ - p_1 q_1}{p_2}\right)$$

Note that q_2 is determined if q_1 is specified, so it is sufficient to maximize U with respect to q_1

$$\frac{dU}{dq_1} = f_1 + f_2\left(-\frac{p_1}{p_2}\right) = 0$$

and

$$\frac{f_1}{f_2} = \frac{p_1}{p_2}$$

NOTE: The utility function may be written

$$U = f(q_1, q_2) \qquad \text{where } q_2 = \frac{y^\circ - p_1 q_1}{p_2} = g(q_1).$$

Then

$$\frac{dU}{dq_1} = \frac{\partial f}{\partial q_1} \cdot \frac{\partial q_1}{\partial q_1} + \frac{\partial f}{\partial q_2} \cdot \frac{\partial q_2}{\partial q_1}$$

$$= f_1 + f_2\left(-\frac{p_1}{p_2}\right)$$

Thus for a maximum the ratio of the marginal utilities must equal the ratio of prices, or equivalently,

$$\frac{f_1}{p_1} = \frac{f_2}{p_2}$$

and marginal utility divided by price must be the same for both commodities. This condition is necessary, but not sufficient, for occurrence of a maximum. The second-order condition for a maximum requires that

$$\frac{d^2U}{dq_1^2} = f_{11} + 2f_{12}\left(-\frac{p_1}{p_2}\right) + f_{22}\left(-\frac{p_1}{p_2}\right)^2 < 0$$

or

$$f_{11}p_2^2 - 2f_{12}p_1p_2 + f_{22}p_1^2 < 0$$

It can be shown, as follows, that the second-order condition for a maximum requires that the utility curves are convex from below. Obtain the total derivative $\frac{d^2q_2}{dq_1^2}$ by further differentiating $\frac{dq_2}{dq_1} = -\frac{f_1}{f_2}$

$$\frac{d^2q_2}{dq_1^2} = \left[\frac{\partial}{\partial q_1}\left(\frac{dq_2}{dq_1}\right)\right]\left[\frac{\partial q_1}{\partial q_1}\right] + \left[\frac{\partial}{\partial q_2}\left(\frac{dq_2}{dq_1}\right)\right]\left[\frac{\partial q_2}{\partial q_1}\right]$$

But

$$\frac{\partial}{\partial q_1}\left(\frac{dq_2}{dq_1}\right) = \frac{\partial}{\partial q_1}\left(-\frac{f_1}{f_2}\right) = -\frac{f_{11}f_2 - f_1f_{12}}{f_2^2}$$

$$\frac{\partial q_1}{\partial q_1} = 1$$

$$\frac{\partial}{\partial q_2}\left(\frac{dq_2}{dq_1}\right) = \frac{\partial}{\partial q_2}\left(-\frac{f_1}{f_2}\right) = -\frac{f_{12}f_2 - f_1f_{22}}{f_2^2}$$

$$\frac{\partial q_2}{\partial q_1} = -\frac{f_1}{f_2}$$

Thus

$$\frac{d^2q_2}{dq_1^2} = -\frac{f_{11}f_2 - f_1f_{12} + (f_{12}f_2 - f_1f_{22})\left(-\dfrac{f_1}{f_2}\right)}{f_2^2}$$

$$= -\frac{1}{f_2^3}(f_{11}f_2^2 - 2f_{12}f_1f_2 + f_{22}f_1^2)$$

Substituting $f_1 = \dfrac{p_1}{p_2} f_2$,

$$\frac{d^2 q_2}{dq_1^2} = -\frac{1}{f_2^3}\left(f_{11}f_2^2 - 2f_{12}f_2^2\frac{p_1}{p_2} + f_{22}f_2^2\frac{p_1^2}{p_2^2}\right)$$

$$= -\frac{1}{f_2 p_2^2}(f_{11}p_2^2 - 2f_{12}p_1 p_2 + f_{22}p_1^2)$$

But the second-order condition for a maximum requires that

$$f_{11}p_2^2 - 2f_{12}p_1 p_2 + f_{22}p_1^2 < 0$$

and, since $f_2 > 0$,

$$\frac{d^2 q_2}{dq_1^2} > 0$$

and the indifference curves are convex from below. Since $\dfrac{dq_2}{dq_1} = -\dfrac{f_1}{f_2} = -\dfrac{p_1}{p_2}$ and prices are positive, the indifference curves are negatively sloped. Thus if the utility function has a maximum, the indifference curves are of the general form shown in Fig. 3.5.

Example

If $U = q_1 q_2$, $p_1 = 15$, $p_2 = 5$, and the consumer's income for the period is 150, the budget constraint is

$$150 - 15q_1 - 5q_2 = 0$$

$$q_2 = \frac{150 - 15q_1}{5} = 30 - 3q_1$$

and

$$U = 30q_1 - 3q_1^2$$

$$\frac{dU}{dq_1} = 30 - 6q_1$$

If $\dfrac{dU}{dq_1} = 0$, $q_1 = 5$, $q_2 = 15$, and $\dfrac{d^2 U}{dq_1^2} = -6$, so the consumer maximizes utility subject to his budget constraint by purchasing 5 units of Q_1 and 15 units of Q_2. Note that

$$\frac{f_1}{f_2} = \frac{q_2}{q_1} = \frac{15}{5} = \frac{p_1}{p_2}$$

as required for a maximum.

Alternatively, the constrained maximum can be obtained using Lagrange multipliers

$$Z = f(q_1, q_2) - \lambda(y^\circ - p_1 q_1 - p_2 q_2)$$

$$\frac{\partial Z}{\partial q_1} = f_1 + \lambda p_1 = 0$$

$$\frac{\partial Z}{\partial q_2} = f_2 + \lambda p_2 = 0$$

$$\frac{\partial Z}{\partial \lambda} = y^\circ - p_1 q_1 - p_2 q_2 = 0$$

Thus

$$\lambda = -\frac{f_1}{p_1} = -\frac{f_2}{p_2}$$

and

$$\frac{f_1}{f_2} = \frac{p_1}{p_2}$$

and so forth, as above.

□ KUHN-TUCKER CONDITIONS

The method of Lagrange multipliers can be modified to determine the maximum of a function of two variables subject to one inequality constraint as follows: Assume that the inequality constraint holds as an equality constraint and obtain the maximum using the method of Lagrange multipliers; if $\lambda > 0$, this maximum is also the maximum subject to the inequality constraint; if $\lambda \leq 0$, the maximum determined without regard to the constraint satisfies the constraint and is thus also the constrained maximum. Corresponding statements hold for determining the minimum of a function of two variables subject to one inequality constraint.

This procedure can be generalized to include multiple inequality constraints, some of which may be satisfied as equalities and others as inequalities in any particular problem. In the more general procedure, the conditions necessary for a maximum or minimum subject to inequality constraints are known as the Kuhn-Tucker conditions. These conditions are given for the general case in Chapter 8; for the case of a function of two variables subject to one inequality constraint the Kuhn-Tucker conditions are stated as follows.

A point (x, y) is a local maximum of $f(x, y)$ subject to $g(x, y) \leq 0$ only if there exists a nonnegative λ such that λ and (x, y) satisfy the following conditions:

$$\frac{\partial f(x, y)}{\partial x} - \lambda \frac{\partial g(x, y)}{\partial x} = 0$$

$$\frac{\partial f(x, y)}{\partial y} - \lambda \frac{\partial g(x, y)}{\partial y} = 0$$

$$\lambda g(x, y) = 0$$

$$g(x, y) \le 0$$

These conditions are also sufficient if $f(x, y)$ is concave and the constraint is concave. Since a maximum point of $f(x, y)$ is a minimum point of $-f(x, y)$, this result is also applicable to minimizing a convex function subject to a convex constraint.

NOTE: A function $f(x, y)$ is convex in a region if a line segment drawn through any two points on the surface does not fall below the surface. A function of two variables is convex if and only if

$$f[(1 - t)x_1 + tx_2, (1 - t)y_1 + ty_2]$$

$$\le (1 - t)f(x_1, y_1) + tf(x_2, y_2) \qquad \text{for } 0 < t < 1$$

The function is strictly convex if $\le$ can be replaced by $<$; the function is concave if $\le$ can be replaced by $\ge$ and strictly concave if $\le$ can be replaced by $>$.

A second-degree polynomial of the form

$$f(x, y) = Ax^2 + Bxy + Cy^2 + Dx + Ey + F$$

is convex if $4AC - B^2 > 0$ and $A > 0$ ($C > 0$), concave if $4AC - B^2 > 0$ and $A < 0$ ($C < 0$), and not convex or concave everywhere if $4AC - B^2 < 0$. (Note that this result is a reformulation of the conditions for a maximum or minimum of two variables.)

As shown in the following examples, the method of Lagrange multipliers modified for one inequality constraint and the Kuhn-Tucker conditions for one inequality constraint give the same solution. The advantage of the Kuhn-Tucker conditions is that they can be generalized for more than one constraint, while the method of Lagrange multipliers cannot be modified without difficulty for more than one inequality constraint. If the function to be maximized or minimized is linear and the constraints are also linear, the solution may be obtained using linear programming for both equality and inequality constraints.

Note that the following examples are modifications of some of the examples for equality constraints.

Examples

Find the minimum of $f(x, y) = 5x^2 + 6y^2 - xy$ subject to the constraint $x + 2y \ge 24$.

Assuming the inequality constraint to hold as an equality constraint, $\lambda = 51$ (see page 378). Since $\lambda > 0$, the minimum $x = 6$, $y = 9$, assuming the equality constraint is also the minimum assuming the inequality constraint.

Using the Kuhn-Tucker conditions,

$$\frac{\partial f}{\partial x} - \lambda \frac{\partial g}{\partial x} = 10x - y - \lambda = 0$$

$$\frac{\partial f}{\partial y} - \lambda \frac{\partial g}{\partial y} = 12y - x - 2\lambda = 0$$

$$\lambda g = \lambda(x + 2y - 24) = 0$$

$$g = x + 2y - 24 \geq 0$$

Either $\lambda = 0$ or $x + 2y - 24 = 0$. If $\lambda = 0$, $x = y = 0$, but then $x + 2y \geq 24$ is not satisfied. If $x + 2y - 24 = 0$, $x = 24 - 2y$, and

$$240 - 20y - y - \lambda = 0$$

$$12y - 24 + 2y - 2\lambda = 0$$

$$\lambda + 21y = 240$$

$$-2\lambda + 14y = 24$$

$$56y = 504$$

$$y = 9$$

$$x = 6$$

Thus, as above, the minimum of $f(x, y) = 5x^2 + 6y^2 - xy$ subject to $x + 2y \geq 24$ is $x = 6$, $y = 9$.

NOTE: $5x^2 + 6y^2 - xy$ is convex, since $4AC - B^2 = (4)(5)(6) - (1)^2 > 0$ and $A > 0$, $C > 0$.

Find the maximum of $f(x, y) = 12xy - 3y^2 - x^2$ subject to the constraint $x + y \leq 16$.

Assuming the inequality constraint to hold as an equality constraint, $\lambda = 66$ (see page 381). Since $\lambda > 0$ the maximum $x = 9$, $y = 7$, assuming the equality constraint is also the maximum subject to the inequality constraint.

Using the Kuhn-Tucker conditions,

$$\frac{\partial f}{\partial x} - \lambda \frac{\partial g}{\partial x} = 12y - 2x - \lambda = 0$$

$$\frac{\partial f}{\partial y} - \lambda \frac{\partial g}{\partial y} = 12x - 6y - \lambda = 0$$

$$\lambda g = \lambda(x + y - 16) = 0$$

$$g = x + y - 16 \leq 0$$

Either $\lambda = 0$ or $x + y - 16 = 0$. If $\lambda = 0$, $x = y = 0$, which satisfies $x + y \leq 16$. $f(0, 0) = 0$. If $x + y - 16 = 0$, $x = 16 - y$, and

$$12y - 32 + 2y - \lambda = 0$$

$$192 - 12y - 6y - \lambda = 0$$

$$14y - \lambda = 32$$

$$-18y - \lambda = -192$$

$$32y = 224$$

$$y = 7$$

$$x = 9$$

The solution $x = 9$, $y = 7$, satisfies $12y - 2x - \lambda = 0$ and $12x - 6y - \lambda = 0$ if $\lambda = 66$. $f(9, 7) = 528$. Thus, as above, the maximum of $f(x, y) = 12xy - 3y^2 - x^2$ subject to $x + y \le 16$ is $x = 9$, $y = 7$.

NOTE: $12xy - 3y^2 - x^2$ is concave, since $4AC - B^2 = 4(-1)(-3) - (12)^2 < 0$ and $A < 0$, $C < 0$.

A factory manufactures two types of heavy-duty machines, x and y. The joint-cost function is given by

$$f(x, y) = x^2 + 2y^2 - xy$$

To minimize cost, how many machines of each type should be produced if there must be a total of at least 8 machines?

Assuming the inequality constraint to hold as an equality constraint, $\lambda = 7$ (see page 382). Since $\lambda > 0$, the maximum $x = 5$, $y = 3$, assuming the equality constraint is also the maximum subject to the inequality constraint.

Using the Kuhn-Tucker conditions,

$$\frac{\partial f}{\partial x} - \lambda \frac{\partial g}{\partial x} = 2x - y - \lambda = 0$$

$$\frac{\partial f}{\partial y} - \lambda \frac{\partial g}{\partial y} = 4y - x - \lambda = 0$$

$$\lambda g = \lambda(x + y - 8) = 0$$

$$g = x + y - 8 \ge 0$$

Either $\lambda = 0$ or $x + y - 8 = 0$. If $\lambda = 0$, $x = y = 0$, but then $x + y \ge 8$ is not satisfied. If $x + y - 8 = 0$, $x = 8 - y$, and

$$16 - 2y - y - \lambda = 0$$

$$4y - 8 + y - \lambda = 0$$

$$3y + \lambda = 16$$

$$5y - \lambda = 8$$

$$8y = 24$$

$$y = 3$$

$$x = 5$$

Thus, as above, the minimum of $f(x, y) = x^2 + 2y^2 - xy$ subject to $x + y \geq 8$ is $x = 5$, $y = 3$.

NOTE: $x^2 + 2y^2 - xy$ is convex, since $4AC - B^2 = 4(1)(2) - (1)^2 > 0$ and $A > 0$, $C > 0$.

The relationship between sales S and the amounts x and y spent on two advertising media is given by

$$S = \frac{200x}{5 + x} + \frac{100y}{10 + y}$$

Net profit is $\frac{1}{5}$ of sales minus the cost of advertising. The advertising budget has a maximum of 20; determine how it should be allocated between the two media to maximize net profit.

Assuming the inequality constraint to hold as an equality constraint, $\lambda = -\frac{1}{2}$ (see page 383). Since $\lambda < 0$, the unconstrained maximum is also the maximum subject to the inequality constraint.

$$f(x, y) = \frac{1}{5}\left[\frac{200x}{5 + x} + \frac{100y}{10 + y}\right] - x - y$$

$$\frac{\partial f}{\partial x} = \frac{40(5 + x) - 40x}{(5 + x)^2} - 1$$

$$\frac{\partial f}{\partial y} = \frac{20(10 + y) - 20y}{(10 + y)^2} - 1$$

$$(5 + x)^2 = 200$$

$$x = 10\sqrt{2} - 5$$

$$(10 + y)^2 = 200$$

$$y = 10\sqrt{2} - 10$$

Using the Kuhn-Tucker conditions,

$$\frac{\partial f}{\partial x} - \lambda \frac{\partial g}{\partial x} = \frac{40(5 + x) - 40x}{(5 + x)^2} - 1 - \lambda = 0$$

$$\frac{\partial f}{\partial y} - \lambda \frac{\partial g}{\partial y} = \frac{20(10 + y) - 20y}{(10 + y)^2} - 1 - \lambda = 0$$

$$\lambda g = \lambda(x + y - 25) = 0$$

$$g(x, y) = x + y - 25 \leq 0$$

NOTE: $f(x, y) = \frac{1}{5}\left[\frac{200x}{5 + x} + \frac{100y}{10 + y}\right] - x - y$

Either $\lambda = 0$ or $x + y - 25 = 0$. If $\lambda = 0$,

$$40(5 + x) - 40x = (5 + x)^2,$$

$$(5 + x)^2 = 200$$

$$x = 10\sqrt{2} - 5$$

$$20(10 + y) - 20y = (10 + y)^2$$

$$(10 + y)^2 = 200$$

$$y = 10\sqrt{2} - 10$$

$x = 10\sqrt{2} - 5$, $y = 10\sqrt{2} - 10$, satisfies $x + y \leq 25$. $f(10\sqrt{2} - 5,\ 10\sqrt{2} - 10)$ $= 75 - 40\sqrt{2} \approx 18.44$. If $x + y - 25 = 0$, $x = 25 - y$, and (see page 383)

$$(5 + 25 - y)^2 = (10 + y)^2$$

$$30 - y = 10 + y$$

$$y = 10$$

$$x = 15$$

the solution $x = 15$, $y = 10$, satisfies

$$\frac{200}{(5 + x)^2} - 1 - \lambda = 0$$

$$\frac{200}{(10 + y)^2} - 1 - \lambda = 0$$

if $\lambda = -\frac{1}{2}$. $f(15, 10) = 15$. Thus, as above, the maximum of

$$f(x, y) = \frac{1}{5} \left[\frac{200x}{5 + x} + \frac{100y}{10 + y} \right] - x - y$$

subject to $x + y \leq 25$ is $x = 10\sqrt{2} - 5$, $y = 10\sqrt{2} - 10$.

PROBLEMS

Find the maxima and/or the minima of each of the following functions subject to the given constraints.

1. $f(x, y) = 3x^2 + 4y^2 - xy$ if $2x + y = 21$.

2. $f(x, y) = x^2 + y^2 - 2xy$ if $x^2 + y^2 = 50$.

3. $f(x, y) = x^2 - 10y^2$ if $x - y = 18$.

4. $f(x, y) = 3xy + 4y^2$ if $x^2 + y^2 = 10$.

5. $f(x, y) = x + y$ if $x^2 + y^2 = 1$.

6. $f(x, y) = x^2 + 24xy + 8y^2$ if $x^2 + y^2 = 25$.

7. Find the minimum of $f(x, y) = 4x^2 + 5y^2 - 6y$ if $x + 2y \geq 18$.

8. Find the maximum of $f(x, y) = 16x + 12y - 2x^2 - 3y^2$ if $x + y \leq 11$.

9. Find the minimum of $f(x, y) = 3x^2 + 3y^2$ if $x + y \geq 10$.

10. Find the minimum of $f(x, y) = 12x^2 + 4y^2 - 8xy - 32x$ if $x + y \geq 1$.

11. Find the maximum of $f(x, y) = 10xy - 5x^2 - 7y^2 + 40x$ if $x + y \leq 13$.

12. Find the maximum of $f(x, y) = 6xy - 3x^2 - 4y^2$ if $3x + y \leq 19$.

13. Production P, as a function of two inputs x and y, is given by

$$P = x^2 + 5xy - 4y^2$$

Find the amounts of x and y which maximize production if (a) $2x + 3y = 74$, (b) $2x + 3y \leq 74$.

14. Sales S, as a function of the amounts x and y, spent on two types of promotion is given by

$$S = \frac{240x}{25 + 3x} + \frac{150y}{10 + y}$$

Net profit $= \frac{1}{10} S - x - y$. Find the allocation of x and y which will maximize net profit if $x + y = 15$.

15. Cost of production C, as a function of the numbers produced x and y, of two types of items is given by

$$C = 6x^2 + 3y^2$$

To minimize cost, what numbers of the two items should be produced if (a) $x + y = 18$, (b) $x + y \geq 18$?

16. The cost of repairs C, as a function of the numbers x and y, of inspections at two points in a process is given by

$$C = 2x^2 + 3y^2 + xy - 22x + 5$$

To minimize repair cost, what number of inspections should be made at each point if $x - y = 2$?

17. The number of breakdowns N, as a function of the numbers x and y, of replacements of two parts of a machine is given by

$$N = 3x^2 + y^2 + 2xy - 22x + 6$$

To minimize breakdowns, what numbers of replacements should be made for each part if $2x = y$?

18. The cost of repairs C, as a function of the numbers x and y, of inspections at two points in a process is given by

$$C = 4x^2 + 2y^2 + 5xy - 20x + 30$$

To minimize repair costs, what number of inspections should be made at each point if the total number of inspections is (a) 10, (b) not fewer than 10?

19. Using Lagrange multipliers, determine the maximum profit if the production function is $z = 20 - x^2 + 10x - 2y^2 + 5y$, the prices of the inputs x and y are 2 and 1, respectively, and the price of the output is 5. (See Problem 21, page 374.)

20. Using Lagrange multipliers, determine the maximum profit if the production function is $z = 10 - 2x^2 + xy - y^2 + 5y$, the prices of the inputs x and y are each 3, and the price of the output is 6. (See Problem 22, page 374.)

21. If the consumer's utility function is $U = q_1^2 q_2$, $p_1 = 4$, $p_2 = 5$, and $y^0 = 120$, determine the quantities q_1 and q_2 which he should purchase in order to maximize his derived utility.

22. If the consumer's utility function is $U = q_1 q_2 - q_1^2$, $p_1 = 3$, $p_2 = 6$, and $y^0 = 90$, determine the quantities q_1 and q_2 which he should purchase in order to maximize his derived utility.

ANSWERS TO ODD-NUMBERED PROBLEMS

1. minimum $(8.5, 4)$

3. maximum $(20, 2)$

5. minimum $(-\sqrt{\tfrac{1}{2}}, -\sqrt{\tfrac{1}{2}})$

   maximum $(\sqrt{\tfrac{1}{2}}, \sqrt{\tfrac{1}{2}})$

7. $(4, 7)$

9. $(5, 5)$

11. $(8, 5)$

13. (a) $x = 31$, $y = 4$;
    (b) $x = 31$, $y = 4$

15. (a) $x = 6$, $y = 12$;
    (b) $x = 6$, $y = 12$

17. $x = 1$, $y = 2$

19. $P_{max} = 229\tfrac{3}{5}$, $x = \tfrac{24}{5}$, $y = \tfrac{6}{5}$

21. $q_1 = 20$, $q_2 = 8$

4

INTEGRAL CALCULUS

■ 4.1 **INTRODUCTION**

Integration has two distinct interpretations; it is a procedure which is the inverse of differentiation and it is a method of determining the area under a curve. Each of these interpretations has numerous applications in economics.

As an operation, integration is the inverse of differentiation. Thus if a function is differentiated and the resulting function is then integrated, the result is the original function. As discussed below, this is precisely true only if the constant of integration is specified in some way; otherwise the result may differ from the original function by a constant. In this context, integration is the process of finding a function when its derivative (or rate of change) is known. In economics, integration can be used to find a total cost function when the marginal cost function is given, to find a total revenue function when the marginal revenue function is given, and so forth.

Integration can also be defined as the process of finding the limiting value of a sum of terms when the number of terms increases infinitely and the numerical value of each term approaches zero. It is in this context that integration is interpreted as finding the area under a curve. In fact, integral calculus was developed for the purpose of evaluating areas by supposing them to be divided into an infinite number of infinitesimally small parts whose sum is the area required; the integral sign is the elongated S used by early writers to indicate "sum." In economics total revenue can be evaluated as the area under the

397

marginal revenue curve, consumer's surplus and producer's surplus can be evaluated as areas under demand and supply curves, and so forth.

For either application, integration requires operationally that a function be determined when its derivative is given. Unfortunately, the techniques of integration are inherently more difficult than those of differentiation and there are functions, some of them deceptively simple in appearance, whose integrals cannot be expressed in terms of elementary functions. The simpler cases of integration are accomplished by reversing the corresponding formulas for differentiation; more complicated cases are handled by the use of tables of standard forms, by various procedures of substitution, and, if necessary, by numerical (approximation) methods.

The two interpretations of integration are discussed first using functions that are easily integrated by reversing the formulas for differentiation. Subsequent sections discuss various procedures for integrating more difficult functions.

■ 4.2 INDEFINITE INTEGRATION

The process of determining a function whose derivative is known is called *integration* and the required function is called an *integral* or an *antiderivative* of the given function.

If $F(x)$ is an integral with respect to x of the function $f(x)$, the relationship between them is expressed

$$\int f(x)dx = F(x) + C$$

where the left-hand member is read "integral of f of x with respect to x."

The symbol $\int$ is an *integral sign*, $f(x)$ is the *integrand*, $F(x)$ is a *particular integral*, C is the *constant of integration*, and $F(x) + C$ is the *indefinite integral*.

Note that if $F(x)$ is an integral of $f(x)$ with respect to x, then $F(x) + C$ is also such an integral, where C is any constant, since the derivative of any constant is zero—that is,

$$\frac{d}{dx}[F(x) + C] = \frac{dF(x)}{dx} + \frac{dC}{dx}$$

$$= \frac{dF(x)}{dx}$$

which is $f(x)$ if $F(x)$ is an integral of $f(x)$ with respect to x. Thus a function whose derivative is given is not completely determined, since it contains an arbitrary additive constant, the constant of integration. It is for this reason that the function $\int f(x)dx$ is referred to as the *indefinite* integral of $f(x)$.

It can be shown that two functions which have the same derivative differ at most by a constant; thus if $F(x)$ is an integral of $f(x)$, all integrals of $f(x)$ are included in the set $F(x) + C$, where C is any constant. In many applications of integration, certain information given in the problem (often referred to as an *initial* or *boundary condition*) uniquely specifies the constant of integration.

Geometrically, $y = F(x) + C$ represents a family of curves any one of which can be obtained by shifting the curve $y = F(x)$ (corresponding to $C = 0$) through a vertical displacement C (see Fig. 4.1). The curves represented by $y = F(x) + C$ are parallel to each other in the sense that the slope of the tangent to any one of them at the point having abscissa x is $f(x)$. Thus this family of curves has the property that, given any point (x_0, y_0), there is one and only one curve of the family which passes through this particular point. For the curve to pass through the point, its equation must be satisfied by the coordinates of the point, and this uniquely specifies the value of C—that is,

$$C = y_0 - F(x_0)$$

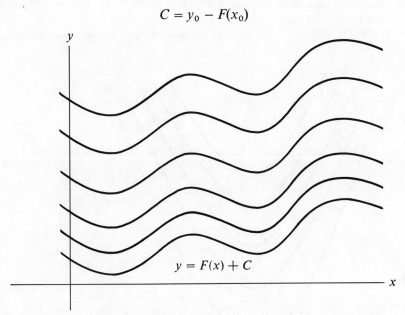

FIGURE 4.1

With C thus determined, a definite function expressing y in terms of x is obtained—that is, the constant of integration is uniquely determined if one point through which the curve representing the integral passes is specified. This specification is referred to as an *initial condition*, because evaluation of the constant of integration was first done in connection with problems in mechanics where initial velocities or positions of moving bodies are specified; however, the terminology is usually appropriate for business or behavioral-science applications as well, since the point most likely to be specified in such cases is the origin or one intercept.

Example

The integral of $f(x) = 4x - 3$ can be obtained by reversing the appropriate formulas for differentiation

$$\int (4x - 3)\, dx = 2x^2 - 3x + C$$

Note that $\dfrac{d}{dx}(2x^2 - 3x + C) = 4x - 3$, regardless of the value of C. Thus, geometrically, the integral is represented by a family of parabolas each corresponding to a different value of C. (See Fig. 4.2.) Suppose it is specified, for example that $f(x) = 5$ when $x = 0$; then

$$2x^2 - 3x + C = 5$$

$$C = 5$$

and

$$F(x) = 2x^2 - 3x + 5$$

which specifies a particular curve of the family given by $F(x) = 2x^2 - 3x + C$. (See Fig. 4.2.)

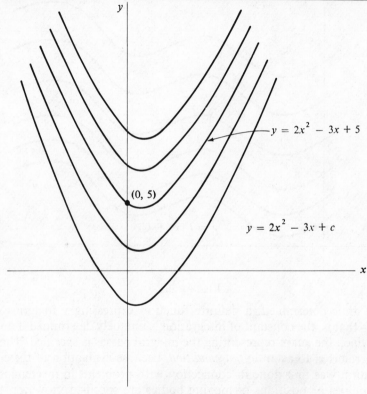

$y = 2x^2 - 3x + 5$

$(0, 5)$

$y = 2x^2 - 3x + c$

FIGURE 4.2

The rules (or standard forms) for integration used in the preceding example are obtained directly by reversing the corresponding rules for differentiation and can be summarized as follows:

1. $\displaystyle\int dx = x + C.$

2. $\displaystyle\int K\, dx = K \int dx$, where K is any constant.

(standard)
rules
for
integration

3. $\int (du + dv) = \int du + \int dv$, where $u = f(x)$ and $v = g(x)$ are differentiable functions of x.

4. $\int x^n \, dx = \dfrac{x^{n+1}}{n+1} + C, n \neq -1.$

5. $\int u^n \, du = \dfrac{u^{n+1}}{n+1} + C, n \neq -1$, where $u = f(x)$ is a differentiable function of x.

Examples

$$\int (8x^2 + 4) \, dx = \frac{8x^3}{3} + 4x + C \qquad \text{(Rules 1, 2, 3, 4)}$$

$$\int x^{3/2} \, dx = \frac{2x^{5/2}}{5} + C \qquad \text{(Rule 4)}$$

$$\int (3x^2 + 2)^3 x \, dx = \frac{1}{6} \int \underbrace{(3x^2 + 2)^3}_{u^3} \underbrace{(6x) \, dx}_{du} \qquad \text{(Rule 2)}$$

$$= \left(\frac{1}{6}\right)\frac{(3x^2 + 2)^4}{4} + C \qquad \text{(Rule 5)}$$

$$= \frac{(3x^2 + 2)^4}{24} + C$$

Alternatively,

$$\int (3x^2 + 2)^3 x \, dx = \int (27x^7 + 54x^5 + 36x^3 + 8x) \, dx$$

$$= \frac{27x^8}{8} + 9x^6 + 9x^4 + 4x^2 + C$$

$$= \frac{81x^8 + 216x^6 + 216x^4 + 96x^2}{24} + C$$

$$= \frac{(3x^2 + 2)^4}{24} + C$$

Note that C in the last step is not equal to C in the preceding step, since

$$(3x^2 + 2)^4 = 81x^8 + 216x^6 + 216x^4 + 96x^2 + 16$$

and the value of C in the last step is thus $16/24$ less than the value of C in the preceding step. It is customary to make no notational distinction when the value of a constant of integration is changed by changing the form of the equation.

Evaluate the following integrals.

(a) $y = \int (x^3 + 2x^{5/2} + 5x^{3/2} + 10x) \, dx \quad$ if $y = 0$ when $x = 0$

$$= \tfrac{1}{4}x^4 + \tfrac{4}{7}x^{7/2} + 2x^{5/2} + 5x^2 + C$$

If $x = 0$, $y = 0$, then $C = 0$ and

$$y = \tfrac{1}{4}x^4 + \tfrac{4}{7}x^{7/2} + 2x^{5/2} + 5x^2$$

(b) $y = \displaystyle\int (x + 2)^2 \, dx \qquad$ if $y = 10$ when $x = 1$

$$= \frac{(x + 2)^3}{3} + C$$

If $x = 1$, $y = 10$, then $C = 1$ and

$$y = \frac{(x + 2)^3}{3} + 1$$

(c) $y = \displaystyle\int (3x^2 + 2x + 6) \, dx \qquad$ if $y = 5$ when $x = 0$

$$= x^3 + x^2 + 6x + C$$

If $x = 0$, $y = 5$, then $C = 5$ and

$$y = x^3 + x^2 + 6x + 5$$

For each of the following find the curve having the given slope and passing through the given point:

(a) $\dfrac{dy}{dx} = \dfrac{x^2 - 4}{x^2}$, $(4, 1)$.

(b) $\dfrac{dy}{dx} = x^2 \sqrt{x}$, $(1, 0)$.

(a) $\displaystyle\int \frac{x^2 - 4}{x^2} \, dx = \int dx - \int \frac{4}{x^2} \, dx$

$$= x + \frac{4x^{-1}}{1} + C$$

$$= x + \frac{4}{x} + C$$

Thus

$$y = x + \frac{4}{x} + C$$

$$1 = 4 + 1 + C$$

$$C = -4$$

so

$$y = x + \frac{4}{x} - 4$$

$$= \frac{x^2 - 4x + 4}{x}$$

$$= \frac{(x-2)^2}{x} \text{ is the required curve.}$$

(b) $\int x^2 \sqrt{x} \, dx = \int x^{5/2} \, dx$

$$= \frac{x^{7/2}}{\frac{7}{2}} + C$$

$$= \tfrac{2}{7} x^{7/2} + C$$

Thus

$$y = \tfrac{2}{7} x^{7/2} + C$$

$$0 = \tfrac{2}{7} + C$$

$$C = -\tfrac{2}{7}$$

so

$$y = \tfrac{2}{7} x^{7/2} - \tfrac{2}{7}$$

$$= \tfrac{2}{7}(x^{7/2} - 1)$$

$$= \tfrac{2}{7}(x^3 \sqrt{x} - 1) \text{ is the required curve.}$$

PROBLEMS

Evaluate the following integrals.

1. $\int (x^2 - \sqrt{x} + 4) \, dx$

2. $\int (2 - 7t)^{2/3} \, dt$

3. $\int \sqrt{2 + 5y} \, dy$

4. $\int \frac{dx}{(3x + 2)^2}$

5. $\int \frac{3r \, dr}{\sqrt{1 - r^2}}$

6. $\int x\sqrt{2x^2 + 1} \, dx$

7. $\int \left(\sqrt{x} + \frac{1}{\sqrt{x}} \right) dx$

8. $\int \frac{(z + 1) \, dz}{\sqrt[3]{z^2 + 2z + 2}}$

9. $\int \frac{(1 - 2x)^2 \, dx}{\sqrt{2x}}$ $= \int (1 - 4x + 4x^2)(2x)^{-\frac{1}{2}}$

$= \int 2x^2 \ldots$

10. $\int \frac{dx}{x\sqrt{2x}}$

11. $\int (x\sqrt{x} - 5)^2 \, dx = \int (x^{3/2} - 5)^2$

12. $\int \frac{(x^3 - 1) \, dx}{x - 1} = \int \frac{(x-1)(x^2 + x + 1)}{(x-1)}$

13. $\int (2x + 3) \, dx$

14. $\displaystyle\int (x^2 - \sqrt{x})\, dx$

15. $\displaystyle\int \sqrt{2 + 5y}\, dy$

16. Find the equation of the curve having slope $\dfrac{dy}{dx} = 2x - 5$ and passing through the point $(5, 4)$.

17. Find the equation of the curve having slope $\dfrac{dy}{dx} = (x + 1)(x + 2)$ and passing through the point $(-3, -3/2)$.

18. If $\dfrac{dy}{dx} = 2x - 3$ and $y = 2$ if $x = 3$, find the value of y if $x = 5$.

19. If $\dfrac{dp}{dx} = \dfrac{1}{\sqrt{2ax}}$ and $p = 2a$ if $x = \frac{1}{2}a^3$, find the value of p if $x = 2a^3$.

20. Find the equation of the curve for which $y''' = 2$ and which has a slope of -2 at its point of inflection $(1, 3)$.

21. Find the equation of the curve for which $y'' = \dfrac{4}{x^3}$ and which is tangent to the line $2x + y = 5$ at the point $(1, 3)$.

22. Find the equation of the curve for which $y'' = 6x^2$ and which passes through the points $(0, 2)$ and $(-1, 3)$.

23. Find the equation of the curve for which $y'' = x$ and which passes through the point $(1, 2)$ with a slope of $\frac{5}{2}$.

24. Find the equation of the curve which has a slope of zero at the point $(0, 2)$, has a point of inflection at $(-1, \frac{10}{3})$, and has $y''' = 4$.

ANSWERS TO ODD-NUMBERED PROBLEMS

1. $\frac{1}{3}x^3 - \frac{2}{3}x^{3/2} + 4x + C$

3. $\frac{2}{15}(2 + 5y)^{3/2} + C$

5. $3\sqrt{1 - r^2} + C$

7. $\frac{2}{3}x^{3/2} + 2x^{1/2} + C$

9. $\sqrt{2x}(1 - \frac{4}{3}x + \frac{8}{5}x^2) + C$

11. $\frac{1}{4}x^4 - 4x^{5/2} + 25x + C$

13. $x^2 + 3x + C$

15. $\frac{2}{15}(2 + 5y)^{3/2} + C$

17. $y = \frac{1}{3}x^3 + \frac{3}{2}x^2 + 2x$

19. $p(2a^3) = 3a$

21. $y = \dfrac{2}{x} + 1$

23. $y = \frac{1}{6}x^3 + 2x - \frac{1}{6}$

■ 4.3 **APPLICATIONS OF INDEFINITE INTEGRATION IN BUSINESS AND ECONOMICS**

As noted in the discussion of differentiation, in economics the variation of one quantity y with respect to another quantity x is frequently discussed in terms of two concepts—an *average* variation and a *marginal* variation. Just as its marginal variation can be obtained by differentiating a function, the function (apart from a constant) can be obtained by integrating its marginal variation.

□ *COST*

If the total cost y of producing and marketing x units of a commodity is given by the function

$$y = f(x)$$

Then the *average cost* per unit is

$$\frac{y}{x} = \frac{f(x)}{x}$$

and the *marginal cost* is

$$\frac{dy}{dx} = f'(x)$$

That is, marginal cost is the derivative $f'(x)$ of the total cost function $y = f(x)$ with respect to x. Thus total cost is the integral with respect to x of the marginal cost function; that is,

$$y = \int f'(x)\,dx = f(x) + C$$

To obtain a unique total cost function by integrating the corresponding marginal cost function, an initial condition must be specified. Frequently this specification is in terms of a fixed cost or initial overhead, that is, the cost when $x = 0$.

Examples

Marginal cost y' as a function of units produced x is given by

$$y' = 1.064 - 0.005x$$

Find the total and average cost functions if fixed cost is 16.3.

$$y = \int (1.064 - 0.005x)\,dx$$

$$= 1.064x - 0.0025x^2 + C$$

If $x = 0$, $y = 16.3$, and thus $C = 16.3$ and

$$y = 16.3 + 1.064x - 0.0025x^2 \qquad \text{(total cost)}$$

$$\frac{y}{x} = \frac{16.3}{x} + 1.064 - 0.0025x \qquad \text{(average cost)}$$

Marginal cost y' as a function of units produced x is given by

$$y' = 2 + 60\hat{x} - 5x^2$$

Find the total and average cost functions if fixed cost is 65.

$$y = \int (2 + 60x - 5x^2)\, dx$$

$$= 2x + 30x^2 - \tfrac{5}{3}x^3 + C$$

If $x = 0$, $y = 65$, and thus $C = 65$ and

$$y = 65 + 2x + 30x^2 - \tfrac{5}{3}x^3 \qquad \text{(total cost)}$$

$$\frac{y}{x} = \frac{65}{x} + 2 + 30x - \tfrac{5}{3}x^2 \qquad \text{(average cost)}$$

☐ *REVENUE*

For any demand function

$$y = f(x)$$

where y is the price per unit and x is the number of units, *total revenue R* is the product of x and y; that is,

$$R = xy = x \cdot f(x)$$

Marginal revenue with respect to demand is the derivative with respect to x of the total revenue

$$\frac{dR}{dx} = R'(x)$$

Thus total revenue is the integral with respect to x of the marginal revenue function; that is,

$$R = \int R'(x)dx$$

And, since

$$\int R'(x)dx = R(x) + C$$

an initial condition must be specified to obtain a unique total revenue function by integrating the corresponding marginal revenue function. The initial condition that revenue is zero if demand is zero can be used to evaluate the constant of integration.

Note that *average revenue* or revenue per unit is the price per unit, y, and thus the average revenue curve and the demand curve are identical.

Examples

If the marginal revenue function is

$$R'(x) = 8 - 6x - 2x^2$$

determine the total revenue and demand functions.

$$R(x) = \int (8 - 6x - 2x^2)\,dx$$

$$= 8x - 3x^2 - \tfrac{2}{3}x^3 + C$$

If $x = 0$, $R = 0$, and thus $C = 0$ and

$$R = 8x - 3x^2 - \tfrac{2}{3}x^3$$

$$y = \frac{R}{x} = 8 - 3x - \tfrac{2}{3}x^2$$

If the marginal revenue function is

$$R'(x) = 12 - 8x + x^2$$

determine the revenue and demand functions.

$$R(x) = \int (12 - 8x + x^2)\,dx$$

$$= 12x - 4x^2 + \tfrac{1}{3}x^3 + C$$

If $x = 0$, $R = 0$, and thus $C = 0$ and

$$R = 12x - 4x^2 + \tfrac{1}{3}x^3$$

$$y = \frac{R}{x} = 12 - 4x + \tfrac{1}{3}x^2$$

$$= \frac{(6 - x)^2}{3}$$

☐ *NATIONAL INCOME, CONSUMPTION, AND SAVINGS*

If the consumption function is given by

$$c = f(x)$$

where c is total national consumption and x is total national income, then the *marginal propensity to consume* is the derivative with respect to x of the consumption function

$$\frac{dc}{dx} = f'(x)$$

and, assuming $x = c + s$, where s is savings, the *marginal propensity to save* is

$$\frac{ds}{dx} = 1 - \frac{dc}{dx}$$

Total national consumption is the integral with respect to x of the marginal propensity to consume,

$$c = \int f'(x)\,dx = f(x) + C$$

An initial condition must be specified to obtain a unique consumption function by integrating the corresponding marginal propensity to consume.

Examples

The marginal propensity to consume (in billions of dollars) is

$$\frac{dc}{dx} = 0.7 + \frac{0.2}{\sqrt{x}}$$

When income is zero, consumption is 8 billion dollars. Find the consumption function.

$$c = \int \left(0.7 + \frac{0.2}{\sqrt{x}}\right) dx$$

$$= 0.7x + 0.4\sqrt{x} + C$$

If $x = 0$, $c = 8$, and thus $C = 8$ and

$$c = 8 + 0.7x + 0.4\sqrt{x}$$

The marginal propensity to save is $\frac{1}{3}$. When income is zero, consumption is 11 billion dollars. Find the consumption function.

$$\frac{dc}{dx} = 1 - \frac{ds}{dx} = \tfrac{2}{3}$$

$$c = \int \tfrac{2}{3}\, dx$$

$$= \tfrac{2}{3}x + C$$

If $x = 0$, $c = 11$, and thus $C = 11$ and

$$c = \tfrac{2}{3}x + 11$$

PROBLEMS

1. If the marginal revenue is a constant different from zero, show that price is constant.

2. If $R'(x) = 0$ and $R(0) \neq 0$, what is the nature of the demand curve?

3. If marginal cost is constant, show that the cost function is a straight line.

4. The marginal propensity to consume (in billions of dollars) is

$$\frac{dc}{dx} = 0.6 + \frac{0.5}{2x^{1/2}}$$

When income is zero, consumption is 10 billion dollars. Find the consumption function.

5. The marginal cost function for production is $y' = 10 + 24x - 3x^2$; if the (total) cost of producing 1 unit is 25, find the total cost function and the average cost function.

6. The marginal propensity to save is $\frac{1}{2}$. When income is zero, consumption is 6 billion dollars. Find the consumption function.

7. If marginal revenue is $R' = 15 - 9x - 3x^2$, find the revenue and demand functions.

8. If marginal revenue is $R' = \dfrac{3}{x^2} - \dfrac{2}{x}$, find the revenue and demand functions if $R(1) = 6$.

9. If marginal revenue is $R' = 10 - 5x$, find the revenue and demand functions.

10. If marginal revenue is $R' = 20 - 3x^2$, find the revenue and demand functions.

11. The marginal propensity to consume (in billions of dollars) is

$$\frac{dc}{dx} = 0.5 + \frac{1}{3x^{1/3}}$$

When income is zero, consumption is 6 billion dollars. Find the consumption function.

12. The marginal propensity to save (in billions of dollars) is

$$\frac{dc}{ds} = 1 - 0.4 - \frac{1}{6x^{2/3}}$$

When income is zero, consumption is 9 billion dollars. Find the consumption function.

ANSWERS TO ODD-NUMBERED PROBLEMS

5. $y = 10x + 12x^2 - x^3 + 4$

   $\bar{y} = 10 + 12x - x^2 + \dfrac{4}{x}$

7. $R = 15x - \frac{9}{2}x^2 - x^3$
   $y = 15 - \frac{9}{2}x - x^2$

9. $R = 10x - \frac{5}{2}x^2$
   $y = 10 - \frac{5}{2}x$

11. $C = 0.5x + 0.5x^{2/3} + 6$

■ 4.4 DEFINITE INTEGRATION

As noted above, finding the areas of figures was one of the problems that led to the development of integral calculus. In elementary geometry the area of a rectangle is shown to be equal to the product of its width and its height, and from this the areas of other figures bounded by straight-line segments are obtained by elementary geometrical methods. However, these methods are not directly applicable to figures bounded (entirely or in part) by curved lines. In general, to find areas of curvilinear figures, the method of limits must be used —for example, the area of a circle is obtained in geometry by considering it to be the common limit of sets of regular inscribed and circumscribed polygons as the number of their sides is indefinitely increased. This use of the method of limits leads to the interpretation of the definite integral as the area under a curve.

Consider the problem of determining the area bounded by the continuous positive curve $y = f(x)$, the x-axis, and the lines $x = a$ and $x = b$. Divide the base $[a, b]$ into n subintervals and denote the points of division by $a = x_1$, $x_2, \ldots, x_n, x_{n+1} = b$ and the lengths of the n subintervals as $\Delta x_i = x_{i+1} - x_i$; $i = 1, \ldots, n$. Erect ordinates at the points of division and inscribe rectangles (see Fig. 4.3).

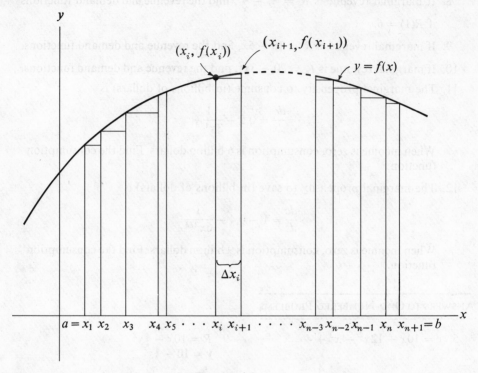

FIGURE 4.3

The areas of these inscribed rectangles are $f(x_1)\Delta x_1, f(x_2)\Delta x_2, \ldots, f(x_n)\Delta x_n$ and their sum is

$$\sum_{i=1}^{n} f(x_i)\Delta x_i$$

By increasing the number of inscribed rectangles, that is, by letting $n \to \infty$ and max $\Delta x_i \to 0$, the area under the curve between a and b which is not included in the rectangles is decreased and, in fact, approaches zero.

DEFINITION: The area bounded by the continuous positive function

$$y = f(x)$$

the x-axis, and two fixed ordinates $x = a$, $x = b$ is

$$A = \lim_{\substack{n \to \infty \\ \max \Delta x_i \to 0}} \sum_{i=1}^{n} f(x_i)\Delta x_i$$

NOTE: The same limit would be obtained by circumscribing rather than inscribing the rectangles—that is,

$$\lim_{\substack{n \to \infty \\ \max \Delta x_i \to 0}} \sum_{i=1}^{n} f(x_i)\Delta x_i = \lim_{\substack{n \to \infty \\ \max \Delta x_i \to 0}} \sum_{i=1}^{n} f(x_{i+1})\Delta x_i$$

If the curve is nonmonotonic, the argument is modified by using, respectively, the minimum or maximum values of the function in the intervals rather than $f(x_i)$ or $f(x_{i+1})$. In fact, *any* point in an interval can be used without affecting the result.

If $f(x)$ is continuous for the interval $[a, b]$, then $\displaystyle\lim_{\substack{n \to \infty \\ \max \Delta x_i \to 0}} \sum_{i=1}^{n} f(x_i)\,\Delta x_i$ exists, $f(x)$ is said to be *integrable* over the interval $[a, b]$, and it can be shown that

$$\text{Area} = \lim_{\substack{n \to \infty \\ \max \Delta x_i \to 0}} \sum_{i=1}^{n} f(x_i)\,\Delta x_i = \int_{a}^{b} f(x)\,dx$$

by the following argument.

Consider the area between a fixed ordinate at $x = a$ and a variable (movable) ordinate at $x = b$ (see Fig. 4.4) and denote the area *abgh* by A. When x takes

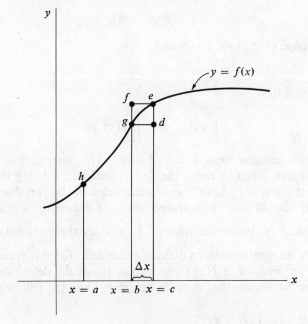

FIGURE 4.4

a small increment Δx, A takes an increment $\Delta A = $ area *bceg*. Note that

$$\text{Area}(bcdg) < \text{Area}(bceg) < \text{Area}(bcef)$$

$$(bg)(\Delta x) < \Delta A < (ce)(\Delta x)$$

$$bg < \frac{\Delta A}{\Delta x} < ce$$

and let $\Delta x \to 0$. (If it happens that $ce < bg$, the inequality signs can be reversed without affecting the argument.) Then, since y is a continuous function of x, *ce* approaches *bg* and

$$\frac{dA}{dx} = bg = y = f(x)$$

$$dA = f(x)\,dx$$

Integrating,

$$A = \int f(x)\,dx$$

Denote $\int f(x)\,dx$ by $F(x) + C$. Then $A = F(x) + C$. Note that $A = 0$ when $x = a$ and thus

$$0 = F(a) + C$$
$$C = -F(a)$$

and

$$A = F(x) - F(a)$$

For the area $abgh$ (Fig. 4.4), $x = b$ and

$$A$$

which is denoted by

$$\int_a^b y\,dx \quad \text{or} \quad \int_a^b f(x)\,dx$$

and is read "the integral from a to b of $y\,dx$." This operation is referred to as *integration between limits*, a being the *lower limit* and b being the *upper limit*. (In this context the word "limit" means the value of the variable at one end of its range; this should not be confused with the meaning of the word in the theory of limits.) In the evaluation of $\int_a^b f(x)\,dx$ the constant of integration disappears; the integral thus has a definite value and, for this reason, is referred to as the *definite integral* of $f(x)$ from a to b. From the definition of a definite integral, it can be shown that definite integrals have the following properties.

1. $\displaystyle\int_a^b f(x)\,dx = -\int_b^a f(x)\,dx.$

2. $\displaystyle\int_a^a f(x)\,dx = 0.$

3. $\displaystyle\int_a^b f(x)\,dx = \int_a^c f(x)\,dx + \int_c^b f(x)\,dx,$ where $a \le c \le b.$

Example

(a) $\displaystyle\int_1^3 y(y^2 - 4)^2\,dy = \tfrac{1}{2}\int_1^3 (2y)(y^2 - 4)^2\,dy$

DEFINITE INTEGRATION | 413

$$= \left[\frac{(y^2 - 4)^3}{6} \right]_1^3$$

$$= \tfrac{125}{6} - \left(-\tfrac{27}{6} \right)$$

$$= \tfrac{152}{6} = \tfrac{76}{3}$$

$$\int_3^1 y(y^2 - 4)^2 \, dy = \left[\frac{(y^2 - 4)^3}{6} \right]_3^1$$

$$= -\tfrac{27}{6} - \tfrac{125}{6}$$

$$= -\tfrac{152}{6} = -\tfrac{76}{3}$$

and

$$\int_1^3 y(y^2 - 4)^2 \, dy = -\int_3^1 y(y^2 - 4)^2 \, dy$$

(b) $\displaystyle \int_{-1}^{-1} \sqrt{1 - z} \, dz = \left[-\tfrac{2}{3}(1 - z)^{3/2} \right]_{-1}^{-1}$

$$= -\tfrac{2}{3}(2)^{3/2} - [-\tfrac{2}{3}(2)^{3/2}]$$

$$= 0$$

(c) $\displaystyle \int_1^4 \frac{v + 1}{\sqrt{v}} \, dv = \int_1^4 (v^{1/2} + v^{-1/2}) \, dv$

$$= \left[\tfrac{2}{3}v^{3/2} + 2v^{1/2} \right]_1^4$$

$$= \tfrac{16}{3} + 4 - \tfrac{2}{3} - 2$$

$$= \tfrac{20}{3}$$

$$\int_1^4 \frac{v + 1}{\sqrt{v}} \, dv = \int_1^2 \frac{v + 1}{\sqrt{v}} \, dv + \int_2^4 \frac{v + 1}{\sqrt{v}} \, dv$$

$$= \left[\tfrac{2}{3}v^{3/2} + 2v^{1/2} \right]_1^2 + \left[\tfrac{2}{3}v^{3/2} + 2v^{1/2} \right]_2^4$$

$$= \tfrac{2}{3}(2)^{3/2} + 2^{3/2} - \tfrac{2}{3} - 2 + \tfrac{16}{3} + 4 - \tfrac{2}{3}(2)^{3/2} - 2^{3/2}$$

$$= \tfrac{20}{3}$$

The previous result concerning evaluation of area by integration is known as the *fundamental theorem of integral calculus* and can be summarized in somewhat more rigorous form as follows:

Let $f(x)$ be continuous and positive for the interval $x = a$ to $x = b$. Let this interval be divided into n subintervals of lengths $\Delta x_1, \Delta x_2, \ldots, \Delta x_n$ and points be chosen, one in each subinterval, their abscissas being $x_1, x_2, \ldots, x_n$, respectively. Then

$$\lim_{\substack{n \to \infty \\ \max \Delta x_i \to 0}} \sum_{i=1}^n f(x_i) \, \Delta x_i = \int_a^b f(x) \, dx = F(b) - F(a)$$

The importance of this theorem results from the fact that it permits the evaluation of the limit of a sum of terms by integration and that this limit can be interpreted as the area under a curve. Specifically, the definite integral $\int_a^b f(x)\,dx$ can be interpreted as the area bounded by the continuous positive curve $y = f(x)$, the x-axis, and the lines $x = a$ and $x = b$.

Examples

Find the area bounded by the curve
$$y = x^3 + 3x^2$$
the x-axis, and the lines $x = 0$ and $x = 2$ (see Fig. 4.5).

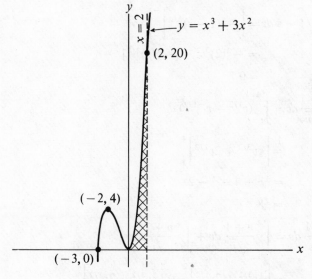

FIGURE 4.5

$$A = \int_0^2 (x^3 + 3x^2)dx = \left[\frac{x^4}{4} + x^3\right]_0^2 = 12$$

Find the area bounded by the curve
$$x^2y = x^2 - 4$$
the x-axis, and the lines $x = 2$ and $x = 4$ (see Fig. 4.6.)

$$A = \int_2^4 \frac{x^2 - 4}{x^2}\,dx = \int_2^4 \left(1 - \frac{4}{x^2}\right)dx = \left[x + 4x^{-1}\right]_2^4$$
$$= 4 + 1 - 2 - 2$$
$$= 1$$

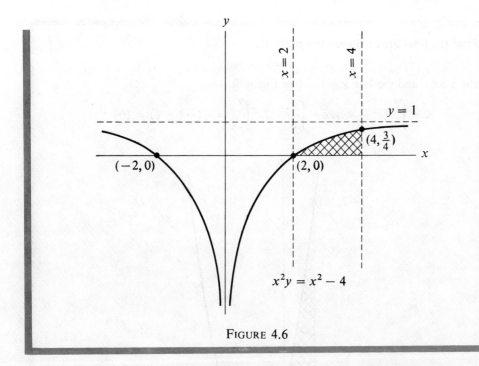

FIGURE 4.6

Find the area in the first quadrant bounded by the x-axis and the curve

$$y = 6x + x^2 - x^3$$

(see Fig. 4.7).

$$A = \int_0^3 (6x + x^2 - x^3)\, dx = \left[3x^2 + \frac{x^3}{3} - \frac{x^4}{4}\right]_0^3 = 27 + 9 - \frac{81}{4} = 15\tfrac{3}{4}$$

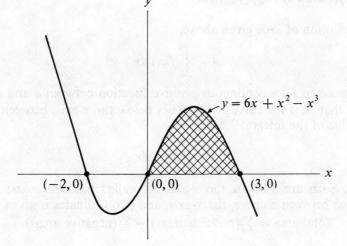

FIGURE 4.7

Find the total area between the parabola

$$y = x^2 - 4x$$

the x-axis, and the line $x = -2$ (see Fig. 4.8).

$$A = \int_{-2}^{0} (x^2 - 4x)dx = \left[\frac{x^3}{3} - 2x^2\right]_{-2}^{0} = -(-\tfrac{8}{3} - 8) = 10\tfrac{2}{3}$$

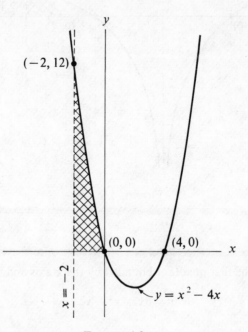

FIGURE 4.8

● **Interpretation of Negative Areas**

In the definition of area given above,

$$A = \int_{a}^{b} f(x)\, dx$$

$f(x)$ is assumed to be a continuous positive function between a and b. If $f(x)$ is negative, that is, if the curve $y = f(x)$ lies below the x-axis, between a and b, then the value of the integral

$$A = \int_{a}^{b} f(x)\, dx$$

is negative. Such areas below the x-axis are called *negative areas*; the total absolute area between a curve, the x-axis, and two ordinates is given by

$$\text{Total area} = \sum (\text{positive areas}) - \sum (\text{negative areas})$$

NOTE: This is equivalent to saying that area is equal to the absolute value of the integral and thus is always positive.

Examples

Find the area bounded by the curve
$$y = 2x + x^2 - x^3$$
the x-axis, and the lines $x = -1$ and $x = 1$ (see Fig. 4.9).

$$A = \int_0^1 (2x + x^2 - x^3)dx - \int_{-1}^0 (2x + x^2 - x^3)\,dx$$

$$= \left[x^2 + \frac{x^3}{3} - \frac{x^4}{4}\right]_0^1 - \left[x^2 + \frac{x^3}{3} - \frac{x^4}{4}\right]_{-1}^0$$

$$= [(1 + \tfrac{1}{3} - \tfrac{1}{4}) - 0] - [0 - (1 - \tfrac{1}{3} - \tfrac{1}{4})]$$

$$= \tfrac{13}{12} - (-\tfrac{5}{12}) \text{ (positive area minus negative area)}$$

$$= \tfrac{3}{2}$$

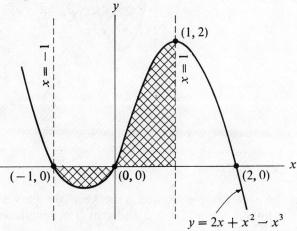

FIGURE 4.9

Find the area bounded by the curve
$$y = x^3 - 4x$$
and the x-axis (see Fig. 4.10).

$$A = \int_{-2}^0 (x^3 - 4x)\,dx - \int_0^2 (x^3 - 4x)\,dx$$

$$= \left[\frac{x^4}{4} - 2x^2\right]_{-2}^0 - \left[\frac{x^4}{4} - 2x^2\right]_0^2$$

$$= [0 - (4 - 8)] - [(4 - 8) - 0]$$

$$= 4 - (-4)$$

$$= 8$$

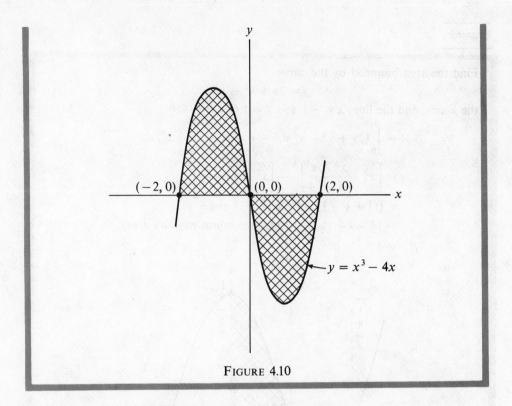

FIGURE 4.10

● Area Between Two Curves

Suppose that the area to be evaluated is between the curves $y_1 = f(x)$ and $y_2 = g(x)$ and the lines $x = a$ and $x = b$ and that (for definiteness) $f(x) \leq g(x)$ for $a \leq x \leq b$ (see Fig. 4.11). Then

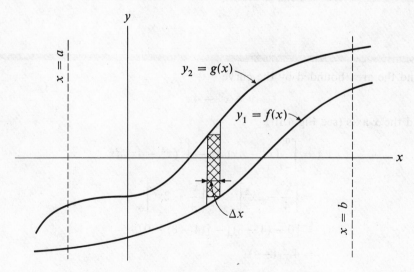

FIGURE 4.11

$$A = \int_a^b [g(x) - f(x)] \, dx$$

Note that this formula includes negative areas (with appropriate signs) in the total area between the curves.

Examples

Find the area bounded by the curves

$$y = x^2 \quad \text{and} \quad y = x$$

(see Fig. 4.12).

Finding the points of intersection of the curves

$$y = x = x^2$$

$$x(1 - x) = 0$$

$$x = 0, 1$$

If $x = 0$, $y = 0$; if $x = 1$, $y = 1$. Thus

$$A = \int_0^1 (x - x^2) \, dx = \left[\frac{x^2}{2} - \frac{x^3}{3} \right]_0^1$$

$$= \tfrac{1}{2} - \tfrac{1}{3}$$

$$= \tfrac{1}{6}$$

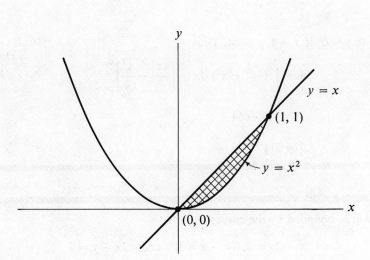

FIGURE 4.12

Find the area bounded by the curves
$$y = x^3 \quad \text{and} \quad y = 4x^2$$
(see Fig. 4.13).
Finding the points of intersection of the curves
$$y = x^3 = 4x^2$$
$$x^2(x - 4) = 0$$
$$x = 0, 4$$

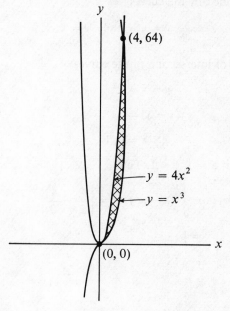

FIGURE 4.13

If $x = 0$, $y = 0$; if $x = 4$, $y = 64$. Thus
$$A = \int_0^4 (4x^2 - x^3)\, dx = \left[\frac{4x^3}{3} - \frac{x^4}{4}\right]_0^4$$
$$= \tfrac{256}{3} - 64$$
$$= 21\tfrac{1}{3}$$

Find the area bounded by the curves
$$x + 2y = 2, \quad y - x = 1, \quad \text{and} \quad 2x + y = 7$$
(see Fig. 4.14).

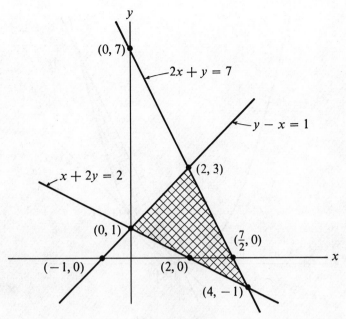

FIGURE 4.14

$$A = \int_0^2 \left[(1+x) - \left(\frac{2-x}{2} \right) \right] dx + \int_2^4 \left[(7-2x) - \left(\frac{2-x}{2} \right) \right] dx$$

$$= \int_0^2 \tfrac{3}{2}x \, dx + \int_2^4 (6 - \tfrac{3}{2}x) \, dx = \left[\frac{3x^2}{4} \right]_0^2 + \left[6x - \frac{3x^2}{4} \right]_2^4$$

$$= 3 + 24 - 12 - 12 + 3$$

$$= 6$$

Find the area bounded by the curves

$$y = x^2, \quad y = x, \quad \text{and} \quad y = 2x$$

(see Fig. 4.15).
Finding the points of intersection of the curves

$$
\begin{array}{ll}
y = x = x^2 & y = 2x = x^2 \\
x(x - 1) = 0 & x(x - 2) = 0 \\
x = 0, 1 & x = 0, 2 \\
\text{If } x = 0, y = 0 & \text{If } x = 0, y = 0 \\
\text{If } x = 1, y = 1 & \text{If } x = 2, y = 4
\end{array}
$$

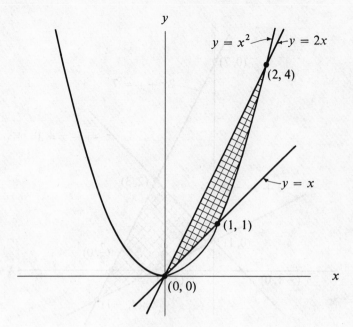

FIGURE 4.15

Thus

$$A = \int_0^1 (2x - x)\,dx + \int_1^2 (2x - x^2)\,dx$$

$$= \left[\frac{x^2}{2}\right]_0^1 + \left[x^2 - \frac{x^3}{3}\right]_1^2$$

$$= \tfrac{1}{2} + 4 - \tfrac{8}{3} - 1 + \tfrac{1}{3}$$

$$= \tfrac{7}{6}$$

NOTE: In evaluating an area it is theoretically of no importance whether horizontal or vertical elements of area are used (see Fig. 4.11); the choice depends on the number and difficulty of the integrals needed to determine the particular area. In the above example either choice involves approximately the same amount of calculation.

The area bounded by the curves

$$y = x^2 \quad \text{and} \quad y = x$$

could have been determined using horizontal elements of area as follows:

$$A = \int_0^1 (y^{1/2} - y)\,dy = \left[\frac{2y^{3/2}}{3} - \frac{y^2}{2}\right]_0^1 = \tfrac{2}{3} - \tfrac{1}{2} = \tfrac{1}{6}$$

The area bounded by the curves

$$y = x^3 \quad \text{and} \quad y = 4x^2$$

could have been determined using horizontal elements of area as follows:

$$A = \int_0^{64} \left(y^{1/3} - \frac{y^{1/2}}{2} \right) dy = \left[\frac{3y^{4/3}}{4} - \frac{y^{3/2}}{3} \right]_0^{64}$$

$$= 3(64) - \tfrac{8}{3}(64) = 21\tfrac{1}{3}$$

The area bounded by the curves

$$x + 2y = 2, \quad y - x = 1, \quad \text{and} \quad 2x + y = 7$$

could have been determined using horizontal elements of area as follows:

$$A = \int_{-1}^{1} \left[\left(\frac{7-y}{2} \right) - (2 - 2y) \right] dy + \int_{1}^{3} \left[\left(\frac{7-y}{2} \right) - (y - 1) \right] dy$$

$$= \int_{-1}^{1} \tfrac{3}{2}(y + 1)\, dy + \int_{1}^{3} \tfrac{3}{2}(3 - y)\, dy$$

$$= \left[\frac{3y^2}{4} + \tfrac{3}{2}y \right]_{-1}^{1} + \left[\tfrac{9}{2}y - \frac{3y^2}{4} \right]_{1}^{3}$$

$$= \tfrac{3}{4} + \tfrac{3}{2} - \tfrac{3}{4} + \tfrac{3}{2} + \tfrac{27}{2} - \tfrac{27}{4} - \tfrac{9}{2} + \tfrac{3}{4}$$

$$= 6$$

The area bounded by the curves

$$y = x^2, \quad y = x, \quad \text{and} \quad y = 2x$$

could have been determined using horizontal elements of area as follows:

$$A = \int_0^1 \left(y - \frac{y}{2} \right) dy + \int_1^4 \left(y^{1/2} - \frac{y}{2} \right) dy$$

$$= \left[\frac{y^2}{4} \right]_0^1 + \left[\frac{2y^{3/2}}{3} - \frac{y^2}{4} \right]_1^4$$

$$= \tfrac{1}{4} + \tfrac{16}{3} - 4 - \tfrac{2}{3} + \tfrac{1}{4}$$

$$= \tfrac{7}{6}$$

PROBLEMS

Evaluate the following integrals.

1. $\displaystyle\int_0^1 (x^2 - 2x + 3)\, dx$

9. $\displaystyle\int_a^{2a} (a + z)\, dz$

2. $\displaystyle\int_{-1}^1 (v + 1)^2\, dv$

10. $\displaystyle\int_1^2 \frac{x^2 - 1}{x^4}\, dx$

3. $\displaystyle\int_0^2 (4x + 1)^{1/2}\, dx$

11. $\displaystyle\int_1^8 (u^{1/3} - u^{-1/3})\, du$

4. $\displaystyle\int_0^1 \frac{dx}{(2x + 1)^3}$

12. $\displaystyle\int_{-1}^0 (2x + x^2 - x^3)\, dx$

5. $\displaystyle\int_{-3}^{-2} t(t + 1)^2\, dt$

13. $\displaystyle\int_a^{2a} (a^3 + 3ax^2 + x^3)\, dx$

6. $\displaystyle\int_2^5 \left(x^2 + \frac{1}{x^2}\right) dx$

14. $\displaystyle\int_0^a (\sqrt{a} - \sqrt{x})^2\, dx$

7. $\displaystyle\int_1^3 (2\theta + 1)(3 - \theta)\, d\theta$

15. $\displaystyle\int_1^4 (\sqrt{z} - z)^2\, dz$

8. $\displaystyle\int_{-1}^1 (x^2 + 1)^2\, dx$

16. $\displaystyle\int_{-1}^2 (x^2 + x)(3x + 1)\, dx$

Sketch each of the following curves and find the area bounded by the curve, the x-axis, and the given ordinates.

17. $y = \sqrt{x}$; $x = 1$, $x = 16$

18. $y = 2x + 1$; $x = 0$, $x = 4$

19. $y = x^{99}$; $x = 0$, $x = 1$

20. $y = 3x^2$; $x = 1$, $x = 3$

21. $y = x^2 - 3x$; $x = -1$, $x = 4$

22. $y = -x^2 + 4x$ (and x-axis)

23. $f(x) = \begin{cases} x^2 & x \le 2 \\ -x + 6 & x > 2 \end{cases}$ $x = 0$, $x = 3$

24. $f(x) = \begin{cases} 2x + 3 & x \le 3 \\ -x + 12 & x > 3 \end{cases}$ $x = 2$, $x = 5$

25. Find the area between the curve $y = 2x^4 - x^2$, the x-axis, and the two minimum ordinates.

26. Find the area bounded by the coordinate axes and the parabolic arc $\sqrt{x} + \sqrt{y} = \sqrt{a}$.

Draw a sketch and find the area bounded by the following curves.

27. $y^2 = 2x$
    $y = x - 4$

28. $x^2 = 2ay$
    $y = 2a$

29. $y = x - x^2$
    $y = -x$

30. $y^2 = 4ax$
    $x^2 = 4ay$

31. $y^2 = x$
    $y = x^3$

32. $y = (x - 1)^3$
    $y = x^2 - x - 1$

33. $y^2 = 5a^2 - ax$
    $y^2 = 4ax$

34. $x^2y = 4$
    $y = 7 - 3x$

35. $y = x^2$
    $y = 8 - x^2$
    $y = 4x + 12$

36. $y^3 = x^2$
    $2x + y + 1 = 0$
    $x - y = 4$

37. $y = x^2$
    $y = x + 2$
    $y = -3x + 18$

38. $y = 4x - 4$
    $y = \tfrac{1}{3}x^2$
    $y = 6 - x$

39. $y = x^3 + 3x^2 + 2$
    $y = x^3 + 6x^2 - 25$

40. $y = 25 - x^2$
    $y = (5 - x)^2$

41. $y = x^3 - 3x^2 - 10x$
    $y = -6x$

42. $y = (x + 2)(x - 1)(x - 5)$
    $y = (x + 2)(x - 1)$

43. $y = x(x - 3)(x + 3)$
    $y = -5x$

44. $y = x^3 + 3x^2 + 6$
    $y = x^3 + 4x^2 + 5x$

45. $y = x^3 - 5x^2 - 8x + 12$
    $y = x^3 - 6x^2 + 21$

HINTS

31. $y^2 = x$ and $y = x^3$ intersect $(0, 0)$ and $(1, 1)$
34. $x^2y = 4$ and $y = 7 - 3x$ intersect $(1, 4)$ and $(2, 1)$
36. $y^3 = x^2$ and $2x + y + 1 = 0$ intersect $(-1, 1)$
    $y^3 = x^2$ and $x - y = 4$ intersect $(8, 4)$
45. $x^3 - 5x^2 - 8x + 12 = (x + 2)(x - 1)(x - 6)$

ANSWERS TO ODD-NUMBERED PROBLEMS

1. $\tfrac{7}{3}$
3. $\tfrac{13}{3}$
5. $-\tfrac{73}{12}$
7. $\tfrac{26}{3}$
9. $\tfrac{5}{2}a^2$
11. $\tfrac{27}{4}$
13. $\tfrac{47}{4}a^4$
15. $\tfrac{37}{10}$
17. 42
19. 0.01

21. $\frac{49}{6}$

23. $\frac{37}{6}$

25. $\frac{7}{120}$

27. 18

29. $\frac{4}{3}$

31. $\frac{5}{12}$

33. $\frac{40}{3}a^2$

35. 64

37. $\frac{23}{6}$

39. 108

41. $160\frac{3}{4}$

43. 8

45. $166\frac{2}{3}$

■ 4.5 APPLICATIONS OF DEFINITE INTEGRATION IN BUSINESS AND ECONOMICS

Definite integration has a variety of applications in business and economics; the concepts of *consumers' surplus* and *producers' surplus* are two examples of such applications. Other examples involve the determination of the revenue produced for a firm by a factor of production over a period of time, in relation to the cost of that factor over the same time period. In such examples the point in time at which revenue produced equals cost of the factor can also be determined.

□ *CONSUMERS' SURPLUS*

A demand function represents the quantities of a commodity that would be bought at various prices. If the market price is y_0 and the corresponding market demand is x_0, then those consumers who would be willing to pay more than this market price gain from the fact that the price is only y_0 (see Fig. 4.16).

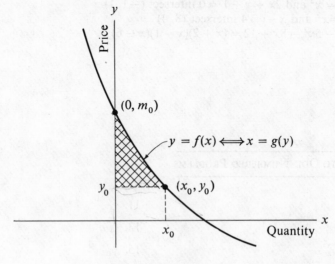

FIGURE 4.16

Under certain economic assumptions the total consumer gain is represented by the area below the demand curve and above the line $y = y_0$. This area is designated by Marshall as *consumers' surplus* and is evaluated as

$$\text{Consumers' surplus} = \int_0^{x_0} f(x)\, dx - x_0 y_0$$

where the demand function is $y = f(x)$, or as

$$\text{Consumers' surplus} = \int_{y_0}^{m_0} g(y)\, dy$$

where the demand function is $x = g(y)$ and m_0 is the value of y when $x = 0$, that is, m_0 is the y-intercept of the demand function:

$$\text{Consumers' surplus} = \int_0^{x_0} f(x)\, dx - x_0 y_0 = \int_{y_0}^{m_0} g(y)\, dy$$

Examples

If the demand function is $y = 85 - 4x - x^2$, find the consumers' surplus (a) if $x_0 = 5$, (b) if $y_0 = 64$ (see Fig. 4.17).

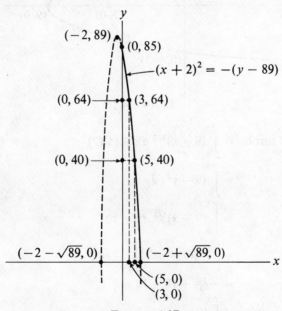

FIGURE 4.17

(a) Consumers' surplus $= \displaystyle\int_0^5 (85 - 4x - x^2)\, dx - (5)(40)$

$$= \left[85x - 2x^2 - \frac{x^3}{3} \right]_0^5 - 200$$

$$= 333\tfrac{1}{3} - 200$$

$$= 133\tfrac{1}{3}$$

(b) Consumers' surplus $= \displaystyle\int_0^3 (85 - 4x - x^2)\,dx - (3)(64)$

$$= \left[85x - 2x^2 - \frac{x^3}{3}\right]_0^3 - 192$$

$$= 228 - 192$$

$$= 36$$

If the demand function is $y = \sqrt{9 - x}$ and $x_0 = 5$, find the consumers' surplus by two methods (see Fig. 4.18).

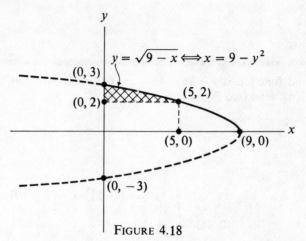

FIGURE 4.18

Consumers' surplus $= \displaystyle\int_0^5 (9 - x)^{1/2}\,dx - (5)(2)$

$$= \int_2^3 (9 - y^2)\,dy$$

$$= \int_0^5 (9 - x)^{1/2}\,dx - 10$$

$$= \left[-\tfrac{2}{3}(9 - x)^{3/2}\right]_0^5 - 10$$

$$= -\tfrac{16}{3} + 18 - 10 = \tfrac{8}{3}$$

or

Consumers' surplus $= \displaystyle\int_2^3 (9 - y^2)\,dy$

$$= \left[9y - \frac{y^3}{3}\right]_2^3$$

$$= 27 - 9 - 18 + \tfrac{8}{3} = \tfrac{8}{3}$$

$$= \tfrac{8}{3} \text{ (as above)}$$

The quantity sold and the corresponding price, under a monopoly, are determined by the demand function $y = 16 - x^2$ and by the marginal cost $y' = 6 + x$ in such a way as to maximize profit. Determine the corresponding consumers' surplus (see Fig. 4.19).

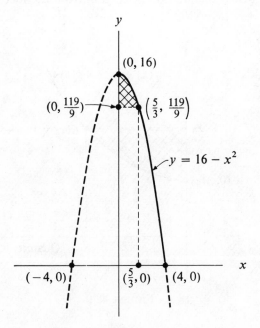

FIGURE 4.19

$$\text{Revenue} = 16x - x^3$$

$$\text{Marginal revenue} = 16 - 3x^2$$

Profit is maximized when marginal revenue equals marginal cost—that is,

$$16 - 3x^2 = 6 + x$$

$$3x^2 + x - 10 = 0$$

$$(3x - 5)(x + 2) = 0$$

$$x = \tfrac{5}{3}, -2$$

$$x_0 = \tfrac{5}{3} \qquad y_0 = \tfrac{119}{9}$$

$$\text{Consumers' surplus} = \int_0^{5/3} (16 - x^2)\, dx - (\tfrac{5}{3})(\tfrac{119}{9})$$

$$= \left[16x - \frac{x^3}{3} \right]_0^{5/3} - \tfrac{595}{27}$$

$$= \tfrac{80}{3} - \tfrac{125}{81} - \tfrac{595}{27}$$

$$= \tfrac{250}{81} \approx 3.09$$

□ *PRODUCERS' SURPLUS*

A supply function represents the respective quantities of a commodity that would be supplied at various prices. If the market price is y_0 and the corresponding market supply is x_0, then those producers who would be willing to supply the commodity below this market price gain from the fact that the price is y_0.

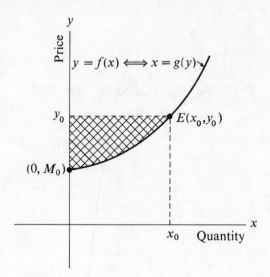

FIGURE 4.20

Under certain economic assumptions the total producer gain is represented by the area above the supply curve and below the line $y = y_0$ and is known as *producers' surplus* (see Fig. 4.20). This area is evaluated as

$$\text{Producers' surplus} = x_0 y_0 - \int_0^{x_0} f(x)\, dx$$

where the supply function is $y = f(x)$ and as

$$\text{Producers' surplus} = \int_{M_0}^{y_0} g(y)\, dy$$

where the supply function is $x = g(y)$ and M_0 is the value of y when $x = 0$ (that is, M_0 is the y-intercept of the supply function).

$$\text{Producers' surplus} = x_0 y_0 - \int_0^{x_0} f(x)\, dx = \int_{M_0}^{y_0} g(y)\, dy$$

Examples

If the supply law is $y = (x + 2)^2$ and the price is fixed at $y_0 = 25$, find the producers' surplus by two methods (see Fig. 4.21).

Producers' surplus $= (3)(25) - \int_0^3 (x+2)^2\,dx = \int_4^{25}(y^{1/2}-2)\,dy$

$$75 - \int_0^3 (x+2)^2\,dx = 75 - \left[\frac{(x+2)^3}{3}\right]_0^3 = 75 - \tfrac{125}{3} + \tfrac{8}{3} = 36$$

Alternatively,

$$\int_4^{25}(y^{1/2}-2)\,dy = \left[\frac{2y^{3/2}}{3} - 2y\right]_4^{25} = \tfrac{250}{3} - 50 - \tfrac{16}{3} + 8 = 36$$

Producers' surplus $= 36$

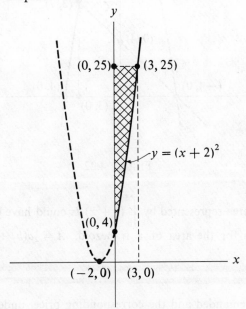

FIGURE 4.21

The quantity demanded and the corresponding price, under pure competition, are determined by the demand and supply functions $y = 16 - x^2$ and $y = 4 + x$, respectively. Determine the corresponding producers' surplus (see Fig. 4.22).

$$y = 16 - x^2 = 4 + x$$
$$x^2 + x - 12 = 0$$
$$(x + 4)(x - 3) = 0$$
$$x = 3,\ -4$$
$$x_0 = 3 \qquad y_0 = 7$$

$$\text{Producers' surplus} = (3)(7) - \int_0^3 (4 + x)\,dx$$

$$= 21 - \left[4x + \frac{x^2}{2}\right]_0^3$$

$$= 21 - 12 - \tfrac{9}{2}$$

$$= \tfrac{9}{2}$$

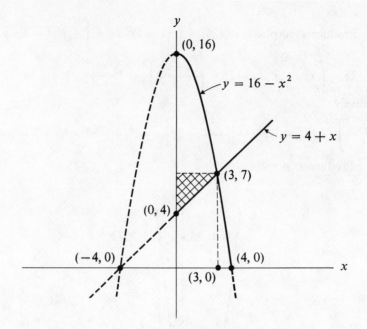

FIGURE 4.22

NOTE: The area represented by $\int_0^3 (4 + x)\,dx$ could have been evaluated also by the formula for the area of a trapezoid, $A = \frac{1}{2}a(b_1 + b_2)$—that is, $A = \frac{3}{2}(4 + 7) = \frac{33}{2}$.

The quantity demanded and the corresponding price, under pure competition, are determined by the demand and supply functions $y = 36 - x^2$ and $y = 6 + \dfrac{x^2}{4}$, respectively. Determine the corresponding consumers' surplus and producers' surplus (see Fig. 4.23).

$$y = 36 - x^2 = 6 + \frac{x^2}{4}$$
$$5x^2 = 120$$
$$x^2 = 24$$
$$x = \pm 2\sqrt{6}$$
$$x_0 = 2\sqrt{6} \qquad y_0 = 12$$

$$\text{Consumers' surplus} = \int_0^{2\sqrt{6}} (36 - x^2)\,dx - (2\sqrt{6})(12)$$

$$= \left[36x - \frac{x^3}{3} \right]_0^{2\sqrt{6}} - 24\sqrt{6}$$

$$= 72\sqrt{6} - 16\sqrt{6} - 24\sqrt{6}$$

$$= 32\sqrt{6} \approx 78.4$$

$$\text{Producers' surplus} = (2\sqrt{6})(12) - \int_0^{2\sqrt{6}} \left(6 + \frac{x^2}{4}\right) dx$$

$$= 24\sqrt{6} - \left[6x + \frac{x^3}{12}\right]_0^{2\sqrt{6}}$$

$$= 24\sqrt{6} - 12\sqrt{6} - 4\sqrt{6}$$

$$= 8\sqrt{6} \approx 19.6$$

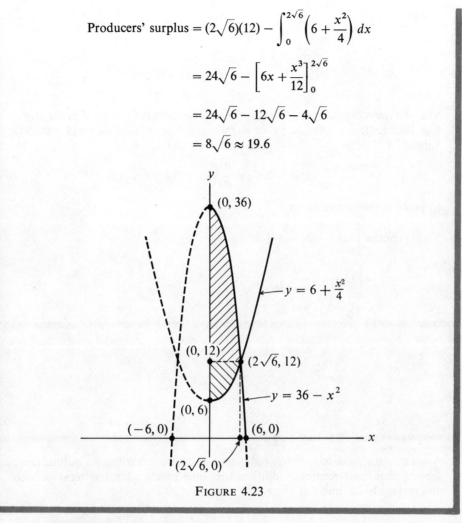

FIGURE 4.23

☐ REVENUE VS. COST

In economics integration can be used to determine total profit or total net earnings in various contexts. In general, profit is maximized (assuming pure competition) when marginal revenue equals marginal cost, and total profit is the integral of the difference of marginal revenue minus marginal cost from zero quantity to the quantity for which profit is maximized.

Examples

Find the profit-maximizing output and the total profit at that point if the marginal revenue and marginal cost functions are given by

$$MR = 25 - 5x - 2x^2$$
$$MC = 10 - 3x - x^2$$

Putting $MR - MC = 0$,

$$25 - 5x - 2x^2 - 10 + 3x + x^2 = 0$$
$$15 - 2x - x^2 = 0$$
$$(5 + x)(3 - x) = 0$$
$$x = -5, 3$$

The first derivative of $MR - MC$ is the second derivative of total profit and its sign thus indicates whether profit is maximized or minimized for a particular value of x

$$\frac{d}{dx}(MR - MC) = \frac{d^2P}{dx^2} = -2 - 2x = -8$$

so profit is maximized for $x = 3$.

$$\text{Total profit} = \int_0^3 (15 - 2x - x^2)\, dx$$

$$= \left[15 - x^2 - \frac{x^3}{3} \right]_0^3$$

$$= 45 - 9 - 9 = 27$$

A manufacturing company has purchased a machine that has an output representing additional earnings (additional revenue minus additional cost of labor and materials) at time t of

$$E(t) = 225 - \tfrac{1}{4}t^2$$

where $E(t)$ is in units of \$10,000 and t is years. The additional repair and maintenance cost at time t is

$$R(t) = 2t^2$$

where $R(t)$ is in units of \$10,000 and t is years. First, suppose that the machine can be disposed of at any time with no cost or salvage value. Then the machine should be disposed of at the time when additional earnings equals additional cost of repair and maintenance (see Fig. 4.24).

Additional earnings equals additional cost of repair and maintenance if

$$225 - \tfrac{1}{4}t^2 = 2t^2$$
$$225 = \tfrac{9}{4}t^2$$
$$t^2 = 100$$
$$t = 10$$

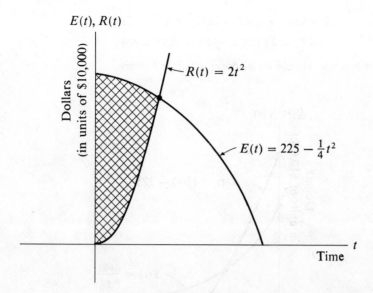

FIGURE 4.24

Thus the machine should be disposed of after 10 years. The total net earnings (earnings minus cost of repair and maintenance) after 10 years is

$$\int_0^{10} [E(t) - R(t)]\, dt = \int_0^{10} (225 - \tfrac{9}{4}t^2)\, dt$$

$$= \left[225t - \tfrac{3}{4}t^3 \right]_0^{10}$$

$$= 2250 - 750$$

$$= 1500 \text{ or } \$1,500,000$$

Now suppose the machine has a salvage value at time t of

$$S(t) = \frac{6480}{6 + t}$$

where $S(t)$ is in units of \$10,000 and t is years. Then the company will maximize its net earnings if it disposes of the machine at time T when the net earnings after T equals the salvage value at T (see Fig. 4.25).

Net earnings after T equals salvage value at T if

$$\frac{6480}{6 + T} = \int_T^{10} (225 - \tfrac{9}{4}t^2)\, dt$$

$$\frac{6480}{6 + T} = 1500 - 225T + \tfrac{3}{4}T^3$$

$$6480 = 9000 - 1350T + \tfrac{9}{2}T^3 + 1500T - 225T^2 + \tfrac{3}{4}T^4$$

$$0 = 2520 + 150T - 225T^2 + \tfrac{9}{2}T^3 + \tfrac{3}{4}T^4$$
$$= (T - 4)(\tfrac{3}{4}T^3 + \tfrac{15}{2}T^2 - 195T - 630)$$

Thus the machine should be disposed of after 4 years.

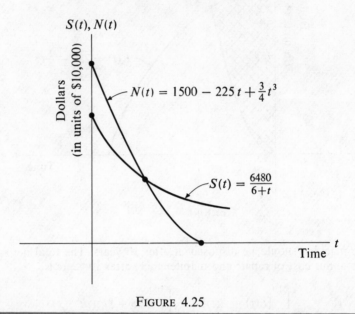

FIGURE 4.25

A company is considering adding salesmen to its staff. The cost of employing additional salesmen is

$$5y^2 = 48x$$

where y is cost in units of \$10,000 and x is number of additional salesmen employed, and the additional revenue is

$$(R - 2)^2 = 4(x + 10)$$

where R is revenue in units of \$10,000 and x is number of salesmen employed. (Assume the cost and revenue functions are continuous, although actually they are meaningful only for integer values of x.) The company should employ additional salesmen until the cost of doing so equals the additional revenue obtained (see Fig. 4.26).

The cost of employing additional salesmen equals the additional revenue obtained if $R = y$:

$$(R - 2)^2 = 4(x + 10)$$
$$R^2 - 4R + 4 = 4x + 40$$
$$R^2 - 4R - 36 = 4x$$

Thus $R = y$ if

$$y^2 - 4y - 36 = \frac{5y^2}{12}$$

$$7y^2 - 48y - 432 = 0$$

$$(7y + 26)(y - 12) = 0$$

$$y = 12$$

$$x = 15$$

and 15 additional salesmen should be employed. The total resulting net revenue (total revenue minus cost) is

$$\int_0^{12} [\tfrac{5}{48}y^2 - \tfrac{1}{4}y^2 + y + 9] \, dy = \int_0^{12} [y + 9 - \tfrac{7}{48}y^2] \, dy$$

$$= \left[\frac{y^2}{2} + 9y - \tfrac{7}{144}y^3\right]_0^{12}$$

$$= 72 + 108 - 84$$

$$= 96 \text{ or } \$96,000$$

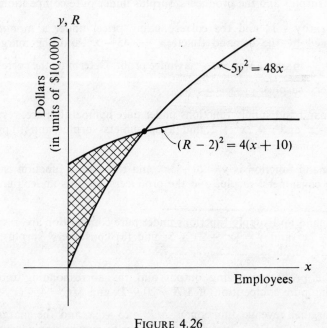

FIGURE 4.26

PROBLEMS

1. If the demand function is $y = 39 - x^2$, find the consumers' surplus if (a) $x_0 = \tfrac{5}{2}$ and (b) the commodity is free (that is, $y_0 = 0$).

2. If the demand function is $y = 16 - x^2$ and the supply function is $y = 2x + 1$, find consumers' surplus and producers' surplus under pure competition.

3. If the supply function is $y = \sqrt{9 + x}$ and $x_0 = 7$, find the producers' surplus.

4. If the supply function is $y = 4e^{x/3}$ and $x_0 = 3$, find the producers' surplus.

5. The demand and supply functions (under pure competition) are $y = \frac{1}{4}(9 - x)^2$ and $y = \frac{1}{4}(1 + 3x)$, respectively. If an additive tax of 3 per unit quantity is imposed on the commodity, determine the decrease in consumers' surplus.

6. The quantity sold and the corresponding price are determined, under a monopoly, by the demand function $y = \frac{1}{4}(10 - x)^2$ and the total cost $y = \frac{x^3}{4} + 5x$ in such a way as to maximize profit. Determine the corresponding consumers' surplus.

7. The quantity sold and the corresponding price under monopoly are determined by the demand function $y = 20 - 4x^2$ and the marginal cost $y' = 2x + 6$ in such a way as to maximize profit. Determine the corresponding consumers' surplus.

8. If the demand function is that part of the equilateral hyperbola $y = \frac{8}{x + 1} - 2$ in the first quadrant, and the supply curve is $y = \frac{1}{2}(x + 3)$, find the consumers' surplus and the producers' surplus under pure competition.

9. The quantity sold and the corresponding price, under a monopoly, are determined by the demand function $y = 45 - x^2$ and the marginal cost $y' = 6 + \frac{x^2}{4}$ in such a way as to maximize profit. Determine the corresponding consumers' surplus.

10. The demand and supply functions under pure competition are, respectively, $y = 14 - x^2$ and $y = 2x^2 + 2$; find (a) consumers' surplus, and (b) producers' surplus.

11. The demand function is $y = 20 - 3x^2$ and the supply function is $y = 2x^2$; find the consumers' surplus and the producers' surplus under pure competition.

12. The demand and supply functions under pure competition are, respectively, $y = 32 - 2x^2$ and $y = \frac{1}{3}x^2 + 2x + 5$; find (a) consumers' surplus, and (b) producers' surplus.

13. Find the profit-maximizing output and the corresponding total profit (assuming pure competition) if $MR = 20 - 2x$ and $MC = 4 + (x - 4)^2$.

14. The marginal revenue function is $MR = 25 - 3x$ and the marginal cost function is $MC = 25 - 7x + x^2$. Find the profit-maximizing output and the corresponding total profit under pure competition.

15. If $MR = 44 - 9x$ and $MC = 20 - 7x + 2x^2$, find the profit-maximizing output and the corresponding total profit under pure competition.

16. Assuming pure competition, find the profit-maximizing output and the corresponding total profit if $MR = 24 - 6x - x^2$ and $MC = 4 - 2x - x^2$.

17. If $MR = 15 - 5x$ and $MC = 10 - 3x + 3x^2$, find the profit-maximizing output and the corresponding total profit assuming pure competition.

18. A manufacturing company has purchased a machine whose output represents earnings at time t given by $y^2 = 6(t + 9)$, where y is in units of $10,000 and t is years. The repair and maintenance cost at time t is given by $(y + 4)^2 = 8(t + 17)$, where y is in units of $10,000 and t is years. Assuming

the machine can be disposed of at any time with no cost or salvage value, how many years should it be kept to maximize total net earnings (earnings minus cost of repair and maintenance)?

19. A company is considering purchasing additional companion units for its computer. The savings (in time and mistakes) from added units is given by $y = 3x^2 + 11$, where y is in units of $11,000 and x is number of units added. The cost of repair and maintenance is given by $y = 4x^2 + 2$, where y is in units of $1000 and x is the number of units added. To maximize total net revenue (revenue minus cost of repair and maintenance), how many units should be added and what is the associated savings? Assume the units are added in a specified order and that the savings and cost curves are continuous.

20. A company is considering adding advertising personnel. The cost of adding such personnel is given by $y = \frac{1}{2}x$, where y is in units of $5000 and x is the number of personnel added. Additional revenue from adding personnel is $R^2 = 4x$, where R is in units of $5000 and x is number of personnel added. What number of advertising personnel should be added to maximize profit (revenue minus cost) and what is the associated additional revenue? Assume continuous functions.

ANSWERS TO ODD-NUMBERED PROBLEMS

---

1. (a) 31.25
   (b) $26\sqrt{13}$

3. $\frac{10}{3}$

5. $\frac{121}{12}$

7. $\frac{8}{3}$

9. $16\sqrt{3}$ (approx. 27.71)

11. c.s. $= 16$
    p.s. $= \frac{32}{3}$

13. $x = 6; P_{max} = 36$

15. $x = 3; P_{max} = 45$

17. $x = 1, P_{max} = 3$

19. 18

■ **4.6 SPECIAL METHODS OF INTEGRATION**

□ *STANDARD FORMS FOR INTEGRATION*

Differential calculus provides a general rule for differentiation, from which particular rules are derived. Unfortunately, there is no corresponding general rule for integration and the integral of any given expression must be obtained through knowledge of the results of differentiation. Thus integration is inherently more difficult than differentiation; to expedite the process of integrating a given expression, tables of known integrals, called *standard forms*, have been compiled. The simplest of these standard forms are obtained directly by reversing the corresponding rules for differentiation; additional standard forms are derived from the results of more complicated differentiation. Note that a formula for integration can be derived from the result of any differentiation; the most frequently occurring of such formulas are given in tables of standard forms.

In the following list of standard forms, the first 14 formulas are obtained by reversing the corresponding rules for differentiation (the first 5 of these are discussed at the beginning of the chapter); the last 12 formulas are examples of standard forms derived from the results of more complicated differentiation.

1. $\int dx = x + C.$

2. $\int K \, dx = K \int dx$, where K is any constant.

3. $\int [du + dv] = \int du + \int dv$, where $u = f(x)$ and $v = g(x)$ are differentiable functions of x.

4. $\int x^n dx = \frac{x^{n+1}}{n+1} + C, n \neq -1.$

5. $\int u^n du = \frac{u^{n+1}}{n+1} + C, n \neq -1$, where $u = f(x)$ is a differentiable function of x.

6. $\int \frac{1}{u} \, du = \ln u + C$, where $u = f(x)$ is a differentiable function of x.

7. $\int e^u du = e^u + C$, where $u = f(x)$ is a differentiable function of x.

8. $\int a^u du = \frac{a^u}{\ln a} + C$, where $u = f(x)$ is a differentiable function of x.

9. $\int \sin u \, du = -\cos u \, du + C.$

10. $\int \cos u \, du = \sin u \, du.$

11. $\int \sec^2 u \, du = \tan u + C.$

12. $\int \csc^2 u \, du = -\cot u + C.$

13. $\int \sec u \tan u \, du = \sec u + C.$

14. $\int \csc u \cot u \, du = -\csc u + C.$

15. $\int \tan u \, du = -\ln \cos u + C = \ln \sec u + C.$

16. $\int \cot u \, du = \ln \sin u + C.$

17. $\int \sec u \, du = \ln (\sec u + \tan u) + C.$

18. $\int \csc u \, du = \ln (\csc u - \cot u) + C.$

19. $\int \dfrac{du}{a^2 - u^2} = \dfrac{1}{2a} \ln \dfrac{a + u}{a - u} + C, \, u^2 < a^2.$

20. $\int \dfrac{du}{u^2 - a^2} = \dfrac{1}{2a} \ln \dfrac{u - a}{u + a} + C, \, u^2 > a^2.$

21. $\int \dfrac{du}{\sqrt{u^2 + a^2}} = \ln (u + \sqrt{u^2 + a^2}) + C.$

22. $\int \sqrt{u^2 + a^2} \, du = \dfrac{u}{2} \sqrt{u^2 + a^2} + \dfrac{a^2}{2} \ln (u + \sqrt{u^2 + a^2}) + C.$

23. $\int u e^u du = e^u (u - 1) + C.$

24. $\int \ln u \, du = u \ln u - u + C.$

25. $\int u^n \ln u \, du = u^{n+1} \left[\dfrac{\ln u}{n + 1} - \dfrac{1}{(n + 1)^2} \right] + C.$

26. $\int \dfrac{du}{u \ln u} = \ln(\ln u) + C.$

The first step in the procedure for integrating a given expression consists of comparing it with various standard forms. If an expression is identical with a standard form, its integral is known; if an expression is not identical with a standard form, there are various methods by which it may in some cases be reduced to a standard form. Some of these methods are discussed in later sections.

Examples

Evaluate the following integrals.

(a) $\int \dfrac{x \, dx}{x^2 + 1} = \dfrac{1}{2} \int \dfrac{2x \, dx}{x^2 + 1}$

$\qquad = \dfrac{1}{2} \ln(x^2 + 1) + C$

(b) $\int x e^{-x^2} dx = -\dfrac{1}{2} \int -2x e^{-x^2} dx$

$\qquad = -\dfrac{1}{2} e^{-x^2} + C$

(c) $\int a^{2x-1}\,dx = \frac{1}{2}\int 2a^{2x-1}\,dx$

$$= \frac{a^{2x-1}}{2\ln a} + C$$

(d) $\int \sin 3x \cos^2 3x\,dx = -\frac{1}{3}\int (-3\sin 3x)(\cos^2 3x)\,dx$

$$= -\frac{1}{9}\cos^3 3x + C$$

(e) $\int \dfrac{\sin ax\,dx}{\sqrt{b + \cos ax}} = -\dfrac{1}{a}\int (-a\sin ax)(b + \cos ax)^{-1/2}\,dx$

$$= -\frac{2}{a}\sqrt{b + \cos ax} + C$$

(f) $\int \dfrac{\sec^2 by\,dy}{a + c\tan by} = \dfrac{1}{bc}\int \dfrac{(bc\sec^2 by)\,dy}{a + c\tan by}$

$$= \frac{1}{bc}\ln(a + c\tan by) + C$$

Evaluate the following integrals.

(a) $\int \dfrac{4 + 6x}{6 - (4x + 3x^2)^2}\,dx = \dfrac{1}{2\sqrt 6}\ln\left(\dfrac{\sqrt{6} + 4x + 3x^2}{\sqrt{6} - 4x - 3x^2}\right) + C$

(b) $\int 4x^3 e^{x^2}\,dx = 2e^{x^2}(x^2 - 1) + C$

(c) $\int \dfrac{x^2}{x^3 \ln x^3}\,dx = \frac{1}{3}\ln(\ln x^3) + C$

(d) $\int (2x - 3)(x^2 - 3x - 1)^4 \ln(x^2 - 3x - 1)\,dx$

$$= (x^2 - 3x - 1)^5\left[\frac{\ln(x^2 - 3x - 1)}{5} - \frac{1}{25}\right] + C$$

(e) $\int (x^2 + 2x + 6)^{1/2}\,dx = \int \sqrt{(x + 1)^2 + (\sqrt 5)^2}\,dx$

$$= \frac{x + 1}{2}(x^2 + 2x + 6)^{1/2} + \frac{5}{2}\ln[(x + 1) + (x^2 + 2x + 6)^{1/2}] + C$$

(f) $\int (x^2 + 2x)\ln(x^3 + 3x^2 + 14)\,dx$

$$= \frac{1}{3}[(x^3 + 3x^2 + 14)\ln(x^3 + 3x^2 + 14) - (x^3 + 3x^2 + 14)] + C$$

☐ *INTEGRATION BY PARTS*

When an expression involving products or logarithms cannot be evaluated directly by the use of standard forms, one of the most useful techniques for transforming it to a standard form is the formula for integration by parts. This formula is based on the inverse of the formula for differentiation of a product.

If u and v are functions of a single independent variable x, then from the formula for the differentiation of a product,

$$\frac{d}{dx}(uv) = u\frac{dv}{dx} + v\frac{du}{dx}$$

$$u\frac{dv}{dx} = \frac{d}{dx}(uv) - v\frac{du}{dx}$$

and, integrating with respect to x,

$$\int u\, dv = uv - \int v\, du$$

This is the *formula for integration by parts.* Clearly, the usefulness of this formula depends on the appropriate choice of u and dv, so that $\int v\, du$ and $\int dv$ can be evaluated, even though $\int u\, dv$ cannot.

Unfortunately, there is no general rule for separating a given expression into two factors u and dv in order to apply the formula for integration by parts. However, note that

1. dx is always a part of dv.
2. dv must be integrable.
3. When the expression to be integrated is the product of two functions, it is usually advisable to choose the most complicated looking one that can be integrated as part of dv in order to make $\int v\, du$ as easily integrable as possible.

It may be necessary to apply the formula for integration by parts more than once, as in example (e) below.

Example

Evaluate the following integrals. Note that (a), (b), and (d) are special cases, respectively, of the standard forms (23), (24), and (25) above and can also be evaluated by their use.

(a) $\displaystyle\int xe^{ax}\, dx = \frac{xe^{ax}}{a} - \int \frac{e^{ax}}{a}\, dx + C$

$\displaystyle = \frac{xe^{ax}}{a} - \frac{e^{ax}}{a^2} + C \qquad\qquad u = x \qquad dv = e^{ax}\, dx$

$\displaystyle = \frac{e^{ax}}{a}\left(x - \frac{1}{a}\right) + C \qquad\qquad du = dx \qquad v = \frac{e^{ax}}{a}$

(b) $\displaystyle\int \ln x\, dx = x \ln x - \int x\left(\frac{1}{x}\right)dx + C$

$\displaystyle = x \ln x - x + C \qquad\qquad u = \ln x \qquad dv = dx$

$\displaystyle = x(\ln x - 1) + C \qquad\qquad du = \frac{1}{x}\, dx \qquad v = x$

(c) $\int x \sin \dfrac{x}{a} dx = -ax \cos \dfrac{x}{a} + \int a \cos \dfrac{x}{a} dx + C$

$\qquad\qquad = -ax \cos \dfrac{x}{a} + a^2 \sin \dfrac{x}{a} + C \qquad\quad u = x \qquad dv = \sin \dfrac{x}{a} dx$

$\qquad\qquad = a^2 \sin \dfrac{x}{a} - ax \cos \dfrac{x}{a} + C \qquad\quad du = dx \qquad v = -a \cos \dfrac{x}{a}$

(d) $\int e^x \cos x \, dx = e^x \sin x - \int e^x \sin x \, dx + C$

$\qquad\qquad = e^x \sin x - \left[-e^x \cos x + \int e^x \cos x \, dx \right] + C$

$\qquad\qquad = e^x \sin x + e^x \cos x - \int e^x \cos x \, dx + C$

$\int e^x \cos x \, dx = \dfrac{1}{2} e^x(\sin x + \cos x) + C$

$$\begin{aligned} u &= e^x & dv &= \cos x \, dx \\ du &= e^x & v &= \sin x \\ u &= e^x & dv &= \sin x \, dx \\ du &= e^x & v &= -\cos x \end{aligned}$$

(e) $\int x^2 e^{-x} dx = -x^2 e^{-x} + 2 \int x e^{-x} dx + C$

$\qquad\qquad = -x^2 e^{-x} + 2 \left[-x e^{-x} + \int e^{-x} dx \right] + C$

$\qquad\qquad = -x^2 e^{-x} - 2x e^{-x} - 2 e^{-x} + C \qquad u = x^2 \qquad dv = e^{-x} dx$

$\qquad\qquad = -e^{-x}(x^2 + 2x + 2) + C \qquad\qquad du = 2x \, dx \qquad v = -e^{-x}$

$$\begin{aligned} u &= x & dv &= e^{-x} dx \\ du &= dx & v &= -e^{-x} \end{aligned}$$

(f) $\int \dfrac{\ln(x + 1) \, dx}{\sqrt{x + 1}} = 2(x + 1)^{1/2} \ln(x + 1) - 2 \int \dfrac{1}{x + 1} (x + 1)^{1/2} dx + C$

$\qquad\qquad = 2(x + 1)^{1/2} \ln(x + 1) - 4(x + 1)^{1/2} + C$

$\qquad\qquad = 2(x + 1)^{1/2} [\ln(x + 1) - 2] + C$

$$\begin{aligned} u &= \ln(x + 1) & dv &= (x + 1)^{-1/2} dx \\ du &= \dfrac{dx}{x + 1} & v &= 2(x + 1)^{1/2} \end{aligned}$$

PROBLEMS

Evaluate the following integrals.

1. $\int x e^{x^2} dx$

2. $\int \sin^2 x \cos x \, dx$

3. $\int \sin ax \cos ax \, dx$

4. $\int \sec^2 \frac{x}{a} \tan \frac{x}{a} \, dx$

5. $\int \left(\frac{\sec 2x}{1 + \tan 2x} \right)^2 dx$

6. $\int (x^2 + 1)5^{x^3 + 3x} \, dx = \frac{1}{3}(3x^2+3)5^{x^3+3x}$

7. $\int \frac{\cos x \, dx}{1 + \sin x}$ $= \frac{5^{x^3+3x}}{3 \ln 5}$

8. $\int e^{\cos z} \sin z \, dz$

9. $\int \frac{dx}{\sin^2 ax}$ $= \int \csc^2 ax$

10. $\int \frac{du}{\cos^2 u}$

11. $\int \sec ax \, dx$

12. $\int \frac{dt}{1 + \cos t}$

13. $\int \frac{xe^x \, dx}{(1 + x)^2}$

14. $\int xe^{-x} \, dx$

15. $\int x^2 e^x \, dx$

16. $\int xe^{2x} \, dx$

17. $\int t \ln t \, dt$

18. $\int z^2 e^{-3z} \, dz$

19. $\int e^x (x + 1)^2 \, dx$

20. $\int (x^{1/2} + x^{1/4})^2 \, dx$ (moltiplie $(x^{\frac{1}{2}} + x^{\frac{1}{4}})^2$ ...)

21. $\int \frac{(x + 1) \, dx}{(x + 1)^2 + (a + 1)^2}$

22. $\int (x + 1) \ln x \, dx$ $f'(x) \quad f(x)$

23. $\int (x^2 + 3x + 4)^3 (2x + 3) \, dx$

24. $\int e^{3x^2 + 6x + 10}(x + 1) \, dx$

25. $\int (x^{1/3} + x^{2/3})^2 \, dx$

26. $\int \frac{6x^2 + 8x + 8}{x^3 + 2x^2 + 4x} \, dx$

27. $\int \frac{(x^3 + x) \, dx}{\sqrt[4]{x^4 + 2x^2 + 1}}$

28. $\int \left(x^2 + \frac{1}{x} + 6x \right) dx$

29. $\int xe^{-3x} \, dx$

30. $\int \frac{x^3 + 2}{x^4 + 8x + 10} \, dx$

31. $\int \frac{\sin v \, dv}{1 + \cos v}$

32. $\int \frac{dx}{1 + \sin x}$

33. $\int u \sin u^2 \, du$

34. $\int (x + \sin 2x) \, dx$

35. $\int xa^x \, dx$

36. $\int x^n \ln x \, dx$

37. $\int \frac{\sin x \, dx}{\sqrt{2 - \cos x}}$

38. $\int \frac{\sec^2 \theta \, d\theta}{\sqrt{1 + 2 \tan \theta}}$

39. $\int x \cos x \, dx$

40. $\int e^{-ax} \sin nx \, dx$

41. $\int \theta \sec^2 \theta \, d\theta$

42. $\int y^2 \sin ny \, dy$

ANSWERS TO ODD-NUMBERED PROBLEMS

1. $\frac{1}{2}e^{x^2} + C$

3. $\frac{\sin^2 ax}{2a} + C$

5. $-\frac{1}{2(1 + \tan 2x)} + C$

7. $\ln(1 + \sin x) + C$

9. $-\frac{1}{a}\cot ax + C$

11. $\frac{1}{a}\ln(\sec ax + \tan ax) + C$

13. $\frac{e^x}{1 + x} + C$

15. $e^x(x^2 - 2x + 2) + C$

17. $\frac{1}{2}t^2 \ln t - \frac{t^2}{4} + C$

19. $e^x(x^2 + 1) + C$

21. $\frac{1}{2}\ln[(x + 1)^2 + (a + 1)^2] + C$

23. $\frac{1}{4}(x^2 + 3x + 4)^4 + C$

25. $\frac{3}{5}x^{5/3} + x^2 + \frac{3}{7}x^{7/3} + C$

27. $\frac{1}{3}(x^4 + 2x^2 + 1)^{3/4} + C$

29. $-\frac{1}{9}e^{-3x}(3x + 1) + C$

31. $-\ln(1 + \cos v) + C$

33. $-\frac{1}{2}\cos u^2 + C$

35. $\frac{a^x}{\ln a}\left(x - \frac{1}{\ln a}\right) + C$

37. $2\sqrt{2 - \cos x} + C$

39. $x \sin x + \cos x + C$

41. $\theta \tan \theta + \ln \cos \theta + C$

□ *INTEGRATION BY PARTIAL FRACTIONS*

A rational algebraic function, by definition, can be expressed as the quotient of two polynomials. In theory, every rational function has an integral that is expressible in terms of elementary functions. If a rational function cannot be integrated directly, the method of partial fractions is frequently useful to transform the rational fraction into a sum of simpler functions which can be integrated by standard forms. The method of partial fractions is appropriate *only* for proper fractions, that is, for fractions in which the polynomial in the numerator is of lower degree than the polynomial in the denominator. Any improper fraction, that is, a fraction in which the polynomial in the numerator is of the same or higher degree than the polynomial in the denominator, can be reduced by division to the sum of a polynomial (easily integrated) and a proper fraction (integrated by the method of partial fractions). The method of integration by partial fractions consists of the following steps:

1. Express the denominator of the fraction as the product of linear factors of the form $ax + b$ and irreducible quadratic factors of the form $ax^2 + bx + c$ —although this is not always easy in practice, it is always possible in theory for any polynomial in x with real coefficients.

2. Determine the form of the partial fractions—several cases arise, depending on the nature of the factors occurring in the denominator:

Factor Occurring in Denominator	*Corresponding Partial Fraction*

(a) Distinct linear factor: $ax + b$

$$\frac{A}{ax + b}$$

where A is a constant to be determined

(b) Repeated linear factor: $(ax + b)^n$

$$\frac{A_1}{ax + b} + \frac{A_2}{(ax + b)^2} + \cdots + \frac{A_n}{(ax + b)^n}$$

where $A_1 \ldots, A_n$ are constants to be determined

(c) Distinct quadratic factor: $ax^2 + bx + c$

$$\frac{Ax + B}{ax^2 + bx + c}$$

where A and B are constants to be determined

(d) Repeated quadratic factor: $(ax^2 + bx + c)^n$

$$\frac{A_1 x + B_1}{ax^2 + bx + c} + \frac{A_2 x + B_2}{(ax^2 + bx + c)^2} + \cdots + \frac{A_n x + B_n}{(ax^2 + bx + c)^n}$$

where A_i and B_i, $i = 1, 2, \ldots, n$ are constants to be determined

3. Determine the constants occurring in the numerators of the partial fractions. When a rational fraction is separated into partial fractions, the resulting equation is an identity—that is, it is true for all meaningful values of the variables. The method for evaluating the constants occurring in partial fractions, as illustrated in the example below, is based on the algebraic theorem which states that if two polynomials of the same degree are identical, the coefficients of like powers of the variable in both polynomials must be equal.

4. Integrate the partial fractions using standard forms.

Example

Evaluate the following integrals.

(a) $\displaystyle \int \frac{(x + 3)\, dx}{x^2 + 3x + 2} = \int \frac{(x + 3)\, dx}{(x + 1)(x + 2)} = \int \left[\frac{A}{x + 1} + \frac{B}{x + 2} \right] dx$

$$x + 3 = A(x + 2) + B(x + 1)$$

$$= (A + B)x + (2A + B)$$

so

$$A + B = 1$$

$$2A + B = 3$$

$$A = 2$$

$$B = -1$$

and

$$\int \frac{(x + 3)\, dx}{(x + 1)(x + 2)} = \int \frac{2\, dx}{x + 1} - \int \frac{dx}{x + 2}$$

$$= 2 \ln(x + 1) - \ln(x + 2) + C$$

$$= \ln\left[\frac{(x + 1)^2}{x + 2}\right] + C$$

(b) $\displaystyle\int \frac{(x^2 - 3x - 8)}{x^2 - 2x + 1} \, dx = \int \left[1 - \frac{x + 9}{(x - 1)^2}\right] dx = x + \int \left[\frac{A}{x - 1} + \frac{B}{(x - 1)^2}\right] dx$

$$x + 9 = A(x - 1) + B$$

$$= Ax - (A - B)$$

so

$$A = 1$$

$$A - B = -9$$

$$B = 10$$

and

$$\int \frac{(x^2 - 3x - 8) \, dx}{x^2 - 2x + 1} = x - \int \frac{dx}{x - 1} - \int \frac{10 \, dx}{(x - 1)^2}$$

$$= x - \ln(x - 1) + \frac{10}{x - 1} + C$$

(c) $\displaystyle\int \frac{t \, dt}{t^4 + 6t^2 + 5} = \int \frac{t \, dt}{(t^2 + 5)(t^2 + 1)} = \int \left[\frac{A_1 t + B_1}{t^2 + 5} + \frac{A_2 t + B_2}{t^2 + 1}\right] dt$

$$t = (A_1 t + B_1)(t^2 + 1) + (A_2 t + B_2)(t^2 + 5)$$

$$= (A_1 + A_2)t^3 + (B_1 + B_2)t^2 + (A_1 + 5A_2)t + (B_1 + 5B_2)$$

so

$$A_1 + A_2 = 0$$

$$B_1 + B_2 = 0$$

$$A_1 + 5A_2 = 1$$

$$B_1 + 5B_2 = 0$$

$$A_2 = \tfrac{1}{4}$$

$$A_1 = -\tfrac{1}{4}$$

$$B_1 = B_2 = 0$$

and

$$\int \frac{t \, dt}{(t^2 + 5)(t^2 + 1)} = -\tfrac{1}{4} \int \frac{t \, dt}{t^2 + 5} + \tfrac{1}{4} \int \frac{t \, dt}{t^2 + 1}$$

$$= -\tfrac{1}{8} \ln(t^2 + 5) + \tfrac{1}{8} \ln(t^2 + 1) + C$$

$$= \tfrac{1}{8} \ln\left(\frac{t^2 + 1}{t^2 + 5}\right) + C$$

(d) $\displaystyle\int \frac{dz}{z(z^2+1)^2} = \int \left[\frac{A_0}{z} + \frac{A_1 z + B_1}{z^2+1} + \frac{A_2 z + B_2}{(z^2+1)^2}\right] dz$

$$1 = A_0(z^2+1)^2 + (A_1 z + B_1)z(z^2+1) + (A_2 z + B_2)z$$
$$= A_0(z^4 + 2z^2 + 1) + A_1(z^4 + z^2) + B_1(z^3 + z) + A_2 z^2 + B_2 z$$
$$= (A_0 + A_1)z^4 + B_1 z^3 + (2A_0 + A_1 + A_2)z^2$$
$$+ (B_1 + B_2)z + A_0$$

so

$$A_0 + A_1 = 0$$
$$B_1 = 0$$
$$2A_0 + A_1 + A_2 = 0$$
$$B_1 + B_2 = 0$$
$$A_0 = 1$$
$$A_1 = -1$$
$$A_2 = -1$$
$$B_2 = 0$$

and

$$\int \frac{dz}{z(z^2+1)^2} = \int \frac{dz}{z} - \int \frac{z\,dz}{z^2+1} - \int \frac{z\,dz}{(z^2+1)^2}$$

$$= \ln z - \tfrac{1}{2}\ln(z^2+1) + \frac{1}{2(z^2+1)} + C$$

$$= \tfrac{1}{2}\ln\left(\frac{z^2}{z^2+1}\right) + \frac{1}{2(z^2+1)} + C$$

(e) $\displaystyle\int \frac{dx}{x^3 + 5x^2 + 4x} = \int \frac{dx}{x(x+1)(x+4)} = \int \left[\frac{A}{x} + \frac{B}{x+1} + \frac{C}{x+4}\right] dx$

$$1 = A(x+1)(x+4) + Bx(x+4) + Cx(x+1)$$
$$= A(x^2 + 5x + 4) + B(x^2 + 4x) + C(x^2 + x)$$
$$= (A + B + C)x^2 + (5A + 4B + C)x + 4A$$

so

$$A + B + C = 0$$
$$5A + 4B + C = 0$$
$$4A = 1$$
$$A = \tfrac{1}{4}$$
$$4A + 3B = 0$$
$$B = -\tfrac{1}{3}$$
$$C = \tfrac{1}{12}$$

and

$$\int \frac{dx}{x(x + 1)(x + 4)} = \tfrac{1}{4} \int \frac{dx}{x} - \tfrac{1}{3} \int \frac{dx}{x + 1} + \tfrac{1}{12} \int \frac{dx}{x + 4}$$

$$= \tfrac{1}{4} \ln x - \tfrac{1}{3} \ln(x + 1) + \tfrac{1}{12} \ln(x + 4) + C$$

$$= \tfrac{1}{12} \ln \left[\frac{x^3(x + 4)}{(x + 1)^4} \right] + C$$

(f) $\displaystyle \int \frac{(x^3 - 2x)\, dx}{x^4 - 81} = \int \frac{(x^3 - 2x)\, dx}{(x - 3)(x + 3)(x^2 + 9)}$

$$= \int \left[\frac{A}{x - 3} + \frac{B}{x + 3} + \frac{Cx + D}{x^2 + 9} \right] dx$$

$$x^3 - 2x = A(x + 3)(x^2 + 9) + B(x - 3)(x^2 + 9) + (Cx + D)(x^2 - 9)$$

$$= A(x^3 + 3x^2 + 9x + 27) + B(x^3 - 3x^2 + 9x - 27)$$
$$+ C(x^3 - 9x) + D(x^2 - 9)$$

$$= (A + B + C)x^3 + (3A - 3B + D)x^2 + (9A + 9B - 9C)x$$
$$+ (27A - 27B - 9D)$$

so

$$\begin{array}{ll} A + B + C = 1 & A + B = \tfrac{7}{18} \\ 3A - 3B + D = 0. & 3A - 3B = 0 \\ 9A + 9B - 9C = -2 & 2A = \tfrac{7}{18} \\ 27A - 27B - 9D = 0 & A = \tfrac{7}{36} \\ 18D = 0 & B = \tfrac{7}{36} \\ D = 0 & \\ 18C = 11 & \\ C = \tfrac{11}{18} & \end{array}$$

and

$$\int \frac{(x^3 - 2x)\, dx}{(x - 3)(x + 3)(x^2 + 9)} = \tfrac{7}{36} \int \frac{dx}{x - 3} + \tfrac{7}{36} \int \frac{dx}{x + 3} + \tfrac{11}{18} \int \frac{x\, dx}{x^2 + 9}$$

$$= \tfrac{7}{36} \ln(x - 3) + \tfrac{7}{36} \ln(x + 3) + \tfrac{11}{36} \ln(x^2 + 9) + C$$

$$= \tfrac{1}{36} \ln[(x - 3)^7(x + 3)^7(x^2 + 9)^{11}] + C$$

$$= \tfrac{1}{36} \ln[(x^2 - 9)^7(x^2 + 9)^{11}] + C$$

NOTE: In this particular problem the correct solution is also obtained by using the factors $(x^2 - 9)(x^2 + 9)$; however, in general, *irreducible* quadratic factors and linear factors must be used.

□ *INTEGRATION BY SUBSTITUTION; RATIONALIZATION*

As discussed in the preceding section, all rational functions are integrable in terms of elementary functions; however, only a relatively small number of algebraic functions which are not rational can be integrated in terms of elementary functions. In some cases, by substitution of a new variable, functions which are not rational can be transformed into equivalent functions which are rational. These equivalent functions are integrable either by partial fractions or directly by standard forms. The method of integrating a function that is not rational by transforming it into a rational function by substitution is called *integration by rationalization* and is useful for various classes of functions. Two of the most common of these are discussed in the following sections.

1. An expression involving fractional powers of x only can be transformed into a rational form by the substitution

$$x = z^n$$

where n is the least common denominator of the fractional exponents of x.

2. An expression involving fractional powers of $(a + bx)$ only can be transformed into a rational form by the substitution

$$a + bx = z^n$$

where n is the least common denominator of the fractional exponents of $(a + bx)$.

Example

Evaluate the following integrals.

(a) $\displaystyle\int \frac{x^{1/2}\, dx}{1 + x^{3/4}}$:

$$x = z^4$$

$$dx = 4z^3\, dz$$

$$\int \frac{x^{1/2}\, dx}{1 + x^{3/4}} = \int \frac{z^2 \cdot 4z^3\, dz}{1 + z^3}$$

$$= 4 \int \frac{z^5\, dz}{z^3 + 1}$$

$$= 4 \int \left[z^2 - \frac{z^2}{z^3 + 1} \right] dz$$

$$= \tfrac{4}{3}z^3 - \tfrac{4}{3} \ln(z^3 + 1) + C$$

$$= \tfrac{4}{3}x^{3/4} - \tfrac{4}{3} \ln(x^{3/4} + 1) + C$$

(b) $\displaystyle\int \frac{x\,dx}{(a+bx)^{3/2}}$:

$$a + bx = z^2$$

$$b\,dx = 2z\,dz$$

$$dx = \frac{2}{b}z\,dz$$

$$\int \frac{x\,dx}{(a+bx)^{3/2}} = \frac{2}{b^2}\int \frac{(z^2-az)\cdot z\,dz}{z^3}$$

$$= \frac{2}{b^2}\int \frac{(z^3-az)\,dz}{z^3}$$

$$= \frac{2}{b^2}\int \left[1-\frac{a}{z^2}\right]dz$$

$$= \frac{2}{b^2}\left[z+\frac{a}{z}\right]+C$$

$$= \frac{2}{b^2}\left[\frac{z^2+a^2}{z}\right]+C$$

$$= \frac{2}{b^2}\left[\frac{2a+bx}{(a+bx)^{1/2}}\right]+C$$

(c) $\displaystyle\int \frac{(5x+9)\,dx}{(x-9)x^{3/2}}$:

$$x = z^2$$

$$dx = 2z\,dz$$

$$\int \frac{(5x+9)\,dx}{(x-9)x^{3/2}} = \int \frac{(5x^2+9)\cdot 2z\,dz}{(z^2-9)z^3}$$

$$= 2\int \frac{(5z^2+9)\,dz}{z^2(z-3)(z+3)}$$

$$= 2\int \left[\frac{A}{z}+\frac{B}{z^2}+\frac{C}{z-3}+\frac{D}{z+3}\right]dz$$

$$5z^2+9 = Az(z^2-9)+B(z^2-9)+Cz^2(z+3)+Dz^2(z-3)$$

$$= A(z^3-9z)+B(z^2-9)+C(z^3+3z^2)+D(z^3-3z^2)$$

so

$$\begin{aligned} A+C+D &= 0 & C+D &= 0 \\ B+3C-3D &= 5 & 3C-3D &= 6 \\ -9A &= 0 & 2C &= 2 \\ -9B &= 9 & C &= 1 \\ A &= 0 & D &= -1 \\ B &= -1 & & \end{aligned}$$

and

$$\int \frac{(5x+9)\,dx}{(x-9)x^{3/2}} = 2\left[-\int \frac{dz}{z^2} + \int \frac{dz}{z-3} - \int \frac{dz}{z+3}\right]$$

$$= 2\left[\frac{1}{z} + \ln(z-3) - \ln(z+3)\right] + C$$

$$= 2\left[\frac{1}{z} + \ln\left(\frac{z-3}{z+3}\right)\right] + C$$

$$= 2\left[\frac{1}{x^{1/2}} + \ln\left(\frac{x^{1/2}-3}{x^{1/2}+3}\right)\right] + C$$

(d) $\displaystyle\int \frac{dx}{x - x^{4/3}}$:

$$x = z^3$$

$$dx = 3z^2\,dz$$

$$\int \frac{dx}{x - x^{4/3}} = \int \frac{3z^2\,dz}{z^3 - z^4}$$

$$= 3\int \frac{dz}{z(1-z)}$$

$$= 3\int \left[\frac{A}{z} + \frac{B}{1-z}\right] dz$$

$$1 = A(1-z) + Bz$$

so

$$-A + B = 0$$

$$A = 1$$

$$B = -1$$

and

$$\int \frac{dx}{x - x^{4/3}} = 3\left[\int \frac{dz}{z} - \int \frac{dz}{1-z}\right]$$

$$= 3[\ln z - \ln(1-z)] + C$$

$$= 3\ln\left(\frac{z}{1-z}\right) + C$$

$$= 3\ln\left(\frac{x^{1/3}}{1-x^{1/3}}\right) + C$$

(e) $\displaystyle\int y(a+y)^{1/3}\,dy$:

$$a + y = z^3$$

$$dy = 3z^2\,dz$$

$$\int y(a + y)^{1/3}\, dy = \int (z^3 - a) \cdot z \cdot 3z^2\, dz$$

$$= 3 \int (z^6 - az^3)\, dz$$

$$= 3 \int (z^6 - az^3)\, dz$$

$$= 3 \left[\frac{z^7}{7} - \frac{az^4}{4} \right] + C$$

$$= \tfrac{3}{28} [z^4 (4z^3 - 7a)] + C$$

$$= \tfrac{3}{28} [(a + y)^{4/3} (4a + 4y - 7a)] + C$$

$$= \tfrac{3}{28} [(a + y)^{4/3} (4y - 3a)] + C$$

(f) $\displaystyle \int \frac{x^2\, dx}{(4x + 1)^{5/2}}$:

$$4x + 1 = z^2$$

$$4\, dx = 2z\, dz$$

$$dx = \tfrac{1}{2} z\, dz$$

$$\int \frac{x^2\, dx}{(4x + 1)^{5/2}} = \int \frac{\tfrac{1}{16}(z^2 - 1)^2 \cdot \tfrac{1}{2} z\, dz}{z^5}$$

$$= \tfrac{1}{32} \int \frac{(z^4 - 2z^2 + 1)\, dz}{z^4}$$

$$= \tfrac{1}{32} \int \left[1 - \frac{2}{z^2} + \frac{1}{z^4} \right] dz$$

$$= \tfrac{1}{32} \left[z + \frac{2}{z} - \frac{1}{3z^3} \right] + C$$

$$= \tfrac{1}{32} \left[\frac{3z^4 + 6z^2 - 1}{3z^3} \right] + C$$

$$= \tfrac{1}{32} \left[\frac{3(4x + 1)^2 + 6(4x + 1) - 1}{3(4x + 1)^{3/2}} \right] + C$$

$$= \frac{6x^2 + 6x + 1}{12(4x + 1)^{3/2}} + C$$

□ INTEGRATION BY MISCELLANEOUS SUBSTITUTIONS

The substitutions considered in the preceding section made integration possible by rationalizing the function to be integrated. There are also a number of functions that can be integrated by means of substitutions which do not rationalize them. Unfortunately, no general rules can be given for these substitutions and they must be determined by trial and error, guided by experience. For example, a very useful substitution of this type is the *reciprocal substitution*:

$$x = \frac{1}{z} \qquad dx = \frac{-dz}{z^2}$$

Example

Evaluate the following integrals.

(a) $\displaystyle\int \frac{(x - x^3)^{1/3} \, dx}{x^4}$:

$$x = \frac{1}{z}$$

$$dx = \frac{-dz}{z^2}$$

$$\int \frac{(x - x^3)^{1/3} \, dx}{x^4} = -\int \frac{\left(\dfrac{1}{z} - \dfrac{1}{z^3}\right)^{1/3} \dfrac{dz}{z^2}}{\dfrac{1}{z^4}}$$

$$= -\int \frac{(z^2 - 1)^{1/3} \, dz}{\dfrac{1}{z}}$$

$$= \int z(z^2 - 1)^{1/3} \, dz$$

$$= -\tfrac{3}{8}(z^2 - 1)^{4/3} + C$$

$$= -\tfrac{3}{8}\left(\frac{1}{x^2} - 1\right)^{4/3} + C$$

(b) $\displaystyle\int \frac{dx}{x\sqrt{1 + x + x^2}}$ using the standard form

$$\int \frac{du}{\sqrt{a + bu + cu^2}} = \frac{1}{\sqrt{c}} \ln(2cu + b + 2\sqrt{c}\sqrt{a + bu + cu^2}) + C$$

$$x = \frac{1}{z}$$

$$dx = \frac{-dz}{z^2}$$

$$\int \frac{dx}{x\sqrt{1+x+x^2}} = -\int \frac{\frac{dz}{z^2}}{\frac{1}{z}\sqrt{1+\frac{1}{z}+\frac{1}{z^2}}}$$

$$= -\int \frac{dz}{z\sqrt{\frac{z^2+z+1}{z^2}}}$$

$$= -\int \frac{dz}{\sqrt{z^2+z+1}}$$

$$= -\ln(2z+1+2\sqrt{z^2+z+1}) + C$$

$$= -\ln\left(\frac{2}{x}+1+2\sqrt{\frac{1}{x^2}+\frac{1}{x}+1}\right) + C$$

$$= -\ln\left(\frac{2+x}{x}+2\sqrt{\frac{1+x+x^2}{x^2}}\right) + C$$

$$= -\ln\left(\frac{2+x+2\sqrt{1+x+x^2}}{x}\right) + C$$

$$= \ln\left(\frac{x}{2+x+2\sqrt{1+x+x^2}}\right) + C$$

PROBLEMS

Evaluate each of the following integrals using partial fractions.

1. $\displaystyle\int \frac{(4x-2)\,dx}{x^3-x^2-2x}$

2. $\displaystyle\int \frac{(4x^3+2x^2+1)\,dx}{4x^3-x}$

3. $\displaystyle\int \frac{z^2\,dz}{(z-1)^3}$

4. $\displaystyle\int \frac{(y^4-8)\,dy}{y^3+2y^2}$

5. $\displaystyle\int \frac{(4x^2+6)\,dx}{x^3+3x}$.

6. $\displaystyle\int \frac{(x^3+3x)\,dx}{(x^2+1)^2}$

7. $\displaystyle\int \frac{t^5\,dt}{(t^2+4)^2}$

8. $\displaystyle\int \frac{(2t^2-8t-8)\,dt}{(t-2)(t^2+4)}$

Evaluate each of the following integrals by rationalization.

9. $\displaystyle\int \frac{y\,dy}{\sqrt{2+4y}}$

10. $\displaystyle\int \frac{dt}{2\sqrt{t}+\sqrt[3]{t}}$

11. $\displaystyle\int \frac{(x^{3/2}-x^{1/3})\,dx}{6x^{1/4}}$

12. $\displaystyle\int \frac{(\sqrt{x+1}+1)\,dx}{\sqrt{x+1}-1}$

13. $\displaystyle\int \frac{dx}{1+\sqrt[3]{x+2}}$

14. $\displaystyle\int \frac{dx}{1+\sqrt{x}}$

Evaluate each of the following integrals by reciprocal substitution.

15. $\int \dfrac{dx}{x^2\sqrt{x^2 + a^2}}$

18. $\int \dfrac{\sqrt{4 - x^2}\ dx}{x^4}$

16. $\int \dfrac{\sqrt{x^2 - a^2}\ dx}{x^4}$

19. $\int \dfrac{-dx}{x\sqrt{1 + 4x + 5x^2}}$

17. $\int \dfrac{dx}{x\sqrt{2x - x^2}}$

20. $\int \dfrac{dx}{x^2\sqrt{2x - x^2}}$

ANSWERS TO ODD-NUMBERED PROBLEMS

1. $\ln\left[\dfrac{x(x - 2)}{(x + 1)^2}\right] + C$

7. $\dfrac{t^2}{2} - 4\ln(t^2 + 4) - \dfrac{8}{t^2 + 4} + C$

3. $\ln(z - 1) + \dfrac{3 - 4z}{2(z - 1)^2} + C$

9. $\tfrac{1}{6}(2 + 4y)^{1/2}(y - 1) + C$

5. $\ln[x^2(x^2 + 3)] + C$

11. $\tfrac{2}{27}x^{9/4} - \tfrac{2}{13}x^{13/12} + C$

13. $\tfrac{3}{2}(x + a)^{2/3} - 3(x + a)^{1/3} + 3\ln[(x + a)^{1/3} + 1] + C$

15. $-\dfrac{\sqrt{x^2 + a^2}}{a^2 x} + C$

17. $-\left(\dfrac{2 - x}{x}\right)^{1/2} + C$

19. $\ln\left(\dfrac{1 + 2x + \sqrt{1 + 4x + 5x^2}}{x}\right) + C$

■ 4.7 NUMERICAL (APPROXIMATE) METHODS OF INTEGRATION

Approximate integration is useful in many practical problems when an integral cannot be expressed in terms of elementary functions or when an integrand is defined by an empirical table of values or by an empirical graph. Three methods of approximate integration are discussed in the following sections: the *trapezoidal rule* (linear approximation), *Simpson's rule* (quadratic approximation), and *Taylor's expansion* (series approximation). In all three of these methods, the function to be integrated is replaced by an approximation whose integral is known. The trapezoidal rule and Simpson's rule (but not Taylor's expansion) can also be used when the integrand is defined empirically by a table of values or a graph, rather than by a function.

The methods discussed in this section and several other approximation methods are used to evaluate integrals using electronic computers. Approximate integration, even of quite difficult integrals, can be done efficiently using a computer. One of the purposes of the following discussion is to explain the principles involved in such approximation.

□ *THE TRAPEZOIDAL RULE*

The trapezoidal rule uses a series of straight-line segments to approximate the given function $f(x)$; it is in this sense a method of linear approximation.

Suppose the problem is to evaluate $\int_a^b f(x)\,dx$. Divide the interval $[a, b]$ into n equal parts, each of length Δx, and denote the points of division by $a = x_0, x_1, \ldots, x_n = b$. Erect ordinates at the points of division and denote them by $y_0 = f(x_0), y_1 = f(x_1), \ldots, y_n = f(x_n)$. Join the ends of consecutive ordinates to form trapezoids (see Fig. 4.27). Then

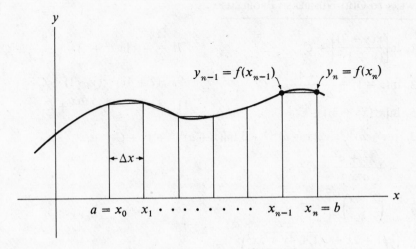

FIGURE 4.27

Area of first trapezoid $= \frac{1}{2}(y_0 + y_1)\Delta x$
Area of second trapezoid $= \frac{1}{2}(y_1 + y_2)\Delta x$

.
.
.

Area of nth trapezoid $= \frac{1}{2}(y_{n-1} + y_n)\Delta x$

and the total area of the n trapezoids is

$$\Delta x\left[\tfrac{1}{2}y_0 + \sum_{i=1}^{n-1} y_i + \tfrac{1}{2}y_n\right]$$

The trapezoidal rule for approximate integration is thus

$$\int_a^b f(x)dx \simeq \Delta x\left[\tfrac{1}{2}(y_0 + y_n) + \sum_{i=1}^{n-1} y_i\right]$$

● **Notes Concerning the Accuracy of the Trapezoidal Rule**

1. As the number of divisions n increases, the sum of the areas of the trapezoids more closely approximates the area under the curve.
2. The trapezoidal rule gives a closer approximation to the area under the curve than does the sum of the areas of the corresponding rectangles—that is,

$$\left|\int_a^b f(x)\,dx - \Delta x\left[\tfrac{1}{2}(y_0 + y_n) + \sum_{i=1}^{n-1} y_i\right]\right| < \left|\int_a^b f(x)\,dx - \Delta x \sum_{i=0}^{n-1} y_i\right|$$

and

$$\left|\int_a^b f(x)\,dx - \Delta x\left[\tfrac{1}{2}(y_0 + y_n) + \sum_{i=1}^{n-1} y_i\right]\right| < \left|\int_a^b f(x)\,dx - \Delta x \sum_{i=1}^{n} y_i\right|$$

3. The integral $\int_a^b f(x)\,dx$ is bounded by $\Delta x \sum_{i=0}^{n-1} y_i$ and $\Delta x \sum_{i=1}^{n} y_i$; depending on which bound is smaller,

$$\Delta x \sum_{i=0}^{n-1} y_i \le \int_a^b f(x)\,dx \le \Delta x \sum_{i=1}^{n} y_i$$

or

$$\Delta x \sum_{i=1}^{n} y_i \le \int_a^b f(x)\,dx \le \Delta x \sum_{i=0}^{n-1} y_i$$

The trapezoidal rule averages these two bounds.

Example

Evaluate $\int_2^4 x(16 - x^2)^{1/2}\,dx$ by the trapezoidal rule using $n = 4$.

i	0	1	2	3	4
x_i	2.0	2.5	3.0	3.5	4.0
$f(x_i) = y_i$	$4\sqrt{3} \simeq 6.928$	$\tfrac{5}{4}\sqrt{39} \simeq 7.806$	$3\sqrt{7} \simeq 7.938$	$\tfrac{7}{4}\sqrt{15} \simeq 6.778$	0

$$\int_2^4 x(16 - x^2)^{1/2}\,dx \simeq \Delta x\left[\tfrac{1}{2}(y_0 + y_4) + \sum_{i=1}^{3} y_i\right]$$

$$\simeq 0.5[\tfrac{1}{2}(6.928) + (7.806 + 7.938 + 6.778)]$$

$$\simeq 0.5[3.464 + 22.522]$$

$$\simeq 12.993$$

NOTE: $\Delta x \sum_{i=1}^{n} y_i \le \int_a^b f(x)\,dx \le \Delta x \sum_{i=0}^{n-1} y_i$

$$11.261 \le \int_2^4 x(16 - x^2)^{1/2}\,dx \le 14.725$$

□ *SIMPSON'S RULE*

Simpson's rule uses a series of parabolic arcs to approximate the given function $f(x)$; it is in this sense a method of quadratic approximation. Simpson's rule provides a closer approximation than the trapezoidal rule for any given number of subdivisions of the interval over which the integral is to be evaluated.

A parabola with vertical axis can be passed through any three points and the area under a parabolic arc through three equidistant points can be obtained by the following rule: If a parabola with vertical axis is passed through the extremities of three equidistant ordinates y_0, y_1, y_2 with distance Δx between consecutive ordinates, the area bounded by the parabola, the x-axis, and the extreme ordinates y_0 and y_2 is given by

$$A = \frac{\Delta x}{3}(y_0 + 4y_1 + y_2)$$

Again suppose the problem is to evaluate $\int_a^b f(x)\, dx$. Divide the interval $[a, b]$ into n equal parts, where n *must now be an even number*, each of length Δx, and denote the points of division by $a = x_0, x_1, \ldots, x_n = b$. Erect the corresponding ordinates $y_0, y_1, \ldots, y_n$; consider these ordinates in groups of three: $y_0, y_1, y_2; y_2, y_3, y_4; y_4, y_5, y_6; \ldots; y_{n-2}, y_{n-1}, y_n$, and pass a parabolic arc with vertical axis through each set of three points (see Fig. 4.28). The areas under these parabolic arcs are, respectively,

$$A_1 = \frac{\Delta x}{3}(y_0 + 4y_1 + y_2)$$

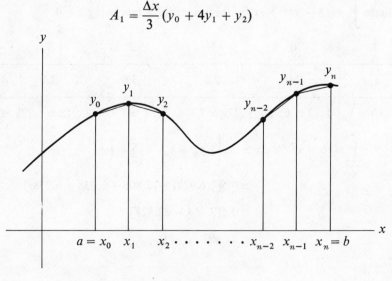

FIGURE 4.28

$$A_2 = \frac{\Delta x}{3}(y_2 + 4y_3 + y_4)$$

.
.
.

$$A_n = \frac{\Delta x}{3}(y_{n-2} + 4y_{n-1} + y_n)$$

and the sum of these areas is

$$\frac{\Delta x}{3}[y_0 + 4y_1 + 2y_2 + 4y_3 + 2y_4 + \cdots + 2y_{n-2} + 4y_{n-1} + y_n]$$

Simpson's rule for approximate integration is thus

$$\int_a^b f(x)\, dx \simeq \frac{\Delta x}{3}[y_0 + 4y_1 + 2y_2 + \cdots + 2y_{n-2} + 4y_{n-1} + y_n]$$

As in the case of the trapezoidal rule, as the number of divisions n increases, the sum of the areas under the parabolic arcs more closely approximates the area under the curve.

Example

$\int_2^4 x(16 - x^2)^{1/2}\, dx$ by Simpson's rule using $n = 4$.

i	0	1	2	3	4
x_i	2.0	2.5	3.0	3.5	4.0
$(x_i) = y_i$	$4\sqrt{3} \simeq 6.928$	$\frac{5}{4}\sqrt{39} \simeq 7.806$	$3\sqrt{7} \simeq 7.938$	$\frac{7}{4}\sqrt{15} \simeq 6.778$	0

$$\int_2^4 x(16 - x)^{1/2}\, dx \simeq \frac{\Delta x}{3}[y_0 + 4(y_1 + y_3) + 2y_2 + y_4]$$

$$\simeq \frac{0.5}{3}[6.928 + 4(7.806 + 6.778) + 2(7.938) + 0]$$

$$\simeq \frac{0.5}{3}[6.928 + 58.336 + 15.876]$$

$$\simeq 13.523$$

NOTE:

$$\int_2^4 x(16 - x^2)^{1/2}\, dx = \left[-\tfrac{1}{3}(16 - x^2)^{3/2}\right]_2^4 = 0 + \tfrac{1}{3}(12)^{3/2} = 8\sqrt{3} \simeq 13.856,$$

and, as noted above, Simpson's rule gives a closer approximation than does the trapezoidal rule. Note also that the exact answer is in fact within the bounds given by the trapezoidal rule.

☐ *TAYLOR'S EXPANSION*

Taylor's theorem may be used to expand a function $f(x)$ in an infinite series; $\int_c^d f(x)\, dx$ may then be evaluated approximately by integrating the series term by term and evaluating as many terms as necessary to obtain the required accuracy. For this procedure to be valid, the series must converge to $f(x)$ for all values of x in the interval $[c, d]$ over which the integral is to be evaluated. Usually, by expanding the series about a value of a such that $c \leq a \leq d$, the required accuracy can be obtained with fewer terms.

Thus, providing the convergence conditions are met,

$$\int_c^d f(x)\, dx = \int_c^d \left[f(a) + \frac{f'(a)}{1!}(x - a) + \frac{f''(a)}{2!}(x - a)^2 + \cdots \right.$$

$$\left. + \frac{f^{(n)}(a)}{n!}(x - a)^n + \cdots \right] dx$$

$$= \left[f(a)x + \frac{f'(a)}{2!}(x - a)^2 + \frac{f''(a)}{3!}(x - a)^3 + \cdots \right.$$

$$\left. + \frac{f^{(n-1)}(a)}{n!}(x - a)^n + \cdots \right]_c^d$$

where, in general, $c \leq a \leq d$.

Examples

Evaluate $\displaystyle \int_0^{1/2} \frac{x^2\, dx}{x + 1}$ using Taylor's series.

$f(x) = \dfrac{x^2}{x + 1}$ $\qquad\qquad$ $f(\tfrac{1}{4}) = \dfrac{\frac{1}{16}}{\frac{5}{4}} = \dfrac{1}{20}$

$f'(x) = \dfrac{2x(x + 1) - x^2}{(x + 1)^2} = \dfrac{x^2 + 2x}{(x + 1)^2}$ $\qquad$ $f'(\tfrac{1}{4}) = \dfrac{\frac{1}{16} + \frac{1}{2}}{(\frac{5}{4})^2} = \dfrac{9}{25}$

$f''(x) = \dfrac{(2x + 2)(x + 1)^2 - (x^2 + 2x)(2x + 2)}{(x + 1)^4}$ $\qquad$ $f''(\tfrac{1}{4}) = \dfrac{2}{(\frac{5}{4})^3} = \dfrac{128}{125}$

$\qquad = \dfrac{2}{(x + 1)^3}$

$f'''(x) = \dfrac{-6(x + 1)^2}{(x + 1)^6} = -\dfrac{6}{(x + 1)^4}$ $\qquad$ $f'''(\tfrac{1}{4}) = -\dfrac{6}{(\frac{5}{4})^4} = -\dfrac{1536}{625}$

$f^{(IV)}(x) = \dfrac{24(x + 1)^3}{(x + 1)^8} = \dfrac{24}{(x + 1)^5}$ $\qquad$ $f^{(IV)}(\tfrac{1}{4}) = \dfrac{24}{(\frac{5}{4})^5} = \dfrac{24576}{3125}$

$\qquad \vdots \qquad\qquad\qquad\qquad\qquad\qquad\qquad \vdots$

$f^{n-1}(x) = (-1)^{n-1}\dfrac{(n - 1)!}{(x + 1)^n}$ $\qquad$ $f^{n-1}(\tfrac{1}{4}) = (-1)^{n-1}\dfrac{(n - 1)!}{(\frac{5}{4})^n}$

$$\int_c^d f(x)dx = \left[f(a)x + \frac{f'(a)}{2!}(x - a)^2 + \frac{f''(a)}{3!}(x - a)^3 + \cdots \right.$$

$$+ \frac{f^{(n-1)}(a)}{n!}(x-a)^n + \cdots \Bigg]_c^d$$

Letting $a = \frac{1}{4}$,

$$\int_0^{1/2} \frac{x^2\, dx}{x+1} \simeq \left[\tfrac{1}{20}x + \frac{9}{25 \cdot 2!}(x-\tfrac{1}{4})^2 + \frac{128}{125 \cdot 3!}(x-\tfrac{1}{4})^3 \right.$$

$$\left. - \frac{1536}{625 \cdot 4!}(x-\tfrac{1}{4})^4 + \frac{24756}{3125 \cdot 5!}(x-\tfrac{1}{4})^5 \right]_0^{1/2}$$

$$\simeq \left(\frac{1}{40} + \frac{9}{25 \cdot 2!}\cancel{\left(\frac{1}{4}\right)^2} + \frac{128}{125 \cdot 3!}\left(\frac{1}{4}\right)^3 - \frac{1536}{625 \cdot 4!}\cancel{\left(\frac{1}{4}\right)^4} + \frac{24576}{3125 \cdot 5!}\left(\frac{1}{4}\right)^5 \right)$$

$$- \left(0 + \frac{9}{25 \cdot 2!}\cancel{\left(-\frac{1}{4}\right)^2} + \frac{128}{125 \cdot 3!}\left(-\frac{1}{4}\right)^3 \right.$$

$$\left. - \frac{1536}{625 \cdot 4!}\cancel{\left(-\frac{1}{4}\right)^4} + \frac{24576}{3125 \cdot 5!}\left(-\frac{1}{4}\right)^5 \right)$$

$$\simeq \frac{1}{40} + \frac{2}{375} + \frac{2}{15625}$$

$$\simeq 0.025 + 0.0053333 + 0.000128$$

$$\simeq 0.0304613$$

or 0.0305 to four decimal places.

NOTE: Using standard forms,

$$\int_0^{1/2} \frac{x^2}{x+1}\, dx = \int_0^{1/2}\left(x - 1 + \frac{1}{x+1} \right) dx = \left[\frac{x^2}{2} - x + \ln(x+1) \right]_0^{1/2}$$

$$= (\tfrac{1}{8} - \tfrac{1}{2} + \ln \tfrac{3}{2}) - (0 - 0 + 0)$$

$$= -\tfrac{3}{8} + \ln \tfrac{3}{2}$$

$$\simeq -0.375 + 0.4055$$

$$\simeq 0.0305 \text{ to four decimal places}$$

Evaluate $\int_0^1 x^3\, dx$ using (a) trapezoidal rule, (b) Simpson's rule, (c) Taylor's series, and (d) exactly.

Divide the range into 10 equal parts as summarized in the following table:

i	0	1	2	3	4	5
x_i	0	0.1	0.2	0.3	0.4	0.5
$f(x_i) = y_i$	0	0.001	0.008	0.027	0.064	0.125

i	6	7	8	9	10
x_i	0.6	0.7	0.8	0.9	1.0
$f(x_i) = y_i$	0.216	0.343	0.512	0.729	1.00

(a) trapezoidal rule: $\int_a^b f(x)\, dx \simeq \Delta x \left[\frac{1}{2}(y_0 + y_n) + \sum_{i=1}^{n-1} y_i \right]$:

$$\int_0^1 x^3\, dx \simeq 0.1[\tfrac{1}{2}(0 + 1.000) + 2.025]$$

$$\simeq 0.2525$$

(b) Simpson's rule:

$$\int_a^b f(x)\, dx \simeq \frac{\Delta x}{3}[y_0 + 4y_1 + 2y_2 + 4y_3 + \cdots + 4y_{2n-1} + y_n]:$$

$$\int_0^1 x^3\, dx \simeq \frac{0.1}{3}[(0 + 1.000) + 2(0.800) + 4(1.225)]$$

$$\simeq 0.25$$

(c) $\int_c^d f(x)\, dx = \left[f(a)x + \frac{f'(a)}{2!}(x - a)^2 + \frac{f''(a)}{3!}(x - a)^3 + \cdots \right]_c^d$:

Letting $a = \frac{1}{2}$,

$$\int_0^1 x^3\, dx = \left[f(\tfrac{1}{2})x + \frac{f'(\tfrac{1}{2})}{2!}(x - \tfrac{1}{2})^2 + \frac{f''(\tfrac{1}{2})}{3!}(x - \tfrac{1}{2})^3 + \cdots \right]_0^1$$

$$f(x) = x^3 \qquad f(\tfrac{1}{2}) = \tfrac{1}{8}$$

$$f'(x) = 3x^2 \qquad f'(\tfrac{1}{2}) = \tfrac{3}{4}$$

$$f''(x) = 6x \qquad f''(\tfrac{1}{2}) = 3$$

$$f'''(x) = 6 \qquad f'''(\tfrac{1}{2}) = 6$$

$$f^{(\mathrm{IV})}(x) = 0 \qquad f^{(\mathrm{IV})}(\tfrac{1}{2}) = 0$$

$$\int_0^1 x^3\, dx = \left[\tfrac{1}{8}x + \frac{\tfrac{3}{4}}{2!}(x - \tfrac{1}{2})^2 + \frac{3}{3!}(x - \tfrac{1}{2})^3 + \frac{6}{4!}(x - \tfrac{1}{2})^4 \right]_0^1$$

$$= \left(\frac{1}{8} + \frac{3}{2!} \left(\frac{1}{2} \right)^2 + \frac{3}{3!} \left(\frac{1}{2} \right)^3 + \frac{6}{4!} \left(\frac{1}{2} \right)^4 \right)$$

$$- \left(0 + \frac{3}{2!} \left(-\frac{1}{2} \right)^2 + \frac{3}{3!} \left(-\frac{1}{2} \right)^3 + \frac{6}{4!} \left(-\frac{1}{2} \right)^4 \right)$$

$$= 0.125 + 0.125$$

$$= 0.250$$

(d) $\int_0^1 x^3 \, dx = \left[\frac{x^4}{4} \right]_0^1 = \frac{1}{4} - 0 = 0.25$

NOTE: Both Simpson's rule and the Taylor's series expansion provide the exact answer for this particular problem. Because of the nature of the approximation (quadratic), Simpson's rule is exact for any quadratic or cubic function. The Taylor's series expansion is exact if all further terms are zero—that is, if n terms are used and the nth derivative of $f(x)$ is zero. Because Simpson's rule is exact, the answer could have been obtained by dividing the range into only two parts:

i	0	1	2
x_i	0	0.5	1
$f(x_i) = y_i$	0	.125	1

$$\int_0^1 x^3 \, dx = \frac{0.5}{3} [1 + 4(.125)] = 0.25$$

However, using $n = 2$ instead of $n = 10$ would reduce the accuracy of the trapezoidal rule:

$$\int_0^1 x^3 \, dx = 0.5[\tfrac{1}{2}(1) + .125] = 0.3125$$

Evaluate $\int_2^6 \frac{dx}{x^2 - 1}$ using (a) trapezoidal rule, (b) Simpson's rule, (c) Taylor's series, and (d) exactly.

Divide the range into four equal parts as summarized in the following table:

i	0	1	2	3	4
x_i	2	3	4	5	6
$f(x_i) = y_i$	$\frac{1}{3}$	$\frac{1}{8}$	$\frac{1}{15}$	$\frac{1}{24}$	$\frac{1}{35}$
	(0.3333)	(0.1250)	(0.0667)	(0.0417)	(0.0286)

(a) trapezoidal rule: $\int_a^b f(x)\,dx \simeq \Delta x\left[\frac{1}{2}(y_0 + y_n) + \sum_{i=1}^{n-1} y_i\right]$:

$$\int_2^6 \frac{dx}{x^2 - 1} \simeq 1[\tfrac{1}{2}(0.3333 + 0.0286) + 0.2334]$$

$$\simeq 0.4143$$

(b) Simpson's rule: $\int_a^b f(x)\,dx \simeq \dfrac{\Delta x}{3}\left[y_0 + 4y_1 + 2y_2 + \cdots + 4y_{2n-1} + y_n\right]$:

$$\int_2^6 \frac{dx}{x^2 - 1} \simeq \tfrac{1}{3}[(0.3333 + 0.0286) + 4(0.1250 + 0.0417) + 2(0.0667)]$$

$$\simeq 0.3870$$

(c) $\displaystyle\int_c^d f(x)\,dx = \left[f(a)x + \frac{f'(a)}{2!}(x-a)^2 + \frac{f''(a)}{3!}(x-a)^3 + \cdots\right]_c^d$

Letting $a = 4$,

$$\int_2^6 \frac{dx}{x^2-1} \simeq \left[f(4)x + \frac{f'(4)}{2!}(x-4)^2 + \frac{f''(4)}{3!}(x-4)^3 + \frac{f'''(4)}{4!}(x-4)^4 \right.$$

$$\left. + \frac{f^{(IV)}(4)}{5!}(x-4)^5\right]_2^6$$

$f(x) = (x^2 - 1)^{-1}$ $\qquad\qquad\qquad$ $f(4) = \frac{1}{15}$

$f'(x) = -1(x^2 - 1)^{-2}(2x)$

$\quad = -2x(x^2 - 1)^{-2}$ $\qquad\qquad\qquad$ $f'(4) = \dfrac{-8}{(15)^2}$

$f''(x) = -2(x^2 - 1)^{-2} - 2x(-2)(x^2 - 1)^{-3}(2x)$ $\qquad$ $f''(4) = \dfrac{98}{(15)^3}$

$\quad = (x^2 - 1)^{-3}[-2x^2 + 2 + 8x^2]$

$\quad = 2(3x^2 + 1)(x^2 - 1)^{-3}$ $\qquad\qquad\qquad$ $f'''(4) = \dfrac{-(96)(17)}{(15)^4}$

$f'''(x) = 2(6x)(x^2 - 1)^{-3}$

$\quad + 2(3x^2 + 1)(-3)(x^2 - 1)^{-4}(2x)$ $\qquad$ $f^{(IV)}(4) = \dfrac{(24)(144)}{(15)^5}$

$\quad = (x^2 - 1)^{-4}[12x^3 - 12x - 36x^3 - 12x]$

$\quad = -24x(x^2 + 1)(x^2 - 1)^{-4}$

$f^{(IV)}(x) = -24(3x^2 + 1)(x^2 - 1)^{-4} - 24(x^3 + x)(-4)(x^2 - 1)^{-5}(2x)$

$\quad = -24(x^2 - 1)^{-5}[3x^4 - 2x^2 - 1 - 8x^4 - 8x^2]$

$\quad = 24(5x^4 + 10x^2 + 1)(x^2 - 1)^{-5}$

$$\int_2^6 \frac{dx}{x^2-1} \simeq \left[\tfrac{1}{15}x - \frac{8}{(15)^2 \cdot 2!}(x-4)^2 + \frac{98}{(15)^3 \cdot 3!}(x-4)^3\right.$$

$$\left. - \frac{(96)(17)}{(15)^4 \cdot 4!}(x-4)^4 + \frac{(24)(1441)}{(15)^5 \cdot 5!}(x-4)^5\right]_2^6$$

$$\simeq \left(\frac{6}{15} - \frac{8}{(15)^2 \cdot 2!}(2)^2 + \frac{98}{(15)^3 \cdot 3!}(2)^3 \right.$$

$$\left. - \frac{(96)(17)}{(15)^4 \cdot 4!}(2)^4 + \frac{(24)(1441)}{(15)^5 \cdot 5!}(2)^5 \right)$$

$$- \left(\frac{2}{15} - \frac{8}{(15)^2 \cdot 2!}(-2)^2 + \frac{98}{(15)^3 \cdot 3!}(-2)^3 \right.$$

$$\left. - \frac{(96)(17)}{(15)^4 \cdot 4!}(-2)^4 + \frac{(24)(1441)}{(15)^5 \cdot 5!}(-2)^5 \right)$$

$$\simeq 0.2667 + 0.0774 + 0.0240$$

$$\simeq 0.3681$$

(d) $\displaystyle \int_2^6 \frac{dx}{x^2 - 1} = \left[\frac{1}{2} \ln \left(\frac{x-1}{x+1} \right) \right]_2^6 = \frac{1}{2}[\ln \frac{5}{7} - \ln \frac{1}{3}]$

$$= \frac{1}{2}[\ln 5 - \ln 7 + \ln 3]$$

$$\simeq \frac{1}{2}[1.6094 - 1.9459 + 1.0986]$$

$$\simeq 0.3811$$

NOTE: $\displaystyle \int \frac{du}{u^2 - a^2} = \frac{1}{2a} \ln \left(\frac{u-a}{u+a} \right) + C.$

It should be noted that the seemingly better results from part (b) are due to the truncation effects of using only 4 terms in (c). Taylor's series is more accurate than Simpson's rule.

PROBLEMS

Evaluate each of the following integrals approximately using (a) trapezoidal rule, (b) Simpson's rule, (c) Taylor's series, and (d) exactly.

1. $\displaystyle \int_0^3 (x^4 + 3x^2)\, dx$, $n = 6$

2. $\displaystyle \int_3^5 \frac{dx}{x}$, $n = 4$

3. $\displaystyle \int_{-2}^2 e^{2x}\, dx$, $n = 4$

4. $\displaystyle \int_{-2}^2 e^{1/2x}\, dx$, $n = 4$

Evaluate each of the following integrals by expanding the function in a Taylor's series; comment on the interval of convergence and the accuracy of the evaluation.

5. $\displaystyle \int_0^1 (x^4 - x^3 + \frac{1}{2})\, dx$

6. $\displaystyle \int_0^2 (5x^4 + \frac{1}{3}x^3 + 6x)\, dx$

7. $\displaystyle \int_0^2 \left(\frac{x^4}{4} + x^3 + 2x^2 + 1 \right) dx$

8. $\displaystyle \int_2^4 (x^3 - 6x + 3)\, dx$

1. (a) 78.218; (b) 75.625; (c) 75.6; (d) 75.6
3. (a) 35.832; (b) 28.904; (c) 27.173; (d) 27.290
5. $\frac{9}{20}$ (exact, no problem of interval of convergence)
7. $12\frac{14}{15}$ (exact, no problem of interval of convergence)

■ 4.8 MULTIPLE INTEGRATION

The definite integral $\int_a^b f(x)\,dx$ is defined with respect to the function $f(x)$ over an interval $a \le x \le b$. Similarly, the *double integral*

$$\iint_R f(x, y)\,dy\,dx$$

is defined with respect to the function $f(x, y)$ over a bounded region, R, of the xy-plane.

Just as the definite integral of $f(x)$ can be interpreted in terms of area, the double integral can be interpreted in terms of volume. (See Fig. 4.29.) The function $f(x, y)$ is assumed to be positive over the region R and the volume computed is that below the surface $z = f(x, y)$ and above the region R in the xy-plane.

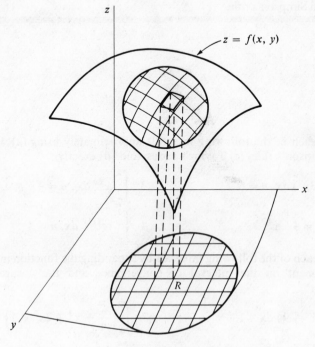

FIGURE 4.29

The evaluation of double integrals is most easily accomplished by successive *partial integration*, which is the inverse of partial differentiation. That is, to evaluate a double integral, a function of two independent variables is integrated with respect to one of the variables while the other variable is considered as constant; the result of this partial integration is then integrated with respect to the other variable. For this purpose the double integral

$$\iint_R f(x, y) \, dy \, dx \qquad \text{or} \qquad \int_a^b \int_{h(x)}^{g(x)} f(x, y) \, dy \, dx$$

where a and b are constants, can be written as the *iterated integral*

$$\int_a^b \left[\int_{h(x)}^{g(x)} f(x, y) \, dy \right] dx$$

To evaluate this expression, $f(x, y)$ is first integrated partially with respect to y and evaluated for the appropriate limits; the result is a function of x which is then integrated with respect to x and evaluated for the appropriate limits. Similarly,

$$\int_a^b \int_{h(y)}^{g(y)} f(x, y) \, dx \, dy \qquad \text{or} \qquad \int_a^b \left[\int_{h(y)}^{g(y)} f(x, y) \, dx \right] dy$$

is first integrated partially with respect to x and then with respect to y.

For functions of more than two independent variables, this process can be generalized using multiple integrals; there are relatively few applications requiring more than triple integration. It is important to note that multiple integration is performed from the inside outward; thus the first integral sign belongs to the last differential and so forth. Note also that when an integration is performed with respect to a variable, that variable is eliminated completely from the remaining integral.

Examples

Evaluate the double integral $\displaystyle\int_0^1 \int_{x^2}^x \sqrt{\frac{x}{y}} \, dy \, dx.$

$$\int_0^1 \int_{x^2}^x \sqrt{\frac{x}{y}} \, dy \, dx = \int_0^1 \left[2x^{1/2} y^{1/2} \right]_{x^2}^x dx$$

$$= \int_0^1 (2x - 2x^{3/2}) \, dx$$

$$= \left[x^2 - \frac{4x^{5/2}}{5} \right]_0^1$$

$$= 1 - \tfrac{4}{5} = \tfrac{1}{5}$$

Evaluate the double integral $\displaystyle\int_0^a \int_0^{\sqrt{a^2-y^2}} x \, dx \, dy.$

$$\int_0^a \int_0^{\sqrt{a^2-y^2}} x \, dx \, dy = \int_0^a \left[\frac{x^2}{2} \right]_0^{\sqrt{a^2-y^2}} dy$$

$$= \int_0^a \frac{a^2-y^2}{2} \, dy$$

$$= \left[\frac{a^2 y}{2} - \frac{y^3}{6} \right]_0^a$$

$$= \frac{a^3}{2} - \frac{a^3}{6} = \frac{a^3}{3}$$

Evaluate the double integral $\displaystyle\int_{-1}^1 \int_1^{e^y} \frac{1}{xy} \, dx \, dy$.

$$\int_{-1}^1 \int_1^{e^y} \frac{1}{xy} \, dx \, dy = \int_{-1}^1 \left[\int_1^{e^y} \frac{1}{xy} \, dx \right] dy$$

$$= \int_{-1}^1 \left[\frac{1}{y} \ln x \right]_1^{e^y} dy$$

$$= \int_{-1}^1 dy$$

$$= \left[y \right]_{-1}^1$$

$$= 1 - (-1) = 2$$

Evaluate the double integral $\displaystyle\int_0^1 x^2 \int_0^1 e^{xy} \, dy \, dx$.

$$\int_0^1 x^2 \int_0^1 e^{xy} \, dy \, dx = \int_0^1 \left[x e^{xy} \right]_0^1 dx$$

$$= \int_0^1 (x e^x - x) \, dx$$

$$= \left[e^x(x-1) - \frac{x^2}{2} \right]_0^1$$

$$= -\tfrac{1}{2} - (-1) = \tfrac{1}{2}$$

Evaluate the triple integral $\displaystyle\int_0^1 \int_0^x \int_0^{x+y} (x + y + z) \, dz \, dy \, dx$.

$$\int_0^1 \int_0^x \int_0^{x+y} (x + y + z) \, dz \, dy \, dx = \int_0^1 \int_0^x \left[xy + yz + \frac{z^2}{2} \right]_0^{x+y} dy \, dx$$

$$= \int_0^1 \int_0^x \left[x^2 + xy + xy + y^2 + \frac{(x+y)^2}{2} \right] dy \, dx$$

$$= \int_0^1 \int_0^x \left(\frac{3x^2}{2} + 3xy + \frac{3y^2}{2} \right) dy \, dx$$

$$= \int_0^1 \left[\frac{3x^2 y}{2} + \frac{3xy^2}{2} + \frac{y^3}{2} \right]_0^x dx$$

$$= \int_0^1 \frac{7x^3}{2} \, dx$$

$$= \left[\frac{7x^4}{8} \right]_0^1$$

$$= \tfrac{7}{8}$$

Evaluate the triple integral $\int_1^2 y \int_y^{y^2} \int_0^{\ln x} e^z \, dz \, dx \, dy$

$$\int_1^2 y \int_y^{y^2} \int_0^{\ln x} e^z \, dz \, dx \, dy = \int_1^2 y \int_y^{y^2} \left[e^z \right]_0^{\ln x} dx \, dy$$

$$= \int_1^2 y \int_y^{y^2} (x - 1) \, dx \, dy$$

$$= \int_1^2 y \left[\frac{x^2}{2} - x \right]_y^{y^2} dy$$

$$= \int_1^2 \left(\frac{y^5}{2} - y^3 - \frac{y^3}{2} + y^2 \right) dy$$

$$= \left[\frac{y^6}{12} - \frac{3y^4}{8} + \frac{y^3}{3} \right]_1^2$$

$$= (\tfrac{16}{3} - 6 + \tfrac{8}{3}) - (\tfrac{1}{12} - \tfrac{3}{8} + \tfrac{1}{3})$$

$$= \tfrac{47}{24}$$

PROBLEMS

Evaluate the following multiple integrals.

1. $\int_0^1 \int_0^2 (x + 2) \, dy \, dx$

2. $\int_0^2 \int_1^3 (x + y) \, dx \, dy$

3. $\int_0^1 \int_{y^2}^y x^{1/2} \, dx \, dy$

4. $\int_0^2 \int_1^{x^2} y \, dy \, dx$

5. $\int_0^{-1} \int_{y+1}^{2y} xy \, dx \, dy$

6. $\int_0^1 \int_0^{x^2} e^{y/x} \, dy \, dx$

7. $\int_b^a \int_0^b \int_a^{2a} x^2 y^2 z \, dz \, dy \, dx$

8. $\int_0^1 \int_{y^2}^1 \int_0^{1-x} x \, dz \, dx \, dy$

9. $\displaystyle\int_0^1 \int_0^{1-x} \int_0^{1-y^2} z \, dz \, dy \, dx$

10. $\displaystyle\int_0^1 \int_0^x \int_0^{x+y} e^{x+y+z} dz \, dy \, dx$

11. $\displaystyle\int_{-1}^1 \int_y^{2y} x^2 y \, dx \, dy$

12. $\displaystyle\int_{-3}^0 \int_0^y y^2 e^{xy} \, dx \, dy$

13. $\displaystyle\int_1^2 \int_0^{x^2} (xy+1) \, dy \, dx$

14. $\displaystyle\int_0^3 \int_x^{x+1} (x+y) \, dy \, dx$

15. $\displaystyle\int_{-1}^1 \int_{x-1}^{x+1} (x-y-1) \, dy \, dx$

16. $\displaystyle\int_0^2 \int_y^{y+2} y \, dx \, dy$

ANSWERS TO ODD-NUMBERED PROBLEMS

1. 5

3. $\frac{1}{10}$

5. $\frac{11}{24}$

7. $\frac{1}{6}a^2 b^3 (a^3 - b^3)$

9. $\frac{11}{60}$

11. $\frac{14}{15}$

13. $\frac{91}{12}$

15. -4

5

DIFFERENTIAL EQUATIONS

■ 5.1 **INTRODUCTION**

In many problems the relationships between or among variables are most appropriately stated as rates of change of one or more variables as functions of the rates of change or the values of other variables. For example, in physics, equations involving rates of change in energy are used in the derivation of the laws of conservation of energy; in economics it is assumed that the rate at which price approaches its equilibrium value depends on the magnitude of the discrepancy between the quantities supplied and demanded.

Rates of change can be stated in either of two mathematical forms, depending on whether time (or, more generally, any variable with respect to which changes are considered) is viewed as continuous or discrete. When changes are considered to occur continuously or instantaneously, rates of change are stated as derivatives and equations involving them are differential equations. When changes are considered as occurring discretely or discontinuously at certain points in time or as average changes over a period of time, rates of change are stated as differences in the values of variables at different points in time and equations involving them are difference equations. Differential equations are the limiting case of difference equations as the time period between changes or over which an average change is computed approaches zero.

This chapter discusses differential equations, that is, equations involving derivatives. Chapter 6 discusses difference equations, that is, equations involving differences between values of variables at different points in time or with respect to different values of another variable.

473

■ 5.2 DEFINITION AND CLASSIFICATION OF DIFFERENTIAL EQUATIONS

A *differential equation* is an equation that involves derivatives of one or more unknown functions. Differential equations are classified according to type, order, and degree.

If a differential equation involves derivatives of an unknown function with respect to one independent variable, it is an *ordinary differential equation*; if it involves partial derivatives of an unknown function of two or more independent variables, it is a *partial differential equation*.

The *order* of a differential equation is the order of the highest derivative occurring in the equation.

When a differential equation is rational and integrable with respect to all the derivatives which occur in it, its degree with respect to the derivative of highest order is the *degree* of the differential equation.

Example

(a) $\dfrac{dy}{dx} = 2x$ is an ordinary differential equation of first order and first degree

(b) $x\,dy - y\,dx = 0$ is an ordinary differential equation of first order and first degree

(c) $\dfrac{d^2y}{dx^2} + y = 0$ is an ordinary differential equation of second order and first degree

(d) $\left(\dfrac{dy}{dx}\right)^2 = 4 - y^2$ is an ordinary differential equation of first order and second degree

(e) $\dfrac{\partial z}{\partial x} + \dfrac{\partial z}{\partial y} = z$ is a partial differential equation of first order and first degree

(f) $\dfrac{\partial^2 u}{\partial x^2} + \dfrac{\partial^2 u}{\partial y^2} = 0$ is a partial differential equation of second order and first degree

Note that many of the equations in Chapter 4 are differential equations, since any equation involving at least one derivative is a differential equation. If a differential equation can be written in the form

$$\frac{d^n y}{dx^n} = f(x)$$

its solution is obtained in a straightforward manner by (successive) integration, as in Chapter 4.

Examples

Find the general solution of the differential equation $\dfrac{dy}{dx} = \cos x + 2x$.

If $\dfrac{dy}{dx} = \cos x + 2x$,

$$y = \sin x + x^2 + C$$

Show that $4y = \dfrac{1}{3x} + c_1 x^5 + c_2 x$ is a solution of $x^2 \dfrac{d^2 y}{dx^2} - 5x \dfrac{dy}{dx} + 5y = \dfrac{1}{x}$.

$$4 \frac{dy}{dx} = -\frac{1}{3x^2} + 5c_1 x^4 + c_2$$

$$4 \frac{d^2 y}{dx^2} = \frac{2}{3x^3} + 20c_1 x^3$$

and thus

$$\tfrac{1}{4}\left(\frac{2}{3x} + 20c_1 x^5\right) - \tfrac{5}{4}\left(-\frac{1}{3x} + 5c_1 x^5 + c_2 x\right) + \tfrac{5}{4}\left(\frac{1}{3x} + c_1 x^5 + c_2 x\right) = \frac{1}{x}$$

$$\underbrace{(\tfrac{2}{12} + \tfrac{5}{12} + \tfrac{5}{12})\frac{1}{x}}_{\dfrac{1}{x}} + \underbrace{(5 - \tfrac{25}{4} + \tfrac{5}{4})c_1 x^5}_{0} + \underbrace{(-\tfrac{5}{4} + \tfrac{5}{4})c_2 x}_{0} = \frac{1}{x}$$

The methods discussed in this chapter are appropriate for solving several types of differential equations whose solutions cannot be obtained by straight-forward integration.

Five types of differential equations of first order and first degree are discussed in some detail; second-order differential equations and first-degree differential equations of higher order are discussed briefly.

□ SOLUTIONS OF ORDINARY DIFFERENTIAL EQUATIONS

A solution of an ordinary differential equation is a function not containing derivatives or differentials, which satisfies the differential equation. Such a solution may be expressed as an explicit or implicit function.

The *general solution* of an nth-order differential equation is a solution containing n independent arbitrary constants of integration.

A *particular solution* of a differential equation is a solution that can be obtained from the general solution by giving specific values to the arbitrary constants of the general solution.

Some differential equations also have *singular solutions* that cannot be obtained as particular solutions; such exceptional cases are not considered here.

As in simple integration, the constants of integration of a differential equation are specified by *boundary conditions* or *initial conditions*. A condition of the form $y = y_0$, when $x = x_0$ is a boundary condition; the special case $x = x_0$, when $x = 0$ is an initial condition.

Clearly, the problem of the solution or integration of a differential equation is an extension of the problem of simple integration. As for simple integration, most frequently a particular solution of a differential equation is needed for practical applications. To obtain such a particular solution it is usually necessary first to find the general solution of the differential equation and then to obtain the arbitrary constants from the given data—that is, from the initial conditions of the problem. A constant of integration may be written in various forms, such as C, $2C$, C^2, $\sqrt{C}$, e^C, $\ln C$; frequently solutions of differential equations may be expressed in simpler form by proper choice of the form of the constant or constants of integration. When the form of a constant of integration is changed, the constant is frequently still written using the same notation with the understanding that it is a "generic constant." Until the numerical value of a constant is determined, its form has no real meaning and thus the constant is written in the simplest way possible.

In each of the following examples a differential equation and its solution are given and the solution is shown to satisfy the differential equation. Methods for obtaining solutions of differential equations are then discussed.

Examples

Show that $y = \dfrac{x^2}{3} + \dfrac{C}{x}$ is a solution of $x\dfrac{dy}{dx} + y = x^2$.

$$\frac{dy}{dx} = \frac{2x}{3} - \frac{C}{x^2}$$

and thus

$$\underbrace{x\left(\frac{2x}{3} - \frac{C}{x^2}\right) + \frac{x^2}{3} + \frac{C}{x}}_{x\frac{dy}{dx} + y} = x^2$$

Show that $y = c_1 e^{kx} + c_2 e^{-kx}$ is a solution of $\dfrac{d^2y}{dx^2} - k^2 y = 0$.

$$\frac{dy}{dx} = c_1 k e^{kx} - c_2 k e^{-kx}$$

$$\frac{d^2y}{dx^2} = c_1 k^2 e^{kx} + c_2 k^2 e^{-kx}$$

and thus

$$\underbrace{c_1 k^2 e^{kx} + c_2 k^2 e^{-kx} - k^2(c_1 e^{kx} + c_2 e^{-kx})}_{\dfrac{d^2y}{dx^2} - k^2 y} = 0$$

Show that $y = c_1 e^x + c_2 e^{-2x}$ is a solution of $\dfrac{d^2 y}{dx^2} + \dfrac{dy}{dx} - 2y = 0$ and find a particular solution that satisfies the condition $y = \dfrac{dy}{dx} = 1$ when $x = 0$.

$$\frac{dy}{dx} = c_1 e^x - 2c_2 e^{-2x}$$

$$\frac{d^2 y}{dx^2} = c_1 e^x + 4c_2 e^{-2x}$$

and thus

$$\underbrace{c_1 e^x + 4c_2 e^{-2x} + c_1 e^x - 2c_2 e^{-2x}}_{\dfrac{d^2 y}{dx^2} + \dfrac{dy}{dx}} \underbrace{- 2c_1 e^x - 2c_2 e^{-2x}}_{-2y} = 0$$

If $y = y' = 1$ when $x = 0$,

$$c_1 + c_2 = c_1 - 2c_2 = 1$$

$$c_1 + c_2 = c_1 - 2c_2 \Rightarrow c_2 = 0$$

and thus $c_1 = 1$, so the particular solution is $y = e^x$.

Show that $y = 2Cx^2 + C^2$ is a solution of $\left(\dfrac{dy}{dx}\right)^2 + 8x^3\left(\dfrac{dy}{dx}\right) = 16x^2 y$ and find a particular solution that satisfies the condition $y = -1$ when $x = 1$.

$$\frac{dy}{dx} = 4Cx$$

and thus

$$\underbrace{16C^2 x^2 + 8x^3(4Cx)}_{\left(\dfrac{dy}{dx}\right)^2 + 8x^3\left(\dfrac{dy}{dx}\right)} = \underbrace{16x^2(2Cx^2 + C^2)}_{16x^2 y}$$

If $y = -1$ when $x = 1$,

$$-1 = 2C + C^2$$

$$C^2 + 2C + 1 = 0$$

$$(C + 1)^2 = 0$$

$$C = -1,$$

so the particular solution is $y = 1 - 2x^2$.

Show that $y^2 = c_1 x^2 + c_2 x$ is a solution of

$$x^2 y \frac{d^2 y}{dx^2} + \left(x \frac{dy}{dx} - y \right)^2 = 0$$

and find a particular solution that satisfies the condition $y = 2$ and $\frac{dy}{dx} = 1$ when $x = 1$.

$$2y \frac{dy}{dx} = 2c_1 x + c_2$$

$$\frac{dy}{dx} = \frac{2c_1 x + c_2}{2\sqrt{c_1 x^2 + c_2 x}}$$

$$\frac{d^2 y}{dx^2} = \frac{4c_1 \sqrt{c_1 x^2 + c_2 x} - (2c_1 x + c_2)^2 (c_1 x^2 + c_2 x)^{-1/2}}{4(c_1 x^2 + c_2 x)}$$

$$= \frac{c_1}{(c_1 x^2 + c_2 x)^{1/2}} - \frac{(2c_1 x + c_2)^2}{4(c_1 x^2 + c_2 x)^{3/2}}$$

and thus

$$\underbrace{c_1 x^2 - \frac{x^2(2c_1 x + c_2)}{4(c_1 x^2 + c_2 x)}}_{\textstyle x^2 y \frac{d^2 y}{dx^2}} + \underbrace{\left(\frac{x(2c_1 x + c_2)}{2\sqrt{c_1 x^2 + c_2 x}} - \sqrt{c_1 x^2 + c_2 x} \right)^2}_{\textstyle \left(x \frac{dy}{dx} - y \right)^2} = 0$$

$$c_1 x^2 - \frac{x^2(2c_1 x + c_2)^2}{4(c_1 x^2 + c_2 x)} + \frac{x^2(2c_1 x + c_2)^2}{4(c_1 x^2 + c_2 x)} - x(2c_1 x + c_2) + (c_1 x^2 + c_2 x) = 0$$

If $y = 2$ and $\frac{dy}{dx} = 1$ when $x = 1$,

$$2 = \sqrt{c_1 + c_2}$$

$$1 = \frac{2c_1 + c_2}{2\sqrt{c_1 + c_2}}$$

$$4 = c_1 + c_2$$

$$4 = 2c_1 + c_2$$

$$c_1 = 0$$

$$c_2 = 4,$$

so the particular solution is $y^2 = 4x$.

Show that $(x - c_1)^2 + y^2 = c_2$ is a solution of

$$y \frac{d^2 y}{dx^2} + \left(\frac{dy}{dx} \right)^2 + 1 = 0$$

and find a particular solution that satisfies the condition $y = 3$, and $\dfrac{dy}{dx} = -\frac{4}{3}$ when $x = 5$.

$$2y \frac{dy}{dx} = -2(x - c_1)$$

$$\frac{dy}{dx} = -\frac{x - c_1}{\sqrt{c_2 - (x - c_1)^2}}$$

$$\frac{d^2 y}{dx^2} = \frac{-\sqrt{c_2 - (x - c_1)^2} + (x - c_1)(\frac{1}{2})[c_2 - (x - c_1)^2]^{-1/2}(-2)(x - c_1)}{c_2 - (x - c_1)^2}$$

$$= \frac{-1}{\sqrt{c_2 - (x - c_1)^2}} - \frac{(x - c_1)^2}{[c_2 - (x - c_1)^2]^{3/2}}$$

and thus

$$\underbrace{-1 - \frac{(x - c_1)^2}{c_2 - (x - c_1)^2}}_{y\frac{d^2 y}{dx^2}} + \underbrace{\left[-\frac{x - c_1}{\sqrt{c_2 - (x - c_1)^2}}\right]^2}_{\left(\frac{dy}{dx}\right)^2} + 1 = 0$$

If $y = 3$ and $\dfrac{dy}{dx} = -\frac{4}{3}$ when $x = 5$,

$$3 = \sqrt{c_2 - (5 - c_1)^2}$$

$$= \frac{5 - c_1}{\sqrt{c_2 - (5 - c_1)^2}}$$

$$5 - c_1 = 4$$

$$c_1 = 1$$

$$c_2 = 25,$$

so the particular solution is $y^2 = 25 - (x - 1)^2$.

☐ DIFFERENTIAL EQUATIONS OF THE FIRST ORDER AND FIRST DEGREE

A differential equation of the first order and first degree can be written in the form

$$\frac{dy}{dx} = F(x, y)$$

Note that if $F(x, y)$ is a constant or a function only of x, then the differential equation is solved by the usual methods of integration; it is for the cases in which $F(x, y)$ is in fact a function of both x and y that the following methods are appropriate.

An alternative form, frequently more useful for classifying differential equations of the first order and first degree, is

$$M(x, y)\, dx + N(x, y)\, dy = 0$$

There is one difference between these equations which should be noted. In the first equation y is the dependent variable and x is the independent variable; thus the solution should express y as a function of x and an arbitrary constant. In the second equation the relationship is expressed implicitly and the choice of the dependent and independent variables is a matter of convenience; the solution is frequently also expressed as an implicit function.

Methods for the solution of the following types of differential equations of the first order and first degree are discussed in considerable detail; note that facility in solving a differential equation of any order and degree depends to a very considerable extent on classifying it correctly.

1. *Separable differential equations*: M is a function only of x and N is a function only of y, so the equation is of the form $M(x)\, dx + N(y)\, dy = 0$.

2. *Homogeneous differential equations*: M and N are homogeneous functions of the same degree of homogeneity

3. *Exact differential equations*: $\dfrac{\partial}{\partial y}(M(x, y)) = \dfrac{\partial}{\partial x}(N(x, y))$ so the equation is of the form $\dfrac{\partial F}{\partial x}\, dx + \dfrac{\partial F}{\partial y}\, dy = 0$, where $F(x, y)$ is the solution of the differential equation.

4. *Linear differential equations*: The equation is of the first degree in y and $\dfrac{dy}{dx}$ or in x and $\dfrac{dx}{dy}$ and thus is of the form $\dfrac{dy}{dx} + yP(x) = Q(x)$ or $\dfrac{dx}{dy} + xP(y) = Q(y)$.

5. *Differential equations linear in a function of y or in a function of x*: The equation is of the first degree in $f(y)$ and $\dfrac{d}{dy}f(y)$ or in x and $\dfrac{d}{dx}f(x)$ and thus is of the form $\dfrac{d}{dy}f(y) + f(y)P(x) = Q(x)$ or $\dfrac{d}{dx}f(x) + f(x)P(y) = Q(y)$.

■ 5.3 SEPARABLE DIFFERENTIAL EQUATIONS

If a differential equation can be written in the form

$$M(x)\, dx + N(y)\, dy = 0$$

where, as indicated, M is a function only of x and N is a function only of y, then the variables are said to be *separated* and the general solution of the differential equation is obtained by the usual methods of integration:

$$\int M(x)\,dx + \int N(y)\,dy = C$$

Examples

Solve the equation $(1 + x^2)\dfrac{dy}{dx} + xy = 0$.

$$(1 + x^2)\,dy + xy\,dx = 0$$

$$\frac{x}{1 + x^2}\,dx + \frac{1}{y}\,dy = 0$$

The variables are separated and, integrating,

$$\tfrac{1}{2}\ln(1 + x^2) + \ln y = C$$

$$\ln(y\sqrt{1 + x^2}) = C$$

$$y\sqrt{1 + x^2} = C$$

Note that the constant in the last equation is actually e^C in terms of the preceding equations. As mentioned in the discussion of constants of integration above, until a constant is evaluated to obtain a particular solution, its form is arbitrary and the constant is thus written in the most convenient way.

Solve the equation $y^2\,dx - (1 - x)\,dy = 0$.

$$\frac{1}{x - 1}\,dx + \frac{1}{y^2}\,dy = 0$$

The variables are separated and, integrating,

$$\ln(x - 1) - \frac{1}{y} = C$$

$$y\ln(x - 1) - 1 = Cy$$

$$y\ln[C(x - 1)] = 1$$

or

$$C(x - 1) = e^{1/y}$$

The relationship between net profit P and advertising expenditure x is such that the rate of increase of net profit as advertising expenditure increases is proportional to a constant minus net profit. Find the relationship between net profit and advertising expenditure if $P = P_0$ when $x = 0$ (see Fig. 5.1).

$$\frac{dP}{dx} = k(a - P)$$

$$\frac{dP}{a - P} = k\,dx$$

$$-\ln(a - P) = kx + C$$

$$\ln(a - P) = -kx + C$$

$$a - P = Ce^{-kx}$$

$$P = a - Ce^{-kx}$$

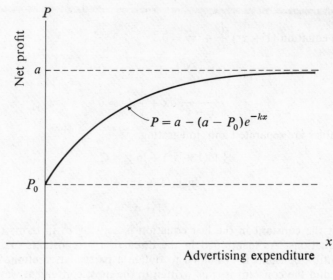

FIGURE 5.1

so

$$P_0 = a - c$$

$$C = a - P_0$$

$$P = a - (a - P_0)e^{-kx}$$

Thus net profit is P_0 with no advertising expenditure and increases with advertising expenditure toward an (asymptotic) maximum of a.

The rate of increase of sales volume s as price p decreases is proportional to sales volume and inversely proportional to price minus a constant. Find the relationship between sales volume and price if $s = s_0$ when $p = p_0$ (see Fig. 5.2).

$$\frac{ds}{dp} = -\frac{as}{p - b}$$

$$\frac{ds}{s} = -\frac{a}{p - b}\,dp$$

$$\ln s = -a\ln(p - b) + C$$

$$\ln s + a \ln(p - b) = C$$

$$s(p - b)^a = C$$

$$s = \frac{C}{(p - b)^a}$$

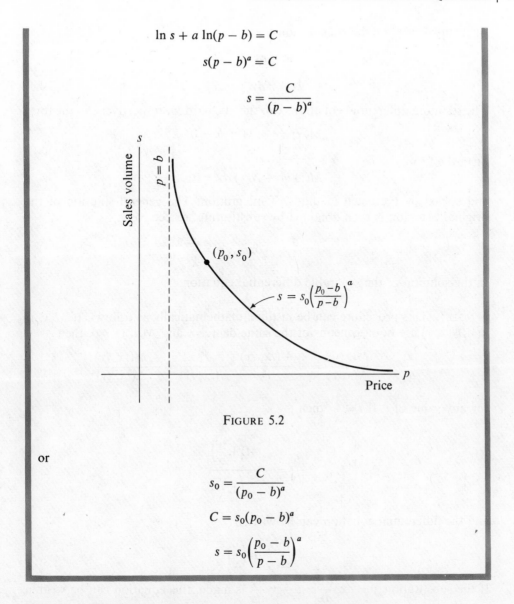

FIGURE 5.2

or

$$s_0 = \frac{C}{(p_0 - b)^a}$$

$$C = s_0(p_0 - b)^a$$

$$s = s_0\left(\frac{p_0 - b}{p - b}\right)^a$$

■ 5.4 HOMOGENEOUS DIFFERENTIAL EQUATIONS

A differential equation of the form

$$M(x, y) \, dx + N(x, y) \, dy = 0$$

is said to be homogeneous if $M(x, y)$ and $N(x, y)$ are homogeneous functions of the same degree in x and y. Recall that $F(x, y)$ is a homogeneous function of degree n in x and y if and only if $F(kx, ky) = k^n F(x, y)$, where k is any constant. When a differential equation is homogeneous, its variables can be separated by the substitution

$$y = vx$$

$$dy = v \, dx + x \, dv$$

or, equivalently, by the substitution

$$x = vy$$

$$dx = v\,dy + y\,dv$$

The resulting differential equations can then be written, respectively, in the form

$$M(x)\,dx + N(v)\,dv = 0$$

or in the form

$$M(v)\,dv + N(y)\,dy = 0$$

and solved by the usual methods of integration. The general solution of the original equation is then obtained by substituting, respectively,

$$v = \frac{y}{x} \quad \text{or} \quad v = \frac{x}{y}$$

in the solution of the separable differential equation.

NOTE: This procedure can be justified mathematically as follows. If $M(x, y)$ and $N(x, y)$ are homogeneous of the same degree n and $N(x, y) \neq 0$, then

$$\frac{dy}{dx} = -\frac{M(x, y)}{N(x, y)} = -\frac{M(tx, ty)}{t^n} \cdot \frac{t^n}{N(tx, ty)} = -\frac{M(tx, ty)}{N(tx, ty)}$$

for any value of t. If $t = \frac{1}{x}$, then

$$\frac{dy}{dx} = -\frac{M\left(1, \frac{y}{x}\right)}{N\left(1, \frac{y}{x}\right)}$$

and the differential equation can be written

$$\frac{dy}{dx} = F\left(\frac{y}{x}\right)$$

If the substitution $y = vx, \frac{dy}{dx} = v + x\frac{dv}{dx}$ is made, this equation can be written

$$v + x\frac{dv}{dx} = F(v)$$

$$(v - F(v))\,dx + x\,dv = 0$$

$$\frac{dx}{x} + \frac{dv}{v - F(v)} = 0$$

and the variables x and v are separated. If $v - F(v) = 0$, then $\frac{y}{x} = \frac{dy}{dx}$ and $M(x, y)\,dx + N(x, y)\,dy = 0$ has the simple form $y\,dx - x\,dy = 0$.

A similar argument shows that the substitution $x = vy$ also results in a new equation in which the variables are separable.

Examples

Solve the equation $(y^2 - xy) \, dx + x^2 \, dy = 0$.

Substituting $y = vx$, $dy = v \, dx + y \, dv$, since the equation is homogeneous (degree 2),

$$(v^2 x^2 - vx^2) \, dx + x^2(v \, dx + y \, dv) = 0$$

$$v^2 x^2 dx + x^3 dv = 0$$

$$\frac{1}{x} dx + \frac{1}{v^2} dv = 0$$

The variables are separated and, integrating,

$$\ln x - \frac{1}{v} = C$$

Substituting $v = \dfrac{y}{x}$,

$$\ln x - \frac{x}{y} = C$$

$$y = \frac{x}{\ln x - C}$$

Solve the equation $(x + y) \, dx + (x - y) \, dy = 0$.

Substituting $x = vy$, $dx = v \, dy + y \, dv$, since the equation is homogeneous (degree 1),

$$(vy + y)(v \, dy + y \, dv) + (vy - y) \, dy = 0$$

$$(vy^2 + y^2) \, dv + (v^2 y + 2vy - y) \, dy = 0$$

$$\frac{v + 1}{v^2 + 2v - 1} \, dv + \frac{1}{y} \, dy = 0$$

The variables are separated and, integrating,

$$\tfrac{1}{2} \ln(v^2 + 2v - 1) + \ln y = C$$

$$y(v^2 + 2v - 1)^{1/2} = C$$

$$y^2(v^2 + 2v - 1) = C$$

Substituting $v = \dfrac{x}{y}$,

$$x^2 + 2xy - y^2 = C$$

The relationship between the manufacturing cost per item M and the number of types of items manufactured N is such that the rate of increase of manufacturing cost as number of types of items increases is equal to the ratio of the cost per item plus the number of types of items divided by the number of types of items. Find the relationship between manufacturing cost per item and number of types of items manufactured if $M = M_0$ when $N = 1$ (see Fig. 5.3).

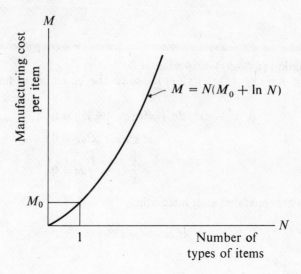

FIGURE 5.3

$$\frac{dM}{dN} = \frac{M + N}{N}$$

$$N\, dM = (M + N)\, dN$$

$$M = vN$$

$$dM = v\, dN + N\, dv$$

$$vN\, dN + N^2 dv - vN\, dN - N\, dN = 0$$

$$dv - \frac{dN}{N} = 0$$

$$v - \ln N = C$$

$$\frac{M}{N} = \ln N + C$$

$$M = N \ln N + NC$$

so

$$M_0 = 0 + C$$

$$C = M_0$$

$$M = N \ln N + NM_0$$

$$M = N(M_0 + \ln N)$$

Suppose that the rate of increase in the cost of ordering and holding y as the size of the order s increases is equal to the ratio of the sum of the squares of the cost and the size divided by twice the product of the cost and the size. Find the relationship between the cost of ordering and holding and the size of the order if $y = 3$ when $s = 1$ (see Fig. 5.4).

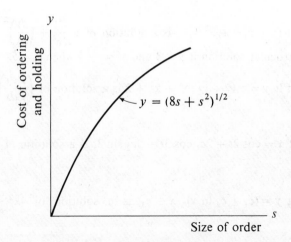

FIGURE 5.4

$$\frac{dy}{ds} = \frac{y^2 + s^2}{2sy}$$

$$2sy\,dy - (y^2 + s^2)\,ds = 0$$

$$y = vs$$

$$dy = v\,ds + s\,dv$$

$$2vs^2(v\,ds + s\,dv) - (v^2s^2 + s^2)\,ds = 0$$

$$(v^2s^2 - s^2)\,ds + 2vs^3dv = 0$$

$$\frac{ds}{s} + \frac{2v}{v^2 - 1}\,dv = 0$$

$$\ln s + \ln(v^2 - 1) = C$$

$$s(v^2 - 1) = C$$

$$s\left(\frac{y^2}{s^2} - 1\right) = C$$

$$y^2 - s^2 = Cs$$

$$y = (Cs + s^2)^{1/2}$$

so

$$3 = (C + 1)^{1/2}$$

$$C = 8$$

$$y = (8s + s^2)^{1/2}$$

PROBLEMS

1. Verify that $y^2 = Cx + \frac{1}{8}C^3$ is a solution of $y = 2x\dfrac{dy}{dx} + y^2\left(\dfrac{dy}{dx}\right)^3$ and find the particular solution if $y' = 1$ when $x = 0$.

2. Verify that $(x - c_1)^2 + y^2 = c_2$ is a solution of $y\dfrac{d^2y}{dx^2} + \left(\dfrac{dy}{dx}\right)^2 + 1 = 0$ and find the particular solution if $y = 3$ and $y' = -\frac{4}{3}$ when $x = 5$.

3. Verify that $\ln y = c_1 e^x + c_2 e^{-x} + x^2 + 2$ is a solution of $\left(\dfrac{1}{y}\dfrac{dy}{dx}\right)^2 - \dfrac{1}{y}\dfrac{dy^2}{dx^2} = x^2 - \ln y$.

4. Verify that $x = \cos 2t + 2c_1 \cos 3t + 3c_2 \sin 3t$ is a solution of $\dfrac{d^2x}{dt^2} + 9x = 5\cos 2t$.

5. Verify that $y = (c_1 + c_2 \ln x)\sqrt{x} + c_3$ is a solution of $4x^2\dfrac{d^3y}{dx^3} + 8x\dfrac{d^2y}{dx^2} + \dfrac{dy}{dx} = 0$.

6. Verify that $y = x^3 + c_1 x^2 + c_2$ is a solution of $\dfrac{d^2y}{dx^2} - \dfrac{1}{x}\dfrac{dy}{dx} - 3x = 0$ and find the particular solution if $y = 1$ when $x = 1$ and $y = 5$ when $x = 2$.

7. Verify that $y = c_1 \cos x + c_2 \sin x - \frac{1}{3}\cos 2x$ is a solution of $\dfrac{d^2y}{dx^2} + y = \cos 2x$.

8. Verify that $y = e^{-x}(x + C)$ is a solution of $\dfrac{dy}{dx} + y = e^{-x}$.

9. Verify that $y = c_1 x + \dfrac{c_2}{x} + c_3$ is a solution of $\dfrac{d^3y}{dx^3} + \dfrac{3}{x}\dfrac{d^2y}{dx^2} = 0$.

Find the general solution for each of the following differential equations.

10. $(y + 2)\,dx + (x - 2)\,dy = 0$

11. $(x^2 + y^2)\,dx - 2xy\,dy = 0$

12. $(xy - x^2)\dfrac{dy}{dx} = y^2$

13. $y^3\,dx - x^3\,dy = 0$

14. $(y + 3)\,dx + \cot x\,dy = 0$

15. $\dfrac{dx}{dt} = 1 - \sin 2t$

16. $\dfrac{d^3y}{dx^3} = e^{-x}$

17. $\dfrac{d^2y}{dx^2} = \dfrac{1}{x^2}$

18. $\sec x \cos^2 y\,dx = \cos x \sin y\,dy$

19. $\sin x \cos^2 y\,dx + \cos^2 x\,dy = 0$

20. $dr + r\cos\theta\,d\theta = 0$

21. $\dfrac{dy}{dx} = \dfrac{x - y}{x + y}$

22. $(xy^2 - x)\,dx + (x^2y + y)\,dy = 0$

23. $\dfrac{dy}{dx} = \dfrac{xy + y}{x + xy}$

24. $\dfrac{dy}{dx} = \dfrac{2x - y}{x + 4y}$

25. $dy = 2xy\,dx$

26. $\dfrac{1}{\rho}\dfrac{d\rho}{d\theta} = \dfrac{\rho^2 - 1}{\rho^2 + 1}\tan\theta$

27. $r\,d\theta + \theta\,dr = 2\,dr$

28. $d\rho + \rho\tan\theta\,d\theta = 0$

29. $(r^2 + 1)\,d\theta + \dfrac{dr}{\sec^2\theta} = 0$

30. $(xy - y^2)\,dx + \left(y^2 - \dfrac{x^2}{2}\right)dy = 0$

31. $\dfrac{y^2}{x} dx + (x - y) dy = 0$

38. $\dfrac{dy}{dx} = \dfrac{x^2}{y^3}$

32. $(xy^3 - x) dx + xy^2 dy = 0$

39. $x\, dy - y\, dx = 0$

33. $\tan x \sin^2 y\, dx + \cos^2 x \cot y\, dy = 0$

40. $(x^2 + 2y^2)\, dx = xy\, dy$

41. $(x^3 - y^3)\, dx + xy^2 dy = 0$

34. $x \dfrac{dy}{dx} - y - x \sin \dfrac{y}{x} = 0$

42. $(x + y)\, dx + x\, dy = 0$

35. $\sin x \cos y\, dx + \cos x \sin y\, dy = 0$

43. $\dfrac{dy}{dx} = e^{x-y}$

36. $\dfrac{dy}{dx} = -\dfrac{y}{x}$

44. $x(2y - 3)\, dx + (x^2 + 1)\, dy = 0$

45. $(x + y)\, dx = x\, dy$

37. $x^3 - 2y^3 + 3xy^2 \dfrac{dy}{dx} = 0$

46. $x\, dy - y\, dx = \sqrt{xy}\, dx$

Find the particular solution for each of the following differential equations under the given conditions.

47. $\dfrac{dy}{dx} = \dfrac{y}{x}$, $y = 3$ when $x = 1$

48. $xy\, dx + \sqrt{1 + x^2}\, dy = 0$, $y = 1$ when $x = 0$

49. $(x^2 + y^2)\, dx = 2xy\, dy$, $y = 0$ when $x = 1$

50. $x\, dy + 2y\, dx = 0$, $y = 1$ when $x = 2$

51. $(xe^{y/x} + y)\, dx = x\, dy$, $y = 0$ when $x = 1$

52. $y^2(y\, dx - x\, dy) + x^3 dx = 0$, $y = 3$ when $x = 1$

53. $x\, dx - 4y\, dy = 0$, $y = 2$ when $x = 5$

54. $x(y + 1)\, dx + y(x + 1)\, dy = 0$, $y = 1$ when $x = 0$

55. $(x - \sqrt{xy})\, dy = y\, dx$, $y = 1$ when $x = 4$

56. $(x + 4)(2y + 6)\, dy + xy^2 dx = 0$, $y = 16$ when $x = 0$

57. $(xy^2 + x^2 y)\, dy - xy^2 dx = 0$, $y = 1$ when $x = 6$

58. $y(x^2 + 6)\, dy + x(y^2 + 1)\, dx$, $y = 3$ when $x = 0$

59. $\dfrac{1}{xy} dx + \dfrac{e^{y^2}}{x^3 - 1} dy = 0$, $y = 0$ when $x = 1$

60. $\dfrac{dy}{dx} = \dfrac{y}{x} + \tan \dfrac{y}{x}$, $y = \pi$ when $x = 6$

61. $\cot y\, dx + \cot x\, dy = 0$, $y = 0$ when $x = 0$

62. The relationship between price p and quantity demanded x is such that the rate of decrease in demand as price increases is proportional to the quantity demanded and inversely proportional to the price plus a constant. Find the demand function if $p = p_0$ when $x = 1$. Sketch the relationship obtained.

63. The rate of increase of total cost y as number of units manufactured x increases is proportional to the number of units manufactured plus a constant

and inversely proportional to the total cost. Find the cost function if $y = y_0$ when $x = 0$. Sketch the relationship obtained.

64. The rate of increase in sales s as advertising effort x increases is equal to a constant minus sales divided by a constant plus advertising effort. Find the relationship between sales and advertising effort if $s = s_0$ when $x = 0$. Sketch the relationship obtained.

65. The relationship between revenue R and quantity demanded x is such that the rate of increase in revenue as quantity demanded increases is equal to twice the cube of the revenue minus the cube of the quantity demanded, all divided by three times the product of the quantity demanded and the square of the revenue. Find the relationship between revenue and quantity demanded if $R = 0$ when $x = 10$. Sketch the relationship obtained.

66. The relationship between average cost $\bar{y}$ and number of units produced x is such that the change in average cost as the number of units increases is equal to the ratio of the number of units minus average cost divided by number of units. Find the relationship between average cost and the number of units produced if $\bar{y} = \frac{9}{2}$ when $x = 1$. Sketch the relationship obtained.

67. The rate of increase in cost y as the number of units manufactured x increases is equal to the ratio of twice the square of the cost minus the square of the number of units divided by the product of the cost and the number of units. Find the relationship between cost and the number of units manufactured if $y = 3$ when $x = 1$. Sketch the relationship obtained.

68. A manufacturer has found the change in the cost of distribution D as sales S increases is equal to a constant times sales plus another constant. If $D = 0$ when $S = 0$, find D as a function of S and sketch the relationship obtained.

69. The rent for an apartment (two-bedroom, standard furnishings) in a college town varies with the distance of the apartment from campus. Suppose this relationship is given by

$$\frac{dy}{dx} = -\left(\frac{k}{x} + a\right) \qquad 1 \le x \le 10$$

where y is monthly rent (in dollars) and x is distance (in miles) and k and a are constants. If $y = 225$ when $x = 1$, find y as a function of x and sketch the relationship obtained.

70. The relationship between the cost of operating a warehouse and the number of gallons of oil stored in the warehouse is given by

$$\frac{dy}{dx} = kx + a$$

where y is the monthly cost of operating the warehouse (in dollars) and x is the number of gallons of oil in storage. If $y = y_0$ (fixed cost) when $x = 0$, find y as a function of x and sketch the relationship obtained.

ANSWERS TO ODD-NUMBERED PROBLEMS

1. $y^2 = 2x + 1$

11. $x^2 - y^2 = Cx$

13. $x^2 - y^2 = Cx^2y^2$

15. $x = t + \frac{1}{2}\cos 2t + C$

17. $y = -\ln x + c_1 x + c_2$

19. $\sec x + \tan y = C$

21. $y^2 + 2xy - x^2 = C$

23. $y - x + \ln \dfrac{y}{x} = C$

25. $y = Ce^{x^2}$

27. $r(\theta - 2) = C$

29. $\tan \theta + \ln \sqrt{r^2 + 1} = C$

31. $y = Ce^{y/x}$

33. $\tan^2 x - \cot^2 y = C$

35. $\cos y = C \sec x$

37. $x^3 + y^3 = Cx^2$

39. $y = Cx$

41. $x^3 e^{y^3/x^3} = C$

43. $e^y - e^x = C$

45. $x = Ce^{y/x}$

47. $y = 3x$

49. $y^2 = x^2 - x$

51. $\ln x + e^{-y/x} = 1$

53. $x^2 - 4y^2 = 9$

55. $2\sqrt{\dfrac{x}{y}} - \ln y = 4$

57. $\ln y - \dfrac{x}{y} + 6 = 0$

59. $2x^3 - 6 \ln x + 3e^{y^2} - 5 = 0$

61. $\cos y = \sec x$

63. $y = (ax^2 + 2abx + y_0^2)^{1/2}$

65. $R = (10x^2 - x^3)^{1/3}$

67. $y = \sqrt{8x^4 + x^2}$

69. $y = 225 + a - ax - k \ln x$

■ 5.5 **EXACT DIFFERENTIAL EQUATIONS**

Recall that the total derivative of a function of x and y, say $F(x, y)$, is given by

$$df(x, y) = \frac{\partial F}{\partial x} dx + \frac{\partial F}{\partial y} dy$$

Thus the differential equation

$$\frac{\partial F}{\partial x} dx + \frac{\partial F}{\partial y} dy = 0$$

has the general solution $F(x, y) = C$ and is said to be an *exact differential equation*.

A differential equation of the general form

$$M(x, y)\, dx + N(x, y)\, dy = 0$$

is said to be an exact differential equation if $M(x, y)\, dx + N(x, y)\, dy$ is the total derivative of some function $F(x, y)$; $M(x, y)$ and $N(x, y)$ are then the partial derivatives of $F(x, y)$ with respect to x and y, respectively.

If the second-order mixed partial derivatives of $F(x, y)$ exist and are continuous, then

$$\frac{\partial}{\partial y} \left(\frac{\partial F}{\partial x} \right) = \frac{\partial}{\partial x} \left(\frac{\partial F}{\partial y} \right)$$

Thus if a differential equation of the form $M(x, y) \, dx + N(x, y) \, dy = 0$ is exact,

$$\frac{\partial}{\partial y} M(x, y) = \frac{\partial}{\partial x} N(x, y)$$

It can be shown that this is also a sufficient condition for exactness; that is,

$$\frac{\partial}{\partial y} M(x, y) = \frac{\partial}{\partial x} N(x, y) \Leftrightarrow M(x, y) \, dx + N(x, y) \, dy = 0 \text{ is exact}$$

If a differential equation is exact, its solution can be found by the following method.

1. Integrate $M(x, y)$ with respect to x replacing the usual constant of integration with a function $f(y)$ of y.

$$F(x, y) = \int M(x, y) \, dx = G(x, y) + f(y)$$

2. Differentiate $F(x, y) = G(x, y) + f(y)$ obtained from step 1 with respect to y and compare this with $N(x, y)$ from the differential equation to be solved to obtain the value of $\frac{\partial}{\partial y} f(y)$.

$$\frac{\partial G}{\partial y} + \frac{\partial}{\partial y} f(y) = \frac{\partial N}{\partial y}$$

$$\frac{\partial}{\partial y} f(y) = \frac{\partial N}{\partial y} - \frac{\partial G}{\partial y}$$

3. Integrate $\frac{\partial}{\partial y} f(y)$ with respect to y to obtain $f(y)$.

$$\int \frac{\partial}{\partial y} f(y) \, dy = f(y)$$

It is not necessary to include the usual constant of integration, since it is introduced in the final step of the solution.

4. The solution, from steps 1 and 3, is

$$F(x, y) = G(x, y) + f(y) + C$$

clearly the solution may also be obtained by integrating first with respect to y.

Examples

Solve the equation $\dfrac{y(2 + x^3 y)}{x^3} \, dx = \dfrac{1 - 2x^3 y}{x^2} \, dy$.

$\dfrac{\partial}{\partial y} \left(\dfrac{y(2 + x^3 y)}{x^3} \right) = \dfrac{2 + 2x^3 y}{x^3} = \dfrac{\partial}{\partial x} \left(-\dfrac{1 - 2x^3 y}{x^2} \right)$, so the equation is exact

$$\frac{\partial F}{\partial x} = \frac{y(2 + x^3 y)}{x^3}$$

$$F(x, y) = -\frac{y}{x^2} + y^2 x + f(y)$$

$$\frac{\partial F}{\partial y} = -\frac{1}{x^2} + 2xy + \frac{\partial}{\partial y} f(y) = -\frac{1}{x^2} + 2xy$$

$$\text{so } \frac{\partial}{\partial y} f(y) = 0 \text{ and } f(y) = C$$

$$F(x, y) = -\frac{y}{x^2} + y^2 x + C$$

and

$$x^3 y^2 - y = Cx^2 \qquad \text{is the solution}$$

Solve the equation $(x^2 - x + y^2) \, dx - (ye^y - 2xy) \, dy = 0$.

$$\frac{\partial}{\partial y}(x^2 - x + y^2) = 2y = \frac{\partial}{\partial x}(-ye^y + 2xy), \text{ so the equation is exact}$$

$$\frac{\partial F}{\partial x} = x^2 - x + y^2$$

$$F(x, y) = \frac{x^3}{3} - \frac{x^2}{2} + xy^2 + f(y)$$

$$\frac{\partial F}{\partial y} = 2xy + \frac{\partial}{\partial y} f(y) = -ye^y + 2xy$$

$$\text{so } \frac{\partial}{\partial y} f(y) = -ye^y$$

$$f(y) = -(y - 1)e^y$$

$$F(x, y) = \frac{x^3}{3} - \frac{x^2}{2} + xy^2 - (y - 1)e^y$$

and

$$2x^3 - 3x^2 + 6xy^2 - 6(y - 1)e^y = C \qquad \text{is the solution}$$

NOTE: Alternatively, the terms of the original equation can be considered in two sets: $x^2 \, dx - x \, dx - ye^y \, dy$ is exact by inspection and can be integrated by the usual methods; $y^2 dx + 2xy \, dy$ can be shown to be exact and integrated by the method above. When this method is used, $f(y)$ is a constant, as illustrated in the following example.

Solve the equation $\dfrac{2xy - 1}{y} \, dx + \dfrac{x + 3y}{y^2} \, dy = 0$ and find the particular solution if $y = 1$ when $x = 2$.

$$2x \, dx + \underbrace{\frac{3}{y} \, dy} - \underbrace{\frac{1}{y} \, dx + \frac{x}{y^2} \, dy} = 0$$

Exact, integrable
by usual methods
to obtain $x^2 + 3 \ln y$

$\frac{\partial}{\partial y}\left(-\frac{1}{y}\right) = \frac{1}{y^2} = \frac{\partial}{\partial x}\left(\frac{x}{y^2}\right)$, so the equation is exact

$$\frac{\partial F}{\partial x} = -\frac{1}{y}$$

$$F(x, y) = -\frac{x}{y} + f(y)$$

$$\frac{\partial F}{\partial y} = \frac{x}{y^2} + \frac{\partial}{\partial y} f(y) = \frac{x}{y^2}$$

$$\frac{\partial}{\partial y} f(y) = 0, \text{ so } f(y) = C$$

$$F(x, y) = -\frac{x}{y} + C$$

$$x^2 + 3 \ln y - \frac{x}{y} = C$$

$$x^2 y - x + 3y \ln y = Cy \qquad \text{is the solution}$$

$$4 - 2 = C, \text{ so } C = 2$$

and

$$x^2 y - x - 2y + 3y \ln y = 0 \qquad \text{is the particular solution for } y = 1, \, x = 2$$

The change in price y with change in quantity demanded x of a particular commodity is given by

$$\frac{dy}{dx} = -\frac{2xy + 24x}{x^2 + 16}$$

Find the relationship between price and quantity demanded if the price is 7.5 when the quantity demanded is 4 (see Fig. 5.5).

$$(2xy + 24x) \, dx + (x^2 + 16) \, dy = 0$$

$$\frac{\partial}{\partial y}(2xy + 24x) = 2x = \frac{\partial}{\partial x}(x^2 + 16), \text{ so the equation is exact}$$

$$\frac{\partial F}{\partial x} = 2xy + 24x$$

$$F(x, y) = x^2 y + 12x^2 + f(y)$$

$$\frac{\partial F}{\partial y} = x^2 + \frac{\partial}{\partial y} f(y) = x^2 + 16$$

$$\text{so } \frac{\partial}{\partial y} f(y) = 16$$

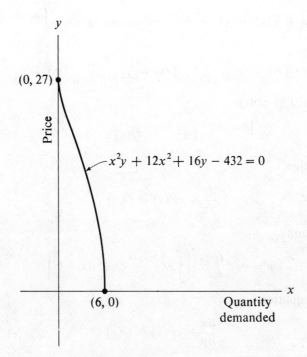

FIGURE 5.5

$$f(y) = 16y$$

$$F(x, y) = x^2y + 12x^2 + 16y$$

$$x^2y + 12x^2 + 16y = C \quad \text{is the solution}$$

$$120 + 192 + 120 = C, \text{ so } C = 432$$

and

$$x^2y + 12x^2 + 16y - 432 = 0 \quad \text{is the particular solution for } x = 4, y = 7.5$$

■ 5.6 LINEAR DIFFERENTIAL EQUATIONS

In some cases a nonexact differential equation can be made exact by multiplying it by a factor; such a factor is called an *integrating factor*, since it permits the equation to be integrated. In general, determination of the appropriate integrating factor for a given differential equation may not be an easy matter; however, for any linear differential equation the appropriate integrating factor can be obtained by the following method.

An equation which is linear in y and $\dfrac{dy}{dx}$ can be written in the form

$$\frac{dy}{dx} + yP(x) = Q(x)$$

If the equation is multiplied by the integrating factor $e^{\int P(x)\,dx}$, the resulting equation

$$e^{\int P(x)\,dx}\,dy + yP(x)e^{\int P(x)\,dx}\,dx = Q(x)e^{\int P(x)\,dx}\,dx$$

can be integrated to obtain

$$ye^{\int P(x)\,dx} = \int e^{\int P(x)\,dx}Q(x)\,dx + C$$

Thus the equation

$$\frac{dy}{dx} + yP(x) = Q(x)$$

has as its solution

$$y = e^{-\int P(x)\,dx}\left[\int e^{\int P(x)\,dx}Q(x)\,dx + C\right]$$

Similarly, the equation

$$\frac{dx}{dy} + xP(y) = Q(y)$$

has $e^{\int P(y)\,dy}$ as an integrating factor and its solution is

$$x = e^{-\int P(y)\,dy}\left[\int e^{\int P(y)\,dy}Q(y)\,dy + C\right]$$

NOTE: Every differential equation of the form $M(x, y)\,dx + N(x, y)\,dy = 0$ which has a solution can be shown to have an infinite number of integrating factors, although their determination may not be easy. An equation of the form

$$\frac{dy}{dx} + yP(x) = Q(x)$$

can be shown to have

$$e^{\int P(x)\,dx}$$

as an integrating factor by the following argument.

Consider first the special case $Q(x) = 0$,

$$\frac{dy}{dx} + yP(x) = 0$$

and multiply by $\dfrac{dx}{dy}$ to obtain

$$\frac{dy}{y} + P(x)\,dx = 0$$

The variables are separated and, integrating,

$$\ln y + P(x)\, dx = \ln C$$

$$ye^{\int P(x)\, dx} = C$$

If this equation is differentiated, the equation $\dfrac{dy}{dx} + yP(x) = 0$ should be obtained.

Differentiating,

$$d\!\left(ye^{\int P(x)\, dx}\right) = e^{\int P(x)\, dx}\, dy + P(x)\, ye^{\int P(x)\, dx}\, dx = 0$$

which is equal to the equation $\dfrac{dy}{dx} + yP(x) = 0$ multiplied by $e^{\int P(x)\, dx}$. Thus

$e^{\int P(x)\, dx}$ is an integrating factor of $\dfrac{dy}{dx} + yP(x) = 0$. Since $e^{\int P(x)\, dx}$ does not

involve y, multiplying the equation $\dfrac{dy}{dx} + yP(x) = Q(x)$ by this factor results in

the right-hand term $Q(x)e^{\int P(x)\, dx}$, which is a function only of x. Thus $e^{\int P(x)\, dx}$ is

an integrating factor of the linear differential equation $\dfrac{dy}{dx} + yP(x) = Q(x)$.

Similarly, $e^{\int P(y)\, dy}$ is an integrating factor for the linear differential equation

$$\dfrac{dx}{dy} + xP(y) = Q(y).$$

Examples

Solve the equation $x^2 dy + (y - 2xy - 2x^2)\, dx = 0$.

$$dy + \frac{1 - 2x}{x^2}\, y\, dx = 2\, dx$$

Integrating factor: $e^{\int [(1 - 2x)/x^2]\, dx} = e^{-(1/x) - \ln x^2} = \dfrac{e^{-1/x}}{x^2}$ and

$$\frac{ye^{-1/x}}{x^2} = \int \frac{2e^{-1/x}}{x^2}\, dx$$

$$= 2e^{-1/x} + C$$

$$y = 2x^2 + Cx^2 e^{1/x}$$

$$= x^2(2 + Ce^{1/x})$$

Solve the equation $y \dfrac{dx}{dy} = 2ye^{3y} + x(3y + 2)$.

$$dx - \frac{3y + 2}{y} x \, dy = 2e^{3y} \, dy$$

Integrating factor: $e^{\int -[(3y+2)/y] \, dy} = e^{-3y - 2 \ln y} = \dfrac{e^{-3y}}{y^2}$ and

$$\frac{xe^{-3y}}{y^2} = \int \frac{2}{y^2} \, dy$$

$$= -\frac{2}{y} + C$$

$$x = -2ye^{3y} + Cy^2 e^{3y}$$

$$= ye^{3y}(Cy - 2)$$

Solve the equation $2y \, dx = (y^4 + x) \, dy$ and find the particular solution if $y = 1$ when $x = 0$.

$$dx - \frac{x}{2y} \, dy = \frac{y^3}{2} \, dy$$

Integrating factor: $e^{\int -dy/2y} = e^{-1/2 \ln y} = y^{-1/2}$ and

$$xy^{-1/2} = \frac{1}{2} \int y^{5/2} \, dy$$

$$= \frac{1}{7} y^{7/2} + C$$

$$x = \frac{1}{7} y^4 + Cy^{1/2}$$

$$7x = y^4 + Cy^{1/2}$$

$$0 = 1 + C \quad \text{so} \quad C = -1$$

and

$$7x = y^4 - y^{1/2} \quad \text{is the particular solution for } x = 0, \, y = 1$$

A manufacturing company has found that the cost c of operating and maintaining its equipment is related to the length x of the interval between overhauls by the equation

$$\frac{dc}{dx} - \frac{b - 1}{x} c = -\frac{ba}{x^2}$$

where a and b are constants. Find c as a function of x if $c = c_0$ when $x = x_0$ (see Fig. 5.6).

$$dc - \frac{(b - 1)}{x} c \, dx = -\frac{ba}{x^2} \, dx$$

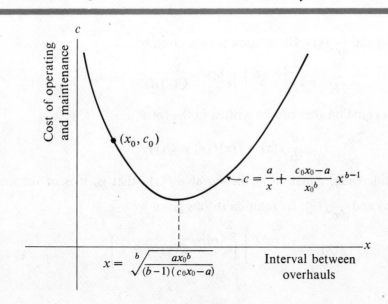

FIGURE 5.6

Integrating factor: $e^{\int -[(b-1)/x]\,dx} = e^{-(b-1)\ln x} = x^{-(b-1)}$ and

$$cx^{-(b-1)} = -ba\int x^{-b-1}$$

$$= ax^{-b} + C$$

$$c = \frac{a}{x} + Cx^{b-1}$$

$$c_0 = \frac{a}{x_0} + Cx_0^{b-1}$$

$$C = \frac{c_0x_0 - a}{x_0^b}$$

$$c = \frac{a}{x} + \frac{C_0x_0 - a}{x_0^b} x^{b-1}$$

■ **5.7 DIFFERENTIAL EQUATIONS LINEAR IN A
FUNCTION OF y OR IN A FUNCTION OF x**

An equation that can be written in the form

$$\frac{d}{dy} f(y) + f(y)P(x) = Q(x)$$

is a linear differential equation in the variable $f(y)$—that is, it is of the first degree in $f(y)$ and $\frac{d}{dy} f(y)$. Its solution is thus given by

$$f(y) = e^{-\int P(x)\,dx} \left[\int e^{\int P(x)\,dx} Q(x)\,dx + C \right]$$

Similarly, an equation that can be written in the form

$$\frac{d}{dx} f(x) + f(x)P(y) = Q(y)$$

is a linear differential equation in the variable $f(x)$—that is, it is of the first degree in $f(x)$ and $\frac{d}{dx} f(x)$. Its solution is thus given by

$$f(x) = e^{-\int P(y)\,dy} \left[\int e^{\int P(y)\,dy} Q(y)\,dy + C \right]$$

Examples

Solve the equation $y\,dx + x(1 - x^2 y^4)\,dy = 0$.

$$dx + \frac{x}{y}\,dy = x^3 y^3\,dy$$

$$x^{-3}\,dx + \frac{x^{-2}}{y}\,dy = y^3\,dy$$

$$-2x^{-3}\,dx - \frac{2x^{-2}}{y}\,dy = -2y^3\,dy$$

Integrating factor: $e^{\int -(2/y)\,dy} = e^{-2\ln y} = y^{-2}$ and

$$x^{-2}y^{-2} = -2\int y\,dy$$

$$x^{-2}y^{-2} = -y^2 + C$$

$$1 + x^2 y^4 = Cx^2 y^2$$

Solve the equation $\frac{dy}{dx} + xy \ln y = xye^{-x^2}$ and find the particular solution if $y = 1$ when $x = 0$.

$$\frac{dy}{y} + x \ln y\,dx = xe^{-x^2}\,dx$$

Integrating factor: $e^{\int x\,dx} = e^{x^2/2}$ and

$$e^{x^2/2} \ln y = \int xe^{-x^2/2}\,dx$$

$$= -e^{-x^2/2} + C$$

$$0 = -1 + C, \quad \text{so} \quad C = 1$$

and

$$\ln y = -e^{-x^2} + e^{-x^2/2}$$

$$= e^{-x^2/2} - e^{-x^2}$$

The cost control unit of a large public accounting firm has found, as it has increased in size, that the average monthly cost y of office supplies is related to the number x of employees (in addition to the unit director) by the equation

$$\frac{dy}{dx} + 2y = y^2 e^{-x}$$

(see Fig. 5.7). Find y as a function of x if $y = 3$ when $x = 0$.

$$y^{-2} \, dy + 2y^{-1} \, dx = e^{-x} \, dx$$

$$-y^{-2} \, dy - 2y^{-1} \, dx = -e^{-x} \, dx$$

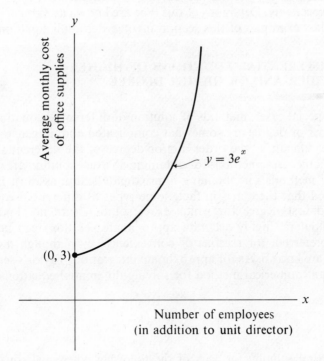

FIGURE 5.7

Integrating factor: $e^{\int -2 \, dx} = e^{-2x}$ and

$$y^{-1} e^{-2x} = -\int e^{-3x} \, dx$$

$$= \tfrac{1}{3}e^{-3x} + C$$

$$3e^x = y + Cye^{3x}$$

$$y = 3e^x + Cye^{3x}$$

$$3 = 3 + 3C, \quad \text{so} \quad C = 0$$

and

$$y = 3e^x$$

NOTE: In general, there is no rule for determining the function $f(y)$ or $f(x)$ in terms of which a differential equation is, or can be made, linear. However, note that equations of the form

$$\frac{dy}{dx} + P(x)y = Q(x)y^n$$

or

$$\frac{dx}{dy} + P(y)x = Q(y)x^n$$

can be made linear in y^{n-1} or x^{n-1} as a result of multiplication by $(1-n)y^{-n}$ or $(1-n)x^{-1}$, respectively. Equations of this type are known as *Bernoulli equations*. The first and last examples of this section involve Bernoulli equations.

■ 5.8 DIFFERENTIAL EQUATIONS OF HIGHER ORDER AND/OR HIGHER DEGREE

Except for special cases, methods of solution of differential equations of even the second order or degree are somewhat complicated and, in general, solution becomes more difficult as the order and/or degree of the differential equation increases. In many cases, methods for obtaining an exact solution are not known and numerical methods for obtaining approximate solutions must be used. It should be noted that there are, in fact, some types of differential equations of first order and first degree for which exact solutions are not known. With electronic computers, highly accurate approximate solutions can be obtained and may be preferred, for reasons of convenience, even though methods for exact solution are known. As for approximate integration, Taylor's series is used in one important numerical method for solving differential equations.

PROBLEMS

Find the general solution for each of the following differential equations.

1. $x\,dy - 3y\,dx = x^2\,dx$

2. $\dfrac{dy}{dx} + 2xy - 2xe^{-x^2} = 0$

3. $y\dfrac{dx}{dy} + (1+y)x - e^y = 0$

4. $y\dfrac{dx}{dy} + 2x - 3y = 0$

5. $x(6xy + 5)\,dx + (2x^3 + 3y)\,dy = 0$

6. $(a_1x + b_1y + c_1)\, dx + (b_1x + b_2y + c_2)\, dy = 0$

7. $y\, dx + 3x^2e^x dx = dy$

8. $(ye^{xy} + 2xy)\, dx + (xe^{xy} + x^2)\, dy = 0$

9. $(x + 1)\dfrac{dy}{dx} + 2y = e^x(x + 1)^{-1}$

10. $(y \cos x - 2 \sin y)\, dx = (2x \cos y - \sin x)\, dy$

11. $(3x^2y + xy^2 + e^x)\, dx + (x^3 + x^2y + \sin y)\, dy = 0$

12. $2y \sin xy\, dx + (2x \sin xy + y^3)\, dy = 0$

13. $(3y \sin x - \cos y)\, dx + (x \sin y - 3 \cos x)\, dy = 0$

14. $(y^2 \csc^2 x + 6xy - 2)\, dx = (2y \cot x - 3x^2)\, dy$

15. $\cos y\, dx - (x \sin y - y^2)\, dy = 0$

16. $2\left(\dfrac{y}{x^3} + \dfrac{x}{y^2}\right)dx = \left(\dfrac{1}{x^2} + \dfrac{2x^2}{y^3}\right)dy$

17. $\dfrac{dy}{dx} + 2y - x = 0$

18. $x\dfrac{dy}{dx} = x^3 + y$

19. $3\dfrac{dy}{dx} + \dfrac{2y}{x + 1} = \dfrac{x}{y^2}$

20. $\dfrac{dx}{dy} + x = e^{-y}$

21. $\dfrac{dy}{dx} - xy = y^{1/2}xe^{x^2}$

22. $\dfrac{dy}{dx} - xy = \dfrac{x}{y}$

23. $y^3\dfrac{dy}{dx} + xy^4 = xe^{-x^2}$

24. $xy\, dy = (x^2 - y^2)\, dx$

25. $(x + y)\, dx + (x - 2y)\, dy = 0$

26. $\dfrac{dy}{dx} + \left(y - \dfrac{1}{y}\right)x = 0$

27. $\dfrac{ds}{dt} - s \cot t = 1 - (t + 2) \cot t$

28. $\dfrac{ds}{dt} + \dfrac{s}{t} = \cos t + \dfrac{\sin t}{t}$

29. $\dfrac{dy}{dx} + y = \cos x - \sin x$

30. $(2x \cos y - e^x)\, dx - x^2 \sin y\, dy = 0$

31. $(y \sin x + xy \cos x)\, dx + (\sin y + e^y)\, dy = 0$

32. $\dfrac{dy}{dx} - xy = e^{\frac{1}{2}x^2} \cos x$

33. $\cos \theta\, \dfrac{dr}{d\theta} = 2 + 2r \sin \theta$

34. $\cos x \sec y\, dx + \sin x \sin y \sec^2 y\, dy = 0$

35. $\dfrac{ds}{dt} + s \tan t = 2t + t^2 \tan t$

36. $\cos y\, dy + (\sin y - 1) \cos x\, dx = 0$

37. $x \tan^2 y\, dy + x\, dy = (2x^2 + \tan y)\, dx$

38. $3y^2\dfrac{dy}{dx} - xy^3 = e^{\frac{1}{2}x^2} \cos x$

39. $(\ln y + y^3 + ye^{xy})\, dx + \left(\dfrac{x}{y} + 3xy^2 + xe^{xy}\right)dy = 0$

40. $dx + (2xy - 4xy^3 - 2y^3 e^{y^4}) \, dy = 0$

41. $\left(y^2 + \dfrac{1}{y} + ye^y \right) dx + \left(2xy - \dfrac{x}{y^2} + xe^y + xye^y \right) dy = 0$

42. $y^2 \dfrac{dx}{dy} + (y^2 + 2y)x - 1 = 0$

43. $x \, dy = (5y + x + 1) \, dx$

44. $\dfrac{xy + 1}{y} \, dx + \dfrac{2y - x}{y^2} \, dy = 0$

45. $\dfrac{dx}{dy} = x + e^y$

46. $x \dfrac{dy}{dx} + 2y = 3x^3 y^{4/3}$

47. $x^2 \dfrac{dy}{dx} + y^2 = xy$

48. $\sin \theta \, d\theta + \cos \theta \, dt = te^t \, dt$

49. $\csc y \cot y \, dy = (\csc y + e^x) \, dx$

50. $x \dfrac{dy}{dx} + y = y^2 x^2 \cos x$

51. $\dfrac{dx}{dy} - x \cot y = e^y (1 - \cot y)$

52. $\dfrac{dy}{dx} + y \tan x = \sec x, \ y = -1$ when $x = 0$

53. $dy + (y \cot x - \sec x) \, dx = 0, \ y = 1$ when $x = 0$

Find the particular solution for each of the following differential equations under the given conditions.

54. $(y^2 + 1) \dfrac{dx}{dy} + 2xy = y^2, \ y = -1$ when $x = 0$

55. $dy = x(1 - e^{2y - x^2}) \, dx, \ y = 0$ when $x = 0$

56. $\left(x^2 + \dfrac{1}{x} + ye^{xy} \right) dx + (e^y + 3y^2 + xe^{xy}) \, dy = 0, \ y = 0$ when $x = 1$

57. $(1 - x^2) \dfrac{dy}{dx} + xy = x(1 - x^2)y^{1/2}, \ y = 1$ when $x = 0$

58. $\dfrac{dy}{dx} + y = y^2 e^{-x}, \ y = 2$ when $x = 0$

59. $y \, dx + 2(x - 2y^2) \, dy = 0, \ y = -1$ when $x = 2$

60. $(y + y^3) \, dx + 4(xy^2 - 1) \, dy = 0, \ y = 1$ when $x = 0$

61. $2y \, dx = (x^2 y^4 + x) \, dy, \ y = 1$ when $x = 1$

62. $(x^2 - 1) \dfrac{dy}{dx} + (x^2 - 1)^2 + 4y = 0, \ y = -6$ when $x = 0$

63. $(ye^x - 2x) \, dx + e^x dy = 0, \ y = 6$ when $x = 0$

64. $\left(\dfrac{2}{y} - \dfrac{y}{x^2} \right) dx + \left(\dfrac{1}{x} - \dfrac{2x}{y^2} \right) dy = 0, \ y = 2$ when $x = 1$

65. $(2y - xy - 3) \, dx + x \, dy = 0, \ y = 1$ when $x = 1$

66. $(ye^y + 2x + y) \, dx + (xe^y + xye^y + 3y^2 + x) \, dy = 0, \ y = 0$ when $x = 2$

67. $\left(3x^2y - \dfrac{2y}{x} - 6x^4\right)dx + dy = 0$, $y = 0$ when $x = -1$

68. $dr = (1 + 2r \cot \theta)\, d\theta$, $r = 3$ when $\theta = \pi/2$

69. The change in net profits P as advertising expenditure x changes is given by

$$\frac{dP}{dx} = k - a(P + x)$$

where a and k are constants. Find P as a function of x if $P = P_0$ when $x = 0$.

70. The change in the cost of ordering and holding C as quantity x changes is given by

$$\frac{dC}{dx} = a - \frac{C}{x}$$

where a is a constant. Find C as a function of x if $C = C_0$ when $x = x_0$.

71. Manufacturing and marketing costs C are related to the number of items x by

$$\frac{dC}{dx} + aC = b + kx$$

where a, b, and k are constants. Find C as a function of x if $C = 0$ when $x = 0$.

72. The change in consumption C of a particular commodity as income I changes is given by

$$\frac{dC}{dI} = C + ke^I$$

where k is a constant. Find C as a function of I if $C = C_0$ when $I = 0$.

ANSWERS TO ODD-NUMBERED PROBLEMS

1. $y = -x^2 + Cx^3$

3. $2xye^y - e^{2y} = C$

5. $4x^3y + 5x^2 + 3y^2 = C$

7. $y = x^3e^x + Ce^x$

9. $y(x + 1)^2 = e^x + C$

11. $2x^3y + x^2y^2 + 2e^x - 2 \cos y = C$

13. $3y \cos x + x \cos y = C$

15. $3x \cos y + y^3 = C$

17. $y = \frac{1}{2}x - \frac{1}{4} + Ce^{-2x}$

19. $12(x + 1)^2y^3 = 3x^4 + 8x^3 + 6x^2 + C$

21. $3y^{1/2} = e^{x^2} + Ce^{x^2/4}$

23. $e^{2x^2}y^4 = 2e^{x^2} + C$

25. $x^2 + 2xy - 2y^2 = C$

27. $s = t + 2 + C \sin t$

29. $y = \cos x + Ce^{-x}$

31. $xy \sin x - \cos y + e^y = C$

33. $r \cos^2\theta = 2 \sin \theta + C$

35. $s = t^2 + C \cos t$

37. $\tan y = 2x^2 + Cx$

39. $x \ln y + xy^3 + e^{xy} = C$

41. $x\left(y^2 + \dfrac{1}{y} + ye^y\right) = C$

43. $20y + 5x + 4 = Cx^5$

45. $x = ye^y + Ce^y$

47. $x = y \ln Cx$

49. $2e^x \csc y + e^{2x} = C$

51. $x = e^y + C \sin y$

53. $y \sin x + \ln \cos x = 0$

55. $x^2 + 1 = e^{x^2 - 2y}$

57. $3y^{1/2} + 1 - x^2 = 4(1 - x^2)^{1/4}$

59. $y^2(x - y^2) = 1$

61. $10x = (9 + xy^4)y^{1/2}$

63. $ye^x - x^2 = 6$

65. $x^2y + 3(x + 1) = 7e^{x-1}$

67. $y = 2x^2 - 2x^2e^{-x^3 - 1}$

69. $P = \dfrac{k+1}{a} - x + \left(P_0 - \dfrac{k+1}{a}\right)e^{-ax}$

71. $C = \dfrac{ab - k}{a^2}(1 - e^{-ax}) + \dfrac{k}{a}x$

■ 5.9 APPLICATIONS OF DIFFERENTIAL EQUATIONS IN ECONOMIC MODELS

There are two general types of economic models, *static* and *dynamic*. Static models concern equilibrium situations, that is, situations which if attained will be maintained. In dynamic models time enters either explicitly as a variable or implicitly in the form of lagged variables. The models discussed in this chapter are very simple dynamic economic models expressed in terms of differential equations.

There are two general classes of variables in economic models, referred to as *endogenous* and *exogenous* variables. Endogenous variables are those variables whose values or levels are to be predicted or explained; exogenous variables are assumed to be determined and known in advance and can be regarded as constant in the model. Endogenous and exogenous come from Greek words meaning "generated from inside" and "generated from outside," respectively. Endogenous variables are predicted from the model; exogenous variables are determined outside the model.

Usually a model is first written in terms of *structural equations* which express relationships among endogenous and exogenous variables. This set of structural equations is then solved (if possible) for what are called *reduced form* equations, each of which expresses an endogenous variable as a function of exogenous variables and parameters. A model is solved by obtaining a reduced form equation for each endogenous variable in the model.

□ DOMAR MACRO MODEL

Consider the model

$$S(t) = \alpha y(t)$$

$$I(t) = \beta \frac{dy}{dt}$$

$$S(t) = I(t)$$

$$\alpha > 0 \qquad \beta > 0$$

where S is saving, I is investment, y is income, and each of these endogenous variables is a function of time.

The first equation states that saving is a fixed proportion of income; the second equation states that investment is proportional to the rate of change of income over time; the third equation states that saving equals investment. Relationships among the variables are thus expressed in general terms in the model; from these relationships, specific functions expressing variations in the variables over time can be obtained.

Since $S(t) = I(t)$, the differential equation

$$\frac{dy}{dt} - \frac{\alpha}{\beta} y = 0$$

is obtained for solution.

$$\frac{1}{y} \frac{dy}{dt} = \frac{\alpha}{\beta}$$

$$\ln y = \frac{\alpha}{\beta} t + C$$

$$y = Ce^{(\alpha/\beta)t}$$

If $y = y_0$ at $t = 0$, then

$$y_0 = C$$

and the particular solution is

$$y = y_0 e^{(\alpha/\beta)t}$$

Note that this solution gives income y as a function of time t. Since $\alpha > 0$, $\beta > 0$, the function has an increasing positive slope, the rate of increase depending on $\frac{\alpha}{\beta}$. Solutions for the remaining variables of the model, I and S, are as follows:

$$I = S = \alpha y = \alpha y_0 e^{(\alpha/\beta)t}$$

☐ *DOMAR DEBT MODELS*

Domar uses a set of models similar to the macro model above to express relationships between national income and national debt. Consider the model

$$\frac{dD}{dt} = \alpha y(t)$$

$$\frac{dy}{dt} = \beta$$

$$y(0) = y_0$$

$$D(0) = D_0$$

$$\alpha > 0 \qquad \beta > 0$$

where D is national debt and y is national income (both endogenous). In this model national income increases at a constant rate β over time and the rate of increase of national debt is a fixed proportion of national income. The third and fourth equations state the initial conditions. Integrating the second equation,

$$y = \beta t + C$$

Since $y = y_0$ when $t = 0$, $C = y_0$ and

$$y = \beta t + y_0$$

Substituting in the first equation of the model,

$$\frac{dD}{dt} = \alpha \beta t + \alpha y_0$$

$$D = \tfrac{1}{2}\alpha \beta t^2 + \alpha y_0 t + C$$

Since $D = D_0$ when $t = 0$, $C = D_0$ and

$$D = \tfrac{1}{2}\alpha \beta t^2 + \alpha y_0 t + D_0$$

The solution of the model is thus

$$D(t) = \tfrac{1}{2}\alpha \beta t^2 + \alpha y_0 t + D_0$$

$$y(t) = \beta t + y_0$$

Domar was interested in the ratio of national debt to national income

$$\frac{D(t)}{y(t)} = \frac{\tfrac{1}{2}\alpha \beta t^2 + \alpha y_0 t + D_0}{\beta t + y_0}$$

or

$$\frac{D(t)}{y(t)} = \frac{D_0}{\beta t + y_0} + \frac{\alpha y_0 t}{\beta t + y_0} + \frac{\tfrac{1}{2}\alpha \beta t^2}{\beta t + y_0}$$

As $t \to \infty$,

$$\frac{D_0}{\beta t + y_0} \to 0$$

$$\frac{\alpha y_0 t}{\beta t + y_0} \to \frac{\alpha y_0}{\beta} \quad \text{(a constant)}$$

$$\frac{\tfrac{1}{2}\alpha \beta t^2}{\beta t + y_0} \to \infty$$

Thus, as $t \to \infty$, $\dfrac{D(t)}{y(t)} \to \infty$ and, for this model, the ratio of national debt to national income increases over time without limit.

☐ A SECOND DOMAR DEBT MODEL

Consider now a second version of the Domar debt model obtained by modifying the second equation in the above model so that income increases by a constant proportion:

$$\frac{dD}{dt} = \alpha y(t)$$

$$\frac{dy}{dt} = \beta y(t)$$

$$y(0) = y_0$$

$$D(0) = D_0$$

$$\alpha > 0 \qquad \beta > 0$$

Integrating the second equation,

$$\ln y = \beta t + C$$

$$y = Ce^{\beta t}$$

Since $y = y_0$ when $t = 0$, $C = y_0$ and

$$y = y_0 e^{\beta t}$$

Substituting in the first equation of the model,

$$\frac{dD}{dt} = \alpha y_0 e^{\beta t}$$

$$D = \frac{\alpha}{\beta} y_0 e^{\beta t} + C$$

Since $D = D_0$ when $t = 0$, $C = D_0 - \frac{\alpha}{\beta} y_0$ and

$$D = D_0 - \frac{\alpha}{\beta} y_0 + \frac{\alpha}{\beta} y_0 e^{\beta t}$$

or

$$D = D_0 + \frac{\alpha}{\beta} y_0 (e^{\beta t} - 1)$$

The solution of the model is thus

$$D(t) = D_0 + \frac{\alpha}{\beta} y_0 (e^{\beta t} - 1)$$

$$y(t) = y_0 e^{\beta t}$$

The ratio of national debt to national income is

$$\frac{D(t)}{y(t)} = \frac{D_0}{y_0 e^{\beta t}} + \frac{\alpha}{\beta} \left(1 - \frac{1}{e^{\beta t}} \right)$$

As $t \to \infty$,

$$\frac{D_0}{y_0 e^{\beta t}} \to 0$$

$$\frac{\alpha}{\beta} \left(1 - \frac{1}{e^{\beta t}} \right) \to \frac{\alpha}{\beta}$$

Thus, as $t \to \infty$, $\dfrac{D(t)}{y(t)} \to \dfrac{\alpha}{\beta}$, a (finite) constant.

□ *EVANS PRICE ADJUSTMENT MODEL*

This is a model of a particular market for some commodity. The demand and supply equations are the same as those for the usual simple linear model and can be solved for the equilibrium price in the usual way. In addition, there is an equation stating that the rate of change of price over time is proportional to the excess demand $(d - s)$. This factor of proportionality is positive, implying that a positive excess demand causes a rise in price and a negative excess demand causes a fall in price.

$$d(t) = \alpha_0 + \alpha_1 p(t)$$

$$s(t) = \beta_0 + \beta_1 p(t)$$

$$\frac{dp}{dt} = \gamma(d - s)$$

$$\alpha_1 > 0 \qquad \beta_1 > 0 \qquad \gamma > 0$$

where d is demand, s is supply, and p is price. Substituting the first two equations into the third equation,

$$\frac{dp}{dt} = \gamma[\alpha_0 - \beta_0 + (\alpha_1 - \beta_1)p]$$

$$= \gamma(\alpha_1 - \beta_1)(p - p_e)$$

where $p_e = \dfrac{\alpha_0 - \beta_0}{\beta_1 - \alpha_1}$ is the equilibrium price in the model obtained in the usual way by solving $d(t) = s(t)$ for $p(t)$, the equilibrium price. Letting $\lambda = \gamma(\alpha_1 - \beta_1)$,

$$\frac{dp}{dt} = \lambda(p - p_e)$$

$$\frac{1}{p - p_e} \frac{dp}{dt} = \lambda$$

$$\ln(p - p_e) = \lambda t + C$$

$$p - p_e = Ce^{\lambda t}$$

$$p = p_e + Ce^{\lambda t}$$

Since $p = p_0$ when $t = 0$, $C = p_0 - p_e$ and

$$p = p_e + (p_0 - p_e)e^{\lambda t}$$

where, as above, $p_e = \dfrac{\alpha_0 - \beta_0}{\beta_1 - \alpha_1}$ and $\lambda = \gamma(\alpha_1 - \beta_1)$. Since $\lambda < 0$, $p \to p_e$ as $t \to \infty$.

□ *INCOME-CONSUMPTION-INVESTMENT MODEL*

This is a differential-equation form of the income-consumption-investment model where current consumption and investment are linear functions of current income and income changes at a rate that is proportional to excess demand, that is, to consumption plus investment minus income.

$$C_\delta(t) = \alpha Y_\delta(t)$$

$$I_\delta(t) = \gamma Y_\delta(t)$$

$$\frac{dY_\delta}{dt} = \lambda(C_\delta + I_\delta - Y_\delta)$$

$$Y_\delta(0) = Y_0 - Y_e$$

$$\alpha > 0 \qquad \gamma > 0 \qquad \lambda > 0$$

where C_δ, I_δ, and Y_δ are deviations of consumption, investment, and income, respectively, from their equilibrium values C_e, I_e, and Y_e. Substituting the first two equations into the third equation,

$$\frac{dY_\delta}{dt} = \lambda(\alpha + \gamma - 1) Y_\delta$$

$$\frac{dY_\delta}{Y_\delta} = \lambda(\alpha + \gamma - 1)\, dt$$

$$\ln Y_\delta = \lambda(\alpha + \gamma - 1)t + C$$

$$Y_\delta = Ce^{\lambda(\alpha+\gamma-1)t}$$

Since $Y_\delta = Y_0 - Y_e$ when $t = 0$, $C = Y_0 - Y_e$ and

$$Y_\delta = (Y_0 - Y_e)e^{\lambda(\alpha+\gamma-1)t}$$

That is,

$$Y = Y_e + (Y_0 - Y_e)e^{\lambda(\alpha+\gamma-1)t}$$

And, if $\alpha + \lambda < 1$, $e^{\lambda(\alpha+\gamma-1)t} \to 0$ and $Y \to Y_e$ as $t \to \infty$.

PROBLEMS

1. Demand and supply (per unit time) of a product are given respectively by x and y, where p is unit price:

$$x = ap + b \qquad y = cp + d$$

Suppose that price changes in such a way that the excess of demand over supply is decreased at a rate proportional to the excess. Show that

(a) $\dfrac{d}{dt}(x - y) = -k(x - y)$

(b) $\dfrac{dp}{dt} + k(p - \bar{p}) = 0$, where $\bar{p} = \dfrac{b - d}{c - a}$

(c) The unit price tends to an equilibrium value $\bar{p}$ and

$$p = \bar{p} + (p_0 - \bar{p})e^{-kt}$$

where p_0 is the initial price at $t = 0$

2. Consider the model

$$\frac{dD}{dt} = \alpha y(t) + \beta$$

$$\frac{dy}{dt} = \gamma y(t)$$

$$y(0) = y_0$$

$$D(0) = D_0$$

$$\alpha > 0 \qquad \beta > 0 \qquad \gamma > 0$$

where D is national debt and y is national income.
(a) Solve the model
(b) Determine the limit as $t \to \infty$ of the ratio of national debt to national income

3. Consider the model

$$\frac{dR}{dt} = \frac{\alpha}{S(t)}$$

$$\frac{dS}{dt} = -\lambda S(t)$$

$$R(0) = 0$$

$$S(0) = S_0 \text{ (original cost)}$$

$$\alpha > 0 \qquad \lambda > 0$$

where R is running cost of a car and S is resale value. Solve the model.

4. The increase in the number of new products tested y as amount x allocated to research and development increases equals a constant times the product of the number of new products tested and the amount allocated to research and development plus another constant times the ratio of the amount allocated to research and development divided by the number of new products tested. Find the relationship between the number of new products tested and the amount allocated to research and development if $y = y_0$ when $x = 0$.

5. Consider the model

$$\frac{dR}{dt} = \frac{\alpha}{S(t)} + \beta$$

$$\frac{dS}{dt} = -\lambda S(t)$$

$$R(0) = R_0$$

$$S(0) = S_0$$

$$\alpha > 0 \qquad \beta \geq 0 \qquad \lambda > 0$$

where R is the cost of repairing and operating a machine and S is salvage value of the machine. Find R and S as functions of time t.

6. Consider the model

$$\frac{dw}{dt} = \frac{1}{\alpha y(t)} + k e^{\beta t}$$

$$\frac{dy}{dt} = \beta y(t)$$

$$w(0) = w_0$$

$$y(0) = y_0$$

$$\beta > 0 \qquad \alpha > \frac{k}{\beta y_0}$$

where w is per capita consumption of wheat products and y is per capita income. Find w and y as functions of time and determine the limit as $t \to \infty$ of the ratio of per capita consumption of wheat to per capita income.

ANSWERS TO ODD-NUMBERED PROBLEMS

3. $S(t) = S_0 e^{-\lambda t}$

$R(t) = \dfrac{\alpha}{\lambda S_0}(e^{\lambda t} - 1)$

5. $S = S_0 e^{-\lambda t}$

$R = R_0 + \beta t + \dfrac{\alpha}{\lambda S_0}(e^{\lambda t} - 1)$

6

DIFFERENCE EQUATIONS

■ 6.1 **INTRODUCTION**

When variables are thought of as changing discretely or discontinuously rather than continuously or instantaneously, difference equations rather than differential equations are appropriate for expressing relationships among the changes. Difference equations are frequently useful in business and economic analyses since many economic data are recorded for uniformly spaced periods of time—for example, gross national product may be given for a year; net profit for a quarter; quantities produced, bought, or sold for a month.

In many analyses, time is the independent variable and the study is focused on changes in other variables over time. Such studies of variables over discrete sets of time values are referred to as *period analyses*, and difference equations provide the basis for such analyses. Recall that when the time periods (or, more generally, the changes in the independent variable) are made smaller and smaller, difference equations approach differential equations as a limiting case.

For generality, the following discussion of the classification and solution of difference equations is in terms of an independent variable x. In many economic and business analyses, including the models discussed later, the independent variable time is denoted by t.

■ 6.2 DEFINITION AND CLASSIFICATION OF DIFFERENCE EQUATIONS

Suppose that y is a function of x, $y = f(x)$, where y is defined for integer values of x, $x = 0, 1, 2, 3, \ldots$. In the context of difference equations, the functional relationship $y = f(x)$ is frequently indicated by y_x. The change in y as x changes from x to $x + 1$ is the *first difference* of y_x and is written

$$\Delta y_x = y_{x+1} - y_x \quad \text{(read ``delta'' } y_x)$$

Note that Δy_x is also a function of x; Δ is an *operator* and provides the rule for computing Δy_x from the sequence $y_0, y_1, y_2, \ldots$. Similarly, higher-order differences are obtained as differences of differences by applying the operator Δ:

The second difference of y_x is $\Delta^2 y_x = \Delta(\Delta y_x) = \Delta y_{x+1} - \Delta y_x$

$$= (y_{x+2} - y_{x+1}) - (y_{x+1} - y_x)$$

$$= y_{x+2} - 2y_{x+1} + y_x$$

The third difference of y_x is $\Delta^3 y_x = \Delta(\Delta^2 y_x) = \Delta y_{x+2} - 2\Delta y_{x+1} + \Delta y_x$

$$= (y_{x+3} - y_{x+2}) - 2(y_{x+2} - y_{x+1}) + (y_{x+1} - y_x)$$

$$= y_{x+3} - 3y_{x+2} + 3y_{x+1} - y_x$$

$$\vdots$$

The kth difference of y_x is $\Delta^k y_x = \Delta(\Delta^{k-1} y_x) = \sum_{i=0}^{k} \frac{k!}{(k-i)! i!} (-1)^i y_{x+k-i}$

Example

If $y = 2x^2 - 3$,

$$\Delta^2 y_x = \Delta y_{x+1} - \Delta y_x$$
$$= [2(x+2)^2 - 3] - [2(x+1)^2 - 3] - \{[2(x+1)^2 - 3] - [2x^2 - 3]\}$$
$$= 4x + 6 - 4x + 2 = 4$$

Note that

$$y_{x+2} - 2y_{x+1} + y_x = [2(x+2)^2 - 3] - 2[2(x+1)^2 - 3] + [2x^2 - 3]$$
$$= 4 = \Delta^2 y_x$$

A difference equation states a relationship involving differences or, equivalently, a relationship involving the values of a dependent variable for a discrete set of (lagged) values of the independent variable. In the following discussion, the values of the independent variable are assumed to be equally spaced; for convenience, the independent variable is redefined if necessary so that its values are successive positive integers.

□ *LINEAR DIFFERENCE EQUATIONS*

A difference equation is said to be *linear* if it involves the dependent variable only in expressions of the first degree—that is, without higher powers or cross-products. Thus a difference equation is linear if it can be written in the form

$$a_0(x)y_{x+n} + a_1(x)y_{x+n-1} + \cdots + a_{n-1}(x)y_{x+1} + a_n(x)y_x = g(x)$$

where $a_0, a_1, \ldots, a_{n-1}, a_n$ and g are functions of x (but not of y_x) defined for $x = 0, 1, 2, \ldots$.

A linear difference equation is of *order n* if, when written in this form, both a_0 and a_n are unequal to zero for all values of x under consideration—that is, a linear difference equation is of order n if it involves values of y corresponding to values of x differing by n but by not more than n. Difference equations that are not linear are, in general, very difficult to solve and are seldom used. The following discussion is therefore confined to linear difference equations.

Example

Each of the following difference equations is linear and of the order indicated.

(a) $y_{x+2} - 7y_{x+1} + 5y_x = 3x$ order 2
(b) $3y_{x+2} + 4y_{x+1} = 2x$ order 1
(c) $18y_{x+2} - 6y_x = 5x$ order 2
(d) $8^x y_{x+3} - 3^x y_{x+2} + 9^x y_{x+1} + 2y_x = 3$ order 3

Note that an nth-order difference equation can be written either as an implicit function of the values of the variable y at n different values of x (that is, the *lagged* values of y),

$$f[y_{x+n}, y_{x+n-1}, \ldots, y_x] = 0$$

or, since knowledge of $n + 1$ adjacent values of y permits calculation of the value of y and its first n differences, an nth-order difference equation can also be written as a function of y and its first n differences,

$$F[\Delta^n y_x, \Delta^{n-1} y_x, \ldots, \Delta y_x, y_x] = 0$$

Example

(a) $\Delta y_x = 0$ can be written
$$y_{x+1} - y_x = 0 \qquad \text{(order 1)}$$

(b) $\Delta y_x - 2y_x = 5$ can be written
$$y_{x+1} - y_x - 2y_x = 5$$
$$y_{x+1} - 3y_x - 5 = 0 \qquad \text{(order 1)}$$

(c) $\Delta^2 y_x + 3\Delta y_x - 3y_x = x$ can be written

$$\Delta(y_{x+1} - y_x) - 3(y_{x+1} - y_x) - 3y_x = x$$

$$y_{x+2} - y_{x+1} - y_{x+1} + y_x - 3y_{x+1} + 3y_x - 3y_x = x$$

$$y_{x+2} - 5y_{x+1} + y_x - x = 0 \qquad \text{(order 2)}$$

(d) $\Delta^3 y_x + \Delta^2 y_x + \Delta y_x + y_x = 0$ can be written

$$\Delta^2(y_{x+1} - y_x) + \Delta(y_{x+1} - y) + y_{x+1} - y_x + y_x = 0$$

$$\Delta(y_{x+2} - y_{x+1} - y_{x+1} + y_x) + y_{x+2} - y_{x+1} - y_{x+1} + y_x + y_{x+1} = 0$$

$$y_{x+3} - y_{x+2} - 2y_{x+2} + 2y_{x+1} + y_{x+1} - y_x + y_{x+2} - y_{x+1} + y_x = 0$$

$$y_{x+3} - 2y_{x+2} + 2y_{x+1} = 0$$
$$\text{(order 2)}$$

☐ SOLUTIONS OF DIFFERENCE EQUATIONS

A *solution* of a difference equation is a functional relation not involving differences, which is defined for all nonnegative integers and which satisfies the difference equation.

The *general solution* of an nth-order difference equation is a solution containing n arbitrary constants. It can be shown that the general solution of a difference equation is unique.

A *particular solution* of a difference equation is a solution that can be obtained from the general solution by giving particular values to the arbitrary constants of the general solution. As in the case of differential equations, the arbitrary constants of a difference equation are specified by *boundary conditions* or *initial conditions*. The general solution of an nth-order difference equation includes n arbitrary constants, and a particular solution thus requires the specification of n boundary conditions.

In each of the following examples a proposed solution is shown to satisfy a given difference equation and a particular solution is determined for the specified boundary condition(s). Methods for obtaining solutions of linear first- and second-order difference equations with constant coefficients are then discussed. Similar methods of solution are appropriate for higher-order difference equations.

Examples

Show that $y_x = x + c$ is a solution of $y_{x+1} - y_x = 1$ and find a particular solution if $y_0 = 1$.

$$y_{x+1} - y_x = 1$$

$$(x + 1 + c) - (x + c) = 1,$$

$$\text{so } y_x = x + c \qquad \text{is a solution}$$

$$1 = 0 + c, \text{ so } c = 1$$

and

$$y_x = x + 1 \qquad \text{is the particular solution when } y_0 = 1$$

Show that $y_x = \dfrac{x(x-1)}{2} + c$ is a solution of $y_{x+1} - y_x = x$ and find a particular solution if $y_0 = 2$.

$$y_{x+1} - y_x = x$$

$$\frac{(x+1)x}{2} + c - \left(\frac{x(x-1)}{2} + c\right) = x$$

$$\frac{x(x+1-x+1)}{2} = x$$

$$\frac{2x}{2} = x,$$

$$\text{so } y_x = \frac{x(x-1)}{2} + c \qquad \text{is a solution}$$

$$2 = 0 + c, \text{ so } c = 2$$

and

$$y_x = \frac{x(x-1)}{2} + 2 \qquad \text{is the particular solution when } y_0 = 2$$

Show that $y_x = c_1 + c_2(-1)^x$ is a solution of $y_{x+2} - y_x = 0$ and find a particular solution if $y_0 = 2$, $y_1 = 5$.

$$y_{x+2} - y_x = 0$$

$$c_1 + c_2(-1)^{x+2} - [c_1 + c_2(-1)^x] = 0$$

$$c_2[(-1)^{x+2} - (-1)^x] = 0,$$

$$\text{so } y_x = c_1 + c_2(-1)^x \qquad \text{is a solution}$$

$$2 = c_1 + c_2$$

$$5 = c_1 - c_2$$

$$2c_1 = 7, \text{ so } c_1 = \tfrac{7}{2}, c_2 = -\tfrac{3}{2},$$

and

$$y_x = \tfrac{7}{2} - \tfrac{3}{2}(-1)^x \qquad \text{is the particular solution for } y_0 = 2, y_1 = 5$$

☐ *ANALOGIES BETWEEN DIFFERENCE EQUATIONS*
  AND DIFFERENTIAL EQUATIONS

Note the many analogies in the classification and solution of difference and differential equations; these arise because the derivative of a function is defined as a limit of a difference quotient

$$\frac{dy}{dx} = \lim_{\Delta x \to 0} \frac{\Delta y_x}{\Delta x} = \lim_{\Delta x \to 0} \frac{y_{x+\Delta x} - y_x}{\Delta x}$$

and, as $\Delta x \to 0$, the discrete case (difference equations) approaches as a limit the continuous case (differential equations).

■ 6.3 LINEAR FIRST-ORDER DIFFERENCE EQUATIONS WITH CONSTANT COEFFICIENTS

A linear first-order difference equation can be written in the form

$$a_0(x)y_{x+1} + a_1(x)y_x = g(x), \quad x = 0, 1, 2, \ldots$$

where $a_0(x) \neq 0$ and $a_1(x) \neq 0$. Thus, equivalently,

$$y_{x+1} = -\frac{a_1(x)}{a_0(x)} y_x + \frac{g(x)}{a_0(x)}$$

and, if $a_0(x)$, $a_1(x)$, and $g(x)$ are constants, that is, are not in fact functions of x, then

$$y_{x+1} = Ay_x + B$$

where A and B are constants and $A \neq 0$. ($B = 0$ if and only if $g = 0$ in the original equation.) Thus the difference equation $y_{x+1} = Ay_x + B$ is the general first-order difference equation with constant coefficients.

The solution of this equation can be obtained by induction as follows:

$$y_1 = Ay_0 + B$$

$$y_2 = A(Ay_0 + B) + B$$

$$= A^2y_0 + AB + B$$

$$y_3 = A(A^2y_0 + AB + B) + B$$

$$= A^3y_0 + A^2B + AB + B$$

$$y_4 = A(A^3y_0 + A^2B + AB + B) + B$$

$$= A^4y_0 + A^3B + A^2B + AB + B$$

$$\vdots$$

$$y_x = A^xy_0 + B(1 + A + A^2 + A^3 + \cdots + A^{x-1})$$

and thus, noting that $1 + A + A^2 + A^3 + \cdots + A^{x-1}$ is a geometric series with sum $\dfrac{1 - A^x}{1 - A}$, the solution of $y_{x+1} = Ay_x + B$ is

$$y_x = A^xy_0 + B\frac{1 - A^x}{1 - A} \quad \text{for } A \neq 1 \quad x = 0, 1, 2, \ldots$$

$$y_x = y_0 + Bx \qquad \text{for } A = 1 \quad x = 0, 1, 2, \ldots$$

Note that this solution, obtained by induction, does in fact satisfy the equation $y_{x+1} = Ay_x + B$, since

For $A \neq 1$,

$$y_{x+1} = Ay_x + B$$

$$= A\left(A^x y_0 + B\frac{1 - A^x}{1 - A}\right) + B$$

$$= A^{x+1} y_0 + B\left(\frac{A - A^{x+1} + 1 - A}{1 - A}\right)$$

$$= A^{x+1} y_0 + B\frac{1 - A^{x+1}}{1 - A}$$

For $A = 1$,

$$y_{x+1} = y_x + B$$

$$= (y_0 + Bx) + B$$

$$= y_0 + B(x + 1)$$

There are three special cases of the equation $y_{x+1} = Ay_x + B$ which occur frequently in descriptions of business and economic data.

(1) First-order difference a constant:

$$y_{x+1} - y_x = B \text{ (special case: } A = 1)$$

$$\text{Solution: } y_x = y_0 + Bx$$

(2) First-order difference proportional to the variable:

$$y_{x+1} - y_x = \alpha y_{x+1} \left(\text{special case: } A = \frac{1}{1 - \alpha}, \, B = 0\right)$$

$$\text{Solution: } y_x = \left(\frac{1}{1 - \alpha}\right)^x y_0$$

(3) First-order difference a linear function of the variable:

$$y_{x+1} - y_x = \alpha y_{x+1} + \beta \left(\text{special case: } A = \frac{1}{1 - \alpha}, \, B = \frac{1}{1 - \alpha}\right)$$

$$\text{Solution: } y_x = \left(\frac{1}{1 - \alpha}\right)^x y_0 + \frac{\beta}{\alpha}\left[\left(\frac{1}{1 - \alpha}\right)^x - 1\right]$$

Examples of solutions of linear first-order difference equations with constant coefficients and of economic models in which they occur are given in the following sections.

Examples

Solve the equation $2y_{x+1} = 4y_x + 3$ and find the particular solution if $y_0 = \frac{1}{2}$.

$$2y_{x+1} = 4y_x + 3$$

$$y_{x+1} = 2y_x + \tfrac{3}{2}$$

$$y_x = 2^x y_0 + \tfrac{3}{2}\left(\frac{1-2^x}{-1}\right)$$

$$y_x = 2^x y_0 - \tfrac{3}{2}(1 - 2^x)$$

$$y_x = (y_0 + \tfrac{3}{2})2^x - \tfrac{3}{2}$$

$$\text{if } y_0 = \tfrac{1}{2}, \quad y_x = 2^{x+1} - \tfrac{3}{2}$$

Solve the equation $3y_{x+1} = 3y_x - 7$ and find the particular solution if $y_0 = 3$.

$$3y_{x+1} = 3y_x - 7$$

$$y_{x+1} = y_x - \tfrac{7}{3}x$$

$$y_x = y_0 - \tfrac{7}{3}x$$

$$\text{if } y_0 = 3, \quad y_x = 3 - \tfrac{7}{3}x$$

Solve the equation $6y_{x+1} + 2y_x = 0$ and find the particular solution if $y_0 = 2$.

$$6y_{x+1} + 2y_x = 0$$

$$y_{x+1} = -\tfrac{1}{3}y_x$$

$$y_x = (-\tfrac{1}{3})^x y_0$$

$$\text{if } y_0 = 2, \quad y_x = 2(-\tfrac{1}{3})^x$$

Solve the equation $8 - 9y_x + 3y_{x+1} = 0$ and find the particular solution if $y_0 = \tfrac{1}{3}$.

$$8 - 9y_x + 3y_{x+1} = 0$$

$$y_{x+1} = 3y_x - \tfrac{8}{3}$$

$$y_x = 3^x y_0 - \tfrac{8}{3}\left(\frac{1-3^x}{-2}\right)$$

$$y_x = 3^x y_0 + \tfrac{4}{3}(1 - 3^x)$$

$$y_x = (y_0 - \tfrac{4}{3})3^x + \tfrac{4}{3}$$

$$\text{if } y_0 = \tfrac{1}{3}, \quad y_x = \tfrac{4}{3} - 3^x$$

■ 6.4 BEHAVIOR OF THE SOLUTION SEQUENCE

A sequence is a succession of terms formed according to some rule or, equivalently, a sequence is a function defined for positive integer values of the independent variable. The solution of a difference equation is thus a sequence. When the independent variable is time, this sequence is sometimes referred to as the time path of the dependent variable. For a linear first-order difference equation, the specification of y_0 determines (or generates) the solution sequence $y_0, y_1, y_2, y_3, \ldots$; each term is found according to the difference equation

$$y_{x+1} = Ay_x + B \qquad x = 0, 1, 2, \ldots$$

or, equivalently, according to its solution,

$$y_x = A^x y_0 + B \frac{1 - A^x}{1 - A} \qquad \text{for } A \neq 1 \quad x = 0, 1, 2, \ldots$$

$$y_x = y_0 + Bx \qquad \text{for } A = 1 \quad x = 0, 1, 2, \ldots$$

When A and B are given, specification of y_0 thus determines a solution sequence of real numbers.

The behavior of the solution sequence of a difference equation is of interest for many applications; this behavior depends on the values of y_0, A and B as shown in Table 6.1. A sketch typical of each type of behavior is given in Fig. 6.1, labeled to match the corresponding case in the table.

The results given in the table can be summarized in the following theorem.

THEOREM: The linear first-order difference equation

$$y_{x+1} = Ay_x + B \qquad x = 0, 1, 2, \ldots$$

has the solution

$$y_x = A^x(y_0 - y^*) + y^* \qquad \text{if } A \neq 1 \quad x = 0, 1, 2, \ldots$$

$$y_x = y_0 + Bx \qquad \text{if } A = 1 \quad x = 0, 1, 2, \ldots$$

where $y^* = \dfrac{B}{1 - A}$. If $-1 < A < 1$, the solution sequence converges to y^*; otherwise it diverges, unless $y_x = y_0$.

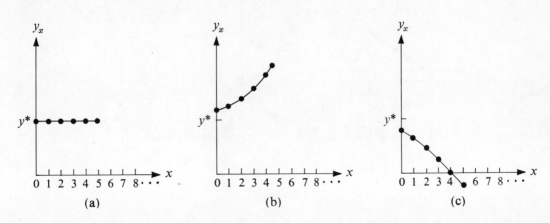

(a)   (b)   (c)

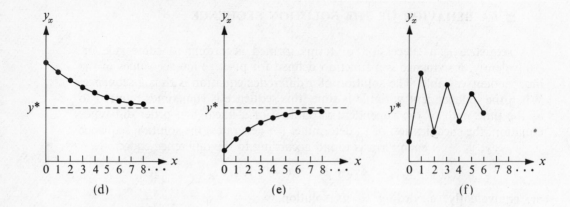

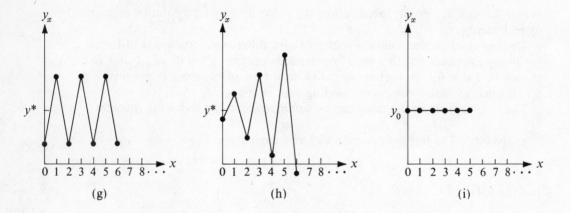

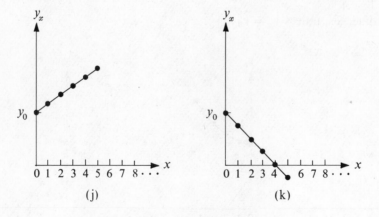

FIGURE 6.1

Table 6.1

BEHAVIOR OF THE SOLUTION SEQUENCE FOR $y_{x+1} = Ay_x + B$

Case	A	B	y_0	$y_x, x = 1, 2, \ldots$	Behavior of the solution sequence
(a)	$A \neq 1$		$y_0 = y^*$	$y_x = y^*$	Constant: $y_x = y^*$
(b)	$A > 1$		$y_0 > y^*$	$y_x > y^*$	Diverges to $+\infty$ (monotone increasing)
(c)	$A > 1$		$y_0 < y^*$	$y_x < y^*$	Diverges to $-\infty$ (monotone decreasing)
(d)	$0 < A < 1$		$y_0 > y^*$	$y_x > y^*$	Converges to y^* (monotone decreasing)
(e)	$0 < A < 1$		$y_0 < y^*$	$y_x < y^*$	Converges to y^* (monotone increasing)
(f)	$-1 < A < 0$		$y_0 \neq y^*$		Converges to y^* (damped oscillatory)
(g)	$A = -1$		$y_0 \neq y^*$		Diverges (oscillates finitely)
(h)	$A < -1$		$y_0 \neq y^*$		Diverges (oscillates infinitely)
(i)	$A = 1$	$B = 0$		$y_x = y_0$	Constant: $y_x = y_0$
(j)	$A = 1$	$B > 0$		$y_x > y_0$	Diverges to $+\infty$ (monotone increasing)
(k)	$A = 1$	$B < 0$		$y_x < y_0$	Diverges to $-\infty$ (monotone decreasing)

Examples

Solve each of the following difference equations, determine the behavior of the solution sequence, and calculate the first few values of the solution sequence.

(a) $6y_{x+1} + 2y_x - 3 = 0$, $y_0 = 1$.
(b) $5y_{x+1} - 4y_x - 15 = 0$, $y_0 = 5$.
(c) $5y_{x+1} - 25y_x - 1 = 0$, $y_0 = 0$.

(a) $6y_{x+1} + 2y_x - 3 = 0$, $y_0 = 1$.

$$y_{x+1} = -\tfrac{1}{3}y_x + \tfrac{1}{2}$$

$$y_x = (-\tfrac{1}{3})^x y_0 + \tfrac{1}{2}\left(\frac{1 - (-\tfrac{1}{3})^x}{1 - (-\tfrac{1}{3})}\right)$$

$$= (-\tfrac{1}{3})^x y_0 + \tfrac{3}{8}(1 - (-\tfrac{1}{3})^x)$$

$$= (-\tfrac{1}{3})^x (y_0 - \tfrac{3}{8}) + \tfrac{3}{8}$$

$$= \tfrac{5}{8}(-\tfrac{1}{3})^x + \tfrac{3}{8}$$

$A = -\tfrac{1}{3}$, $B = \tfrac{1}{2}$, $y^* = \tfrac{3}{8}$; case (f)—converges to y^*, damped oscillatory.
$y_0 = 1$, $y_1 = \tfrac{1}{6}$, $y_2 = \tfrac{4}{9}$, $y_3 = \tfrac{19}{54}$, $y_4 = \tfrac{31}{81}$, and so forth.

526 | DIFFERENCE EQUATIONS

(b) $5y_{x+1} - 4y_x - 15 = 0$, $y_0 = 10$.

$$y_{x+1} = \tfrac{4}{5}y_x + 3$$

$$y_x = (\tfrac{4}{5})^x y_0 + 3\left(\frac{1 - (\tfrac{4}{5})^x}{1 - \tfrac{4}{5}}\right)$$

$$= (\tfrac{4}{5})^x y_0 + 15(1 - (\tfrac{4}{5})^x)$$

$$= (\tfrac{4}{5})^x (y_0 - 15) + 15$$

$$= 15 - 5(\tfrac{4}{5})^x$$

$A = \tfrac{4}{5}$, $B = 3$, $y^* = 15$; case (d)—converges to y^*, monotone increasing.
$y_0 = 10$, $y_1 = 11$, $y_2 = 11\tfrac{4}{5}$, $y_3 = 12\tfrac{11}{25}$, $y_4 = 12\tfrac{119}{125}$, and so forth.

(c) $5y_{x+1} - 25y_x - 1 = 0$, $y_0 = 0$.

$$y_{x+1} = 5y_x + \tfrac{1}{5}$$

$$y_x = 5^x y_0 + \tfrac{1}{5}\left(\frac{1 - 5^x}{1 - 5}\right)$$

$$= 5^x y_0 - \tfrac{1}{20}(1 - 5^x)$$

$$= 5^x(y_0 + \tfrac{1}{20}) - \tfrac{1}{20}$$

$$= \tfrac{1}{20}(5^x - 1)$$

$A = 5$, $B = \tfrac{1}{5}$, $y^* = -\tfrac{1}{20}$; case (b)—diverges to $+\infty$, monotone increasing.
$y_0 = 0$, $y_1 = \tfrac{1}{5}$, $y_2 = \tfrac{6}{5}$, $y_3 = \tfrac{31}{5}$, $y_4 = \tfrac{156}{5}$, and so forth.

If money earns simple interest, the amount on deposit at any interest date is equal to the amount on deposit one period (usually a year) previously plus the interest earned in that period on the initial principal invested. If S_0 is the initial deposit, S_t is the amount on deposit after t periods, and r is the interest rate per period, then

$$S_{t+1} = S_t + rS_0 \qquad t = 0, 1, 2, \ldots$$

which has the solution

$$S_t = S_0(1 + tr) \qquad t = 0, 1, 2, \ldots$$

When the initial amount accumulates at compound interest, the interest earned during any period is computed on the total sum on deposit at the beginning of that period, rather than on the initial deposit, and

$$S_{t+1} = S_t + iS_t = (1 + i)S_t \qquad t = 0, 1, 2, \ldots$$

where i is the interest rate per conversion period; thus

$$S_t = (1 + i)^t S_0 \qquad t = 0, 1, 2 \ldots$$

The amount on deposit diverges to $+\infty$ linearly for simple interest [case (j)] and more rapidly for compound interest [case (b)].

□ *EQUILIBRIUM AND STABILITY*

If a difference equation has a constant function $y_x = y^*$ as its solution, then the value y^* of this function is called an *equilibrium* or *stationary* value of y_x. An equilibrium value y^* (or the corresponding difference equation) is said to be *stable* if every solution of the difference equation converges to y^*, independent of the initial conditions. This is the type of stability referred to in economic literature as "perfect stability of the first kind."

A displacement from the equilibrium value is equivalent to a new solution with different initial conditions, and thus a stable equilibrium can be defined as one for which *any* displacement from equilibrium is followed by a sequence of values of y which again converge to equilibrium.

THEOREM: For the difference equation

$$y_{x+1} = Ay_x + B$$

an equilibrium value of y is given by

$$y^* = \frac{B}{1 - A} \qquad \text{if } A \neq 1$$

and y^* is stable if and only if $-1 < A < 1$, unless y_x is constant.

Note that this theorem is closely related to the preceding theorem, which states that the solution sequence converges to y^* if $-1 < A < 1$ and diverges otherwise, unless $y_x = y_0$. Thus stable equilibrium occurs only for cases (a), (d), (e), (f), and (i) of Table 6.1.

■ **6.5 APPLICATIONS OF DIFFERENCE EQUATIONS IN ECONOMIC MODELS**

The following very simple economic models are examples of the use of first-difference equations to express the dependence of the value of a variable on its value in the preceding period.

□ *THE HARROD MODEL*

The following model for national income analysis has been proposed by Harrod.

$$S_t = \alpha Y_t$$

$$I_t = \beta(Y_t - Y_{t-1})$$

$$S_t = I_t$$

$$Y_0 = Y_0 \text{ (known value at } t = 0)$$

$$\alpha > 0 \qquad \beta > 0$$

where S is saving, I is investment, Y is income, and each of these variables is a function of time t.

From the first three equations of the model, the difference equation

$$\alpha Y_t = \beta(Y_t - Y_{t-1})$$

or

$$Y_t = \left(\frac{\beta}{\beta - \alpha}\right) Y_{t-1}$$

is obtained for solution and

$$Y_t = \left(\frac{\beta}{\beta - \alpha}\right)^t Y_0$$

$$I_t = S_t = \alpha \left(\frac{\beta}{\beta - \alpha}\right)^t Y_0$$

Assuming $Y_0 > 0$, the behavior of the solution sequence depends on the value of the constant $\frac{\beta}{\beta - \alpha}$. Since Y represents income and is assumed to be nonnegative,

$$\frac{\beta}{\beta - \alpha} \geq 0$$

and from the model, $\alpha > 0$, $\beta > 0$, and thus

$$\frac{\beta}{\beta - \alpha} > 1$$

Since $Y^* = 0$, the sequence $\{Y_t\}$ is monotone increasing, diverging to $+\infty$ [case (b)]. Since $\alpha > 0$, the sequences $\{I_t\}$ and $\{S_t\}$ are also monotone increasing, diverging to $+\infty$. Clearly, none of the variables of this model have equilibrium values.

NOTE: The above is one of the classical models used to study the growth of national income in an expanding economy; models for which the solution sequences do not diverge have also been considered.

□ *THE GENERAL COBWEB MODEL*

The adjustment of supply and demand can be studied using the following model.

Supply: $q_t = \alpha + \beta p_{t-1}$

Demand: $p_t = \gamma + \delta q_t$

$q_0 = q_0$ (known value at $t = 0$)

where p is price, q is quantity, and both are functions of time t. Combining the first two equations and eliminating p,

$$q_t = \alpha + \beta\gamma + \beta\delta q_{t-1}$$

This difference equation can be solved in the usual way; however, it is the behavior of the solution sequence that is of interest. Since $\beta > 0$, $\delta < 0$, their product $\beta\delta < 0$, and the solution sequences are thus always oscillatory. The equilibrium point is

$$(p^*, q^*) = \left(\frac{\gamma + \alpha\delta}{1 - \beta\delta}, \frac{\alpha + \beta\gamma}{1 - \beta\delta}\right)$$

If $-1 < \beta\delta < 0$, the sequences $\{p_t\}$ and $\{q_t\}$ are damped and converge to

(p^*, q^*); if $\beta\delta = -1$, the sequences oscillate finitely; if $\beta\delta < -1$, the sequences oscillate infinitely. Thus the equilibrium is stable only if $-1 < \beta\delta < 0$.

NOTE: If the supply curve is written so that its slope is with respect to the quantity variable, the slope is $\dfrac{1}{\beta}$. Thus the equilibrium is stable if and only if the slope of the demand curve is less (in numerical value) than the slope of the supply curve.

□ *CONSUMPTION MODEL*

The following is a simple model for consumption.

$$C_t + S_t = Y_t$$

$$Y_t = \alpha S_{t-1}$$

$$C_t = \gamma Y_t$$

$$Y_0 = Y_0 \text{ (known value at } t = 0)$$

$$\alpha > 0 \qquad 0 < \gamma < 1$$

where γ is the marginal propensity to consume, C is consumption, S is saving, Y is income, and each of these variables is a function of time t.

Substituting the second and third equations in the first equation of the model, the difference equation

$$Y_{t+1} = \alpha(1 - \gamma)Y_t$$

is obtained for solution and

$$Y_t = (\alpha - \alpha\gamma)^t Y_0$$

$$C_t = \gamma(\alpha - \alpha\gamma)^t Y_0$$

$$= (\alpha - \alpha\gamma)^t C_0$$

$$S_t = (1 - \gamma)(\alpha - \alpha\gamma)^t Y_0$$

$$= (\alpha - \alpha\gamma)^t S_0$$

The sequences $\{Y_t\}$, $\{C_t\}$, and $\{S_t\}$ are monotone increasing and diverge to $+\infty$ if $\alpha(1 - \gamma) > 1$, are monotone decreasing and converge to $y^* = 0$ if $\alpha(1 - \gamma) < 1$, and are constant if $\alpha(1 - \gamma) = 1$.

□ *INCOME-CONSUMPTION-INVESTMENT MODEL*

When time is considered in periods rather than continuously, the income-consumption-investment model stated in terms of differential equations in Chapter 5 can be stated in terms of difference equations, as follows.

$$C_t = \alpha Y_t + \beta$$

$$I_t = \gamma Y_t + g$$

$$\Delta Y_{t-1} = \theta[C_{t-1} + I_{t-1} - Y_{t-1}]$$

$$Y_0 = Y_0$$

$$\alpha > 0, \qquad \gamma > 0, \qquad \theta > 0$$

Rewriting the third equation and substituting the first and second equations into it,

$$Y_t - Y_{t-1} = \theta[C_{t-1} + I_{t-1} - Y_{t-1}]$$

$$Y_t = \theta[C_{t-1} + I_{t-1}] + (1 - \theta) Y_{t-1}$$

$$= \theta[\alpha Y_{t-1} + \beta + \gamma Y_{t-1} + g] + (1 - \theta) Y_{t-1}$$

$$= [\theta(\alpha + \gamma) + (1 - \theta)] Y_{t-1} + \theta\beta + \theta g$$

$$= [\theta(\alpha + \gamma) + (1 - \theta)]^t Y_0 + \theta(\beta + g) \frac{1 - [\theta(\alpha + \gamma) + (1 - \theta)]^t}{1 - [\theta(\alpha + \gamma) + (1 - \theta)]}$$

The solution is stable if

$$-1 < \theta(\alpha + \gamma) + (1 - \theta) < 1$$

$$-\frac{1}{\theta} < \alpha + \gamma + \frac{1}{\theta} - 1 < \frac{1}{\theta}$$

$$1 - \frac{2}{\theta} < \alpha + \gamma < 1$$

But $\alpha + \gamma > 0$ and, in practice, $\theta < 2$ since response to disequilibrium of supply and demand is not likely to result in a change in supply twice as large as the discrepancy. Thus the stability condition is $\alpha + \gamma < 1$, as for the differential-equation form of the model.

PROBLEMS

1. Show that $y_x = \dfrac{c}{1 + cx}$ is a solution of $y_{x+1} = \dfrac{y_x}{1 + y_x}$ and find a particular solution if $y_0 = -4$.

2. Show that $y_x = c_1 + c_2 2^x$ is a solution of $y_{x+2} - 3y_{x+1} + 2y_x = 0$ and find a particular solution if $y_0 = 1$, $y_1 = 2$.

3. Show that $y_x = c_1 + c_2 2^x - x$ is a solution of $y_{x+2} - 3y_{x+1} + 2y_x = 1$ and find a particular solution if $y_0 = 0$, $y_1 = 3$.

4. Show that $y_x = c_1 + c_2 2^x + c_3 3^x$ is a solution of $y_{x+3} - 6y_{x+2} + 11y_{x+1} - 6y_x = 0$ and find a particular solution if $y_0 = 1$, $y_1 = 1$, $y_2 = -1$.

5. Show that $y_x = c_1 + c_2 x + c_3 x^2 + c_4 x^3$ is a solution of $y_{x+4} - 4y_{x+3} + 6y_{x+2} - 4y_{x+1} + y_x = 0$ and find a particular solution if $y_0 = 1$, $y_1 = 5$, $y_2 = 9$, $y_3 = 7$.

Solve each of the following difference equations.

6. $y_{x+1} + y_x - 2 = 0$

7. $3y_{x+1} = 2y_x + 3$

8. $2y_{x+1} + y_x - 3 = 0$

9. $y_{x+1} + 3y_x = 0$

Solve each of the following difference equations, determine the behavior of the solution sequence, and calculate the first few values of the solution sequence.

10. $y_{x+1} = 7y_x + 6$, $y_0 = 1$

11. $8y_{x+1} + 4y_x - 3 = 0$, $y_0 = \frac{1}{2}$

12. $16y_{x+1} - 6y_x = 1$, $y_0 = \frac{1}{10}$

13. $3y_{x+1} - 2y_x - 3 = 0$, $y_0 = 5$

14. $3y_{x+1} - y_x = \frac{6}{5}$, $y_0 = \frac{2}{5}$

15. $y_{x+1} = 3y_x - 1$, $y_0 = \frac{1}{2}$

16. $y_{x+1} + 3y_x + 1 = 0$, $y_0 = 1$

17. $2y_{x+1} - y_x = 2$, $y_0 = 4$

18. $y_{x+1} = y_x - 1$, $y_0 = 5$

19. $7y_{x+1} + 2y_x - 7 = 0$, $y_0 = 1$

20. $y_{x+1} + y_x + 2 = 0$, $y_0 = 3$

21. $15y_{x+1} - 10y_x - 3 = 0$, $y_0 = 1$

22. $5y_{x+1} - y_x - 60 = 0$, $y_0 = 15$

23. $y_{x+1} + 4y_x + 12 = 0$, $y_0 = 6$

24. $8y_{x+1} + y_x - 4 = 0$, $y_0 = \frac{1}{3}$

25. $4y_{x+1} - y_x - 3 = 0$, $y_0 = \frac{1}{2}$

26. $4y_{x+1} + 3y_x - 4 = 0$, $y_0 = 1$

27. $3y_{x+1} - 2y_x - 6 = 0$, $y_0 = 4$

28. $9y_{x+1} + 5y_x - 18 = 0$, $y_0 = 1$

29. $y_{x+1} - y_x - 10 = 0$, $y_0 = 2$

30. In the Harrod model, graph $\{Y_t\}$ for each of the following cases and comment on the plausibility of each.

Case	α	β	Y_0
(a)	$\frac{1}{5}$	2	100
(b)	$-\frac{1}{5}$	2	100
(c)	-4	2	100
(d)	$\frac{1}{5}$	2	-100

31. In the Cobweb model, suppose the supply curve has negative slope—state the conditions for stable equilibrium.

32. Derive the solution of the Kahn model:

$$C_t = \alpha Y_{t-1} + \beta$$
$$Y_t = C_t + I_t$$

where C is consumption, Y is income, and I is investment.

33. Solve the following model, determine the behavior of the solution sequences, and state any additional "logical" restrictions on the parameters.

$$S_t = \alpha Y_t + \beta$$
$$I_t = \gamma(Y_t - Y_{t-1})$$
$$S_t = \delta I_t$$
$$Y_0 = Y_0$$
$$\alpha > 0 \quad \beta > 0 \quad \gamma > 0 \quad \delta > 0$$

where S is savings, Y is income, and I is investment.

34. Solve the following simplified Metzler inventory model:

$$y_t = u_t + v_0$$
$$u_t = \beta y_{t-1}$$

$$y_0 = y_0$$

$$0 < \beta < 1$$

where y is income produced, u is the number of units produced for sale, with units of measurement appropriately chosen, v_0 is the constant noninduced investment, and β is the marginal propensity to consume (of this year's consumption with respect to last year's income).

35. Consider the model

$$p_t = 2 - q_t$$

$$q_{t+1} = p^*_{t+1} + 1$$

$$p^*_{t+1} = \alpha \rho_{t+1} + (1 - \alpha) p_t$$

$$p_0 = p_0$$

$$0 \le \alpha \le 1$$

where q is the quantity supplied, p is the actual price, p^* is the supplier's estimated price for the next period, and ρ is a public forecast for the price. (Note that $\alpha = 1$ implies that the suppliers have perfect confidence in the public forecast; $\alpha = 0$ implies they have no confidence in the public forecast.) Defining Δ_{t+1} by the equation

$$\Delta_{t+1} = p^*_{t+1} - \rho_{t+1}$$

show that $\Delta_t = 1 - 2p_t$.

36. Solve the following model of the growth of national income in an expanding economy:

$$Y_t = C_t + I_t$$

$$C_t = \alpha + \beta Y_t$$

$$Y_{t+1} - Y_t = \gamma I_t$$

$$Y_0 = Y_0 \qquad C_0 = C_0 \qquad I_0 = I_0$$

$$\alpha \ge 0 \qquad 0 < \beta < 1 \qquad \gamma > 0$$

where Y is income, C is consumption, and I is investment.

ANSWERS TO ODD-NUMBERED PROBLEMS

1. $y_x = \dfrac{4}{4x - 1}$

3. $y_x = 4(2^x - 1) - x$

5. $y_x = 1 + 2x + 3x^2 - x^3$

7. $y_x = (\frac{2}{3})^x (y_0 - 3) + 3$

9. $y_x = (-3)^x y_0$

11. $y_x = \frac{1}{4}(-\frac{1}{2})^x + \frac{1}{4}$; damped oscillatory, converges to $y^* = \frac{1}{4}$; $y_0 = \frac{1}{2}$, $y_1 = \frac{1}{8}$, $y_2 = \frac{5}{16}$, $y_3 = \frac{7}{32}$, $y_4 = \frac{17}{64}$, $y_5 = \frac{31}{128}$

13. $y_x = 2(\frac{2}{3})^x + 3$; monotone decreasing, converges to $y^* = 3$; $y_0 = 5$, $y_1 = 4\frac{1}{3}$, $y_2 = 3\frac{8}{9}$, $y_3 = 3\frac{16}{27}$, $y_4 = 3\frac{32}{81}$, $y_5 = 3\frac{64}{243}$

15. $y_x = \frac{1}{2}$; constant

17. $y_x = 2(\frac{1}{2})^x + 2$; monotone decreasing, converges to $y^* = 2$; $y_0 = 4$, $y_1 = 3$, $y_2 = \frac{5}{2}$, $y_3 = \frac{9}{4}$, $y_4 = \frac{17}{8}$, $y_5 = \frac{33}{16}$

19. $y_x = \frac{2}{9}(-\frac{2}{7})^x + \frac{7}{9}$; damped oscillatory, converges to $y^* = \frac{7}{9}$; $y_0 = 1$, $y_1 = \frac{5}{7}$, $y_2 = \frac{39}{49}$, $y_3 = \frac{265}{343}$, $y_4 = \frac{1871}{2401}$, $y_5 = \frac{13065}{16807}$

21. $y_x = \frac{2}{5}(\frac{2}{3})^x + \frac{3}{5}$; monotone decreasing, converges to $y^* = \frac{3}{5}$; $y_0 = 1$, $y_1 = \frac{13}{15}$, $y_2 = \frac{7}{9}$, $y_3 = \frac{97}{135}$, $y_4 = \frac{55}{81}$, $y_5 = \frac{29}{45}$

23. $y_x = \frac{42}{5}(-4)^x - \frac{12}{5}$; divergent, oscillates infinitely; $y_0 = 6$, $y_1 = -36$, $y_2 = 132$, $y_3 = -540$, $y_4 = 2148$, $y_5 = -8604$

25. $y_x = -(\frac{1}{2})(\frac{1}{4})^x + 1$; monotone increasing, converges to $y^* = 1$; $y_0 = \frac{1}{2}$, $y_1 = \frac{7}{8}$, $y_2 = \frac{31}{32}$, $y_3 = \frac{127}{128}$, $y_4 = \frac{511}{512}$, $y_5 = \frac{2047}{2048}$

27. $y_x = -2(\frac{2}{3})^x + 6$; monotone increasing, converges to $y^* = 6$; $y_0 = 4$, $y_1 = \frac{14}{3}$, $y_2 = \frac{46}{9}$, $y_3 = \frac{146}{27}$, $y_4 = , \frac{454}{81}$, $y_5 = \frac{1394}{243}$

29. $y_x = 2 + 10x$; monotone increasing, diverges to $+\infty$; $y_0 = 2$, $y_1 = 12$, $y_2 = 22$, $y_3 = 32$, $y_4 = 42$, $y_5 = 52$

31. If $\delta < 0$ and $\beta < 0$, the approach to equilibrium will not be oscillatory and $|\delta\beta| < 1$ (the stability condition) indicates that the demand curve must be flatter than the supply curve.

33. $Y_t = \left(\dfrac{\delta\gamma}{\delta\gamma - \alpha}\right)^t \left(Y_0 + \dfrac{\beta}{\alpha}\right) - \dfrac{\beta}{\alpha}$ approaches $+\infty$

$S_t = \left(\dfrac{\delta\gamma}{\delta\gamma - \alpha}\right)^t (\alpha Y_0 + \beta)$ approaches $+\infty$

$I_t = \left(\dfrac{\delta\gamma}{\delta\gamma - \alpha}\right)^t \left(\dfrac{\alpha}{\delta} Y_0 + \dfrac{\beta}{\delta}\right)$ approaches $+\infty$

$\delta\gamma > \alpha$

■ 6.6 LINEAR SECOND-ORDER DIFFERENCE EQUATIONS WITH CONSTANT COEFFICIENTS

The general second-order difference equation with constant coefficients can be written in the form

$$y_{x+2} + A_1 y_{x+1} + A_2 y_x = g(x)$$

Consider first the special case $g(x) = 0$

$$y_{x+2} + A_1 y_{x+1} + A_2 y_x = 0$$

An equation whose constant term is zero is sometimes said to be homogeneous. Thus $y_{x+2} + A_1 y_{x+1} + A_2 y_x = 0$ is the general homogeneous second-order linear difference equation with constant coefficients. Note that the definition of a homogeneous equation must be distinguished from the definition of a homogeneous function.

In order to obtain the solution of

$$y_{x+2} + A_1 y_{x+1} + A_2 y_x = 0$$

form the auxiliary equation

$$m^2 + A_1 m + A_2 = 0$$

and solve for its roots, if necessary using the quadratic formula

$$m_1 = \frac{-A_1 + \sqrt{A_1^2 - 4A_2}}{2}$$

$$m_2 = \frac{-A_1 - \sqrt{A_1^2 - 4A_2}}{2}$$

These roots m_1 and m_2 may be real and unequal, real and equal, or complex (involving the square root of a negative number). The form of the solution of the equation $y_{x+2} + A_1 y_{x+1} + A_2 y_x = 0$ depends on the nature of the roots m_1 and m_2 as summarized below. Note that the general solution for a second-order difference equation includes two arbitrary constants and that a particular solution is specified by two boundary conditions, that is, by two consecutive values of y.

Case 1. m_1 and m_2 are real and unequal ($m_1 \neq m_2$)
      solution: $y_x = C_1 m_1^x + C_2 m_2^x$

Case 2. m_1 and m_2 are real and equal ($m_1 = m_2 = m$)
      solution: $y_x = C_1 m^x + C_2 x m^x$

Case 3. m_1 and m_2 are complex ($m_1 = a + bi$, $m_2 = a - bi$ where $i = \sqrt{-1}$)
      solution: $y_x = r^x(C_1 \cos \theta x + C_2 \sin \theta x)$ where $r = \sqrt{a^2 + b^2}$ and θ is the angle whose $\tan = a/b$. Alternatively, $\sin \theta = a/r$, $\cos \theta = b/r$.

Note that a and b can be interchanged in these definitions, since the trigonometric functions are periodic. For convenience, the solution is usually written for θ in the first quadrant.

Examples

Obtain the general solution for the difference equation

$$y_{x+2} - 5y_{x+1} + 6y_x = 0$$

and the particular solution if $y_0 = 2$, $y_1 = 5$.
    The auxiliary equation is

$$m^2 - 5m + 6 = 0$$

and

$$m_1 = \frac{5 + \sqrt{25 - 24}}{2} = 3$$

$$m_2 = \frac{5 - \sqrt{25 - 24}}{2} = 2$$

Thus the general solution is

$$y_x = C_1 3^x + C_2 2^x$$

If $y_0 = 2$, $y_1 = 5$,

$$2 = C_1 + C_2$$
$$5 = 3C_1 + 2C_2$$
$$C_2 = 1$$
$$C_1 = 1$$

and the particular solution is

$$y_x = 3^x + 2^x$$

Obtain the general solution for the difference equation

$$y_{x+2} - 4y_{x+1} + 4y_x = 0$$

and the particular solution if $y_0 = 1$, $y_1 = 6$.
   The auxiliary equation is

$$m^2 - 4m + 4 = 0$$

and

$$m_1 = \frac{4 + \sqrt{16 - 16}}{2} = 2$$

$$m_2 = \frac{4 - \sqrt{16 - 16}}{2} = 2$$

Thus the general solution is

$$y_x = C_1 2^x + C_2 x 2^x$$

If $y_0 = 1$, $y_1 = 6$,

$$1 = C_1 + 0$$
$$6 = 2C_1 + 2C_2$$
$$C_1 = 1$$
$$C_2 = 2$$

and the particular solution is

$$y_x = 2^x + x 2^{x+1}$$

Obtain the general solution for the difference equation

$$y_{x+2} - y_{x+1} + \tfrac{1}{2} y_x = 0$$

and the particular solution if $y_0 = 3$, $y_1 = \tfrac{1}{2}$.
   The auxiliary equation is

$$m^2 - m + \tfrac{1}{2} = 0$$

and

$$m_1 = \frac{1 + \sqrt{1-2}}{2} = \tfrac{1}{2} + \tfrac{1}{2}i$$

$$m_2 = \frac{1 - \sqrt{1-2}}{2} = \tfrac{1}{2} - \tfrac{1}{2}i$$

$$r = \sqrt{(\tfrac{1}{2})^2 + (\tfrac{1}{2})^2} = \frac{\sqrt{2}}{2}$$

$$\tan\theta = 1, \quad \text{so } \theta = \tfrac{1}{4}\pi$$

Thus the general solution is

$$y_x = \left(\frac{\sqrt{2}}{2}\right)^x (C_1 \cos\tfrac{1}{4}\pi x + C_2 \sin\tfrac{1}{4}\pi x)$$

If $y_0 = 3$, $y_1 = \tfrac{5}{2}$,

$$3 = (1)[C_1(1) + C_2(0)]$$

$$C_1 = 0$$

$$\frac{5}{2} = \frac{\sqrt{2}}{2}\left[3\left(\frac{\sqrt{2}}{2}\right) + C_2\left(\frac{\sqrt{2}}{2}\right)\right]$$

$$\tfrac{5}{2} = \tfrac{3}{2} + \tfrac{1}{2}C_2$$

$$C_2 = 2$$

and the particular solution is

$$y_x = \left(\frac{\sqrt{2}}{2}\right)^x (3\cos\tfrac{1}{4}\pi x + 2\sin\tfrac{1}{4}\pi x)$$

□ BEHAVIOR OF THE SOLUTION SEQUENCE

The behavior of the solution sequence depends on both the difference equation and the initial conditions; the roots of the auxiliary equation indicate the limiting behavior of the solution sequence as follows.

Case 1. Real roots, $m_1 \neq m_2$

If m_1 is the root with the greater absolute value, that is, $|m_1| > |m_2|$, then the limiting behavior of the solution sequence $\{C_1 m_1^x + C_2 m_2^x\}$ is the same as that of $\{C_1 m_1^x\}$, provided $C_1 \neq 0$.

This can be shown by writing

$$C_1 m_1^x + C_2 m_2^x = m_1^x[C_1 + C_2(m_2/m_1)^x]$$

Since $-1 < m_2/m_1 < 1$, $(m_2/m_1)^x \to 0$ as $x \to \infty$ and

$$\frac{C_1 m_1^x}{C_1 m_1^x + C_2 m_2^x} = \frac{C_1}{C_1 + C_2(m_2|m_1)^x} \to \frac{C_1}{C_1} = 1 \text{ as } x \to \infty$$

Thus the limiting behavior of $\{C_1 m_1^x + C_2 m_2^x\}$ is the same as the limiting behavior of $\{C_1 m_1^x\}$ if $|m_1| > |m_2|$. The limiting behavior of $\{C_1 m_1^x\}$ is discussed in the preceding sections concerning solution sequences of first-order difference equations. Recall that

If $|m_1| \leq 1$, the sequence converges

If $|m_1| > 1$, the sequence diverges

If $-1 < m_1 < 0$, the sequence is damped oscillatory

If $m < -1$, the sequence oscillates infinitely

If $C_1 = 0$, the solution sequence is $\{C_2 m_2^x\}$ and similar considerations are applicable to this sequence. Note that if $C_1 = 0$, $y_0 = C_2$ and $y_1 = C_2 m_2$.

Case 2. Real roots, $m_1 = m_2 = m$

The solution sequence is $\{(C_1 + C_2 x)m^x\}$, which diverges if $|m| > 1$ unless $C_1 = C_2 = 0$ and also diverges if $|m| = 1$ unless $C_2 = 0$. If $|m| < 1$, the sequence $\{xm^x\}$ converges to zero and $\{(C_1 + C_2 x)m^x\}$ also converges to zero. If m is negative, the sequence is oscillatory.

Case 3. Complex roots, $m_1 = a + bi$, $m_2 = a - bi$

The solution sequence is oscillatory; it converges to zero if $0 < \sqrt{a^2 + b^2} < 1$ and diverges if $\sqrt{a^2 + b^2} > 1$.

A complete classification of the solution sequences of the second-order linear homogeneous difference equation $y_{x+2} + A_1 y_{x+1} + A_2 y_x = 0$ is somewhat involved, since for exceptional initial values C_1 or C_2 or both are zero. There is one case in which the solution sequence for a homogeneous second-order linear difference equation converges to zero for every possible pair of initial values, as summarized in the following theorem.

THEOREM: If $\rho = \max(|m_1|, |m_2|)$, where m_1 and m_2 are the roots of the auxiliary equation of the homogeneous second-order difference equation

$$y_{x+2} + A_1 y_{x+1} + A_2 y_x = 0$$

then $\rho < 1$ is a necessary and sufficient condition for the solution sequence $\{y_x\}$ to converge with limit 0 for all initial values y_0 and y_1.

More specifically, the definition of ρ is as follows.

Case 1. m_1 and m_2 real and unequal
$\rho = \max(|m_1|, |m_2|)$

Case 2. m_1 and m_2 real and equal, $m_1 = m_2 = m$
$\rho = |m|$

Case 3. m_1 and m_2 complex, $m_1 = a + bi$, $m_2 = a - bi$
$\rho = \sqrt{a^2 + b^2}$

Example

In the preceding example the general solution for the difference equation $y_{x+2} - 5y_{x+1} + 6y_x = 0$ is found to be

$$y_x = C_1 3^x + C_2 2^x$$

and, since $m_1 = 3$ and $m_2 = 2$, $\rho > 1$ and the solution sequence diverges, as can be seen from the first few values of the particular solution $y_x = 3^x + 2^x$: $y_0 = 2$, $y_1 = 5$, $y_2 = 13$, $y_3 = 35$, $y_4 = 97$, $y_5 = 761$, and so forth.

In another previous example, the general solution for the difference equation $y_{x+2} - 4y_{x+1} + 4y_x = 0$ is found to be

$$y_x = C_1 2^x + C_2 x 2^x$$

and, since $m_1 = m_2 = 2$, $\rho > 1$ and the solution sequence diverges, as can be seen from the first few values of the particular solution $y_x = 2^x + x2^{x+1}$: $y_0 = 1$, $y_1 = 6$, $y_2 = 20$, $y_3 = 56$, $y_4 = 144$, $y_5 = 352$, and so forth.

In another previous example, the general solution for the difference equation $y_{x+2} - y_{x+1} + \frac{1}{2}y_x = 0$ is found to be

$$y_x = \left(\frac{\sqrt{2}}{2}\right)^x (C_1 \cos \tfrac{1}{4}\pi x + C_2 \sin \tfrac{1}{4}\pi x)$$

and $\rho = \dfrac{\sqrt{2}}{2} < 1$ so the solution sequence is oscillatory and converges to zero, as can be seen from the first few values of the particular solution

$$y_x = \left(\frac{\sqrt{2}}{2}\right)^x (3 \cos \tfrac{1}{4}\pi x + 2 \sin \tfrac{1}{4}\pi x)$$

$y_0 = 3$, $y_1 = 1$, $y_2 = 1$, $y_3 = -\frac{1}{4}$, $y_4 = -\frac{3}{4}$, $y_5 = \frac{5}{8}$, and so forth.

□ NONHOMOGENEOUS SECOND-ORDER DIFFERENCE EQUATIONS

If the second-order linear homogeneous difference equation

$$y_{x+2} + A_1 y_{x+1} + A_2 y_x = 0$$

has the solution y_x, then the nonhomogeneous difference equation

$$y_{x+2} + A_1 y_{x+1} + A_2 y_x = g(x)$$

has the general solution $y_x + y^*$, where y^* is any (particular) solution of the non-homogeneous equation.

The form of y^* depends on the form of $g(x)$. A number of methods are available for determining y^*, including the *method of undetermined coefficients*, illustrated below.

Suppose that $g(x)$ is a constant, K, that is,

$$y_{x+2} + A_1 y_{x+1} + A_2 y_x = K$$

and suppose $y_x = z_x$ is the solution of the homogeneous equation $y_{x+2} + A_1 y_{x+1} + A_2 y_x = 0$. Determine the solution of the nonhomogeneous equation in the form

$$y_x = z_x + L$$

where L is a constant. Then

$$(z_{x+2} + L) + A_1(z_{x+1} + L) + A_2(z_x + L) = K$$

$$z_{x+2} + A_1 z_{x+1} + A_2 z_x + (1 + A_1 + A_2)L = K$$

But $z_{x+2} + A_1 z_{x+1} + A_2 z_x = 0$, since z_x is a solution of the homogeneous equation, and

$$L = \frac{K}{1 + A_1 + A_2}$$

Thus the solution of the nonhomogeneous equation is

$$y_x = z_x + \frac{K}{1 + A_1 + A_2}$$

where z_x is the solution of the corresponding homogeneous equation.

Example

Find the general solution of the equation

$$y_{x+2} - 6y_{x+1} + 8 = 9$$

and a particular solution if $y_0 = 10$, $y_1 = 25$.

The auxiliary equation of the homogeneous equation is

$$m^2 - 6m + 8 = 0$$

$$(m - 4)(m - 2) = 0$$

$$m_1 = 4$$

$$m_2 = 2$$

The general solution of the homogeneous equation is thus

$$y_x = C_1 4^x + C_2 2^x$$

and the general solution of the nonhomogeneous equation is

$$y_x = C_1 4^x + C_2 2^x + \frac{9}{1 - 6 + 8}$$

$$y_x = C_1 4^x + C_2 2^x + 3$$

If $y_0 = 10$, $y_1 = 25$,

$$C_1 + C_2 = 10 - 3 = 7$$

$$4C_1 + 2C_2 = 25 - 3 = 22$$

$$2C_1 = 8$$

$$C_1 = 4$$

$$C_2 = 3$$

and the particular solution is

$$y_x = 4^{x+1} + (3)2^x + 3$$

Solutions of nonhomogeneous difference equations for which $g(x)$ is not constant, but is in fact a function of x, can be obtained by similar methods.

However, a general rule for determining the form of y^*, the particular solution of a nonhomogeneous difference equation, cannot be stated. The form of y^* depends on the form of $g(x)$. For simpler forms, y^* is similar to $g(x)$, but there are many special cases.

If a nonhomogeneous difference equation is of the form $y_{x+2} + A_1 y_{x+1} + A_2 y_x = g(x)$, where $g(x) = K$, a constant, then if the solution sequence of the corresponding homogeneous equation converges to zero, the solution of the nonhomogeneous equation converges to $\dfrac{K}{1 + A_1 + A_2}$. Similarly, if the solution of the homogeneous equation diverges, as in the preceding example, the solution of the nonhomogeneous equation also diverges.

□ EQUILIBRIUM AND STABILITY

If the difference equation

$$y_{x+2} + A_1 y_{x+1} + A_2 y_x = K$$

where K is a constant, has a constant function y^* as its solutions, then y^* is an *equilibrium* or *stationary value of y* and

$$y^* + A_1 y^* + A_2 y^* = K$$

$$y^* = \frac{K}{1 + A_1 + A_2}, \qquad 1 + A_1 + A_2 \neq 0$$

is an equilibrium value of y.

Note that this equilibrium value has the property that if two consecutive values of a solution of the equation $y_{x+2} + A_1 y_{x+1} + A_2 y_x = K$ are equal to y^*, then all succeeding values are equal to y^*. Substituting $y_x = y_{x+1} = y^* = \dfrac{K}{1 + A_1 + A_2}$ into $y_{x+2} + A_1 y_{x+1} + A_2 y_x = K$,

$$y_{x+2} + A_1 y^* + A_2 y^* = K$$

$$y_{x+2} = K - (A_1 + A_2) y^*$$

$$= K - \frac{K(A_1 + A_2)}{1 + A_1 + A_2}$$

$$= \frac{K}{1 + A_1 + A_2} = y^*$$

The equilibrium value is said to be *stable* or the difference equation $y_{x+2} + A_1 y_{x+1} + A_2 y_x = K$ is said to be *stable* if every solution of the differential equation converges to y^* for every possible set of initial conditions y_0 and y_1, that is, if

$$\lim y_x = y^* \qquad \text{for all } y_0 \text{ and } y_1$$

It can be shown that a necessary and sufficient condition for the equilibrium value $y^* = \dfrac{K}{1 + A_1 + A_2}$ to be stable is $\rho < 1$, where, as above, $\rho = \max(|m_1|, |m_2|)$ and m_1 and m_2 are the roots of the auxiliary equation $m^2 + A_1 m + A_2 = 0$.

It can also be shown that $\rho < 1$ if and only if

$$2 \pm A_1 > 1 - A_2 > 0$$

Thus these inequalities are necessary and sufficient for stability of the equilibrium value y^* and

$$2 \pm A_1 > 1 - A_2 > 0 \Leftrightarrow y^* = \frac{K}{1 + A_1 + A_2}$$

is a stable equilibrium for the difference equation $y_{x+2} + A_1 y_{x+1} + A_2 y_x = K$.

■ 6.7 APPLICATIONS OF SECOND-ORDER DIFFERENCE EQUATIONS IN ECONOMIC MODELS

Second-order difference equations occur in many economic models as an indication of the dependence of the value of a variable on its value for two preceding periods. Second-order difference equations are associated with various types of relationships among variables in the model, as illustrated in the following examples.

□ SAMUELSON'S INTERACTION MODEL

The following model has been proposed by Samuelson for national income analysis.

$$Y_t = C_t + I_t + G_t$$
$$C_t = \alpha Y_{t-1}$$
$$I_t = \beta[C_t - C_{t-1}]$$
$$Y_0 = Y_0$$
$$Y_1 = Y_1$$
$$\alpha > 0, \qquad \beta > 0$$

where Y is national income, C is consumption, I is investment, and G is government expenditure. G is assumed constant (exogenous) from period to period and, for convenience, the units are assumed to be such that $G = 1$. Note that investment in any period is equal to a constant times the increase in consumption of that period over the preceding period; this is referred to as the acceleration principle.

Substituting the second and third equations into the first equation,

$$Y_t = \alpha Y_{t-1} + \beta(\alpha Y_{t-1} - \alpha Y_{t-2}) + 1$$
$$Y_t - \alpha(1 + \beta) Y_{t-1} + \alpha\beta Y_{t-2} - 1 = 0$$

The three types of general solution of the homogeneous equation, depending on the nature of the roots of the auxiliary equation, are

(a) $\quad Y_t = C_1 m_1^t + C_2 m_2^t \qquad$ where $m_1 = \dfrac{\alpha(1 + \beta) + \sqrt{\alpha^2(1 + \beta)^2 - 4\alpha\beta}}{2}$

$$m_2 = \frac{\alpha(1+\beta) - \sqrt{\alpha^2(1+\beta)^2 - 4\alpha\beta}}{2}$$

(b) $Y_t = C_1 m^t + C_2 t m^t$ where $m = \frac{\alpha}{2}(1+\beta)$

(c) $Y_t = r^t(C_1 \cos \theta t + C_2 \sin \theta t)$ where $r = \sqrt{\alpha\beta}$

$$\sin \theta = \frac{\alpha(1+\beta)}{2\sqrt{\alpha\beta}}$$

$$\cos \theta = \left[1 - \frac{\alpha(1+\beta)}{4\beta}\right]^{1/2}$$

A particular solution of the nonhomogeneous equation

$$Y_t - \alpha(1+\beta)Y_{t-1} + \alpha\beta Y_{t-2} - 1 = 0$$

is obtained by substituting $y^* = L$ into the equation,

$$L - \alpha(1+\beta)L + \alpha\beta L - 1 = 0$$

$$L = \frac{1}{1 - \alpha(\alpha+\beta) + \alpha\beta}$$

$$= \frac{1}{1 - \alpha}$$

Thus the solution of the nonhomogeneous equation has the form

(a) $Y_t = C_1 m_1^t + C_2 m_2^t + \dfrac{1}{1-\alpha}$

(b) $Y_t = C_1 m^t + C_2 t m^t + \dfrac{1}{1-\alpha}$

(c) $Y_t = r^t(C_1 \cos \theta t + C_2 \sin \theta t) + \dfrac{1}{1-\alpha}$

where m_1, m_2, m, r, and θ are defined as above and the arbitrary constants can be determined from the initial conditions Y_0 and Y_1.

Clearly it is possible to have an equilibrium solution $y^* = \dfrac{1}{1-\alpha}$ whenever the first two terms of the solution (in any of the three possible forms) tends to zero. It can be shown that $y^* = \dfrac{1}{1-\alpha}$ is the equilibrium value, if one exists, as follows.

If y^* is a constant solution of the difference equation

$$Y_t - \alpha(1+\beta)Y_{t-1} + \alpha\beta Y_{t-2} = 1$$

then

$$y^* - \alpha(1+\beta)y^* + \alpha\beta y^* = 1$$

and the equilibrium value of national income is

$$y^* = \frac{1}{1 - \alpha}, \qquad \alpha \neq 1$$

The stability conditions $1 + A_1 + A_2 > 0$, $1 - A_1 + A_2 > 0$ and $1 - A_2 > 0$ become

$$1 - \alpha(1 + \beta) + \alpha\beta > 0 \qquad \text{or } 1 - \alpha > 0$$
$$1 + \alpha(1 + \beta) + \alpha\beta > 0 \qquad \text{or } 1 + \alpha + 2\alpha\beta > 0$$
$$1 - \alpha\beta > 0$$

Since $\alpha > 0$, $\beta > 0$, the second condition is satisfied and the necessary and sufficient conditions for y^* to be a stable equilibrium value are

$$\alpha < 1$$
$$\alpha\beta < 1$$

That is, both the marginal propensity to consume (one year's consumption with respect to the previous year's income) and its product with the accelerator parameter must be less than 1 for the sequence of income values to converge to y^* for all possible initial conditions.

The convergence to y^* is oscillatory if the roots of the auxiliary equation are complex numbers. This is the case if $A_1^2 - 4A_2$ is negative, that is, if $\alpha^2(1 + \beta)^2 - 4\alpha\beta < 0$.

□ METZLER INVENTORY MODEL

The following model has been proposed by Metzler for analyzing inventory cycles.

$$y_t = u_t + s_t + v_0$$
$$u_t = \beta y_{t-1}$$
$$s_t = \beta(y_{t-1} - y_{t-2})$$
$$0 < \beta < 1$$

where y_t is total income produced in period t, u_t is consumers' goods produced for sale in period t, s_t is consumers' goods produced for inventories in period t, and v_0 is the constant noninduced net investment in each period.

The total income produced in any period is equal to the total production of consumers' goods plus net investment. Sales in any period are a proportion of the income in the preceding period. Production for inventory is equal to the difference between actual and anticipated sales of the preceding period; that is, there is an attempt to keep inventory at a constant level. It is assumed that inventories are sufficient to meet differences between production and consumer demand.

Substituting the second and third equations into the first equation,

$$y_t = \beta y_{t-1} + \beta(y_{t-1} - y_{t-2}) + v_0$$
$$y_t - 2\beta y_{t-1} + \beta y_{t-2} = v_0$$

equivalently, so the t-values can begin at $t = 0$,

$$y_{t+2} - 2\beta y_{t+1} + \beta y_t = v_0$$

The auxiliary equation of the homogeneous difference equation corresponding to the equation $y_{t+2} - 2\beta y_{t+1} + \beta y_t = v_0$ is

$$m^2 - 2\beta m + \beta = 0$$

$$m = \frac{2\beta \pm \sqrt{4\beta^2 - 4\beta}}{2} = \beta \pm \sqrt{\beta^2 - \beta}$$

Since $0 < \beta < 1$, $\beta^2 - \beta < 0$ and the roots are complex numbers

$$m = \beta \pm i\sqrt{\beta(1 - \beta)}$$

Thus

$$r = \sqrt{\beta^2 + \beta(1 - \beta)} = \sqrt{\beta}$$

$$\cos\theta = \frac{\beta}{r} = \sqrt{\beta}$$

$$\sin\theta = \frac{\sqrt{\beta(1 - \beta)}}{r} = \sqrt{1 - \beta}$$

The general solution of the homogeneous equation

$$y_{t+2} - 2\beta y_{t+1} + \beta y_t = 0$$

is thus given by

$$y_t = (\sqrt{\beta})^t(C_1 \cos\theta t + C_2 \sin\theta t)$$

To find a particular solution of the nonhomogeneous equation

$$y_{t+2} - 2\beta y_{t+1} + \beta y_t = v_0$$

substitute $y^* = L$, a constant, into the equation,

$$L - 2\beta L + \beta L = v_0$$

$$L = \frac{v_0}{1 - \beta}$$

and the general solution of the nonhomogeneous equation has the form

$$y_t = (\sqrt{\beta})^t(C_1 \cos\theta t + C_2 \sin\theta t) + \frac{v_0}{1 - \beta}$$

The term involving sines and cosines results in cyclical fluctuations because of its oscillation between positive and negative values. These fluctuations are damped by the factor $(\sqrt{\beta})^t$ since $0 < \beta < 1$. Thus

$$(\sqrt{\beta})^t(C_1 \cos\theta t + C_2 \sin\theta t) \to 0 \qquad \text{as } t \to \infty$$

and

$$y_t \to \frac{v_0}{1 - \beta} \qquad \text{as } t \to \infty$$

as an equilibrium value.

PROBLEMS

Obtain the general solution for each of the following difference equations.

1. $y_{x+2} + 2y_{x+1} + y_x = 0$

2. $y_{x+2} - y_x = 0$

3. $2y_{x+2} - 5y_{x+1} + 2y_x = 0$

4. $3y_{x+2} - 6y_{x+1} + 4y_x = 0$

5. Find the general solution for the difference equation $y_{x+2} + 2y_x = 0$ and the particular solution if $y_0 = 1$, $y_1 = \sqrt{2}$.

6. Find the general solution for the difference equation $y_{x+2} + 3y_{x+1} + 3y_x = 0$ and the particular solution if $y_0 = 3$, $y_1 = 0$.

For each of the following difference equations, obtain the general solution and the particular solution for the specified initial values.

7. $y_{x+2} + 4y_{x+1} + 8y_x = 26, y_0 = 6, y_1 = 3$

8. $y_{x+2} + 8y_{x+1} + 16y_x = 25, y_0 = 0, y_1 = 4$

9. $y_{x+2} - 8y_{x+1} - 9y_x = 24, y_0 = 2, y_1 = 0$

10. $3y_{x+2} - 10y_{x+1} + 3y_x = 8, y_0 = 5, y_1 = 3$

Solve each of the following difference equations, determine the behavior of the solution sequence, and calculate the first few values of the solution sequence.

11. $y_{x+2} - 3y_{x+1} + 3y_x = 5, y_0 = 5, y_1 = 8$

12. $9y_{x+2} - 6y_{x+1} + y_x = 16, y_0 = 0, y_1 = 3$

13. $6y_{x+2} + 5y_{x+1} - y_x = 20, y_0 = 3, y_1 = 8$

14. $4y_{x+2} - y_x = 15, y_0 = 15, y_1 = 10$

15. $8y_{x+2} - 6y_{x+1} + y_x = 9, y_0 = 10, y_1 = 15$

16. $y_{x+2} - 4y_{x+1} + 4y_x = 1, y_0 = 0, y_1 = 1$

17. $y_{x+2} - 5y_{x+1} + 6y_x = 4, y_0 = 0, y_1 = 1$

18. $y_{x+2} - 7y_{x+1} + 12y_x = 2, y_0 = 0, y_1 = 1$

19. $y_{x+2} - 2y_{x+1} + 2y_x = 3, y_0 = 5, y_1 = 6$

20. $y_{x+2} - 4y_x = 9, y_0 = 0, y_1 = 1$

21. $12y_{x+2} - 7y_{x+1} + y_x = 18, y_0 = 0, y_1 = 3$

22. For the Samuelson model, verify the expressions for m_1, m_2, m, r, and θ given in the text.

23. For the Samuelson model, show that the roots of the auxiliary equation are complex if and only if

$$\alpha^2(1 + \beta)^2 - 4\alpha\beta < 0.$$

24. For the Samuelson model, obtain the solution and determine the behavior of the solution sequence if $\alpha = 0.8$ and $\beta = 3$.

25. For the Samuelson model, obtain the solution and determine the behavior of the solution sequence if $\alpha = 0.5$ and $\beta = 1$.

26. For the price-adjustment equation

$$p_{t+2} = \beta r_0 + \beta\alpha(p_{t+1} - p_t)$$

where p is price and β, α, and r_0 are positive constants, determine the limiting behavior of the solution if (a) $\beta\alpha = 1$, (b) $\beta\alpha = \frac{1}{2}$, (c) $\beta\alpha = 2$, (d) $\beta\alpha = \frac{3}{4}$.

27. Consider the following difference equation discussed by Baumol

$$Y_{t+2} - \frac{C}{s} Y_{t+1} + \frac{C}{s} Y_t = 0$$

where Y is warranted income and C and s are positive constants. Show that for $C \geq 4s$ this equation gives an explosive (divergent) solution for warranted income, but for $C < 4s$ warranted income is cyclic.

28. For the Metzler model, note that (total) inventory, denoted by i, is given by

$$i_t = i_{t-1} + s_t + u_t - y_t$$

Obtain an expression for change in inventory, $i_t - i_{t-1}$, in terms of y_t and determine the behavior of this solution sequence.

ANSWERS TO ODD-NUMBERED PROBLEMS

1. $y_x = (C_1 + C_2 x)(-1)^x$

3. $y_x = C_1(\frac{1}{2})^x + C_2(2)^x$

5. $y_x = (\sqrt{2})^x(\cos \frac{1}{2}\pi x + \sin \frac{1}{2}\pi x)$

7. $y_x = (2\sqrt{2})^x(4 \cos \frac{1}{4}\pi x - \frac{7}{2} \sin \frac{1}{4}\pi x) + 2$

9. $y_x = 3(-1)^x + \frac{1}{2}(9)^x - \frac{3}{2}$

11. $y_x = 2(\sqrt{3})^x(\sin \frac{1}{3}\pi x) + 5$, divergent (oscillatory), $y_0 = 5$, $y_1 = 8$, $y_2 = 5 + 3\sqrt{3}$, $y_3 = 5$, $y_4 = 5 - 9\sqrt{3}$, $y_5 = -22$

13. $y_x = -5(-1)^x + (\frac{1}{6})^{x-1} + 2$, divergent (oscillatory), $y_0 = 3$, $y_1 = 8$, $y_2 = -2\frac{5}{6}$, $y_3 = 7\frac{1}{36}$, $y_4 = -2\frac{215}{216}$, $y_5 = 7\frac{1}{1296}$

15. $y_x = 6(\frac{1}{4})^x + (\frac{1}{2})^x + 3$, convergent, $y_0 = 10$, $y_1 = 5$, $y_2 = 3\frac{5}{8}$, $y_3 = 3\frac{7}{32}$, $y_4 = 3\frac{11}{128}$, $y_5 = 3\frac{19}{512}$

17. $y_x = -5(2)^x + 3^{x+1} + 2$, divergent, $y_0 = 0$, $y_1 = 1$, $y_2 = 9$, $y_3 = 43$, $y_4 = 165$, $y_5 = 571$

19. $y_x = (\sqrt{2})^x(2 \cos \frac{1}{4}\pi x + \sin \frac{1}{4}\pi x) + 3$, divergent (oscillatory), $y_0 = 5$, $y_1 = 6$, $y_2 = 5$, $y_3 = 1$, $y_4 = -5$, $y_5 = -9$

21. $y_x = -12(\frac{1}{4})^x + 9(\frac{1}{3})^x + 3$, convergent, $y_0 = 0$, $y_1 = 3$, $y_2 = 3\frac{1}{4}$, $y_3 = 3\frac{7}{48}$, $y_4 = 3\frac{37}{576}$, $y_5 = 3\frac{175}{6912}$

25. $y_t = (\frac{1}{2}\sqrt{2})^t(C_1 \cos \frac{1}{4}\pi t + C_2 \sin \frac{1}{4}\pi t) + 2$, convergent (oscillatory) to 2

7

MATRIX ALGEBRA

■ 7.1 INTRODUCTION

In many economic analyses variables are assumed to be related by sets of linear equations. Matrix algebra provides a clear and concise notation for the formulation and solution of such problems, many of which would be almost impossibly complicated in conventional algebraic notation.

In this chapter, vectors, matrices, and operations on them are defined. Linear dependence of a set of vectors and the rank and inverse of a matrix are also discussed and are applied to the solution of simultaneous linear equations. In Chapter 8 further applications of matrix algebra are discussed.

☐ *DEFINITION OF A MATRIX*

A *matrix* is a rectangular array of numbers written in the form

$$\mathbf{A} = \begin{pmatrix} a_{11} & a_{12} \cdots a_{1n} \\ a_{21} & a_{22} \cdots a_{2n} \\ \vdots & \vdots \quad \vdots \\ a_{m1} & a_{m2} \cdots a_{mn} \end{pmatrix} \quad \text{or} \quad \mathbf{A} = \begin{bmatrix} a_{11} & a_{12} \cdots a_{1n} \\ a_{21} & a_{22} \cdots a_{2n} \\ \vdots & \vdots \quad \vdots \\ a_{m1} & a_{m2} \cdots a_{mn} \end{bmatrix}$$

The letters a_{ij} stand for real numbers, the *elements* of the matrix. Note that a_{ij} is the element in the ith row and the jth column of the matrix $\mathbf{A}$; thus the

547

matrix $\mathbf{A}$ is sometimes denoted by (a_{ij}) or by $\{a_{ij}\}$. A matrix that has m rows and n columns is said to be an $m \times n$ (read m by n) matrix or a matrix of *order* $m \times n$. If $m = n$, the matrix is said to be *square*.

Example

$$\begin{pmatrix} 1 & 0 & -2 & 6 \\ 4 & 8 & 3 & -9 \end{pmatrix} \quad \text{is a } 2 \times 4 \text{ matrix}$$

$$\begin{pmatrix} 6 & 6 & 3 \\ 3 & 8 & -2 \\ -1 & 0 & 0 \end{pmatrix} \quad \text{is a } 3 \times 3 \text{ (square) matrix}$$

$$\begin{pmatrix} 5 & 12 & 13 & 2 & 6 \\ -8 & 10 & 9 & 7 & 4 \\ -2 & -1 & -3 & 6 & 10 \end{pmatrix} \quad \text{is a } 3 \times 5 \text{ matrix}$$

$$\begin{pmatrix} 1 & -1 \\ -1 & 1 \end{pmatrix} \quad \text{is a } 2 \times 2 \text{ (square) matrix}$$

Two matrices of the same order are said to be *equal* if and only if all the corresponding elements are equal—that is, if the matrices are identical.

Example

If

$$\mathbf{A} = \begin{pmatrix} 2 & -2 \\ -2 & 2 \end{pmatrix}$$

$$\mathbf{B} = \begin{pmatrix} 2 & -2 & 2 \\ -2 & 2 & -2 \end{pmatrix}$$

$$\mathbf{C} = \begin{pmatrix} -2 & 2 \\ 2 & -2 \end{pmatrix}$$

$$\mathbf{D} = \begin{pmatrix} 2 & -2 \\ -2 & 2 \end{pmatrix}$$

$\mathbf{A} = \mathbf{D}$, but $\mathbf{A} \neq \mathbf{B}$, $\mathbf{A} \neq \mathbf{C}$, and $\mathbf{B} \neq \mathbf{C}$.

□ DEFINITION OF A VECTOR

A matrix that consists of a single column—that is, an $m \times 1$ matrix—is said to be a *column vector* and is written

$$\mathbf{u} = \begin{pmatrix} u_1 \\ u_2 \\ \cdot \\ \cdot \\ u_m \end{pmatrix} \quad \text{or} \quad \mathbf{u} = \begin{bmatrix} u_1 \\ u_2 \\ \cdot \\ \cdot \\ u_m \end{bmatrix}$$

The letters u_i stand for real numbers, the *components* of the vector; u_i is the ith component of the vector **u**. A column vector that has m rows is said to be an *m-component* or an *m-dimensional* vector.

Similarly, a matrix that contains only a single row—that is, a $1 \times n$ matrix— is said to be a <u>*row vector*</u> and is written

$$\mathbf{v} = (v_1, v_2, \ldots v_n) \quad \text{or} \quad \mathbf{v} = [v_1, v_2, \ldots, v_n]$$

The letters v_j stand for real numbers, the *components* of the vector; v_j is the jth component of the vector **v**. A row vector that has n columns is said to be an *n-component* or an *n-dimensional vector*.

Example

$$\begin{pmatrix} -1 \\ -1 \end{pmatrix} \quad \text{is a } 2 \times 1 \text{ matrix, a 2-dimensional column vector}$$

$$\begin{pmatrix} 0 \\ 0 \\ 3 \\ 0 \\ -2 \end{pmatrix} \quad \text{is a } 5 \times 1 \text{ matrix, a 5-dimensional column vector}$$

$(0, 3, 0)$ is a 1×3 matrix, a 3-dimensional row vector

$(-1, -1, 5, -1)$ is a 1×4 matrix, a 4-dimensional row vector

Two row vectors having the same number of rows or two column vectors having the same number of columns are said to be *equal* if and only if all the corresponding elements are equal—that is, if the vectors are identical.

Example

$$\mathbf{u} = (1, 3)$$

$$\mathbf{v} = \begin{pmatrix} 1 \\ 3 \end{pmatrix}$$

$$\mathbf{w} = (1, 3)$$

$$\mathbf{x} = (3, 1)$$

$\mathbf{u} = \mathbf{w}$, but $\mathbf{u} \neq \mathbf{v}$, $\mathbf{u} \neq \mathbf{x}$, and $\mathbf{v} \neq \mathbf{x}$.

NOTE: Frequently it is useful to regard a matrix as being composed of a series of row or column vectors; thus the matrix

$$\begin{pmatrix} 1 & -6 \\ 2 & 2 \\ -3 & 4 \end{pmatrix}$$

can be regarded as consisting of the two column vectors

$$\begin{pmatrix} 1 \\ 2 \\ -3 \end{pmatrix} \quad \text{and} \quad \begin{pmatrix} -6 \\ 2 \\ 4 \end{pmatrix}$$

or, alternatively, of the three row vectors

$$(1, -6) \quad (2, 2) \quad (-3, 4)$$

■ 7.2 MATRIX OPERATIONS

Operations analogous to the operations of addition, subtraction, multiplication, and division of real numbers can be defined for matrices. Since a matrix is an array of numbers, rather than a single number, some of the properties of operations for real numbers do not hold for the analogous matrix operations; specific examples are noted in following sections.

□ ADDITION AND SUBTRACTION OF MATRICES

Matrices can be added or subtracted if and only if they are of the same order. The sum or difference of two $m \times n$ matrices is another $m \times n$ matrix whose elements are the sums or differences of the corresponding elements in the component matrices; thus,
if

$$A = \begin{pmatrix} a_{11} & \dots & a_{1n} \\ \vdots & & \vdots \\ a_{m1} & \dots & a_{mn} \end{pmatrix}$$

$$B = \begin{pmatrix} b_{11} & \dots & b_{1n} \\ \vdots & & \vdots \\ b_{m1} & \dots & b_{mn} \end{pmatrix}$$

then

$$A \pm B = C$$

where

$$C = \begin{pmatrix} a_{11} \pm b_{11} & \dots & a_{1n} \pm b_{1n} \\ \vdots & & \vdots \\ a_{m1} \pm b_{m1} & \dots & a_{mn} \pm b_{mn} \end{pmatrix} = \begin{pmatrix} c_{11} & \dots & c_{1n} \\ \vdots & & \vdots \\ c_{m1} & \dots & c_{mn} \end{pmatrix}$$

that is, $(a_{ij}) + (b_{ij}) = (c_{ij})$, where $c_{ij} = a_{ij} + b_{ij}$ for all i and j.

NOTE: Especially when various operations are being performed on them, the order of matrices is frequently denoted by subscripts, for example, $\mathbf{A}_{m \times n}$ or $(a_{ij})_{m \times n}$.

Example

(a) $\begin{pmatrix} 3 & 2 & -4 \\ 5 & 6 & 8 \\ 3 & 0 & 0 \end{pmatrix} + \begin{pmatrix} 0 & 3 & 8 \\ -5 & -6 & 2 \\ 0 & 0 & -4 \end{pmatrix} = \begin{pmatrix} 3 & 5 & 4 \\ 0 & 0 & 10 \\ 3 & 0 & -4 \end{pmatrix}$

(b) $\begin{pmatrix} 3 & -10 \\ -11 & 25 \end{pmatrix} - \begin{pmatrix} -6 & -4 \\ 22 & -21 \end{pmatrix} = \begin{pmatrix} 9 & -6 \\ -33 & 46 \end{pmatrix}$

(c) $(4, 6, 12) + (-3, 2, -12) = (1, 8, 0)$

(d) $\begin{pmatrix} 1 \\ 1 \\ 2 \\ 4 \\ 1 \end{pmatrix} - \begin{pmatrix} 1 \\ 1 \\ 2 \\ 4 \\ 1 \end{pmatrix} = \begin{pmatrix} 0 \\ 0 \\ 0 \\ 0 \\ 0 \end{pmatrix}$

(e) $\begin{pmatrix} 2 & 3 \\ 6 & 4 \end{pmatrix} + \begin{pmatrix} 1 & 1 \\ -1 & 2 \end{pmatrix} - \begin{pmatrix} 0 & 0 \\ 6 & 4 \end{pmatrix} = \begin{pmatrix} 3 & 4 \\ -1 & 2 \end{pmatrix}$

(f) $\begin{pmatrix} 1 \\ 1 \\ 1 \end{pmatrix} + \begin{pmatrix} 3 \\ 2 \\ 4 \end{pmatrix} - \begin{pmatrix} 6 \\ 8 \\ 10 \end{pmatrix} + \begin{pmatrix} 0 \\ 1 \\ 0 \end{pmatrix} = \begin{pmatrix} -2 \\ -4 \\ -5 \end{pmatrix}$

(g) $(2, 1) + (3, 4) + (6, 7) - (11, 12) = (0, 0)$

(h) $\begin{pmatrix} 1 & 4 \\ 2 & 6 \\ 3 & 8 \end{pmatrix} - \begin{pmatrix} 0 & 5 \\ 7 & 9 \\ 11 & 12 \end{pmatrix} - \begin{pmatrix} 10 & 13 \\ 20 & 0 \\ 1 & 0 \end{pmatrix} = \begin{pmatrix} -9 & -14 \\ -25 & -3 \\ -9 & -4 \end{pmatrix}$

□ MULTIPLICATION OF A MATRIX BY A SCALAR

A real number (a 1×1 matrix) is referred to as a *scalar* when it occurs in operations involving matrices. When a matrix is multiplied by scalar, every element in the matrix is multiplied by that scalar (number); thus, if

$$\mathbf{A} = \begin{pmatrix} a_{11} & \ldots & a_{1n} \\ \vdots & & \vdots \\ a_{m1} & \ldots & a_{mn} \end{pmatrix} \quad \text{and } k \text{ is any constant}$$

then

$$k \times \mathbf{A}_{m \times n} = k\mathbf{A}_{m \times n} = \begin{pmatrix} ka_{11} & \ldots & ka_{1n} \\ \vdots & & \vdots \\ ka_{m1} & \ldots & ka_{mn} \end{pmatrix} = k(a_{ij})_{m \times n} = (ka_{ij})_{m \times n}$$

Example

(a) $\quad 3 \begin{pmatrix} 4 & -3 \\ 8 & -2 \\ -1 & 0 \end{pmatrix} = \begin{pmatrix} 12 & -9 \\ 24 & -6 \\ -3 & 0 \end{pmatrix}$

(b) $\quad 5 \begin{pmatrix} 0 \\ -1 \\ 0 \end{pmatrix} = \begin{pmatrix} 0 \\ -5 \\ 0 \end{pmatrix}$

(c) $\quad -1\,(6, -2, -3) = (-6, 2, 3)$

(d) $\quad a \begin{pmatrix} 5 & 6 & 2 & 4 \\ -3 & -1 & 0 & -6 \end{pmatrix} = \begin{pmatrix} 5a & 6a & 2a & 4a \\ -3a & -a & 0 & -6a \end{pmatrix}$

(e) $\quad -b \begin{pmatrix} 0 \\ -2 \\ 3 \\ -1 \\ 5 \end{pmatrix} = \begin{pmatrix} 0 \\ 2b \\ -3b \\ b \\ -5b \end{pmatrix}$

(f) $\quad c\,(0, 0, 0, 0, 16) = (0, 0, 0, 0, 16c)$

□ MULTIPLICATION OF MATRICES

Two matrices can be multiplied if and only if the number of columns in one matrix is equal to the number of rows in the other matrix. In particular, the matrix product **AB** is defined if and only if the number of columns in **A** is the same as the number of rows in **B**, in this case the matrices **A** and **B** are said to be *conformable* for multiplication and the product matrix has the same number of rows as **A** and the same number of columns as **B**. Thus an $m \times n$ matrix may be multiplied by an $n \times p$ matrix to give an $m \times p$ matrix.

DEFINITION: When a $1 \times n$ row vector multiplies an $n \times 1$ column vector, the result is a scalar, the *inner product* of the two vectors; its value is the sum of products of the components of the vectors. Thus if

$$\mathbf{u} = \begin{pmatrix} u_1 \\ \vdots \\ u_n \end{pmatrix} \quad \text{and} \quad \mathbf{v} = (v_1, \ldots, v_n)$$

then $\mathbf{v}_{1 \times n}\mathbf{u}_{n \times 1} = w$ (a scalar), where $w = v_1 u_1 + v_2 u_2 + \cdots + v_n u_n = \sum_{i=1}^{n} v_i u_i$.

When two matrices are multiplied, the element in the ith and row jth column of the product matrix is the inner product of the ith row vector of the first matrix with the jth column vector of the second matrix. Thus the product of two matrices may be written as a matrix of their inner products: If $\mathbf{A} = (a_{ij})_{m \times n}$ and $\mathbf{B} = (b_{jk})_{n \times p}$, then $\mathbf{AB} = \mathbf{C}$, where

$$\mathbf{C} = (c_{ik})_{m \times p} = \begin{pmatrix} \sum_{j=1}^{n} a_{1j} b_{j1} & \cdots & \sum_{j=1}^{n} a_{1j} b_{jm} \\ \vdots & & \vdots \\ \sum_{j=1}^{n} a_{mj} b_{j1} & \cdots & \sum_{j=1}^{n} a_{mj} b_{jn} \end{pmatrix}$$

that is, $c_{ik} = \sum_{j=1}^{n} a_{ij} b_{jk}$.

Example

(a) $\begin{pmatrix} 1 & 3 & -1 \\ 2 & 0 & 0 \\ 0 & -1 & 6 \end{pmatrix}_{3 \times 3} \begin{pmatrix} 1 & 0 \\ -1 & 2 \\ 1 & 3 \end{pmatrix}_{3 \times 2} = \begin{pmatrix} -3 & 3 \\ 2 & 0 \\ 7 & 16 \end{pmatrix}_{3 \times 2}$

(b) $(-1, 0, 6, 3, 2)_{1 \times 5} \begin{pmatrix} 3 & 0 \\ 4 & 0 \\ -2 & 3 \\ 1 & 8 \\ 0 & -2 \end{pmatrix}_{5 \times 2} = (-12, 38)_{1 \times 2}$

In matrix multiplication, the sequence in which multiplication is performed is very important. If $\mathbf{A}$ is $m \times n$ and $\mathbf{B}$ is $n \times m$, then it is possible to obtain both of the product matrices $\mathbf{AB}$ and $\mathbf{BA}$—however, in general $\mathbf{AB} \neq \mathbf{BA}$. In the matrix product $\mathbf{AB}$, $\mathbf{A}$ is said to *premultiply* $\mathbf{B}$ or, alternatively, $\mathbf{B}$ is said to *postmultiply* $\mathbf{A}$. Since, in general, premultiplication and postmultiplication give different results, even when both are defined, care must be taken to preserve the appropriate sequence in all matrix multiplications. This precaution is not necessary in the multiplication of numbers.

Example

(a)
$$\begin{pmatrix} 4 & 6 & -1 & 3 \\ 0 & -1 & 2 & 1 \end{pmatrix}_{2 \times 4} \begin{pmatrix} 1 & 2 \\ -1 & 1 \\ 1 & 6 \\ 2 & 3 \end{pmatrix}_{4 \times 2} = \begin{pmatrix} 3 & 17 \\ 5 & 14 \end{pmatrix}_{2 \times 2}$$

$$\begin{pmatrix} 1 & 2 \\ -1 & 1 \\ 1 & 6 \\ 2 & 3 \end{pmatrix}_{4 \times 2} \begin{pmatrix} 4 & 6 & -1 & 3 \\ 0 & -1 & 2 & 1 \end{pmatrix}_{2 \times 4} = \begin{pmatrix} 4 & 4 & 3 & 5 \\ -4 & -7 & 3 & -2 \\ 4 & 0 & 11 & 9 \\ 8 & 9 & 4 & 9 \end{pmatrix}_{4 \times 4}$$

(b)
$$\begin{pmatrix} 5 & -6 \\ -1 & 0 \\ 0 & 3 \end{pmatrix}_{3 \times 2} \begin{pmatrix} -1 & 8 & -3 \\ 0 & 10 & -4 \end{pmatrix}_{2 \times 3} = \begin{pmatrix} -5 & -20 & 9 \\ 1 & -8 & 3 \\ 0 & 30 & -12 \end{pmatrix}_{3 \times 3}$$

$$\begin{pmatrix} -1 & 8 & -3 \\ 0 & 10 & -4 \end{pmatrix}_{2 \times 3} \begin{pmatrix} 5 & -6 \\ -1 & 0 \\ 0 & 3 \end{pmatrix}_{3 \times 2} = \begin{pmatrix} -13 & -3 \\ -10 & -12 \end{pmatrix}_{2 \times 2}$$

(c)
$$\begin{pmatrix} -1 & 3 & 1 \\ 2 & 0 & -2 \\ 0 & 4 & 5 \end{pmatrix}_{3 \times 3} \begin{pmatrix} 0 & 2 & 3 \\ 8 & -1 & 9 \\ -2 & 0 & 5 \end{pmatrix}_{3 \times 3} = \begin{pmatrix} 22 & -5 & 29 \\ 4 & 4 & -4 \\ 22 & -4 & 61 \end{pmatrix}_{3 \times 3}$$

$$\begin{pmatrix} 0 & 2 & 3 \\ 8 & -1 & 9 \\ -2 & 0 & 5 \end{pmatrix}_{3 \times 3} \begin{pmatrix} -1 & 3 & 1 \\ 2 & 0 & -2 \\ 0 & 4 & 5 \end{pmatrix}_{3 \times 3} = \begin{pmatrix} 4 & 12 & 11 \\ -10 & 60 & 55 \\ 2 & 14 & 23 \end{pmatrix}_{3 \times 3}$$

NOTE: When a row vector premultiplies a column vector, the result is their inner product, a scalar whose value is the sum of the products of the elements of the two vectors. When an $n \times 1$ column vector premultiplies a $1 \times n$ row vector, the result is an $n \times n$ square matrix whose elements are the squares and products of the individual vectors; thus if

$$\mathbf{u} = \begin{pmatrix} u_1 \\ \vdots \\ u_n \end{pmatrix} \quad \text{and} \quad \mathbf{v} = (v_1, \ldots, v_n)$$

then, as above, $\mathbf{v}_{1 \times n} \mathbf{u}_{n \times 1} = w$ (a scalar) where $w \sum_{i=1}^{n} v_i u_i$, and $\mathbf{u}_{n \times 1} \mathbf{v}_{1 \times n} = \mathbf{x}_{n \times n}$ (a square matrix), where $x_{ij} = u_i v_j$.

Example

(a)
$$(1, 3, 6) \begin{pmatrix} -2 \\ 4 \\ -1 \end{pmatrix} = -2 + 12 - 6 = 4$$

$$\begin{pmatrix} -2 \\ 4 \\ -1 \end{pmatrix} (1, 3, 6) = \begin{pmatrix} -2 & -6 & -12 \\ 4 & 12 & 24 \\ -1 & -3 & -6 \end{pmatrix}$$

(b) $(1, 0, 0, 2, -3) \begin{pmatrix} 0 \\ -1 \\ -4 \\ -3 \\ -2 \end{pmatrix} = 0 + 0 + 0 - 6 + 6 = 0$

$$\begin{pmatrix} 0 \\ -1 \\ -4 \\ -3 \\ -2 \end{pmatrix} (1, 0, 0, 2, -3) = \begin{pmatrix} 0 & 0 & 0 & 0 & 0 \\ -1 & 0 & 0 & -2 & 3 \\ -4 & 0 & 0 & -8 & 12 \\ -3 & 0 & 0 & -6 & 9 \\ -2 & 0 & 0 & -4 & 6 \end{pmatrix}$$

Although the sequence in which two matrices are multiplied affects the result, the order in which three or more matrices are multiplied does not affect the result, provided the sequence is preserved. That is,

$$\mathbf{A}_{m \times n} \mathbf{B}_{n \times p} \mathbf{C}_{p \times q} = \mathbf{A}_{m \times n} (\mathbf{B}_{n \times p} \mathbf{C}_{p \times q}) = (\mathbf{A}_{m \times n} \mathbf{B}_{n \times p}) \mathbf{C}_{p \times q}$$

Thus addition of matrices is commutative (that is $\mathbf{A} + \mathbf{B} = \mathbf{B} + \mathbf{A}$) and both addition and subtraction are associative [that is, $\mathbf{A} \pm \mathbf{B} \pm \mathbf{C} = \mathbf{A} \pm (\mathbf{B} \pm \mathbf{C}) = (\mathbf{A} \pm \mathbf{B}) \pm \mathbf{C}$]; multiplication of matrices is *not* commutative (that is, $\mathbf{AB} \neq \mathbf{BA}$) but is associative [that is, $\mathbf{ABC} = \mathbf{A(BC)} = \mathbf{(AB)C}$].

Examples

$$\begin{pmatrix} 1 & -1 & 0 \\ 2 & -3 & 4 \\ 0 & 0 & 1 \end{pmatrix}_{3 \times 3} \begin{pmatrix} 3 \\ 1 \\ -1 \end{pmatrix}_{3 \times 1} (0, 2, -1)_{1 \times 3} = \begin{pmatrix} 1 & -1 & 0 \\ 2 & -3 & 4 \\ 0 & 0 & 1 \end{pmatrix}_{3 \times 3} \begin{pmatrix} 0 & 6 & -3 \\ 0 & 2 & -1 \\ 0 & -2 & 1 \end{pmatrix}_{3 \times 3}$$

$$= \begin{pmatrix} 0 & 4 & -2 \\ 0 & -2 & 1 \\ 0 & -2 & 1 \end{pmatrix}_{3 \times 3}$$

Alternatively, by associativity,

$$\begin{pmatrix} 1 & -1 & 0 \\ 2 & -3 & 4 \\ 0 & 0 & 1 \end{pmatrix}_{3 \times 3} \begin{pmatrix} 3 \\ 1 \\ -1 \end{pmatrix}_{3 \times 1} (0, 2, 1)_{1 \times 3} = \begin{pmatrix} 2 \\ -1 \\ -1 \end{pmatrix}_{3 \times 1} (0, 2, -1)_{1 \times 3}$$

$$= \begin{pmatrix} 0 & 4 & -2 \\ 0 & -2 & 1 \\ 0 & -2 & 1 \end{pmatrix}_{3 \times 3}$$

$$\begin{pmatrix} 1 & -1 \\ 6 & 10 \end{pmatrix}_{2 \times 2} \begin{pmatrix} 5 & -2 & 3 \\ -8 & 0 & 6 \end{pmatrix}_{2 \times 3} \begin{pmatrix} -1 \\ 0 \\ -4 \end{pmatrix}_{3 \times 1} = \begin{pmatrix} 1 & -1 \\ 6 & 10 \end{pmatrix}_{2 \times 2} \begin{pmatrix} -17 \\ -16 \end{pmatrix}_{2 \times 1}$$

$$= \begin{pmatrix} -1 \\ -262 \end{pmatrix}_{2 \times 1}$$

Alternatively, by associativity,

$$\begin{pmatrix} 1 & -1 \\ 6 & 10 \end{pmatrix}_{2\times 2} \begin{pmatrix} 5 & -2 & 3 \\ -8 & 0 & 6 \end{pmatrix}_{2\times 3} \begin{pmatrix} -1 \\ 0 \\ -4 \end{pmatrix}_{3\times 1} = \begin{pmatrix} 13 & -2 & -3 \\ -50 & -12 & 78 \end{pmatrix}_{2\times 3} \begin{pmatrix} -1 \\ 0 \\ -4 \end{pmatrix}_{3\times 1}$$

$$= \begin{pmatrix} -1 \\ -262 \end{pmatrix}_{2\times 1}$$

$$\begin{pmatrix} 3 & 4 \\ 4 & 3 \end{pmatrix}_{2\times 2} \begin{pmatrix} 0 & 1 \\ -1 & 0 \end{pmatrix}_{2\times 2} \begin{pmatrix} -6 & -8 & 10 \\ -5 & 5 & 4 \end{pmatrix}_{2\times 3} = \begin{pmatrix} 3 & 4 \\ 4 & 3 \end{pmatrix}_{2\times 2} \begin{pmatrix} -5 & 5 & 4 \\ 6 & 8 & -10 \end{pmatrix}_{2\times 3}$$

$$= \begin{pmatrix} 9 & 47 & -28 \\ -2 & 44 & -14 \end{pmatrix}_{2\times 3}$$

Alternatively, by associativity,

$$\begin{pmatrix} 3 & 4 \\ 4 & 3 \end{pmatrix}_{2\times 2} \begin{pmatrix} 0 & 1 \\ -1 & 0 \end{pmatrix}_{2\times 2} \begin{pmatrix} -6 & -8 & 10 \\ -5 & 5 & 4 \end{pmatrix}_{2\times 3} = \begin{pmatrix} -4 & 3 \\ -3 & 4 \end{pmatrix}_{2\times 2} \begin{pmatrix} -6 & -8 & 10 \\ -5 & 5 & 4 \end{pmatrix}_{2\times 3}$$

$$= \begin{pmatrix} 9 & 47 & -28 \\ -2 & 44 & -14 \end{pmatrix}_{2\times 3}$$

$$(1, -1, 4, 2)_{1\times 4} \begin{pmatrix} 0 \\ 2 \\ -1 \\ 0 \end{pmatrix}_{4\times 1} (-1, 0, 6)_{1\times 3} = (1, -1, 4, 2)_{1\times 4} \begin{pmatrix} 0 & 0 & 0 \\ -2 & 0 & 12 \\ 1 & 0 & -6 \\ 0 & 0 & 0 \end{pmatrix}_{4\times 3}$$

$$= (6, 0, -36)_{1\times 3}$$

Alternatively, by associativity,

$$(1, -1, 4, 2)_{1\times 4} \begin{pmatrix} 0 \\ 2 \\ -1 \\ 0 \end{pmatrix}_{4\times 1} (-1, 0, 6)_{1\times 3} = -6 \times (-1, 0, 6)_{1\times 3}$$

$$= (6, 0, -36)_{1\times 3}$$

■ 7.3 SPECIAL TYPES OF MATRICES

□ DIAGONAL MATRICES

A *diagonal matrix* is a square matrix that has zeros everywhere except on the main diagonal (that is, the diagonal running from upper left to lower right); thus

$$\mathbf{A} = \begin{pmatrix} a_{11} & \ldots & a_{1n} \\ \vdots & & \vdots \\ a_{n1} & \ldots & a_{nn} \end{pmatrix} = (a_{ij})_{n\times n}$$

is a diagonal matrix if and only if

$a_{ij} = 0$ for $i \neq j$

$a_{ij} \neq 0$ for at least one $i = j$ (if all the elements of a matrix are zero, it is a *null matrix* discussed below)

An $n \times n$ diagonal matrix may be indicated by the notation

$$\mathbf{A} = \begin{pmatrix} a_{11} & & \bigcirc \\ & \ddots & \\ \bigcirc & & a_{nn} \end{pmatrix} \quad \text{or} \quad \begin{pmatrix} a_1 & & \bigcirc \\ & \ddots & \\ \bigcirc & & a_n \end{pmatrix}$$

or by

$$\mathbf{D}_n = \begin{pmatrix} d_1 & & \bigcirc \\ & \ddots & \\ \bigcirc & & d_n \end{pmatrix}$$

Example

$$\begin{pmatrix} 1 & 0 & 0 \\ 0 & -3 & 0 \\ 0 & 0 & 10 \end{pmatrix} \quad \text{and} \quad \begin{pmatrix} -1 & 0 & 0 & 0 \\ 0 & 0 & 0 & 0 \\ 0 & 0 & 0 & 0 \\ 0 & 0 & 0 & 7 \end{pmatrix}$$

are diagonal matrices.

□ IDENTITY MATRICES

An *identity matrix* is a diagonal matrix each of whose diagonal elements is a positive one; thus

$$\mathbf{A} = \begin{pmatrix} a_{11} \cdots a_{1n} \\ \vdots \quad\quad \vdots \\ a_{n1} \cdots a_{nn} \end{pmatrix} = (a_{ij})_{n \times n}$$

is an identity matrix if and only if

$$a_{ij} = 0 \quad \text{for } i \neq j$$
$$a_{ij} = 1 \quad \text{for } i = j$$

or equivalently, a diagonal matrix $\mathbf{D}_n$ is an identity matrix if and only if

$$d_i = 1 \quad \text{for } i = 1, 2, \ldots, n$$

An $n \times n$ identity matrix is denoted by $\mathbf{I}_n$.

Example

$$\mathbf{I}_3 = \begin{pmatrix} 1 & 0 & 0 \\ 0 & 1 & 0 \\ 0 & 0 & 1 \end{pmatrix} \quad \text{and} \quad \mathbf{I}_6 = \begin{pmatrix} 1 & 0 & 0 & 0 & 0 & 0 \\ 0 & 1 & 0 & 0 & 0 & 0 \\ 0 & 0 & 1 & 0 & 0 & 0 \\ 0 & 0 & 0 & 1 & 0 & 0 \\ 0 & 0 & 0 & 0 & 1 & 0 \\ 0 & 0 & 0 & 0 & 0 & 1 \end{pmatrix}$$

are the 3×3 and 6×6 identity matrices.

Note that premultiplying or postmultiplying a matrix by the appropriately sized identity matrix leaves it unchanged—that is,

$$\mathbf{A}_{m \times n} = \mathbf{I}_m \mathbf{A}_{m \times n} = \mathbf{A}_{m \times n} \mathbf{I}_n = \mathbf{A}_{m \times n}$$

Examples

$$\begin{pmatrix} 2 & -3 & -6 & 4 \\ -1 & -1 & 0 & 3 \end{pmatrix}_{2 \times 4} = \begin{pmatrix} 1 & 0 \\ 0 & 1 \end{pmatrix}_{2 \times 2} \begin{pmatrix} 2 & -3 & -6 & 4 \\ -1 & -1 & 0 & 3 \end{pmatrix}_{2 \times 4}$$

$$= \begin{pmatrix} 2 & -3 & -6 & 4 \\ -1 & -1 & 0 & 3 \end{pmatrix}_{2 \times 4} \begin{pmatrix} 1 & 0 & 0 & 0 \\ 0 & 1 & 0 & 0 \\ 0 & 0 & 1 & 0 \\ 0 & 0 & 0 & 1 \end{pmatrix}_{4 \times 4}$$

$$= \begin{pmatrix} 2 & -3 & -6 & 4 \\ -1 & -1 & 0 & 3 \end{pmatrix}_{2 \times 4}$$

$$\begin{pmatrix} 3 & 0 & 0 \\ 0 & -2 & 0 \\ 0 & 0 & 6 \end{pmatrix}_{3 \times 3} = \begin{pmatrix} 1 & 0 & 0 \\ 0 & 1 & 0 \\ 0 & 0 & 1 \end{pmatrix}_{3 \times 3} \begin{pmatrix} 3 & 0 & 0 \\ 0 & -2 & 0 \\ 0 & 0 & 6 \end{pmatrix}_{3 \times 3}$$

$$= \begin{pmatrix} 3 & 0 & 0 \\ 0 & -2 & 0 \\ 0 & 0 & 6 \end{pmatrix}_{3 \times 3} \begin{pmatrix} 1 & 0 & 0 \\ 0 & 1 & 0 \\ 0 & 0 & 1 \end{pmatrix}_{3 \times 3}$$

$$= \begin{pmatrix} 3 & 0 & 0 \\ 0 & -2 & 0 \\ 0 & 0 & 6 \end{pmatrix}_{3 \times 3}$$

☐ *NULL MATRICES*

A *null matrix* is an $m \times n$ matrix all of whose elements are zeros; it is denoted by $\mathbf{O}$. When the appropriately sized null matrix is added to or subtracted from another matrix that matrix is unchanged—that is,

$$\mathbf{A}_{m \times n} = \mathbf{A}_{m \times n} \pm \mathbf{O}_{m \times n} = \mathbf{A}_{m \times n}$$

Premultiplying or postmultiplying a matrix by the appropriately sized null matrix results in another null matrix—that is,

$$\mathbf{O}_{k \times m} \mathbf{A}_{m \times n} = \mathbf{O}_{k \times n} \quad \text{and} \quad \mathbf{A}_{m \times n} \mathbf{O}_{n \times 1} = \mathbf{O}_{m \times 1}$$

Examples

$$\begin{pmatrix} 0 & 1 & 0 \\ 10 & 0 & -3 \end{pmatrix}_{2 \times 3} \pm \begin{pmatrix} 0 & 0 & 0 \\ 0 & 0 & 0 \end{pmatrix}_{2 \times 3} = \begin{pmatrix} 0 & 1 & 0 \\ 10 & 0 & -3 \end{pmatrix}_{2 \times 3}$$

$$\begin{pmatrix} 0 & 0 \\ 0 & 0 \\ 0 & 0 \end{pmatrix}_{3 \times 2} \begin{pmatrix} 1 & 6 & 4 & -10 \\ -1 & 20 & -13 & 11 \end{pmatrix}_{2 \times 4} = \begin{pmatrix} 0 & 0 & 0 & 0 \\ 0 & 0 & 0 & 0 \\ 0 & 0 & 0 & 0 \end{pmatrix}_{3 \times 4}$$

$$\begin{pmatrix} 1 & 6 & 4 & -10 \\ -1 & 20 & -13 & 11 \end{pmatrix}_{2 \times 4} \begin{pmatrix} 0 \\ 0 \\ 0 \\ 0 \end{pmatrix}_{4 \times 1} = \begin{pmatrix} 0 \\ 0 \end{pmatrix}_{2 \times 1}$$

■ 7.4 THE TRANSPOSE OF A MATRIX

The *transpose* of an $m \times n$ matrix $\mathbf{A}$ is an $n \times m$ matrix, denoted by $\mathbf{A}'$, whose rows are the columns of $\mathbf{A}$; thus if

$$\mathbf{A}_{m \times n} = \begin{pmatrix} a_{11} & \dots & a_{1n} \\ \vdots & & \vdots \\ a_{m1} & \dots & a_{mn} \end{pmatrix} = (a_{ij})_{m \times n}$$

then the transpose of $\mathbf{A}$ is

$$\mathbf{A}'_{n \times m} = \begin{pmatrix} a_{11} & \dots & a_{1n} \\ \vdots & & \vdots \\ a_{m1} & \dots & a_{mn} \end{pmatrix}' = \begin{pmatrix} a_{11} & \dots & a_{1m} \\ \vdots & & \vdots \\ a_{n1} & \dots & a_{mn} \end{pmatrix} = (a_{ji})_{n \times m} = (a_{ij})'_{m \times n}$$

Note that the transpose of an n-dimensional row vector is an n-dimensional column vector and, similarly, the transpose of an n-dimensional column vector is an n-dimensional row vector. The transpose of a diagonal matrix is that same diagonal matrix.

Example

(a) $\begin{pmatrix} 3 & 2 & 0 \\ -6 & 0 & -1 \end{pmatrix}'_{2 \times 3} = \begin{pmatrix} 3 & -6 \\ 2 & 0 \\ 0 & -1 \end{pmatrix}_{3 \times 2}$

(b) $(6, 2, -1, 0, -5)'_{1 \times 5} = \begin{pmatrix} 6 \\ 2 \\ -1 \\ 0 \\ -5 \end{pmatrix}_{5 \times 1}$

(c) $\begin{pmatrix} 6 & -8 & -10 \\ -2 & 0 & 7 \\ 30 & 40 & 0 \end{pmatrix}'_{3 \times 3} = \begin{pmatrix} 6 & -2 & 30 \\ -8 & 0 & 40 \\ -10 & 7 & 0 \end{pmatrix}_{3 \times 3}$

(d) $\begin{pmatrix} 3 \\ 0 \\ -1 \\ 4 \end{pmatrix}'_{4 \times 1} = (3, 0, -1, 4)_{1 \times 4}$

(e) $\begin{pmatrix} -1 & 5 & -3 \\ 5 & 0 & 4 \\ -3 & 4 & 9 \end{pmatrix}'_{3 \times 3} = \begin{pmatrix} -1 & 5 & -3 \\ 5 & 0 & 4 \\ -3 & 4 & 9 \end{pmatrix}_{3 \times 3}$

(f) $\begin{pmatrix} 6 & 0 & 0 & 0 \\ 0 & -2 & 0 & 0 \\ 0 & 0 & 3 & 0 \\ 0 & 0 & 0 & 5 \end{pmatrix}'_{4 \times 4} = \begin{pmatrix} -6 & 0 & 0 & 0 \\ 0 & -2 & 0 & 0 \\ 0 & 0 & 3 & 0 \\ 0 & 0 & 0 & 5 \end{pmatrix}_{4 \times 4}$

If a (square) matrix and its transpose are equal, that is, $a_{ij} = a_{ji}$ for all i and j, then the matrix is said to be *symmetric* (about its main diagonal). In the preceding example, matrices (e) and (f) are symmetric.

A symmetric matrix that reproduces itself when it is multiplied by itself is said to be *idempotent*. Thus **A** is idempotent if and only if

$$\mathbf{A}' = \mathbf{A}$$

and

$$\mathbf{A}\,\mathbf{A} = \mathbf{A}$$

Examples

The identity matrix (of any size) is idempotent, since

$$\mathbf{I}_n' = \mathbf{I}_n$$

and

$$\mathbf{I}_n\mathbf{I}_n = \mathbf{I}_n$$

The matrix

$$\begin{pmatrix} \frac{1}{5} & \frac{2}{5} \\ \frac{2}{5} & \frac{4}{5} \end{pmatrix}$$

is idempotent, since

$$\begin{pmatrix} \frac{1}{5} & \frac{2}{5} \\ \frac{2}{5} & \frac{4}{5} \end{pmatrix}' = \begin{pmatrix} \frac{1}{5} & \frac{2}{5} \\ \frac{2}{5} & \frac{4}{5} \end{pmatrix}$$

and

$$\begin{pmatrix} \frac{1}{5} & \frac{2}{5} \\ \frac{2}{5} & \frac{4}{5} \end{pmatrix}\begin{pmatrix} \frac{1}{5} & \frac{2}{5} \\ \frac{2}{5} & \frac{4}{5} \end{pmatrix} = \begin{pmatrix} \frac{1}{5} & \frac{2}{5} \\ \frac{2}{5} & \frac{4}{5} \end{pmatrix}$$

☐ *TRANSPOSE OF A SUM OR DIFFERENCE OF MATRICES*

The transpose of a sum or difference of matrices is equal to the sum or difference of the transposes of the matrices; thus

$$(\mathbf{A}_{m \times n} \pm \mathbf{B}_{m \times n} \pm \mathbf{C}_{m \times n})' = \mathbf{A}'_{n \times m} \pm \mathbf{B}'_{n \times m} \pm \mathbf{C}'_{n \times m}$$

that is,

$$(d_{ij})'_{m \times n} = (d_{ji})_{n \times m}$$

where $d_{ij} = a_{ij} \pm b_{ij} \pm c_{ij}$ and $d_{ji} = a_{ji} \pm b_{ji} \pm c_{ji}$.

Examples

If

$$\mathbf{A} = \begin{pmatrix} 3 & 0 & 2 \\ -6 & 8 & -1 \end{pmatrix} \quad \mathbf{B} = \begin{pmatrix} -1 & 6 & -2 \\ 3 & -2 & 1 \end{pmatrix} \quad \mathbf{C} = \begin{pmatrix} 0 & 0 & 6 \\ -2 & 5 & 25 \end{pmatrix}$$

then

$$(\mathbf{A} + \mathbf{B} + \mathbf{C})' = \begin{pmatrix} 2 & 6 & 6 \\ -5 & 11 & 25 \end{pmatrix}' = \begin{pmatrix} 2 & -5 \\ 6 & 11 \\ 6 & 25 \end{pmatrix}$$

or, alternatively,

$$\mathbf{A}' + \mathbf{B}' + \mathbf{C}' = \begin{pmatrix} 3 & -6 \\ 0 & 8 \\ 2 & -1 \end{pmatrix} + \begin{pmatrix} -1 & 3 \\ 6 & -2 \\ -2 & 1 \end{pmatrix} + \begin{pmatrix} 0 & -2 \\ 0 & 5 \\ 6 & 25 \end{pmatrix} = \begin{pmatrix} 2 & -5 \\ 6 & 11 \\ 6 & 25 \end{pmatrix}$$

If

$$\mathbf{A} = \begin{pmatrix} 2 & -1 \\ 0 & -1 \end{pmatrix} \quad \mathbf{B} = \begin{pmatrix} 6 & 8 \\ 10 & -12 \end{pmatrix} \quad \mathbf{C} = \begin{pmatrix} 0 & -1 \\ 0 & 0 \end{pmatrix}$$

then

$$(\mathbf{A} - \mathbf{B} + \mathbf{C})' = \begin{pmatrix} -4 & -10 \\ -10 & 11 \end{pmatrix}' = \begin{pmatrix} -4 & -10 \\ -10 & 11 \end{pmatrix}$$

or, alternatively,

$$\mathbf{A}' - \mathbf{B}' + \mathbf{C}' = \begin{pmatrix} 2 & 0 \\ -1 & -1 \end{pmatrix} - \begin{pmatrix} 6 & 10 \\ 8 & -12 \end{pmatrix} + \begin{pmatrix} 0 & 0 \\ -1 & 0 \end{pmatrix} = \begin{pmatrix} -4 & -10 \\ -10 & 11 \end{pmatrix}$$

□ *TRANSPOSE OF A PRODUCT OF MATRICES*

The transpose of a product of matrices is equal to the product of the transposes of the matrices in reverse sequence; thus

$$(\mathbf{A}_{m \times n} \mathbf{B}_{n \times p} \mathbf{C}_{p \times q})' = \mathbf{C}'_{q \times p} \mathbf{B}'_{p \times n} \mathbf{A}'_{n \times m}$$

Examples

If

$$\mathbf{A} = \begin{pmatrix} 3 & 0 \\ -4 & -1 \end{pmatrix} \qquad \mathbf{B} = \begin{pmatrix} 3 & 5 & -7 \\ 0 & -1 & 8 \end{pmatrix} \qquad \mathbf{C} = \begin{pmatrix} 6 \\ -1 \\ 0 \end{pmatrix}$$

then

$$\mathbf{ABC} = \begin{pmatrix} 39 \\ -53 \end{pmatrix}$$

$$(\mathbf{ABC})' = \begin{pmatrix} 39 \\ -53 \end{pmatrix}'$$

$$= (39, -53)$$

or alternatively,

$$(\mathbf{ABC})' = \mathbf{C}'\mathbf{B}'\mathbf{A}' = (6, -1, 0)\begin{pmatrix} 3 & 0 \\ 5 & -1 \\ -7 & 8 \end{pmatrix}\begin{pmatrix} 3 & -4 \\ 0 & -1 \end{pmatrix}$$

$$= (39, -53)$$

If

$$\mathbf{A} = (3, -1, 0) \qquad \mathbf{B} = \begin{pmatrix} 6 & 0 \\ -7 & 2 \\ 0 & 3 \end{pmatrix} \qquad \mathbf{C} = \begin{pmatrix} 0 \\ 1 \end{pmatrix}$$

then $\mathbf{ABC} = -2$ and $(\mathbf{ABC})' = -2$ (the transpose of a scalar is that scalar), or, alternatively,

$$(\mathbf{ABC})' = \mathbf{C}'\mathbf{B}'\mathbf{A}' = (0, 1)\begin{pmatrix} 6 & -7 & 0 \\ 0 & 2 & 3 \end{pmatrix}\begin{pmatrix} 3 \\ -1 \\ 0 \end{pmatrix} = -2$$

■ 7.5 PARTITIONED MATRICES

It is frequently convenient to partition a matrix, by means of horizontal and vertical lines, into submatrices. These submatrices can then be treated as scalars in performing operations on the original matrix.

The $m \times n$ matrix $\mathbf{A}$ may be partitioned, for example, as follows

$$\mathbf{A} = (\mathbf{A}_1 \mid \mathbf{A}_2)$$

where $\mathbf{A}_1$ is $m \times n_1$, $\mathbf{A}_2$ is $m \times n_2$, and $n_1 + n_2 = n$. The transpose of a partitioned matrix can be written in terms of the transposes of its submatrices; thus

$$\mathbf{A}' = \begin{pmatrix} \mathbf{A}_1' \\ \hline \mathbf{A}_2' \end{pmatrix}$$

Example

If

$$\mathbf{A} = (\mathbf{A}_1 \mid \mathbf{A}_2) = \begin{pmatrix} 4 & -3 & 5 & 0 \\ 2 & -1 & 1 & 6 \\ 8 & -2 & 3 & -7 \end{pmatrix}$$

then

$$\mathbf{A}' = \begin{pmatrix} \mathbf{A}_1' \\ \mathbf{A}_2' \end{pmatrix} \begin{pmatrix} 4 & 2 & 8 \\ -3 & -1 & -2 \\ \hline 5 & 1 & 3 \\ 0 & 6 & -7 \end{pmatrix}$$

If they are partitioned conformably, partitioned matrices can be added, subtracted, or multiplied. If an $m \times n$ matrix $\mathbf{A}$ is partitioned $\mathbf{A} = (\mathbf{A}_1 \mid \mathbf{A}_2)$, where $\mathbf{A}_1$ is $m \times n_1$, $\mathbf{A}_2$ is $m \times n_2$, and $n_1 + n_2 = n$, and an $m \times n$ matrix $\mathbf{B}$ is partitioned $\mathbf{B} = (\mathbf{B}_1 \mid \mathbf{B}_2)$, where $\mathbf{B}_1$ is $m \times n_1$, $\mathbf{B}_2$ is $m \times n_2$, and $n_1 + n_2 = n$, then

$$\mathbf{A} \pm \mathbf{B} = (\mathbf{A}_1 \pm \mathbf{B}_1 \mid \mathbf{A}_2 \pm \mathbf{B}_2)$$

Similarly, if $\mathbf{A} = \begin{pmatrix} \mathbf{A}_1 \\ \hline \mathbf{A}_2 \end{pmatrix}$, where $\mathbf{A}$ is $m \times n$, $\mathbf{A}_1$ is $m_1 \times n$, $\mathbf{A}_2$ is $m_2 \times n$, and $m_1 + m_2 = m$, and $\mathbf{B} = \begin{pmatrix} \mathbf{B}_1 \\ \hline \mathbf{B}_2 \end{pmatrix}$, where $\mathbf{B}$ is $m \times n$, $\mathbf{B}_1$ is $m_1 \times n$, $\mathbf{B}_2$ is $m_2 \times n$, and $m_1 + m_2 = m$, then

$$\mathbf{A} \pm \mathbf{B} = \begin{pmatrix} \mathbf{A}_1 \pm \mathbf{B}_1 \\ \hline \mathbf{A}_2 \pm \mathbf{B}_2 \end{pmatrix}$$

Example

If

$$\mathbf{A} = \begin{pmatrix} 3 & 4 & -2 & 0 \\ -1 & 0 & 5 & 6 \\ 7 & 3 & 3 & 2 \end{pmatrix} \quad \text{and} \quad \mathbf{B} = \begin{pmatrix} -3 & 0 & 2 & 4 \\ -1 & -1 & -2 & 5 \\ 5 & 4 & 3 & 1 \end{pmatrix}$$

then

$$\mathbf{A} + \mathbf{B} = (\mathbf{A}_1 \mid \mathbf{A}_2) + (\mathbf{B}_1 \mid \mathbf{B}_2)$$

$$= \begin{pmatrix} 3 & 4 & -2 & 0 \\ -1 & 0 & 5 & 6 \\ 7 & 3 & 3 & 2 \end{pmatrix} + \begin{pmatrix} -3 & 0 & 2 & 4 \\ -1 & -1 & -2 & 5 \\ 5 & 4 & 3 & 1 \end{pmatrix}$$

$$= \begin{pmatrix} 0 & 4 & 0 & 4 \\ -2 & -1 & 3 & 11 \\ 12 & 7 & 6 & 3 \end{pmatrix} = (\mathbf{A}_1 + \mathbf{B}_1 \mid \mathbf{A}_2 + \mathbf{B}_2)$$

or

$$\mathbf{A} + \mathbf{B} = \begin{pmatrix} \mathbf{A}_1 \\ \hline \mathbf{A}_2 \end{pmatrix} + \begin{pmatrix} \mathbf{B}_1 \\ \hline \mathbf{B}_2 \end{pmatrix}$$

$$= \begin{pmatrix} 3 & 4 & -2 & 0 \\ -1 & 0 & 5 & 6 \\ \hline 7 & 3 & 3 & 2 \end{pmatrix} + \begin{pmatrix} -3 & 0 & 2 & 4 \\ -1 & -1 & -2 & 5 \\ \hline 5 & 4 & 3 & 1 \end{pmatrix}$$

$$= \begin{pmatrix} 0 & 4 & 0 & 4 \\ -2 & -1 & 3 & 11 \\ \hline 12 & 7 & 6 & 3 \end{pmatrix} = \begin{pmatrix} \mathbf{A}_1 + \mathbf{B}_1 \\ \hline \mathbf{A}_2 + \mathbf{B}_2 \end{pmatrix}$$

Many other partitionings are possible and will give the same result.

Partitioning is frequently conceptually convenient when matrices are to be added or subtracted, but the computational advantages of matrix partitioning are associated primarily with multiplication and other more complex operations. Partitioned matrices must be partitioned conformably for multiplication. If an $m \times n$ matrix $\mathbf{A}$ is partitioned $\mathbf{A} = (\mathbf{A}_1 \mid \mathbf{A}_2)$, $\mathbf{A}_1$ is $m \times n_1$, $\mathbf{A}_2$ is $m \times n_2$, and $n_1 + n_2 = n$, and an $n \times p$ matrix $\mathbf{B}$ is partitioned $\mathbf{B} = \begin{pmatrix} \mathbf{B}_1 \\ \hline \mathbf{B}_2 \end{pmatrix}$, where $\mathbf{B}_1$ is $n_1 \times p$ and $\mathbf{B}_2$ is $n_2 \times p$, then

$$\mathbf{AB} = (\mathbf{A}_1 \mid \mathbf{A}_2)\begin{pmatrix} \mathbf{B}_1 \\ \hline \mathbf{B}_2 \end{pmatrix} = \mathbf{A}_1 \mathbf{B}_1 + \mathbf{A}_2 \mathbf{B}_2$$

Example

If

$$\mathbf{A} = \begin{pmatrix} 3 & 0 & -1 \\ -2 & 4 & 1 \\ 1 & -1 & 2 \end{pmatrix} \quad \text{and} \quad \mathbf{B} = \begin{pmatrix} 2 & 1 \\ 1 & 3 \\ -1 & 1 \end{pmatrix}$$

then

$$\mathbf{AB} = \begin{pmatrix} 3 & 0 & -1 \\ -2 & 4 & 1 \\ 1 & -1 & 2 \end{pmatrix}\begin{pmatrix} 2 & 1 \\ 1 & 3 \\ \hline -1 & 1 \end{pmatrix}$$

$$= \begin{pmatrix} 3 & 0 \\ -2 & 4 \\ 1 & -1 \end{pmatrix}\begin{pmatrix} 2 & 1 \\ 1 & 3 \end{pmatrix} + \begin{pmatrix} -1 \\ 1 \\ 2 \end{pmatrix}(-1 \quad 1)$$

$$= \begin{pmatrix} 6 & 3 \\ 0 & 10 \\ 1 & -2 \end{pmatrix} + \begin{pmatrix} 1 & -1 \\ -1 & 1 \\ -2 & 2 \end{pmatrix}$$

$$= \begin{pmatrix} 7 & 2 \\ -1 & 11 \\ -1 & 0 \end{pmatrix}$$

Matrices may be partitioned into more than two submatrices. In fact, it is possible to partition an $m \times n$ matrix into a maximum of mn submatrices;

note that maximum partitioning is equivalent to no partitioning, since each element is treated as a scalar matrix.

Unless there is a logical partitioning in terms of the variables in a problem, matrices should be partitioned for ease of computation; this involves some reasonable compromise between minimizing the number of submatrices and minimizing their maximum size.

Frequently matrices are partitioned once horizontally and once vertically. Thus the $m \times n$ matrix $\mathbf{A}$ may be partitioned

$$\mathbf{A} = \left(\begin{array}{c|c} \mathbf{A}_{11} & \mathbf{A}_{12} \\ \hline \mathbf{A}_{21} & \mathbf{A}_{22} \end{array}\right)$$

where $\mathbf{A}_{11}$ is $m_1 \times n_1$, $\mathbf{A}_{12}$ is $m_1 \times n_2$, $\mathbf{A}_{21}$ is $m_2 \times n_1$, $\mathbf{A}_{22}$ is $m_2 \times n_2$, and $m_1 + m_2 = m$, $n_1 + n_2 = n$. Then

$$\mathbf{A}' = \left(\begin{array}{c|c} \mathbf{A}_{11} & \mathbf{A}_{12} \\ \hline \mathbf{A}_{21} & \mathbf{A}_{22} \end{array}\right)' = \left(\begin{array}{c|c} \mathbf{A}'_{11} & \mathbf{A}'_{12} \\ \hline \mathbf{A}'_{21} & \mathbf{A}'_{22} \end{array}\right)$$

If the $n \times p$ matrix $\mathbf{B}$ is partitioned

$$\mathbf{B} = \left(\begin{array}{c|c} \mathbf{B}_{11} & \mathbf{B}_{12} \\ \hline \mathbf{B}_{21} & \mathbf{B}_{22} \end{array}\right)$$

where $\mathbf{B}_{11}$ is $n_1 \times p_1$, $\mathbf{B}_{12}$ is $n_1 \times p_2$, $\mathbf{B}_{21}$ is $n_2 \times p_1$, $\mathbf{B}_{22}$ is $n_2 \times p_2$, and $n_1 + n_2 = n$, $p_1 + p_2 = p$, then A and B are partitioned conformably for multiplication and

$$\mathbf{AB} = \left(\begin{array}{c|c} \mathbf{A}_{11} & \mathbf{A}_{12} \\ \hline \mathbf{A}_{21} & \mathbf{A}_{22} \end{array}\right)\left(\begin{array}{c|c} \mathbf{B}_{11} & \mathbf{B}_{12} \\ \hline \mathbf{B}_{21} & \mathbf{B}_{22} \end{array}\right)$$

$$= \left(\begin{array}{c|c} \mathbf{A}_{11}\mathbf{B}_{11} + \mathbf{A}_{12}\mathbf{B}_{21} & \mathbf{A}_{11}\mathbf{B}_{12} + \mathbf{A}_{12}\mathbf{B}_{22} \\ \hline \mathbf{A}_{21}\mathbf{B}_{11} + \mathbf{A}_{22}\mathbf{B}_{21} & \mathbf{A}_{21}\mathbf{B}_{12} + \mathbf{A}_{22}\mathbf{B}_{22} \end{array}\right)$$

Example

If

$$\mathbf{A} = \begin{pmatrix} 1 & 3 & 1 \\ -1 & 0 & 1 \\ 2 & -1 & 4 \\ 0 & 2 & -3 \end{pmatrix} \quad \text{and} \quad \mathbf{B} = \begin{pmatrix} 3 & -2 & 1 & 0 & -1 \\ 5 & -1 & 4 & -3 & 2 \\ 3 & -2 & 0 & 1 & -1 \end{pmatrix}$$

then

$$\mathbf{AB} = \left(\begin{array}{c|c} \mathbf{A}_{11} & \mathbf{A}_{12} \\ \hline \mathbf{A}_{21} & \mathbf{A}_{22} \end{array}\right)\left(\begin{array}{c|c} \mathbf{B}_{11} & \mathbf{B}_{12} \\ \hline \mathbf{B}_{21} & \mathbf{B}_{22} \end{array}\right)$$

$$= \left(\begin{array}{cc|c} 1 & 3 & 1 \\ -1 & 0 & 1 \\ 2 & -1 & 4 \\ \hline 0 & 2 & -3 \end{array}\right)\left(\begin{array}{cc|ccc} 3 & -2 & 1 & 0 & -1 \\ 5 & -1 & 4 & -3 & 2 \\ \hline 3 & -2 & 0 & 1 & -1 \end{array}\right)$$

and

$$\mathbf{A}_{11}\mathbf{B}_{11} + \mathbf{A}_{12}\mathbf{B}_{21} = \begin{pmatrix} 1 & 3 \\ -1 & 0 \\ 2 & -1 \end{pmatrix} \begin{pmatrix} 3 & -2 \\ 5 & -1 \end{pmatrix} + \begin{pmatrix} 1 \\ 1 \\ 4 \end{pmatrix} (3 \quad -2)$$

$$= \begin{pmatrix} 18 & -5 \\ -3 & 2 \\ 1 & -3 \end{pmatrix} + \begin{pmatrix} 3 & -2 \\ 3 & -2 \\ 12 & -8 \end{pmatrix}$$

$$= \begin{pmatrix} 21 & -7 \\ 0 & 0 \\ 13 & -11 \end{pmatrix}$$

$$\mathbf{A}_{11}\mathbf{B}_{12} + \mathbf{A}_{12}\mathbf{B}_{22} = \begin{pmatrix} 1 & 3 \\ -1 & 0 \\ 2 & -1 \end{pmatrix} \begin{pmatrix} 1 & 0 & -1 \\ 4 & -3 & 2 \end{pmatrix} + \begin{pmatrix} 1 \\ 1 \\ 4 \end{pmatrix} (0 \quad 1 \quad -1)$$

$$= \begin{pmatrix} 13 & -9 & 5 \\ -1 & 0 & 1 \\ -2 & 3 & -4 \end{pmatrix} + \begin{pmatrix} 0 & 1 & -1 \\ 0 & 1 & -1 \\ 0 & 4 & -4 \end{pmatrix}$$

$$= \begin{pmatrix} 13 & -8 & 4 \\ -1 & 1 & 0 \\ -2 & 7 & -8 \end{pmatrix}$$

$$\mathbf{A}_{21}\mathbf{B}_{11} + \mathbf{A}_{22}\mathbf{B}_{21} = (0 \quad 2) \begin{pmatrix} 3 & -2 \\ 5 & -1 \end{pmatrix} + (-3)(3 \quad -2)$$

$$= (10 \quad -2) + (-9 \quad 6)$$

$$= (1 \quad 4)$$

$$\mathbf{A}_{21}\mathbf{B}_{12} + \mathbf{A}_{22}\mathbf{B}_{22} = (0 \quad 2) \begin{pmatrix} 1 & 0 & -1 \\ 4 & -3 & 2 \end{pmatrix} + (-3)(0 \quad 1 \quad -1)$$

$$= (8 \quad -6 \quad 4) + (0 \quad -3 \quad 3)$$

$$= (8 \quad -9 \quad 7)$$

Thus

$$\mathbf{AB} = \left(\begin{array}{c|c} \mathbf{A}_{11}\mathbf{B}_{11} + \mathbf{A}_{12}\mathbf{B}_{21} & \mathbf{A}_{11}\mathbf{B}_{12} + \mathbf{A}_{12}\mathbf{B}_{12} \\ \hline \mathbf{A}_{21}\mathbf{B}_{11} + \mathbf{A}_{22}\mathbf{B}_{21} & \mathbf{A}_{21}\mathbf{B}_{12} + \mathbf{A}_{22}\mathbf{B}_{22} \end{array} \right)$$

$$= \left(\begin{array}{cc|ccc} 21 & -7 & 13 & -8 & 4 \\ 0 & 0 & -1 & 1 & 0 \\ 13 & -11 & -2 & 7 & -8 \\ \hline 1 & 4 & 8 & -9 & 7 \end{array} \right)$$

which can be verified by direct matrix multiplication.

PROBLEMS

1. Compute the following

(a) $2 \begin{pmatrix} 6 & 1 \\ 0 & -3 \\ -1 & 2 \end{pmatrix} - 3 \begin{pmatrix} 4 & 2 \\ 0 & 1 \\ -5 & -1 \end{pmatrix}$

(b) $\begin{pmatrix} 6 & 0 & -1 \\ 1 & -3 & 2 \end{pmatrix} \begin{pmatrix} 4 & 2 \\ 0 & 1 \\ -5 & -1 \end{pmatrix}$

2. If $\mathbf{U} = (1, -1, 4)$, $\mathbf{X} = (0, 1, 2)$, $\mathbf{V} = \begin{pmatrix} 5 \\ 0 \\ 1 \end{pmatrix}$, and $\mathbf{Y} = \begin{pmatrix} -1 \\ -1 \\ 2 \end{pmatrix}$, find

(a) $\mathbf{UV} + \mathbf{XY}$
(b) $5\mathbf{UV} + 10[\mathbf{X}(2\mathbf{V} - \mathbf{Y})]$

3. If $\mathbf{A}$ is 2×3, $\mathbf{B}$ is 4×3, $\mathbf{C}$ is 3×3, and $\mathbf{D}$ is 3×2, determine the shape of

(a) $\mathbf{AC}$ 2×3   (b) $\mathbf{DA}$ 3×3
(c) $\mathbf{AD}$ 2×2   (d) $\mathbf{BC}$ 4×3
(e) $\mathbf{DAC}$ 3×3   (f) $\mathbf{BCDA}$ 4×3

4. If

$$\mathbf{A} = \begin{pmatrix} 1 & 2 & 3 \\ 0 & -1 & 1 \\ 2 & 3 & 0 \end{pmatrix} \qquad \mathbf{B} = \begin{pmatrix} 3 & 1 & 0 \\ 1 & -1 & 2 \\ 0 & 2 & 1 \end{pmatrix}$$

find $2(\mathbf{AB} - \mathbf{BA})$

5. If

$$\mathbf{A} = \begin{pmatrix} -1 & -2 & -2 \\ 1 & 2 & 1 \\ -1 & -1 & 0 \end{pmatrix} \qquad \mathbf{B} = \begin{pmatrix} -3 & -6 & 2 \\ 2 & 4 & -1 \\ 2 & 3 & 0 \end{pmatrix} \qquad \mathbf{C} = \begin{pmatrix} -5 & -8 & 0 \\ 3 & 5 & 0 \\ 1 & 2 & -1 \end{pmatrix}$$

show that (a) $\mathbf{A}^2 = \mathbf{B}^2 = \mathbf{C}^2 = \mathbf{I}$
(b) $\mathbf{AB} = \mathbf{BA} = \mathbf{C}$
(c) $\mathbf{BC} = \mathbf{CB} = \mathbf{A}$
(d) $\mathbf{AC} = \mathbf{CA} = \mathbf{B}$

6. If

$$\mathbf{A} = \begin{pmatrix} 5 & 4 & -2 \\ 4 & 5 & -2 \\ -2 & -2 & 2 \end{pmatrix}, \text{ show that } \mathbf{A}^2 - 11\mathbf{A} + 10\mathbf{I} = \mathbf{O}$$

7. If

$$\mathbf{A} = \begin{pmatrix} 1 & 0 \\ 1 & 0 \end{pmatrix} \qquad \mathbf{B} = \begin{pmatrix} 0 & 0 \\ 1 & 1 \end{pmatrix} \qquad \mathbf{C} = \begin{pmatrix} 2 & 2 \\ 2 & 2 \end{pmatrix} \qquad \mathbf{D} = \begin{pmatrix} 2 & 3 \\ 4 & 5 \end{pmatrix}$$

find (a) $\mathbf{AB} - 2\mathbf{CD}$
(b) $\mathbf{A}^2$
(c) $(\mathbf{BC})^2$

8. If $\mathbf{U} = (1, 0, 1)$ $\mathbf{V} = \begin{pmatrix} 1 \\ 2 \\ 3 \end{pmatrix}$ $\mathbf{X} = \begin{pmatrix} 4 & 2 & -1 \\ -1 & 3 & 0 \\ 0 & 1 & 1 \end{pmatrix}$ $\mathbf{Y} = \begin{pmatrix} 1 & 0 & 0 \\ 0 & 1 & 0 \\ 0 & 0 & 1 \end{pmatrix}$

find (a) $\mathbf{UV}$
(b) $\mathbf{VU} + \mathbf{X}$
(c) $\mathbf{XY}$

9. If

$$U = \begin{pmatrix} 2 & -2 & -4 \\ -1 & 3 & 4 \\ 1 & -2 & -3 \end{pmatrix} \qquad V = \begin{pmatrix} -1 & 2 & 4 \\ 1 & -2 & -4 \\ -1 & 2 & 4 \end{pmatrix}$$

show that (a) $U^2 = U$ and $V^2 = V$
 (b) $UV = VU = O$
 (c) $U + V = I$

10. If

$$X = \begin{pmatrix} 1 & 2 & 3 \\ 1 & 2 & 3 \\ -1 & -2 & -3 \end{pmatrix}, \text{ show that } X^2 = O$$

11. If

$$A = \begin{pmatrix} 1 & -2 & 1 \\ 2 & 1 & -3 \\ -5 & 2 & 3 \end{pmatrix} \qquad X = \begin{pmatrix} 2 & 5 & -1 & -7 \\ -2 & 1 & 3 & 4 \\ 3 & 2 & 1 & 2 \end{pmatrix}$$

$$Y = \begin{pmatrix} 3 & 6 & 0 & -6 \\ -1 & 2 & 4 & 5 \\ 4 & 3 & 2 & 3 \end{pmatrix}$$

show that $AX = AY$ (although $X \neq Y$).

12. If

$$A = \begin{pmatrix} 1 & -2 \\ 0 & 3 \\ 2 & -1 \end{pmatrix} \qquad B = \begin{pmatrix} 0 & -2 & 3 \\ 0 & 1 & 3 \end{pmatrix} \qquad C = \begin{pmatrix} -2 \\ 3 \\ -3 \end{pmatrix} \qquad D = \begin{pmatrix} -1 \\ 1 \\ 2 \end{pmatrix}$$

find $AB - CD'$.

ANSWERS TO ODD-NUMBERED PROBLEMS

1. (a) $\begin{pmatrix} 0 & -4 \\ 0 & -9 \\ 13 & 7 \end{pmatrix}$

 (b) $\begin{pmatrix} 29 & 13 \\ -6 & -3 \end{pmatrix}$

3. (a) 2×3
 (b) 3×3
 (c) 2×2
 (d) 4×3
 (e) 3×3
 (f) 4×3

7. (a) $\begin{pmatrix} -24 & -32 \\ -24 & -32 \end{pmatrix}$

 (b) $\begin{pmatrix} 1 & 0 \\ 1 & 0 \end{pmatrix}$

 (c) $\begin{pmatrix} 0 & 0 \\ 16 & 16 \end{pmatrix}$

■ **7.6 THE DETERMINANT OF A MATRIX**

The determinant of a matrix is a scalar (number), obtained from the elements of a matrix by specified operations, which is characteristic of the matrix. *N.B.* Determinants are defined only for square matrices.

The determinant of a 2×2 matrix

$$\mathbf{A} = \begin{pmatrix} a_{11} & a_{12} \\ a_{21} & a_{22} \end{pmatrix}$$

is given by

$$\det \mathbf{A} = |\mathbf{A}| = a_{11}a_{22} - a_{12}a_{21}$$

Example

Find the determinant of each of the following matrices.

(a) $\begin{pmatrix} 3 & -6 \\ 4 & 1 \end{pmatrix}$

(b) $\begin{pmatrix} -1 & 0 \\ 6 & 10 \end{pmatrix}$

(a) $\begin{vmatrix} 3 & -6 \\ 4 & 1 \end{vmatrix} = 3 - (-24) = 27$

(b) $\begin{vmatrix} -1 & 0 \\ 6 & 10 \end{vmatrix} = -10 - 0 = -10$

Similarly, the determinant of a 3×3 matrix,

$$\mathbf{A} = \begin{pmatrix} a_{11} & a_{12} & a_{13} \\ a_{21} & a_{22} & a_{23} \\ a_{31} & a_{32} & a_{33} \end{pmatrix}$$

is given by

$$|\mathbf{A}| = a_{11}a_{22}a_{33} + a_{12}a_{23}a_{31} + a_{13}a_{21}a_{32} - a_{11}a_{23}a_{32} - a_{13}a_{22}a_{31} - a_{12}a_{21}a_{33}$$

The terms can be obtained by the rule illustrated in Fig. 7.1, where positive product terms are formed of elements connected by solid lines and negative product terms are formed of elements connected by dashed lines. Note that similar rules are *not* valid for higher-order matrices.

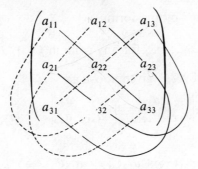

FIGURE 7.1

By definition, a determinant of order n, $|\mathbf{A}| = |a_{ij}|$ with $i, j = 1, 2, \ldots, n$, is the algebraic sum of $n!$ terms, each representing the product of n elements selected one from each row and one from each column in all possible and distinct combinations, having either a positive or negative sign depending on whether the number of inversions in the order of j (after the order of i in the product term has been arranged in numerical ascendency) is even or odd.

Determinants of matrices larger than 3×3 are frequently computed by a procedure known as *expansion by cofactors*. The determinant of the 3×3 matrix above can be written

$$|\mathbf{A}| = a_{11}(a_{22}a_{33} - a_{23}a_{32}) + a_{12}(a_{23}a_{31} - a_{21}a_{33}) + a_{13}(a_{21}a_{32} - a_{22}a_{31})$$

$$= a_{11}\begin{vmatrix} a_{22} & a_{23} \\ a_{32} & a_{33} \end{vmatrix} - a_{12}\begin{vmatrix} a_{21} & a_{23} \\ a_{31} & a_{33} \end{vmatrix} + a_{13}\begin{vmatrix} a_{21} & a_{22} \\ a_{31} & a_{32} \end{vmatrix}$$

Note that each determinant in the sum is the determinant of a submatrix of $\mathbf{A}$ obtained by deleting a particular row and column of $\mathbf{A}$. These determinants are called *minors*.

DEFINITION: Let $\mathbf{M}_{ij}$ denote the $(n - 1) \times (n - 1)$ matrix obtained by deleting the ith row and the jth column of $\mathbf{A}_{n \times n}$. The determinant

$$|\mathbf{M}_{ij}|$$

is a *minor* of the matrix $\mathbf{A}$. The scalar

$$C_{ij} = (-1)^{i+j}|\mathbf{M}_{ij}|$$

is referred to as the *cofactor* or *signed minor* of the element a_{ij} of the matrix $\mathbf{A}$. The $n \times n$ matrix

$$(C_{ij})'$$

is referred to as the *adjoint* of $\mathbf{A}$ and is denoted by adj $\mathbf{A}$.

As noted above, the determinant of a matrix can be obtained by a procedure known as *expansion by cofactors*. The determinant of $\mathbf{A}$ can be expanded in terms of row i by the formula

$$|\mathbf{A}| = \sum_{j=1}^{n} a_{ij}C_{ij} \qquad \text{for any row } i = 1, 2, \ldots, n$$

and in terms of column j by the formula

$$|\mathbf{A}| = \sum_{i=1}^{n} a_{ij}C_{ij} \qquad \text{for any column } j = 1, 2, \ldots, n$$

Thus the determinant of $\mathbf{A}_{3 \times 3}$ given above as

$$|\mathbf{A}| = a_{11}\begin{vmatrix} a_{22} & a_{23} \\ a_{32} & a_{33} \end{vmatrix} - a_{12}\begin{vmatrix} a_{21} & a_{23} \\ a_{31} & a_{33} \end{vmatrix} + a_{13}\begin{vmatrix} a_{21} & a_{22} \\ a_{31} & a_{32} \end{vmatrix}$$

can be written

$$|\mathbf{A}| = a_{11}C_{11} + a_{12}C_{12} + a_{13}C_{13} = \sum_{j=1}^{3} a_{ij}C_{ij}$$

Example

Find the determinant of the matrix

$$\mathbf{A} = \begin{pmatrix} 3 & 0 & -2 \\ 6 & -8 & 1 \\ 0 & 3 & 4 \end{pmatrix}$$

$$|\mathbf{A}| = -96 - 36 + 0 - (0 + 9 + 0)$$

$$= -141$$

Alternatively, expanding in terms of the first row,

$$|\mathbf{A}| = 3 \begin{vmatrix} -8 & 1 \\ 3 & 4 \end{vmatrix} + 0 - 2 \begin{vmatrix} 6 & -8 \\ 0 & 3 \end{vmatrix}$$

$$= 3(-32 - 3) - 2(18 - 0)$$

$$= -105 - 36 = -141$$

Alternatively, expanding in terms of the second column,

$$|\mathbf{A}| = 0 - 8 \begin{vmatrix} 3 & -2 \\ 0 & 4 \end{vmatrix} - 3 \begin{vmatrix} 3 & -2 \\ 6 & 1 \end{vmatrix}$$

$$= 0 - 8(12 - 0) - 3(3 + 12)$$

$$= -96 - 45 = -141$$

Note that cofactors are basically determinants and can be evaluated by further expansion in terms of determinants of lower order. By repeated expansion, an nth-order determinant can be written in terms of second- or third-order determinants which can be evaluated easily. To simplify computation, a determinant should be expanded in terms of the row or column having the largest number of zero elements.

The following properties of determinants are frequently useful in their evaluation:

1. Interchanging the corresponding rows and columns of a determinant does not change its value, that is, $|\mathbf{A}| = |\mathbf{A}'|$.

2. If every element of a row (or of a column) of a determinant is zero, the value of the determinant is zero.

3. If every element of a row (or of a column) of a determinant is multiplied by the same constant, the value of the determinant is multiplied by that constant.

4. If two rows (or two columns) of a determinant are interchanged, the sign of the determinant is changed but its absolute value is unchanged.

5. If two rows (or two columns) of a determinant are identical, the value of the determinant is zero.

6. The value of a determinant is not changed if each element of any row (or of any column), or each element multiplied by the same constant, is added to or subtracted from the corresponding element of any other row (or column).

7. The determinant of the product of two matrices is equal to the product of the determinants of the two matrices, that is, $|\mathbf{AB}| = |\mathbf{A}|\,|\mathbf{B}|$.

8. The determinant of a diagonal matrix is equal to the product of its diagonal elements.

■ 7.7 THE INVERSE OF A MATRIX

If for an $n \times n$ (square) matrix $\mathbf{A}$ there is another $n \times n$ (square) matrix $\mathbf{B}$ such that their product is the identity matrix of size n—that is, if

$$\mathbf{A}_{n \times n} \mathbf{B}_{n \times n} = \mathbf{I}_n = \mathbf{B}_{n \times n} \mathbf{A}_{n \times n}$$

then $\mathbf{B}$ is said to be the *reciprocal* or *inverse* of $\mathbf{A}$ and is written

$$\mathbf{B} = \mathbf{A}^{-1} = (a_{ij})^{-1} = (a^{ij}) = (b_{ij})$$

(it can be shown that $\mathbf{AB} = \mathbf{I} \Leftrightarrow \mathbf{BA} = \mathbf{I}$).

NOTE: In ordinary algebra, division of a quantity x by a quantity y is equivalent to multiplication of x by the reciprocal of y—that is,

$$\frac{x}{y} = xy^{-1}$$

Thus finding the reciprocal or inverse of a matrix is an operation analogous to division in ordinary algebra; however, note that although every nonzero number has a reciprocal, there are square matrices, in addition to the null matrix, which do not have inverses. A matrix that has an inverse is said to be *nonsingular*; a matrix that has no inverse is said to be *singular*.

A matrix that is not square may have a left or right inverse. An $n \times s$ matrix $\mathbf{A}$ is said to have $\mathbf{B}$ as a *left inverse* if $\mathbf{BA} = \mathbf{I}$; in this case $\mathbf{I}$ must be $s \times s$ and $\mathbf{B}$ must be $s \times n$. Similarly, if $\mathbf{AC} = \mathbf{I}$, $\mathbf{C}$ is said to be a *right inverse* of $\mathbf{A}$; in this case $\mathbf{I}$ must be $n \times n$ and $\mathbf{C}$ must be $s \times n$. It can be shown that if $\mathbf{A}$ has both a left inverse $\mathbf{B}$ and a right inverse $\mathbf{C}$, then $\mathbf{B} = \mathbf{C} = \mathbf{A}^{-1}$ and $\mathbf{A}$ is square (and nonsingular).

Obtaining the inverse of a matrix, referred to as *matrix inversion*, is essential for the matrix solution of sets of simultaneous linear equations; such equations arise, for example, in the solution of economic models and in linear programming problems.

Any set of simultaneous linear equations can be written in matrix notation; for example,

$$a_{11}x_1 + a_{12}x_2 + a_{13}x_3 + \cdots + a_{1n}x_n = c_1$$

$$a_{21}x_1 + a_{22}x_2 + a_{23}x_3 + \cdots + a_{2n}x_n = c_2$$

$$\vdots$$

$$a_{m1}x_1 + a_{m2}x_2 + a_{m3}x_3 + \cdots + a_{mn}x_n = c_m$$

can be written

$$\mathbf{A}_{m \times n} \mathbf{x}_{n \times 1} = \mathbf{c}_{m \times 1}$$

If $m = n$ and $\mathbf{A}$ has an inverse—that is, if $\mathbf{A}$ is square and nonsingular, then the set of simultaneous linear equations represented by

$$\mathbf{A}_{n \times n} \mathbf{x}_{n \times 1} = \mathbf{c}_{n \times 1}$$

has the solution

$$\mathbf{x}_{n \times 1} = \mathbf{A}_{n \times n}^{-1} \mathbf{c}_{n \times 1}$$

Solution of simultaneous linear equations is considered in detail in section 7.8.

□ *INVERSION OF 2 × 2 MATRICES*

If $n = 2$, that is, if the set of simultaneous equations consists of two equations in two unknowns,

$$a_{11}x_1 + a_{12}x_2 = c_1$$

$$a_{12}x_1 + a_{22}x_2 = c_2$$

or, in matrix notation,

$$\mathbf{A}_{2 \times 2}\mathbf{x}_{2 \times 1} = \mathbf{c}_{2 \times 1}$$

then $\mathbf{A}_{2 \times 2}^{-1}$ can be obtained fairly easily directly from its definition, as follows. If

$$\mathbf{A} = \begin{pmatrix} a_{11} & a_{12} \\ a_{21} & a_{22} \end{pmatrix}$$

and $\mathbf{A}^{-1}$ is denoted by

$$\mathbf{B} = \begin{pmatrix} b_{11} & b_{12} \\ b_{21} & b_{22} \end{pmatrix}$$

then, by definition, $\mathbf{AB} = \mathbf{I}$, that is,

$$\begin{pmatrix} a_{11} & a_{12} \\ a_{21} & a_{22} \end{pmatrix}\begin{pmatrix} b_{11} & b_{12} \\ b_{21} & b_{22} \end{pmatrix} = \begin{pmatrix} 1 & 0 \\ 0 & 1 \end{pmatrix}$$

and thus

$$\begin{pmatrix} a_{11}b_{11} + a_{12}b_{21} & a_{11}b_{12} + a_{12}b_{22} \\ a_{21}b_{11} + a_{22}b_{21} & a_{21}b_{12} + a_{22}b_{22} \end{pmatrix} = \begin{pmatrix} 1 & 0 \\ 0 & 1 \end{pmatrix}$$

and

$$a_{11}b_{11} + a_{12}b_{21} = 1$$

$$a_{11}b_{12} + a_{12}b_{22} = 0$$

$$a_{21}b_{11} + a_{22}b_{21} = 0$$

$$a_{21}b_{12} + a_{22}b_{22} = 1$$

Solving these four equations for the four b_{ij}'s,

$$b_{11} = \frac{a_{22}}{a_{11}a_{22} - a_{21}a_{12}}$$

$$b_{12} = \frac{-a_{12}}{a_{11}a_{22} - a_{21}a_{12}}$$

$$b_{21} = \frac{-a_{21}}{a_{11}a_{22} - a_{21}a_{12}}$$

$$b_{22} = \frac{a_{11}}{a_{11}a_{22} - a_{21}a_{12}}$$

Note that the denominator of each of these expressions is the *determinant* of $\mathbf{A}$

$$\det \mathbf{A} = \begin{vmatrix} a_{11} & a_{12} \\ a_{21} & a_{22} \end{vmatrix} = a_{11}a_{22} - a_{21}a_{12}$$

If $\det \mathbf{A} = 0$, the b_{ij}'s are not defined and $\mathbf{A}^{-1}$ cannot be obtained. It can be shown in general that a square matrix of any size has an inverse if and only if its determinant is nonzero.

Examples

Determine, if it exists, the inverse of the matrix

$$\begin{pmatrix} -1 & 6 \\ 4 & 3 \end{pmatrix}$$

$\begin{vmatrix} -1 & 6 \\ 4 & 3 \end{vmatrix} = -27$, so the inverse exists

$$b_{11} = \frac{3}{-27} = -\tfrac{1}{9}$$

$$b_{12} = \frac{-6}{-27} = \tfrac{2}{9}$$

$$b_{21} = \frac{-4}{-27} = \tfrac{4}{27}$$

$$b_{22} = \frac{-1}{-27} = \tfrac{1}{27}$$

and thus

$$\begin{pmatrix} -1 & 6 \\ 4 & 3 \end{pmatrix}^{-1} = \begin{pmatrix} -\tfrac{1}{9} & \tfrac{2}{9} \\ \tfrac{4}{27} & \tfrac{1}{27} \end{pmatrix}$$

Note that

$$\begin{pmatrix} -1 & 6 \\ 4 & 3 \end{pmatrix}\begin{pmatrix} -\tfrac{1}{9} & \tfrac{2}{9} \\ \tfrac{4}{27} & \tfrac{1}{27} \end{pmatrix} = \begin{pmatrix} 1 & 0 \\ 0 & 1 \end{pmatrix}$$

Determine, if it exists, the inverse of the matrix

$$\begin{pmatrix} -3 & 15 \\ 1 & -5 \end{pmatrix}$$

$\begin{vmatrix} -3 & 15 \\ 1 & -5 \end{vmatrix} = 0$, so the inverse does not exist (that is, the matrix is singular)

□ *INVERSION OF LARGER MATRICES*

In principle, the inverse of any nonsingular matrix can be obtained from its definition in the same way as was done for a 2×2 matrix. That is, if

$$\mathbf{A} = \begin{pmatrix} a_{11} & a_{12} \cdots a_{1n} \\ a_{21} & a_{22} \cdots a_{2n} \\ \vdots & \vdots & \vdots \\ a_{n1} & a_{n2} \cdots a_{nn} \end{pmatrix}$$

and $\mathbf{B} = \mathbf{A}^{-1}$, then

$$
\mathbf{I}_n = \begin{pmatrix} 1 & & & \bigcirc \\ & 1 & & \\ & & \ddots & \\ \bigcirc & & & 1 \end{pmatrix} = \begin{pmatrix} a_{11} & a_{12} & \cdots & a_{1n} \\ a_{21} & a_{22} & \cdots & a_{2n} \\ \vdots & \vdots & & \vdots \\ a_{n1} & a_{n2} & \cdots & a_{nn} \end{pmatrix} \begin{pmatrix} b_{11} & b_{12} & \cdots & b_{1n} \\ b_{21} & b_{22} & \cdots & b_{2n} \\ \vdots & \vdots & & \vdots \\ b_{n1} & b_{n2} & \cdots & b_{nn} \end{pmatrix}
$$

$$
= \begin{pmatrix} c_{11} & c_{12} & \cdots & c_{1n} \\ c_{21} & c_{22} & \cdots & c_{2n} \\ \vdots & \vdots & & \vdots \\ c_{n1} & c_{n2} & \cdots & c_{nn} \end{pmatrix}
$$

where $c_{ik} = \sum_{j=1}^{n} a_{ij}b_{jk}$ and the n^2 elements of the inverse matrix (b_{jk}) can be obtained by solution of the n^2 equations

$$
\sum_{j=1}^{n} a_{ij}b_{jk} = 1 \qquad \text{if } i = k
$$

$$
\sum_{j=1}^{n} a_{ij}b_{jk} = 0 \qquad \text{if } i \neq k
$$

where $i = 1, 2, \ldots, n$ and $k = 1, 2, \ldots, n$.

For a matrix of any size, this method of inversion is tedious. Fortunately, numerous alternative computational procedures for inverting a matrix are available and inversion is also a standard program for most electronic computers. Two methods of inversion are discussed in following sections; both of these are feasible unless the matrix is quite large and/or its elements consist of several digits.

□ INVERSION USING ROW OR COLUMN OPERATIONS

To solve a system of simultaneous linear equations, certain simple operations are commonly used to convert the original system to an equivalent system— that is, to a system having the same solutions as the original system—which is easier to solve. An equivalent system is obtained if (1) two equations are interchanged, (2) an equation is multiplied by any nonzero constant, and (3) the ith equation is replaced by the sum of the ith equation and k times the jth equation, where k is any nonzero constant.

Similarly, three *elementary row operations* on matrices are defined by (1) interchange of two rows, (2) multiplication of a row by any nonzero scalar, and (3) replacement of the ith row by the sum of the ith row and k times the jth row, where k is any nonzero scalar.

The corresponding operations on the columns of a matrix are *elementary column operations*.

THEOREM: If a matrix $\mathbf{A}$ is converted to the identity matrix by a series of row operations or by a series of column operations, then the same series of operations performed on the identity matrix will convert it to $\mathbf{A}^{-1}$.

There is a standard method, invariably appropriate, for converting a non-singular matrix to the identity matrix or for establishing the singularity of a matrix which cannot be converted to the identity matrix. This standard method is outlined and illustrated below. The generality of the method, which is appropriate for any matrix and which can be programmed for machine computation, makes it especially useful, even though for particular cases a shorter method might be available.

- **Steps in Converting a Square Matrix to the Identity Matrix (Gaussian Elimination)**

1. Divide the first row of the matrix by the entry in its first column; use the resulting row to obtain zeros in the first column of each of the other rows.
2. Divide the second row by the entry in its second column; use the resulting row to obtain zeros in the second column of each of the other rows.

$$\vdots$$

n. Divide the *n*th row by the entry in its *n*th column; use the resulting row to obtain zeros in the *n*th column of each of the other rows.

To find the inverse of a matrix $\mathbf{A}$ it is customary to work with a tableau of the form

$$(\mathbf{A}|\mathbf{I})$$

and change it by the standard procedure given above to the tableau

$$(\mathbf{I}|\mathbf{B})$$

Then, by the theorem above, $\mathbf{B}$ is $\mathbf{A}^{-1}$.

Even if $\mathbf{A}$ has no inverse, this procedure can be started. At some point a tableau will be obtained which is not of the appropriate form and which cannot be changed in the manner outlined above. It can be shown that if the above procedure cannot be completed to obtain $(\mathbf{I}|\mathbf{B})$ from $(\mathbf{A}|\mathbf{I})$, then $\mathbf{A}$ does not have an inverse.

Examples

Find the inverse, if it exists, of the matrix

$$\begin{pmatrix} 0 & -2 & -3 \\ 1 & 3 & 3 \\ -1 & -2 & -2 \end{pmatrix}$$

Following the standard procedure outlined above,

$$\left(\begin{array}{ccc|ccc} 0 & -2 & -3 & 1 & 0 & 0 \\ 1 & 3 & 3 & 0 & 1 & 0 \\ -1 & -2 & -2 & 0 & 0 & 1 \end{array}\right)$$

$$\begin{pmatrix} 1 & 3 & 3 & \bigm| & 0 & 1 & 0 \\ 0 & -2 & -3 & \bigm| & 1 & 0 & 0 \\ -1 & -2 & -2 & \bigm| & 0 & 0 & 1 \end{pmatrix} \begin{matrix} \text{interchanging} \\ \text{first and} \\ \text{second rows} \end{matrix}$$

$$\begin{pmatrix} 1 & 3 & 3 & \bigm| & 0 & 1 & 0 \\ 0 & -2 & -3 & \bigm| & 1 & 0 & 0 \\ 0 & 1 & 1 & \bigm| & 0 & 1 & 1 \end{pmatrix} \quad \text{Step 1}$$

$$\left.\begin{matrix}\begin{pmatrix} 1 & 3 & 3 & \bigm| & 0 & 1 & 0 \\ 0 & 1 & -\frac{3}{2} & \bigm| & -\frac{1}{2} & 0 & 0 \\ 0 & 1 & 1 & \bigm| & 0 & 1 & 1 \end{pmatrix} \\ \\ \begin{pmatrix} 1 & 0 & -\frac{3}{2} & \bigm| & \frac{3}{2} & 1 & 0 \\ 0 & 1 & \frac{3}{2} & \bigm| & -\frac{1}{2} & 0 & 0 \\ 0 & 0 & -\frac{1}{2} & \bigm| & \frac{1}{2} & 1 & 1 \end{pmatrix}\end{matrix}\right\} \text{Step 2}$$

$$\left.\begin{matrix}\begin{pmatrix} 1 & 0 & -\frac{3}{2} & \bigm| & \frac{3}{2} & 1 & 0 \\ 0 & 1 & \frac{3}{2} & \bigm| & -\frac{1}{2} & 0 & 0 \\ 0 & 0 & 1 & \bigm| & -1 & -2 & -2 \end{pmatrix} \\ \\ \begin{pmatrix} 1 & 0 & 0 & \bigm| & 0 & -2 & -3 \\ 0 & 1 & 0 & \bigm| & 1 & 3 & 3 \\ 0 & 0 & 1 & \bigm| & -1 & -2 & -2 \end{pmatrix}\end{matrix}\right\} \text{Step 3}$$

Thus

$$\begin{pmatrix} 0 & -2 & -3 \\ 1 & 3 & 3 \\ -1 & -2 & -2 \end{pmatrix}^{-1} = \begin{pmatrix} 0 & -2 & -3 \\ 1 & 3 & 3 \\ -1 & -2 & -2 \end{pmatrix}$$

Find the inverse, if it exists, of the matrix

$$\begin{pmatrix} 1 & 2 & 3 \\ -1 & 0 & 4 \\ 0 & 2 & 2 \end{pmatrix}$$

Following the standard procedure outlined above,

$$\begin{pmatrix} 1 & 2 & 3 & \bigm| & 1 & 0 & 0 \\ -1 & 0 & 4 & \bigm| & 0 & 1 & 0 \\ 0 & 2 & 2 & \bigm| & 0 & 0 & 1 \end{pmatrix}$$

$$\begin{pmatrix} 1 & 2 & 3 & \bigm| & 1 & 0 & 0 \\ 0 & 2 & 7 & \bigm| & 1 & 1 & 0 \\ 0 & 2 & 2 & \bigm| & 0 & 0 & 1 \end{pmatrix} \quad \text{Step 1}$$

$$\left. \begin{array}{l} \begin{pmatrix} 1 & 2 & 3 & \bigm| & 1 & 0 & 0 \\ 0 & 1 & \frac{7}{2} & \bigm| & \frac{1}{2} & \frac{1}{2} & 0 \\ 0 & 2 & 2 & \bigm| & 0 & 0 & 1 \end{pmatrix} \\ \\ \begin{pmatrix} 1 & 0 & -4 & \bigm| & 0 & -1 & 0 \\ 0 & 1 & \frac{7}{2} & \bigm| & \frac{1}{2} & \frac{1}{2} & 0 \\ 0 & 0 & -5 & \bigm| & -1 & -1 & 1 \end{pmatrix} \end{array} \right\} \text{Step 2}$$

$$\left. \begin{array}{l} \begin{pmatrix} 1 & 0 & -4 & \bigm| & 0 & -1 & 0 \\ 0 & 1 & \frac{7}{2} & \bigm| & \frac{1}{2} & \frac{1}{2} & 0 \\ 0 & 0 & 1 & \bigm| & \frac{1}{5} & \frac{1}{5} & -\frac{1}{5} \end{pmatrix} \\ \\ \begin{pmatrix} 1 & 0 & 0 & \bigm| & \frac{4}{5} & -\frac{1}{5} & -\frac{4}{5} \\ 0 & 1 & 0 & \bigm| & -\frac{1}{5} & -\frac{1}{5} & \frac{7}{10} \\ 0 & 0 & 1 & \bigm| & \frac{1}{5} & \frac{1}{5} & -\frac{1}{5} \end{pmatrix} \end{array} \right\} \text{Step 3}$$

Thus

$$\begin{pmatrix} 1 & 2 & 3 \\ -1 & 0 & 4 \\ 0 & 2 & 2 \end{pmatrix}^{-1} = \begin{pmatrix} \frac{4}{5} & -\frac{1}{5} & -\frac{4}{5} \\ -\frac{1}{5} & -\frac{1}{5} & \frac{7}{10} \\ \frac{1}{5} & \frac{1}{5} & -\frac{1}{5} \end{pmatrix}$$

Find the inverse, if it exists, of the matrix

$$\begin{pmatrix} 1 & 2 & -1 \\ -3 & 4 & 5 \\ -4 & 2 & 6 \end{pmatrix}$$

Following the standard procedure outlined above,

$$\begin{pmatrix} 1 & 2 & -1 & \bigm| & 1 & 0 & 0 \\ -3 & 4 & 5 & \bigm| & 0 & 1 & 0 \\ -4 & 2 & 6 & \bigm| & 0 & 0 & 1 \end{pmatrix}$$

$$\begin{pmatrix} 1 & 2 & -1 & \bigm| & 1 & 0 & 0 \\ 0 & 10 & 2 & \bigm| & 3 & 1 & 0 \\ 0 & 10 & 2 & \bigm| & 4 & 0 & 1 \end{pmatrix}$$

The procedure cannot be continued; thus there is no inverse.

The left-hand matrix of this tableau has two identical rows; the standard procedure thus cannot be completed and the original matrix has no inverse. Note that a matrix having two identical rows corresponds to a set of simultaneous linear equations having two equations with identical coefficients; such a set of equations has no unique solution—if the equations are identical, there are infinitely many solutions; if the equations have different constant terms, there is no solution.

□ *INVERSION USING ADJOINTS AND DETERMINANTS*

An alternative method of matrix inversion involving adjoints and determinants is given by the following theorem.

THEOREM: A square matrix $\mathbf{A}$ is nonsingular if and only if $|\mathbf{A}| \neq 0$. In this case,

$$\mathbf{A}^{-1} = \frac{1}{|\mathbf{A}|} \text{ adj } \mathbf{A}$$

Examples

Find the inverse, if it exists, of the matrix

$$\mathbf{A} = \begin{pmatrix} 0 & -2 & -3 \\ 1 & 3 & 3 \\ -1 & -2 & -2 \end{pmatrix}$$

$$|\mathbf{A}| = 0 + 6 + 6 - (9 + 0 + 4) = -1$$

Alternatively, expanding by elements of the first row,

$$|\mathbf{A}| = 0 + (-2)(-1)^{1+2} \begin{vmatrix} 1 & 3 \\ -1 & -2 \end{vmatrix} + (-3)(-1)^{1+3} \begin{vmatrix} 1 & 3 \\ -1 & -2 \end{vmatrix}$$

$$= 0 + 2(-2 + 3) + (-3)(-2 + 3) = -1$$

or, expanding by elements of the second column,

$$|\mathbf{A}| = (-2)(-1)^{1+2} \begin{vmatrix} 1 & 3 \\ -1 & -2 \end{vmatrix} + (3)(-1)^{2+2} \begin{vmatrix} 0 & -3 \\ -1 & -2 \end{vmatrix} + (-2)(-1)^{3+2} \begin{vmatrix} 0 & -3 \\ 1 & 3 \end{vmatrix}$$

$$= 2(-2 + 3) + 3(0 - 3) + 2(0 + 3) = -1$$

$$C_{11} = (-1)^{1+1} \begin{vmatrix} 3 & 3 \\ -2 & -2 \end{vmatrix} = 0$$

$$C_{12} = (-1)^{1+2} \begin{vmatrix} 1 & 3 \\ -1 & -2 \end{vmatrix} = -(-2 + 3) = -1$$

$$C_{13} = (-1)^{1+3} \begin{vmatrix} 1 & 3 \\ -1 & -2 \end{vmatrix} = -2 + 3 = 1$$

$$C_{21} = (-1)^{2+1} \begin{vmatrix} -2 & -3 \\ -2 & -2 \end{vmatrix} = -(4 - 6) = 2$$

$$C_{22} = (-1)^{2+2} \begin{vmatrix} 0 & -3 \\ -1 & -2 \end{vmatrix} = -3$$

$$C_{23} = (-1)^{2+3} \begin{vmatrix} 0 & -2 \\ -1 & -2 \end{vmatrix} = 2$$

$$C_{31} = (-1)^{3+1} \begin{vmatrix} -2 & -3 \\ 3 & 3 \end{vmatrix} = -6 + 9 = 3$$

$$C_{32} = (-1)^{3+2} \begin{vmatrix} 0 & -3 \\ 1 & 3 \end{vmatrix} = -3$$

$$C_{33} = (-1)^{3+3} \begin{vmatrix} 0 & -2 \\ 1 & 3 \end{vmatrix} = 2$$

Thus

$$\text{adj } \mathbf{A} = (C_{ij})' = \begin{pmatrix} 0 & 2 & 3 \\ -1 & -3 & -3 \\ 1 & 2 & 2 \end{pmatrix}$$

$$\mathbf{A}^{-1} = \frac{1}{|\mathbf{A}|} \text{adj } \mathbf{A} = \begin{pmatrix} 0 & -2 & -3 \\ 1 & 3 & 3 \\ -1 & -2 & -2 \end{pmatrix}$$

(as obtained in the example above by the standard procedure for row operations).

Find the inverse, if it exists, of the matrix

$$\mathbf{A} = \begin{pmatrix} 1 & 2 & 3 \\ -1 & 0 & 4 \\ 0 & 2 & 2 \end{pmatrix}$$

$$|\mathbf{A}| = 0 - 6 + 0 - (0 + 8 - 4) = -10$$

Alternatively, expanding by elements of the first column,

$$|\mathbf{A}| = (-1)^{1+1} \begin{vmatrix} 0 & 4 \\ 2 & 2 \end{vmatrix} - (-1)^{2+1} \begin{vmatrix} 2 & 3 \\ 2 & 2 \end{vmatrix} + 0$$

$$= (0 - 8) + (4 - 6) = -10$$

or, expanding by elements of the second row,

$$|\mathbf{A}| = (-1)(-1)^{2+1} \begin{vmatrix} 2 & 3 \\ 2 & 2 \end{vmatrix} + 0 + 4(-1)^{2+3} \begin{vmatrix} 1 & 2 \\ 0 & 2 \end{vmatrix}$$

$$= (4 - 6) + 0 + (-4)(2 - 0) = -10$$

$$C_{11} = (-1)^{1+1} \begin{vmatrix} 0 & 4 \\ 2 & 2 \end{vmatrix} = -8$$

$$C_{12} = (-1)^{1+2} \begin{vmatrix} -1 & 4 \\ 0 & 2 \end{vmatrix} = 2$$

$$C_{13} = (-1)^{1+3} \begin{vmatrix} -1 & 0 \\ 0 & 2 \end{vmatrix} = -2$$

$$C_{21} = (-1)^{2+1} \begin{vmatrix} 2 & 3 \\ 2 & 2 \end{vmatrix} = -(4 - 6) = 2$$

$$C_{22} = (-1)^{2+2}\begin{vmatrix} 1 & 3 \\ 0 & 2 \end{vmatrix} = 2$$

$$C_{23} = (-1)^{2+3}\begin{vmatrix} 1 & 2 \\ 0 & 2 \end{vmatrix} = -2$$

$$C_{31} = (-1)^{3+1}\begin{vmatrix} 2 & 3 \\ 0 & 4 \end{vmatrix} = 8$$

$$C_{32} = (-1)^{3+2}\begin{vmatrix} 1 & 3 \\ -1 & 4 \end{vmatrix} = -(4+3) = -7$$

$$C_{33} = (-1)^{3+3}\begin{vmatrix} 1 & 2 \\ -1 & 0 \end{vmatrix} = 2$$

Thus

$$\text{adj } \mathbf{A} = (C_{ij})' = \begin{pmatrix} -8 & 2 & 8 \\ 2 & 2 & -7 \\ -2 & -2 & 2 \end{pmatrix}$$

$$\mathbf{A}^{-1} = \frac{1}{|\mathbf{A}|} \text{adj } \mathbf{A} = \begin{pmatrix} \frac{4}{5} & -\frac{1}{5} & -\frac{4}{5} \\ -\frac{1}{5} & -\frac{1}{5} & \frac{7}{10} \\ \frac{1}{5} & \frac{1}{5} & -\frac{1}{5} \end{pmatrix}$$

(as obtained in the example above by the standard procedure for row operations).

Find the inverse, if it exists, of the matrix

$$\mathbf{A} = \begin{pmatrix} 1 & 2 & -1 \\ -3 & 4 & 5 \\ -4 & 2 & 6 \end{pmatrix}$$

$$|\mathbf{A}| = 24 + 6 - 40 - (16 + 10 - 36) = 0$$

Thus **A** is singular.

In general, inversion by row or column operations is less laborious if the elements of the matrix are small whole numbers; inversion by determinant and adjoint is less laborious if the elements of the matrix are large numbers or fractions. For large matrices both of these methods are tedious, and electronic computers should be used, if available.

Unless there is good reason to believe that a matrix is nonsingular, as in some practical applications, it is advisable first to find its determinant, even if inversion by row or column operations is intended. A number of row or column operations may be necessary before the singularity of a matrix becomes apparent using this method of inversion, and much useless computation is thus avoided by establishing the existence of an inverse before attempting (by any method) to compute it.

☐ *INVERSION OF PARTITIONED MATRICES*

It is sometimes convenient to obtain the inverse of a matrix in partitioned form. If an $n \times n$ matrix $\mathbf{A}$ is partitioned

$$\mathbf{A} = \left(\begin{array}{c|c} \mathbf{A}_{11} & \mathbf{A}_{12} \\ \hline \mathbf{A}_{21} & \mathbf{A}_{22} \end{array}\right)$$

where $\mathbf{A}_{11}$ is $n_1 \times n_1$, $\mathbf{A}_{12}$ is $n_1 \times n_2$, $\mathbf{A}_{21}$ is $n_2 \times n_1$, $\mathbf{A}_{22}$ is $n_2 \times n_2$, and $n_1 + n_2 = n$, then

$$\mathbf{A}^{-1} = \begin{pmatrix} \mathbf{A}_{11}^{-1}(\mathbf{I} + \mathbf{A}_{12}\mathbf{B}^{-1}\mathbf{A}_{21}\mathbf{A}_{11}^{-1}) & -\mathbf{A}_{11}^{-1}\mathbf{A}_{12}\mathbf{B}^{-1} \\ -\mathbf{B}^{-1}\mathbf{A}_{21}\mathbf{A}_{11}^{-1} & \mathbf{B}^{-1} \end{pmatrix}$$

where $\mathbf{B} = \mathbf{A}_{22} - \mathbf{A}_{21}\mathbf{A}_{11}^{-1}\mathbf{A}_{12}$ and $\mathbf{A}_{11}$ and $\mathbf{B}$ are nonsingular. This result can be proved directly by multiplication

$$\begin{pmatrix} \mathbf{A}_{11} & \mathbf{A}_{12} \\ \mathbf{A}_{21} & \mathbf{A}_{22} \end{pmatrix}\begin{pmatrix} \mathbf{A}_{11}^{-1}(\mathbf{I} + \mathbf{A}_{12}\mathbf{B}^{-1}\mathbf{A}_{21}\mathbf{A}_{11}^{-1}) & -\mathbf{A}_{11}^{-1}\mathbf{A}_{12}\mathbf{B}^{-1} \\ -\mathbf{B}^{-1}\mathbf{A}_{21}\mathbf{A}_{11}^{-1} & \mathbf{B}^{-1} \end{pmatrix} = \begin{pmatrix} \mathbf{T} & 0 \\ 0 & \mathbf{T} \end{pmatrix}$$

since

$$\mathbf{A}_{11}\mathbf{A}_{11}^{-1}(\mathbf{I} + \mathbf{A}_{12}\mathbf{B}^{-1}\mathbf{A}_{21}\mathbf{A}_{11}^{-1}) - \mathbf{A}_{12}\mathbf{B}^{-1}\mathbf{A}_{21}\mathbf{A}_{11}^{-1} = \mathbf{I}$$

$$-\mathbf{A}_{11}\mathbf{A}_{11}^{-1}\mathbf{A}_{12}\mathbf{B}^{-1} + \mathbf{A}_{12}\mathbf{B}^{-1} = 0$$

$$\mathbf{A}_{21}\mathbf{A}_{11}^{-1}(\mathbf{I} + \mathbf{A}_{12}\mathbf{B}^{-1}\mathbf{A}_{21}\mathbf{A}_{11}^{-1}) - \mathbf{A}_{22}\mathbf{B}^{-1}\mathbf{A}_{21}\mathbf{A}_{11}^{-1}$$

$$= (\mathbf{I} + \underbrace{\mathbf{A}_{21}\mathbf{A}_{11}^{-1}\mathbf{A}_{12}\mathbf{B}^{-1} - \mathbf{A}_{22}\mathbf{B}^{-1}}_{(\mathbf{A}_{21}\mathbf{A}_{11}^{-1}\mathbf{A}_{12} - \mathbf{A}_{22})\mathbf{B}^{-1}})\mathbf{A}_{21}\mathbf{A}_{11}^{-1}$$

$$= (\mathbf{I} - \mathbf{B}\mathbf{B}^{-1})\mathbf{A}_{21}\mathbf{A}_{11}^{-1}$$

$$= 0$$

$$-\mathbf{A}_{21}\mathbf{A}_{11}^{-1}\mathbf{A}_{12}\mathbf{B}^{-1} + \mathbf{A}_{22}\mathbf{B}^{-1} = (-\mathbf{A}_{21}\mathbf{A}_{11}^{-1}\mathbf{A}_{12} + \mathbf{A}_{22})\mathbf{B}^{-1}$$

$$= \mathbf{B}\mathbf{B}^{-1}$$

$$= \mathbf{I}$$

Examples

Find the inverse, if it exists, of the matrix

$$\begin{pmatrix} 0 & -2 & -3 \\ 1 & 3 & 3 \\ -1 & -2 & -2 \end{pmatrix}$$

Partitioning the matrix,

$$\left(\begin{array}{cc|c} 0 & -2 & -3 \\ 1 & 3 & 3 \\ \hline -1 & -2 & -2 \end{array}\right) = \left(\begin{array}{c|c} \mathbf{A}_{11} & \mathbf{A}_{12} \\ \hline \mathbf{A}_{21} & \mathbf{A}_{22} \end{array}\right)$$

and

$$\mathbf{A}_{11}^{-1}(\mathbf{I} + \mathbf{A}_{12}\mathbf{B}^{-1}\mathbf{A}_{21}\mathbf{A}_{11}^{-1}) = \begin{pmatrix} \frac{3}{2} & 1 \\ -\frac{1}{2} & 0 \end{pmatrix}\left[\begin{pmatrix} 1 & 0 \\ 0 & 1 \end{pmatrix} + \begin{pmatrix} -3 \\ 3 \end{pmatrix}(-2)(-1 \quad -2)\begin{pmatrix} \frac{3}{2} & 1 \\ -\frac{1}{2} & 0 \end{pmatrix}\right]$$

$$= \begin{pmatrix} \frac{3}{2} & 1 \\ -\frac{1}{2} & 0 \end{pmatrix}\left[\begin{pmatrix} 1 & 0 \\ 0 & 1 \end{pmatrix} + \begin{pmatrix} -6 & -12 \\ 6 & 12 \end{pmatrix}\begin{pmatrix} \frac{3}{2} & 1 \\ -\frac{1}{2} & 0 \end{pmatrix}\right]$$

$$= \begin{pmatrix} \frac{3}{2} & 1 \\ -\frac{1}{2} & 0 \end{pmatrix}\begin{pmatrix} -2 & -6 \\ 3 & 7 \end{pmatrix}$$

$$= \begin{pmatrix} 0 & -2 \\ 1 & 3 \end{pmatrix}$$

where

$$\mathbf{B} = \mathbf{A}_{22} - \mathbf{A}_{21}\mathbf{A}_{11}^{-1}\mathbf{A}_{12} = (-2) - (-1 \quad -2)\begin{pmatrix} \frac{3}{2} & 1 \\ -\frac{1}{2} & 0 \end{pmatrix}\begin{pmatrix} -3 \\ 3 \end{pmatrix}$$

$$= -2 - (-\tfrac{3}{2})$$

$$= -\tfrac{1}{2}$$

and

$$\mathbf{B}^{-1} = (-2)$$

$$-\mathbf{A}_{11}\mathbf{A}_{12}\mathbf{B}^{-1} = \begin{pmatrix} -\frac{3}{2} & -1 \\ \frac{1}{2} & 0 \end{pmatrix}\begin{pmatrix} -3 \\ 3 \end{pmatrix}(-2)$$

$$= \begin{pmatrix} -3 \\ 3 \end{pmatrix}$$

$$-\mathbf{B}^{-1}\mathbf{A}_{21}\mathbf{A}_{11}^{-1} = (2)(-1 \quad -2)\begin{pmatrix} \frac{3}{2} & 1 \\ -\frac{1}{2} & 0 \end{pmatrix} = (-1 \quad -2)$$

$$\mathbf{B}^{-1} = (-2)$$

Thus

$$\begin{pmatrix} 0 & -2 & -3 \\ 1 & 3 & 3 \\ -1 & -2 & -2 \end{pmatrix}^{-1} = \begin{pmatrix} 0 & -2 & -3 \\ 1 & 3 & 3 \\ -1 & -2 & -2 \end{pmatrix}$$

as above.

Find the inverse, if it exists, of the matrix

$$\begin{pmatrix} 1 & 2 & 3 \\ -1 & 0 & 4 \\ 0 & 2 & 2 \end{pmatrix}$$

Partitioning the matrix,

$$\left(\begin{array}{c|cc} 1 & 2 & 3 \\ \hline -1 & 0 & 4 \\ 0 & 2 & 2 \end{array}\right) = \left(\begin{array}{c|c} \mathbf{A}_{11} & \mathbf{A}_{12} \\ \hline \mathbf{A}_{21} & \mathbf{A}_{22} \end{array}\right)$$

and

$$\mathbf{A}_{11}^{-1}(\mathbf{I} + \mathbf{A}_{12}\mathbf{B}^{-1}\mathbf{A}_{21}\mathbf{A}_{11}^{-1}) = (1)\left[(1) + (2 \quad 3)\begin{pmatrix} -\frac{1}{5} & \frac{7}{10} \\ \frac{1}{5} & -\frac{1}{5} \end{pmatrix}\begin{pmatrix} -1 \\ 0 \end{pmatrix}(1)\right]$$

$$= (1)\left[(1) + (\tfrac{1}{5} \quad \tfrac{4}{5})\begin{pmatrix} -1 \\ 0 \end{pmatrix}\right]$$

$$= 1(1 - \tfrac{1}{5})$$

$$= \tfrac{4}{5}$$

where

$$\mathbf{B} = \mathbf{A}_{22} - \mathbf{A}_{21}\mathbf{A}_{11}^{-1}\mathbf{A}_{12} = \begin{pmatrix} 0 & 4 \\ 2 & 2 \end{pmatrix} - \begin{pmatrix} -1 \\ 0 \end{pmatrix}(1)(2 \quad 3)$$

$$= \begin{pmatrix} 0 & 4 \\ 2 & 2 \end{pmatrix} - \begin{pmatrix} -2 & -3 \\ 0 & 0 \end{pmatrix}$$

$$= \begin{pmatrix} 2 & 7 \\ 2 & 2 \end{pmatrix}$$

and

$$\mathbf{B}^{-1} = \begin{pmatrix} -\frac{1}{5} & \frac{7}{10} \\ \frac{1}{5} & -\frac{1}{5} \end{pmatrix}$$

$$-\mathbf{A}_{11}^{-1}\mathbf{A}_{12}\mathbf{B}^{-1} = (-1)(2 \quad 3)\begin{pmatrix} -\frac{1}{5} & \frac{7}{10} \\ \frac{1}{5} & -\frac{1}{5} \end{pmatrix}$$

$$= (-\tfrac{1}{5} \quad -\tfrac{4}{5})$$

$$-\mathbf{B}^{-1}\mathbf{A}_{21}\mathbf{A}_{11}^{-1} = \begin{pmatrix} \frac{1}{5} & -\frac{7}{10} \\ -\frac{1}{5} & \frac{1}{5} \end{pmatrix}\begin{pmatrix} -1 \\ 0 \end{pmatrix}(1)$$

$$= \begin{pmatrix} -\frac{1}{5} \\ \frac{1}{5} \end{pmatrix}$$

$$\mathbf{B}^{-1} = \begin{pmatrix} -\frac{1}{5} & \frac{7}{10} \\ \frac{1}{5} & -\frac{1}{5} \end{pmatrix}$$

Thus

$$\begin{pmatrix} 1 & 2 & 3 \\ -1 & 0 & 4 \\ 0 & 2 & 2 \end{pmatrix}^{-1} = \begin{pmatrix} \frac{4}{5} & -\frac{1}{5} & -\frac{4}{5} \\ -\frac{1}{5} & -\frac{1}{5} & \frac{7}{10} \\ \frac{1}{5} & \frac{1}{5} & -\frac{1}{5} \end{pmatrix}$$

as above.

The following properties of inverses are frequently useful in their evaluation.

1. The inverse of the inverse of a matrix is the original matrix; that is, $(\mathbf{A}^{-1})^{-1} = \mathbf{A}$.

2. The determinant of the inverse of a matrix is equal to the reciprocal of the determinant of the matrix; that is, $|\mathbf{A}^{-1}| = \dfrac{1}{|\mathbf{A}|}$.

3. The inverse of the transpose of a matrix is equal to the transpose of the inverse of the matrix; that is, $(\mathbf{A}')^{-1} = (\mathbf{A}^{-1})'$.

4. The inverse of the product of two matrices is equal to the product of their inverses in reverse order; that is, $(\mathbf{AB})^{-1} = \mathbf{B}^{-1}\mathbf{A}^{-1}$.

PROBLEMS

For each of the following matrices evaluate the determinant and find the inverse, if it exists.

1. $\begin{pmatrix} 1 & 6 \\ 0 & 1 \end{pmatrix}$

2. $\begin{pmatrix} 1 & 0 \\ 0 & 1 \end{pmatrix}$

3. $\begin{pmatrix} 0 & 1 \\ 1 & 0 \end{pmatrix}$

→4. $\begin{pmatrix} 0 & 1 \\ 1 & 6 \end{pmatrix}$

→5. $\begin{pmatrix} 2 & -3 \\ 4 & -6 \end{pmatrix}$

6. $\begin{pmatrix} 2 & 2 \\ -4 & -4 \end{pmatrix}$

7. $\begin{pmatrix} -1 & 3 \\ 2 & 7 \end{pmatrix}$

8. $\begin{pmatrix} -1 & -1 \\ -1 & -1 \end{pmatrix}$

9. $\begin{pmatrix} 0 & -2 & -1 \\ 1 & -3 & 4 \\ -1 & -1 & -1 \end{pmatrix}$

10. $\begin{pmatrix} 3 & 1 & 3 \\ 3 & 3 & 1 \\ 2 & 0 & 3 \end{pmatrix}$

11. $\begin{pmatrix} 3 & 2 & -1 \\ 4 & 3 & -1 \\ -1 & 2 & 4 \end{pmatrix}$

12. $\begin{pmatrix} 1 & 2 & -1 \\ 0 & -3 & 2 \\ 4 & 1 & 0 \end{pmatrix}$

13. If

$$A = \begin{pmatrix} 3 & 2 & -2 \\ 0 & 1 & 4 \\ -1 & 0 & 5 \end{pmatrix} \quad B = \begin{pmatrix} 1 & 0 \\ 0 & 1 \\ 0 & 1 \end{pmatrix} \quad C = \begin{pmatrix} 1 & 1 & 1 \\ 1 & 1 & 1 \end{pmatrix} \quad D = \begin{pmatrix} 3 & -2 \\ 2 & 3 \end{pmatrix}$$

find (a) $\det [(AB)'C' - D]$
(b) $(BC)^{-1}$
(c) $(D^2)^{-1}$

14. If

$$A = \begin{pmatrix} 3 & -1 \\ -4 & 0 \\ 2 & 1 \end{pmatrix} \quad B = \begin{pmatrix} 2 & 1 \\ -1 & -? \\ 1 & 1 \end{pmatrix} \quad C = \begin{pmatrix} 3 & 4 \\ 2 & 2 \end{pmatrix}$$

find (a) $(AI - BC)'$
(b) $(A'B)^{-1}$

15. If

$$A = \begin{pmatrix} 2 & 1 \\ 1 & 2 \end{pmatrix} \quad B = \begin{pmatrix} 1 & 0 \\ 0 & 1 \end{pmatrix} \quad C = \begin{pmatrix} 1 & 2 \\ 3 & 4 \\ 1 & 2 \end{pmatrix} \quad D = \begin{pmatrix} 0 & 1 & 0 \\ 1 & 1 & 1 \end{pmatrix}$$

find (a) $A + B - 2DC$
(b) $A^{-1}B^{-1}$
(c) $C(A + B)B^{-1}$
(d) $CA^{-1}B^{-1}D$

16. If

$$\mathbf{A} = \begin{pmatrix} 0 & 1 & -1 \\ 3 & -2 & 3 \\ 2 & -2 & 3 \end{pmatrix} \qquad \mathbf{B} = \begin{pmatrix} 4 & -3 & 3 \\ 2 & -1 & 2 \\ -3 & 3 & -2 \end{pmatrix}$$

show that (a) $\mathbf{A}^2 = \mathbf{B}^2 = [1/2(\mathbf{A} + \mathbf{B})]^2 = \mathbf{I}$
(b) $(\mathbf{A} - \mathbf{B})^2 = \mathbf{O}$

ANSWERS TO ODD-NUMBERED PROBLEMS

1. $\det = 1$, $\begin{pmatrix} 1 & -6 \\ 0 & 1 \end{pmatrix}$

3. $\det = -1$, $\begin{pmatrix} 0 & 1 \\ 1 & 0 \end{pmatrix}$

5. $\det = 0$, so no inverse

7. $\det = -13$, $\begin{pmatrix} -\frac{7}{13} & \frac{3}{13} \\ \frac{2}{13} & \frac{1}{13} \end{pmatrix}$

9. $\det = 10$, $\begin{pmatrix} \frac{7}{10} & -\frac{1}{10} & -\frac{11}{10} \\ -\frac{3}{10} & -\frac{1}{10} & -\frac{1}{10} \\ -\frac{2}{5} & \frac{1}{5} & \frac{1}{5} \end{pmatrix}$

11. $\det = 1$, $\begin{pmatrix} 14 & -10 & 1 \\ -15 & 11 & -1 \\ 11 & -8 & 1 \end{pmatrix}$

13. (a) -39
(b) Inverse does not exist
(c) $\begin{pmatrix} \frac{5}{169} & \frac{12}{169} \\ -\frac{12}{169} & \frac{5}{169} \end{pmatrix}$

15. (a) $\begin{pmatrix} -3 & -7 \\ -9 & -13 \end{pmatrix}$

(b) $\begin{pmatrix} \frac{2}{3} & -\frac{1}{3} \\ -\frac{1}{3} & \frac{2}{3} \end{pmatrix}$

(c) $\begin{pmatrix} 5 & 7 \\ 13 & 15 \\ 5 & 7 \end{pmatrix}$

(d) $\begin{pmatrix} 1 & 1 & 1 \\ \frac{5}{3} & \frac{7}{3} & \frac{5}{3} \\ 1 & 1 & 1 \end{pmatrix}$

■ 7.8 SIMULTANEOUS LINEAR EQUATIONS

This section concerns simultaneous linear equation systems. Linear dependence of a set of vectors and the related concept of rank of a matrix are defined and applied to the problem of determining whether a set of simultaneous linear equations has a unique solution. Methods of obtaining the solution of a set of simultaneous linear equations, when there is a solution, are also discussed.

□ LINEAR DEPENDENCE AND RANK

A set of m vectors $\mathbf{a}_1$, $\mathbf{a}_2$, ..., $\mathbf{a}_m$ each with n elements is said to be *linearly dependent* if there is a nontrivial linear combination of the vectors that is equal to the zero vector with n elements. That is, if there is a set of numbers λ_1, λ_2, ..., λ_m (not all zero) such that

$$\lambda_1 \mathbf{a}_1 + \lambda_2 \mathbf{a}_2 + \cdots + \lambda_m \mathbf{a}_m = \sum_{i=1}^{m} \lambda_i \mathbf{a}_i = \mathbf{0}$$

then the set of vectors $\mathbf{a}_1$, $\mathbf{a}_2$, ..., $\mathbf{a}_m$ is said to be *linearly dependent*. If there is no set of λ's (except all zeros) such that $\sum_{i=1}^{m} \lambda_i \mathbf{a}_i = 0$, the set of vectors is said to be *linearly independent*.

A matrix can be thought of as a set of row vectors or a set of column vectors. It can be shown that, for any matrix, the number of linearly independent rows is equal to the number of linearly independent columns; this number is said to be the *rank* of the matrix. Thus if a matrix is $m \times n$ and its rank is denoted by r, then $r \leq \min(m, n)$.

Examples

Determine the rank of the matrix

$$\begin{pmatrix} 1 & 4 \\ 5 & 10 \\ 3 & 2 \end{pmatrix}$$

Since 2(first row) + (third row) − (second row) = **0**, the three rows are linearly dependent. However, each pair of two rows is linearly independent; the two columns are also linearly independent. The rank of the matrix is 2.

Determine the rank of the matrix

$$\begin{pmatrix} 3 & 6 \\ 1 & 2 \\ 2 & 4 \end{pmatrix}$$

The three rows are linearly dependent, since

$$(\text{first row}) - (\text{second row}) - (\text{third row}) = \mathbf{0}$$

Each pair of two rows is linearly dependent, since

$$(\text{first row}) - 3(\text{second row}) = \mathbf{0}$$
$$2(\text{first row}) - 3(\text{third row}) = \mathbf{0}$$
$$2(\text{second row}) - (\text{third row}) = \mathbf{0}$$

Note that the two columns are also linearly dependent, since 2(first column) − (second column) = **0**. The rank of the matrix is 1.

The following very useful result provides a systematic method of testing for linear dependence: Consider all the square submatrices of **A** whose determinants are nonzero. The rank of **A** is the order of the largest (in order) of these determinants. Thus one method of computing the rank of a matrix is to look for the largest nonzero determinant; the order of this determinant is the rank of the matrix.

The following properties of rank are useful in determining the rank of a matrix:

1. Since the determinant of a diagonal matrix is equal to the product of its diagonal elements, if **A** is a diagonal matrix, then $r(\mathbf{A})$ is the number of nonzero diagonal elements in **A**. In particular, $r(\mathbf{I}_n) = n$.

2. Since any submatrix of **A'** is the transpose of a submatrix of **A** and since $|\mathbf{B}| = |\mathbf{B}'|$, $r(\mathbf{A}') = r(\mathbf{A})$.

3. The rank of the product of two matrices cannot exceed the smaller rank of the two matrices; that is, $r(\mathbf{AB}) \leq \min\{r(\mathbf{A}), r(\mathbf{B})\}$.

4. If A is an $n \times n$ (square) matrix, then $r(A) = n$ if and only if A is nonsingular; $r(A) < n$ if and only if A is singular. Thus if a square matrix is singular, its rows (and also its columns) are linearly dependent; if it is nonsingular, they are linearly independent.

Consider the solution of a general system of n linear equations in n variables $x_1, x_2, \ldots, x_n$,

$$y = Ax$$

where y is $n \times 1$, A is $n \times n$, and x is $n \times 1$. If A is nonsingular, the unique solution is

$$x = A^{-1}y$$

and, conversely, if $y = Ax$ has a unique solution, A is nonsingular.

More generally, if $y = Ax$, then the whole set of equations is consistent and has at least one solution if $r(A) = r(A \mid y)$. The solution is unique if and only if $r(A) = r(A \mid y) = n$, that is, if and only if A is nonsingular.

The special (homogeneous) case $y = 0$ is frequently of interest. In this case if A is nonsingular, the unique solution is $x = 0$ and there cannot be a nonzero solution. Thus, when the set of equations $Ax = 0$ does not have a nonzero solution, A must be singular.

Suppose that $y = Ax$ and A is $m \times n$ (not square), that is, there are m equations in n variables where m may be less than, equal to, or greater than n; then $r(A) \leq \min(m, n)$.

The following summary concerning solution of simultaneous linear equations applies to the general case of m equations in n variables and also to the special case of n equations in n variables.

if $r(A \mid y) = r(A)$, then all the equations in the set are logically consistent and there is at least one solution

if $r(A \mid y) = r(A) = n$, there is a unique solution

if $r(A \mid y) = r(A) < n$, there are infinitely many solutions and the rows (and columns) of A are linearly dependent

---

Examples

Consider the following set of simultaneous linear equations

$$x + 2y - z = 10$$
$$2x + 4y - 2z = 5$$
$$x + y + z = 6$$

The determinant of the coefficient matrix A is zero

$$\begin{vmatrix} 1 & 2 & -1 \\ 2 & 4 & -2 \\ 1 & 1 & 1 \end{vmatrix} = 4 - 2 - 4 - (-4 - 2 + 4) = 0$$

and the rank of the matrix is 2 since, for example,

$$\begin{vmatrix} 2 & 4 \\ 1 & 1 \end{vmatrix} = 2 - 4 = -2 \neq 0$$

The augmented coefficient matrix (**A** **Y**)

$$\begin{pmatrix} 1 & 2 & -1 & 10 \\ 2 & 4 & -2 & 5 \\ 1 & 1 & 1 & 6 \end{pmatrix}$$

has rank 3 since, for example,

$$\begin{vmatrix} 2 & -1 & 10 \\ 4 & -2 & 5 \\ 1 & 1 & 6 \end{vmatrix} = -24 + 40 - 5 - (20 + 10 - 24) = 5 \neq 0$$

Thus $r(\mathbf{A}) \neq r(\mathbf{A} \mid \mathbf{y})$ and the set of equations has no solution since they are not all consistent. (Note that the first and second equations are clearly inconsistent.)

Consider the following set of simultaneous linear equations

$$\begin{aligned} x + 2y - z &= 10 \\ 2x + 4y - 2z &= 20 \\ x + y + z &= 6 \end{aligned}$$

The coefficient matrix is the same as that for the preceding example and its rank is 2. The augmented coefficient matrix $(\mathbf{A} \mid \mathbf{y})$

$$\begin{pmatrix} 1 & 2 & -1 & 10 \\ 2 & 4 & -2 & 20 \\ 1 & 1 & 1 & 6 \end{pmatrix}$$

is also rank 2, since

$$\begin{vmatrix} 1 & 2 & 10 \\ 2 & 4 & 20 \\ 1 & 1 & 6 \end{vmatrix} = \begin{vmatrix} 1 & -1 & 10 \\ 2 & -2 & 20 \\ 1 & 1 & 6 \end{vmatrix} = \begin{vmatrix} 2 & -1 & 10 \\ 4 & -2 & 20 \\ 1 & 1 & 6 \end{vmatrix} = 0$$

Thus $r(\mathbf{A}) = r(\mathbf{A} \mid \mathbf{y}) = 2 \neq n$, since $n = 3$, and the set of equations has infinitely many solutions; the rows (and columns) of the coefficient matrix are linearly dependent. (Note that the first and second equations are linearly dependent.)

Consider the following set of simultaneous linear equations

$$\begin{aligned} x + 2y - z &= 10 \\ 2x - 4y - 2z &= 5 \\ x + y + z &= 6 \end{aligned}$$

The determinant of the coefficient matrix **A** is nonzero

$$\begin{vmatrix} 1 & 2 & -1 \\ 2 & -4 & -2 \\ 1 & 1 & 1 \end{vmatrix} = -4 - 2 - 4 - (4 - 2 + 4) = -16$$

and the rank of the matrix is 3; the rank of the augmented coefficient matrix is also 3. Thus $r(\mathbf{A}) = r(\mathbf{A} \mid \mathbf{y}) = 3 = n$ and the set of equations has a unique solution.

□ SOLUTION OF SIMULTANEOUS LINEAR EQUATIONS

There are various methods for obtaining the solution of a set of simultaneous linear equations that have a unique solution. Several of these methods are discussed in this section. If one of the methods is applied to a set of linear equations not having a unique solution, the method cannot be completed, thus indicating that there is no unique solution.

As noted above, a set of n simultaneous linear equations in n unknowns can be written in matrix notation as

$$\mathbf{A}_{n \times n} \mathbf{x}_{n \times 1} = \mathbf{c}_{n \times 1}$$

and the solution obtained by inversion of $\mathbf{A}$ can be denoted by

$$\mathbf{x}_{n \times 1} = \mathbf{A}_{n \times n}^{-1} \mathbf{c}_{n \times 1}$$

Alternatively, the standard procedure described previously can be used to change the tableau

$$(\mathbf{A} | \mathbf{c})$$

into the tableau

$$(\mathbf{I} | \mathbf{x})$$

from which the solution can be read directly.

A third matrix method for the solution of simultaneous linear equations is given by *Cramer's rule*: The solution of

$$\mathbf{A}_{n \times n} \mathbf{x}_{n \times 1} = \mathbf{c}_{n \times 1}$$

can be obtained as the ratios of determinants

$$x_1 = \frac{\begin{vmatrix} c_1 & a_{12} & \cdots & a_{1n} \\ c_2 & a_{22} & \cdots & a_{2n} \\ \vdots & \vdots & & \vdots \\ c_n & a_{n2} & \cdots & a_{nn} \end{vmatrix}}{|\mathbf{A}|}$$

$$x_2 = \frac{\begin{vmatrix} a_{11} & c_1 & \cdots & a_{1n} \\ a_{21} & c_2 & \cdots & a_{2n} \\ \vdots & \vdots & & \vdots \\ a_{n1} & c_n & \cdots & a_{nn} \end{vmatrix}}{|\mathbf{A}|}$$

$$\vdots$$

$$x_n = \dfrac{\begin{vmatrix} a_{11} & a_{12} \cdots & c_1 \\ a_{21} & a_{22} \cdots & c_2 \\ \vdots & \vdots & \vdots \\ a_{n1} & a_{n2} \cdots & c_n \end{vmatrix}}{|\mathbf{A}|}$$

For each x_i, $i = 1, 2, \ldots, n$, the denominator is the determinant of the coefficient matrix and the numerator is the determinant of the coefficient matrix with the ith column replaced by the column of constant terms from the right-hand side of the equations. Note that if there is no unique solution for a set of linear equations, $|\mathbf{A}| = 0$ and these quotients are not defined.

Examples

Solve the set of simultaneous linear equations

$$3x_1 + x_2 - x_3 = 2$$

$$x_1 - 2x_2 + x_3 = -9$$

$$4x_1 + 3x_2 + 2x_3 = 1$$

Apply the standard procedure to the tableau

$$(\mathbf{A}\,|\,\mathbf{I}\,|\,\mathbf{c})$$

to obtain the tableau

$$(\mathbf{I}\,|\,\mathbf{A}^{-1}\,|\,\mathbf{x})$$

Then the solution can be read directly from the tableau

$$(\mathbf{I}\,|\,\mathbf{x})$$

or obtained as

$$\mathbf{x} = \mathbf{A}^{-1}\mathbf{c}$$

$$\left(\begin{array}{rrr|rrr|r} 3 & 1 & -1 & 1 & 0 & 0 & 2 \\ 1 & -2 & 1 & 0 & 1 & 0 & -9 \\ 4 & 3 & 2 & 0 & 0 & 1 & 1 \end{array}\right)$$

$$\left(\begin{array}{rrr|rrr|r} 1 & -2 & 1 & 0 & 1 & 0 & -9 \\ 3 & 1 & -1 & 1 & 0 & 0 & 2 \\ 4 & 3 & 2 & 0 & 0 & 1 & 1 \end{array}\right)$$

$$\left(\begin{array}{rrr|rrr|r} 1 & -2 & 1 & 0 & 1 & 0 & -9 \\ 0 & 7 & -4 & 1 & -3 & 0 & 29 \\ 0 & 11 & -2 & 0 & -4 & 1 & 37 \end{array}\right)$$

$$\left(\begin{array}{rrr|rrr|r} 1 & 0 & -\frac{1}{7} & \frac{2}{7} & \frac{1}{7} & 0 & -\frac{5}{7} \\ 0 & 1 & -\frac{4}{7} & \frac{1}{7} & -\frac{3}{7} & 0 & \frac{29}{7} \\ 0 & 0 & \frac{30}{7} & -\frac{11}{7} & \frac{5}{7} & 1 & -\frac{60}{7} \end{array}\right)$$

$$\begin{pmatrix} 1 & 0 & 0 & \frac{7}{30} & \frac{1}{6} & \frac{1}{30} & -1 \\ 0 & 1 & 0 & -\frac{1}{15} & -\frac{1}{3} & \frac{2}{15} & 3 \\ 0 & 0 & 1 & -\frac{11}{30} & \frac{1}{6} & \frac{7}{30} & -2 \end{pmatrix}$$

Thus, reading directly from the tableau,

$$\begin{pmatrix} x_1 \\ x_2 \\ x_3 \end{pmatrix} = \begin{pmatrix} -1 \\ 3 \\ -2 \end{pmatrix}$$

or, using the inverse matrix,

$$\begin{pmatrix} x_1 \\ x_2 \\ x_3 \end{pmatrix} = \begin{pmatrix} \frac{7}{30} & \frac{1}{6} & \frac{1}{30} \\ -\frac{1}{15} & -\frac{1}{3} & \frac{2}{15} \\ -\frac{11}{30} & \frac{1}{6} & \frac{7}{30} \end{pmatrix} \begin{pmatrix} 2 \\ -9 \\ 1 \end{pmatrix} = \begin{pmatrix} -1 \\ 3 \\ 2 \end{pmatrix}$$

Using Cramer's rule,

$$\begin{vmatrix} 3 & 1 & -1 \\ 1 & -2 & 1 \\ 4 & 3 & 2 \end{vmatrix} = -12 - 3 + 4 - (8 + 9 + 2) = -30$$

$$x_1 = \frac{\begin{vmatrix} 2 & 1 & -1 \\ -9 & -2 & 1 \\ 1 & 3 & 2 \end{vmatrix}}{-30} = \frac{-8 + 27 + 1 - (2 + 6 - 18)}{-30} = \frac{30}{-30} = -1$$

$$x_2 = \frac{\begin{vmatrix} 3 & 2 & -1 \\ 1 & -9 & 1 \\ 4 & 1 & 2 \end{vmatrix}}{-30} = \frac{-54 - 1 + 8 - (36 + 3 + 4)}{-30} = \frac{-90}{-30} = 3$$

$$x_3 = \frac{\begin{vmatrix} 3 & 1 & 2 \\ 1 & -2 & -9 \\ 4 & 3 & 1 \end{vmatrix}}{-30} = \frac{-6 + 6 - 36 - (-16 - 81 + 1)}{-30} = \frac{60}{-30} = -2$$

Solve the set of simultaneous linear equations

$$x_1 + x_2 - x_3 = 6$$

$$3x_1 - 4x_2 + 2x_3 = -2$$

$$2x_1 + 5x_2 + x_3 = 0$$

Apply the standard procedure to the tableau

$$(\mathbf{A}\,|\,\mathbf{I}\,|\,\mathbf{c})$$

to obtain the tableau

$$(\mathbf{I}\,|\,\mathbf{A}^{-1}\,|\,\mathbf{x})$$

$$\left(\begin{array}{ccc|ccc|c} 1 & 1 & -1 & 1 & 0 & 0 & 6 \\ 3 & -4 & 2 & 0 & 1 & 0 & -2 \\ 2 & 5 & 1 & 0 & 0 & 1 & 0 \end{array}\right)$$

$$\left(\begin{array}{ccc|ccc|c} 1 & 1 & -1 & 1 & 0 & 0 & 6 \\ 0 & -7 & 5 & -3 & 1 & 0 & -20 \\ 0 & 3 & 3 & -2 & 0 & 1 & -12 \end{array}\right)$$

$$\left(\begin{array}{ccc|ccc|c} 1 & 0 & -\frac{2}{7} & \frac{4}{7} & \frac{1}{7} & 0 & \frac{22}{7} \\ 0 & 1 & -\frac{5}{7} & \frac{3}{7} & -\frac{1}{7} & 0 & \frac{20}{7} \\ 0 & 0 & \frac{36}{7} & -\frac{23}{7} & \frac{3}{7} & 1 & -\frac{144}{7} \end{array}\right)$$

$$\left(\begin{array}{ccc|ccc|c} 1 & 0 & 0 & \frac{7}{18} & \frac{1}{6} & \frac{1}{18} & 2 \\ 0 & 1 & 0 & -\frac{1}{36} & -\frac{1}{12} & \frac{5}{36} & 0 \\ 0 & 0 & 1 & -\frac{23}{36} & \frac{1}{12} & \frac{7}{36} & -4 \end{array}\right)$$

Thus, reading directly from the tableau,

$$\begin{pmatrix} x_1 \\ x_2 \\ x_3 \end{pmatrix} = \begin{pmatrix} 2 \\ 0 \\ -4 \end{pmatrix}$$

or, using the inverse matrix,

$$\begin{pmatrix} x_1 \\ x_2 \\ x_3 \end{pmatrix} = \begin{pmatrix} \frac{7}{18} & \frac{1}{6} & \frac{1}{18} \\ -\frac{1}{36} & -\frac{1}{12} & \frac{5}{36} \\ -\frac{23}{36} & \frac{1}{12} & \frac{7}{36} \end{pmatrix} \begin{pmatrix} 6 \\ -2 \\ 0 \end{pmatrix} = \begin{pmatrix} 2 \\ 0 \\ -4 \end{pmatrix}$$

Using Cramer's rule,

$$\begin{vmatrix} 1 & 1 & -1 \\ 3 & -4 & 2 \\ 2 & 5 & 1 \end{vmatrix} = -4 - 15 + 4 - (8 + 10 + 3) = -36$$

$$x_1 = \frac{\begin{vmatrix} 6 & 1 & -1 \\ -2 & -4 & 2 \\ 0 & 5 & 1 \end{vmatrix}}{-36} = \frac{-24 + 10 - (60 - 2)}{-36} = \frac{72}{-36} = -2$$

$$x_2 = \frac{\begin{vmatrix} 1 & 6 & -1 \\ 3 & -2 & 2 \\ 2 & 0 & 1 \end{vmatrix}}{-36} = \frac{-2 + 24 - (4 + 18)}{-36} = 0$$

$$x_3 = \frac{\begin{vmatrix} 1 & 1 & 6 \\ 4 & -4 & -2 \\ 2 & 5 & 0 \end{vmatrix}}{-36} = \frac{90 - 4 - (-48 - 10)}{-36} = \frac{144}{-36} = -4$$

PROBLEMS

Determine the rank of each of the following matrices.

1. $\begin{pmatrix} 1 & 2 \\ 0 & 1 \end{pmatrix}$

2. $\begin{pmatrix} 1 & 2 & 3 \\ -1 & 0 & 1 \\ 0 & 4 & 8 \end{pmatrix}$

3. $\begin{pmatrix} 1 & -1 & 0 \\ -1 & 2 & 3 \\ 0 & 1 & 2 \end{pmatrix}$

4. $\begin{pmatrix} 1 & -1 & 0 \\ -1 & 1 & 0 \\ 2 & -2 & 0 \end{pmatrix}$

5. $\begin{pmatrix} 1 & 3 \\ 2 & 6 \end{pmatrix}$

6. $\begin{pmatrix} -2 & 1 & 4 \\ 0 & -1 & 5 \\ -2 & 0 & -9 \end{pmatrix}$

7. $\begin{pmatrix} 3 & 1 & -2 \\ 2 & 5 & 4 \\ -4 & 3 & 1 \end{pmatrix}$

8. $\begin{pmatrix} -1 & 2 & -3 \\ 2 & -3 & 1 \\ 0 & 1 & -5 \end{pmatrix}$

9. $\begin{pmatrix} 3 & -1 & 0 & 2 \\ -2 & 1 & 5 & -2 \\ 0 & -4 & 6 & -3 \\ -3 & 5 & -6 & 1 \end{pmatrix}$

10. $\begin{pmatrix} 2 & -1 & 3 & 0 \\ -3 & 3 & 4 & 2 \\ 4 & -5 & -11 & -4 \\ -1 & 2 & 7 & 2 \end{pmatrix}$

For each of the following sets of simultaneous linear equations determine whether there is a unique solution and obtain the solution if there is one.

11. $x + 2y = 1$
    $3x + 4y = 2$

12. $x + y - 2z = 5$
    $2x - 4y + 3z = 6$
    $3x - 3y + z = 11$

13. $x_1 + x_2 + x_3 = 3$
    $2x_1 - x_2 - x_3 = 0$
    $3x_1 - 4x_2 - x_3 = 8$

14. $3x - y + 2z = -2$
    $x + y + z = 5$
    $2x - 2y + z = 3$

15. $x - 5y + 6z = 7$
    $3x + 3y - z = 8$
    $2x + 8y - 7z = 1$

16. $x_1 - 3x_2 = -2$
    $2x_1 + 7x_2 = 3$

17. $x_1 - 4x_2 = -1$
    $3x_1 - 2x_2 - x_3 = 0$
    $x_1 + x_3 = 3$

18. $x_1 + x_2 + x_3 = 9$
    $3x_1 + 2x_3 = 17$
    $x_2 + x_3 = 10$

19. $3x - y = 0$
    $2x + 4y = -14$

20. $3x_1 - 4x_2 = -3$
    $6x_1 + x_2 = 3$

21. $4x_1 - 5x_2 - 7x_3 = 15$
    $3x_1 + 2x_2 - 6x_3 = 8$
    $x_1 - 7x_2 - x_3 = 6$

22. $5x_1 - 2x_2 + x_3 = 12$
    $2x_1 + 2x_2 - 3x_3 = 7$
    $x_1 - 6x_2 + 7x_3 = -2$

23. $2x_1 + 3x_2 + x_3 = 0$
    $4x_1 - 8x_2 - 6x_3 = 2$
    $6x_1 + x_2 - x_3 = 0$

24. $x_1 + 5x_2 - 4x_3 = 0$
    $3x_1 - x_2 + 4x_3 = -4$
    $2x_1 + 3x_2 - 8x_3 = 0$

25. $3x_1 - 3x_2 + 4x_3 = -18$
    $4x_1 - 4x_2 + 4x_3 = -24$
    $2x_1 - 2x_2 + 4x_3 = 6$

26. $x_1 + x_2 + 6x_3 = -2$
    $3x_1 + 2x_2 + x_3 = 0$
    $2x_1 + x_2 + 5x_3 = 2$

27. $x_1 + 2x_2 = 0$
$x_1 + x_2 + x_3 = 2$
$2x_1 + 2x_2 + 3x_3 = 7$

28. $x_1 + x_2 + x_3 = 4$
$2x_1 + 3x_2 + 2x_3 = 5$
$3x_1 + 4x_2 - 3x_3 = -3$

ANSWERS TO ODD-NUMBERED PROBLEMS

1. rank 2
3. rank 3
5. rank 1
7. rank 3
9. rank 3

11. $x = 0, y = \frac{1}{2}$

13. $x_1 = 1, x_2 = 1, x_3 = 1$

15. linearly dependent, no unique solution

17. $x_1 = 1, x_2 = \frac{1}{2}, x_3 = 2$

19. $x = -1, y = -3$

21. inconsistent, no solution

23. $x_1 = -\frac{1}{2}, x_2 = 1, x_3 = -2$

25. inconsistent, no solution

27. $x_1 = -2, x_2 = 1, x_3 = 3$

8

APPLICATIONS
OF MATRIX
ALGEBRA

This chapter discusses the following applications of matrix algebra: maxima and minima of functions of n variables, input-output analysis, linear programming, game theory, and Markov processes.

■ 8.1 MAXIMA AND MINIMA OF FUNCTIONS OF n VARIABLES

The necessary and sufficient conditions for a point to be a maximum or minimum of a function of two variables are discussed in previous sections. These results are a special case ($n = 2$) of the conditions for a maximum or minimum of a function of n variables; the general results are stated below in matrix notation.

□ *UNCONSTRAINED MAXIMA AND MINIMA*

Consider a function of n variables $f(x_1, x_2, \ldots, x_n)$ at a point $x^* = (x_1^*, x_2^*, \ldots, x_n^*)$ such that the n partial derivatives are zero:

$$\frac{\partial f}{\partial x_1}\bigg|_{x^*} = 0, \qquad \frac{\partial f}{\partial x_2}\bigg|_{x^*} = 0, \qquad \ldots, \frac{\partial f}{\partial x_n}\bigg|_{x^*} = 0$$

Define the determinant Δ_n of second-order partial derivatives

$$\Delta_n = \begin{vmatrix} \dfrac{\partial^2 f}{\partial x_1^2} & \dfrac{\partial^2 f}{\partial x_1\,\partial x_2} & \cdots & \dfrac{\partial^2 f}{\partial x_1\,\partial x_n} \\[2ex] \dfrac{\partial^2 f}{\partial x_2\,\partial x_1} & \dfrac{\partial^2 f}{\partial x_2^2} & \cdots & \dfrac{\partial^2 f}{\partial x_2\,\partial x_n} \\[2ex] \vdots & \vdots & & \vdots \\[2ex] \dfrac{\partial^2 f}{\partial x_n\,\partial x_1} & \dfrac{\partial^2 f}{\partial x_n\,\partial x_2} & \cdots & \dfrac{\partial^2 f}{\partial x_n^2} \end{vmatrix}$$

sometimes referred to as a *Hessian determinant*.

The *principal minors* of Δ_n are

$$\Delta_1 = \dfrac{\partial^2 f}{\partial x_1^2}, \ \Delta_2 = \begin{vmatrix} \dfrac{\partial^2 f}{\partial x_1^2} & \dfrac{\partial^2 f}{\partial x_1\,\partial x_2} \\[2ex] \dfrac{\partial^2 f}{\partial x_2\,\partial x_1} & \dfrac{\partial^2 f}{\partial x_2^2} \end{vmatrix}, \ \Delta_3 = \begin{vmatrix} \dfrac{\partial^2 f}{\partial x_1^2} & \dfrac{\partial^2 f}{\partial x_1\,\partial x_2} & \dfrac{\partial^2 f}{\partial x_1\,\partial x_3} \\[2ex] \dfrac{\partial^2 f}{\partial x_2\,\partial x_1} & \dfrac{\partial^2 f}{\partial x_2^2} & \dfrac{\partial^2 f}{\partial x_2\,\partial x_3} \\[2ex] \dfrac{\partial^2 f}{\partial x_3\,\partial x_1} & \dfrac{\partial^2 f}{\partial x_3\,\partial x_2} & \dfrac{\partial^2 f}{\partial x_3^2} \end{vmatrix}, \ldots, \Delta_n$$

The stationary point $x^* = (x_1^*, x_2^*, \ldots, x_n^*)$ is a

Local maximum if $\Delta_1 < 0, \Delta_2 > 0, \Delta_3 < 0, \ldots$

Local minimum if $\Delta_1 > 0, \Delta_2 > 0, \Delta_3 > 0, \ldots$

If neither of these conditions holds, the function must be examined in the region of the stationary point. Note that the conditions for maxima and minima of a function of two variables are a special case of those given above for n variables.

Examples

Determine the maxima or minima (if any) of the function

$$f(x_1, x_2, x_3) = x_1^2 + 2x_2^2 + x_3^2 + x_1 x_2 - 2x_3 - 7x_1 + 12$$

$$\frac{\partial f}{\partial x_1} = 2x_1 + x_2 - 7$$

$$\frac{\partial f}{\partial x_2} = 4x_2 + x_1$$

$$\frac{\partial f}{\partial x_3} = 2x_3 - 2$$

If $\dfrac{\partial f}{\partial x_1} = 0, \ \dfrac{\partial f}{\partial x_2} = 0, \ \dfrac{\partial f}{\partial x_3} = 0$, then

$$2x_1 + x_2 = 7$$

$$x_1 + 4x_2 = 0$$

$$x_2 = -1$$
$$x_1 = 4$$
$$x_3 = 1$$

$$\frac{\partial^2 f}{\partial x_1^2} = 2 \qquad \frac{\partial^2 f}{\partial x_2^2} = 4$$

$$\frac{\partial^2 f}{\partial x_1 \, \partial x_2} = 1 \qquad \frac{\partial^2 f}{\partial x_2 \, \partial x_3} = 0$$

$$\frac{\partial^2 f}{\partial x_1 \, \partial x_3} = 0 \qquad \frac{\partial^2 f}{\partial x_3^2} = 2$$

$$\Delta_1 = 2$$

$$\Delta_2 = \begin{vmatrix} 2 & 1 \\ 1 & 4 \end{vmatrix} = 8 - 1 = 7$$

$$\Delta_3 = \begin{vmatrix} 2 & 1 & 0 \\ 1 & 4 & 0 \\ 0 & 0 & 2 \end{vmatrix} = 16 + 0 + 0 - (0 + 0 + 2) = 14$$

$\Delta_1 > 0, \Delta_2 > 0, \Delta_3 > 0$, so the point $(4, -1, 1)$ is a local minimum of the function $f(x_1, x_2, x_3) = x_1^2 + 2x_2^2 + x_3^2 + x_1 x_2 - 2x_3 - 7x_1 + 12$.

Determine the maxima and minima (if any) of the function

$$f(x, y, z) = e^{-x^2 - y^2 - z^2 + 2y + xz}$$

$$\frac{\partial f}{\partial x} = (-2x + z)e^{-x^2 - y^2 - z^2 + 2y + xz}$$

$$\frac{\partial f}{\partial y} = (-2y + 2)e^{-x^2 - y^2 - z^2 + 2y + xz}$$

$$\frac{\partial f}{\partial z} = (-2z + x)e^{-x^2 - y^2 - z^2 + 2y + xz}$$

If $\dfrac{\partial f}{\partial x} = 0$, $\dfrac{\partial f}{\partial y} = 0$, $\dfrac{\partial f}{\partial z} = 0$, then

$$-2x + z = 0$$
$$x - 2z = 0$$
$$x = z = 0$$
$$y = 1$$

$$\frac{\partial^2 f}{\partial x^2} = [(-2x + z)^2 - 2]e^{-x^2 - y^2 - z^2 + 2y + xz} \qquad \left. \frac{\partial^2 f}{\partial x^2} \right|_{(0,1,0)} = -2e$$

$$\frac{\partial^2 f}{\partial x \, \partial y} = (-2x + z)(-2y + 2)e^{-x^2 - y^2 - z^2 + 2y + xz} \qquad \left. \frac{\partial^2 f}{\partial x \, \partial y} \right|_{(0,1,0)} = 0$$

$$\frac{\partial^2 f}{\partial x \, \partial z} = [(-2x + z)(-2z + x) + 1]e^{-x^2 - y^2 - z^2 + 2y + xz} \qquad \left. \frac{\partial^2 f}{\partial x \, \partial z} \right|_{(0,1,0)} = e$$

$$\frac{\partial^2 f}{\partial y^2} = [(-2y+2)^2 - 2]e^{-x^2-y^2-z^2+2y+xz} \qquad \frac{\partial^2 f}{\partial y^2}\bigg|_{(0,1,0)} = -2e$$

$$\frac{\partial^2 f}{\partial y\, \partial z} = (-2y+2)(-2z+x)e^{-x^2-y^2-z^2+2y+xz} \qquad \frac{\partial^2 f}{\partial y\, \partial z}\bigg|_{(0,1,0)} = 0$$

$$\frac{\partial^2 f}{\partial z^2} = [(-2z+x)^2 - 2]e^{-x^2-y^2-z^2+2y+xz} \qquad \frac{\partial^2 f}{\partial z^2}\bigg|_{(0,1,0)} = -2e$$

$$\Delta_1 = -2e$$

$$\Delta_2 = \begin{vmatrix} -2e & 0 \\ 0 & -2e \end{vmatrix} = 4e$$

$$\Delta_3 = \begin{vmatrix} -2e & 0 & e \\ 0 & -2e & 0 \\ e & 0 & -2e \end{vmatrix} = -8e^3 + 2e^3 = -6e^3$$

$\Delta_1 < 0$, $\Delta_2 > 0$, $\Delta_3 < 0$, so the point $(0, 1, 0)$ is a local maximum of the function $f(x, y, z) = e^{-x^2-y^2-z^2+2y+xz}$.

Total profit is equal to total revenue minus total cost. In a perfectly competitive market, total revenue is equal to the product of the number of units sold and the fixed unit price; thus

$$P = pq - C$$

where P is profit, p is price per unit, q is quantity sold, and C is total cost. If the production function is

$$q = f(x_1, x_2)$$

where x_1 and x_2 are the variable inputs, and the cost function is

$$C = p_1 x_1 + p_2 x_2 + b$$

where p_1 and p_2 are the unit prices of x_1 and x_2, respectively, and b is the cost of the fixed inputs, then

$$P = pf(x_1, x_2) - p_1 x_1 - p_2 x_2 - b$$

Profit is thus a function of x_1 and x_2 and is maximized with respect to these variables as follows.

$$\frac{\partial P}{\partial x_1} = pf_1 - p_1 = 0$$

$$\frac{\partial P}{\partial x_2} = pf_2 - p_2 = 0$$

or

$$pf_1 = p_1$$
$$pf_2 = p_2$$

Since f_1 and f_2 are the marginal products of the two inputs, pf_1 and pf_2 are the values of these marginal products, that is, the rates at which revenue would increase with increase of the respective inputs. Thus the first-order conditions for profit maximization require that each input be increased until the value of its marginal product equals its price. Note that the maximum profit-input combination lies on the expansion path since the conditions $pf_1 = p_1$ and $pf_2 = p_2$ are a special case of the condition $\dfrac{f_1}{f_2} = \dfrac{p_1}{p_2}$.

Second-order conditions require that the principal minors of the Hessian determinant

$$\begin{vmatrix} \dfrac{\partial^2 P}{\partial x_1^2} & \dfrac{\partial^2 P}{\partial x_1 \partial x_2} \\[2mm] \dfrac{\partial^2 P}{\partial x_2 \partial x_1} & \dfrac{\partial^2 P}{\partial x_2^2} \end{vmatrix}$$

alternate in sign. That is, for a maximum it is required that

$$\frac{\partial^2 P}{\partial x_1^2} < 0$$

$$\begin{vmatrix} \dfrac{\partial^2 P}{\partial x_1^2} & \dfrac{\partial^2 P}{\partial x_1 \partial x_2} \\[2mm] \dfrac{\partial^2 P}{\partial x_2 \partial x_1} & \dfrac{\partial^2 P}{\partial x_2^2} \end{vmatrix} > 0$$

Expanding the second determinant,

$$\left(\frac{\partial^2 P}{\partial x_1^2}\right)\left(\frac{\partial^2 P}{\partial x_2^2}\right) - \left(\frac{\partial^2 P}{\partial x_1 \partial x_2}\right)^2 > 0$$

Since $\dfrac{\partial^2 P}{\partial x_1^2} < 0$ and $\left(\dfrac{\partial^2 P}{\partial x_1 \partial x_2}\right)^2 > 0$,

$$\frac{\partial^2 P}{\partial x_2} < 0$$

The second-order partials can be evaluated as

$$\frac{\partial^2 P}{\partial x_1^2} = pf_{11} < 0$$

$$\frac{\partial^2 P}{\partial x_2^2} = pf_{22} < 0$$

and, since $p > 0$, the second-order conditions for maximization require that

$$f_{11} < 0$$
$$f_{22} < 0$$

Thus the second-order conditions for maximization require that both marginal products be decreasing. This is reasonable, since the price of a variable is constant under free competition and thus, if the marginal product of a variable were increasing, profit could be increased by increasing the quantity of the variable.

□ *LAGRANGE MULTIPLIERS*

Consider a function of n variables $f(x_1, x_2, \ldots, x_n)$ subject to the constraint $g(x_1, x_2, \ldots, x_n) = 0$ at a point $x^* = (x_1^*, x_2^*, \ldots, x_n^*)$ which satisfies the $n + 1$ equations

$$\frac{\partial f}{\partial x_1} - \lambda \frac{\partial g}{\partial x_1} = 0$$

$$\frac{\partial f}{\partial x_2} - \lambda \frac{\partial g}{\partial x_2} = 0$$

$$\vdots$$

$$\frac{\partial f}{\partial x_n} - \lambda \frac{\partial g}{\partial x_n} = 0$$

$$\frac{\partial f}{\partial \lambda} - \lambda \frac{\partial g}{\partial \lambda} = 0$$

Note that for $x^* = (x_1^*, x_2^*, \ldots, x_n^*)$, $\lambda = \dfrac{f_{x_i}}{g_{x_i}}$, $i = 1, 2, \ldots, n$. Define the determinant

$$\Delta_{n+1} = \begin{vmatrix} 0 & g_{x_1} & g_{x_2} & \cdots & g_{x_n} \\ g_{x_1} & f_{x_1 x_1} - \lambda g_{x_1 x_1} & f_{x_1 x_2} - \lambda g_{x_1 x_2} & \cdots & f_{x_1 x_n} - \lambda g_{x_1 x_n} \\ g_{x_2} & f_{x_2 x_1} - \lambda g_{x_2 x_1} & f_{x_2 x_2} - \lambda g_{x_2 x_2} & \cdots & f_{x_2 x_n} - \lambda g_{x_2 x_n} \\ \vdots & \vdots & \vdots & & \vdots \\ g_{x_n} & f_{x_n x_1} - \lambda g_{x_n x_1} & f_{x_n x_2} - \lambda g_{x_n x_2} & \cdots & f_{x_n x_n} - \lambda g_{x_n x_n} \end{vmatrix}$$

sometimes referred to as a *bordered Hessian determinant*. In order to determine whether $x^* = (x_1^*, x_2^*, \ldots, x_n^*)$ is a maximum or minimum, the $n - 1$ principal minors of Δ_{n+1}: $\Delta_3, \Delta_4, \ldots, \Delta_{n+1}$ must be evaluated for $x^* = (x_1^*, x_2^*, \ldots, x_n^*)$. Note that Δ_i consists of the first i rows and i columns of Δ_{n+1}. The point $x^* = (x_1^*, x_2^*, \ldots, x_n^*)$ is a

Local (constrained) maximum if $\Delta_3 > 0, \Delta_4 < 0, \Delta_5 > 0, \ldots$

Local (constrained) minimum if $\Delta_3 < 0, \Delta_4 < 0, \Delta_5 < 0, \ldots$

If neither of these conditions holds, the function must be examined in the region of the stationary point. Note that the conditions for constrained maxima and minima of a function of two variables are a special case of those given above for n variables.

Examples

Determine the minimum of the function

$$f(x_1, x_2, x_3) = x_1 x_2 + x_1 x_3 + x_2 x_3 \qquad \text{if} \quad x_1 x_2 x_3 = 125$$

$$F(x_1, x_2, x_3, \lambda) = x_1 x_2 + x_1 x_3 + x_2 x_3 - \lambda(x_1 x_2 x_3 - 125)$$

$$\frac{\partial F}{\partial x_1} = x_2 + x_3 - \lambda x_2 x_3$$

$$\frac{\partial F}{\partial x_2} = x_1 + x_3 - \lambda x_1 x_3$$

$$\frac{\partial F}{\partial x_3} = x_1 + x_2 - \lambda x_1 x_2$$

$$\frac{\partial F}{\partial \lambda} = -(x_1 x_2 x_3 - 125)$$

If $\dfrac{\partial F}{\partial x_1} = 0,\ \dfrac{\partial F}{\partial x_2} = 0,\ \dfrac{\partial F}{\partial x_3} = 0,\ \dfrac{\partial F}{\partial \lambda} = 0$, then

$$x_1 = x_2 = x_3 = \sqrt[3]{125} = 5 \qquad \lambda = \tfrac{2}{5}$$

$$f_{x_1 x_1} = 0 \qquad\qquad f_{x_2 x_2} = 0 \qquad\qquad f_{x_3 x_3} = 0$$

$$f_{x_1 x_2} = 1 \qquad\qquad f_{x_1 x_3} = 1 \qquad\qquad f_{x_2 x_3} = 1$$

$$g_{x_1} = x_2 x_3 = 25 \qquad g_{x_2} = x_1 x_3 = 25 \qquad g_{x_3} = x_1 x_2 = 25$$

$$g_{x_1 x_1} = 0 \qquad\qquad g_{x_2 x_2} = 0 \qquad\qquad g_{x_3 x_3} = 0$$

$$g_{x_1 x_2} = x_3 = 5 \qquad g_{x_1 x_3} = x_2 = 5 \qquad g_{x_2 x_3} = x_1 = 5$$

$$\Delta_3 = \begin{vmatrix} 0 & 25 & 25 \\ 25 & 0 & -1 \\ 25 & -1 & 0 \end{vmatrix} = 0 - 625 - 625 - (0 + 0 + 0) = -1250$$

$$\Delta_4 = \begin{vmatrix} 0 & 25 & 25 & 25 \\ 25 & 0 & -1 & -1 \\ 25 & -1 & 0 & -1 \\ 25 & -1 & -1 & 0 \end{vmatrix}$$

$$= 0 - 25 \begin{vmatrix} 25 & -1 & -1 \\ 25 & 0 & -1 \\ 25 & -1 & 0 \end{vmatrix} + 25 \begin{vmatrix} 25 & 0 & -1 \\ 25 & -1 & -1 \\ 25 & -1 & 0 \end{vmatrix} - 25 \begin{vmatrix} 25 & 0 & -1 \\ 25 & -1 & 0 \\ 25 & -1 & -1 \end{vmatrix}$$

$$= 0 - 25[0 + 25 + 25 - (0 + 25 + 0)] + 25[0 + 25 + 0 - (25 + 25 + 0)]$$
$$- 25[25 + 25 + 0 - (25 + 0 + 0)]$$

$$= 0 - 625 - 625 - 625 = -1875$$

$\Delta_3 < 0$, $\Delta_4 < 0$, so the point $(5, 5, 5)$ is a local minimum of the function $f(x_1, x_2, x_3) = x_1 x_2 + x_1 x_3 + x_2 x_3$ subject to $x_1 x_2 x_3 = 125$.

Determine the maximum of the function

$$f(x, y, z) = -x^2 - 2y^2 - z^2 + xy + z \qquad \text{if} \quad x + y + z = 35$$

$$F(x, y, z, \lambda) = -x^2 - 2y^2 - z^2 + xy + z - \lambda(x + y + z - 35)$$

$$\frac{\partial F}{\partial x} = -2x + y - \lambda$$

$$\frac{\partial F}{\partial y} = 4y + x - \lambda$$

$$\frac{\partial F}{\partial z} = -2z + 1 - \lambda$$

$$\frac{\partial F}{\partial \lambda} = -(x + y + z - 35)$$

If $\dfrac{\partial F}{\partial x} = 0$, $\dfrac{\partial F}{\partial y} = 0$, $\dfrac{\partial F}{\partial z} = 0$, $\dfrac{\partial F}{\partial \lambda} = 0$, then

$$-2x + y = -4y + x = -2z + 1$$

$$3x = 5y$$

$$x = \tfrac{5}{3}y$$

$$-2z + 1 = y - \tfrac{10}{3}y = -\tfrac{7}{3}y$$

$$z = \frac{1 + \tfrac{7}{3}y}{2}$$

$$\tfrac{5}{3}y + y + \frac{1 + \tfrac{7}{3}y}{2} = 35$$

$$\tfrac{10}{3}y + 2y + 1 + \tfrac{7}{3}y = 70$$

$$\tfrac{23}{3}y = 69$$

$$y = 9$$

$$x = 15$$

$$z = 11$$

$$\lambda = -21$$

$$
\begin{array}{lll}
f_{xx} = -2 & f_{yy} = -4 & f_{zz} = -2 \\
f_{xy} = 1 & f_{xz} = 0 & f_{yz} = 0 \\
g_x = 1 & g_y = 1 & g_z = 1 \\
g_{xx} = 0 & g_{yy} = 0 & g_{zz} = 0 \\
g_{xy} = 0 & g_{xz} = 0 & g_{yz} = 0
\end{array}
$$

$$\Delta_3 = \begin{vmatrix} 0 & 1 & 1 \\ 1 & -2 & 1 \\ 1 & 1 & -4 \end{vmatrix} = (0 + 1 + 1) - (-2 + 0 - 4) = 8$$

$$\Delta_4 = \begin{vmatrix} 0 & 1 & 1 & 1 \\ 1 & -2 & 1 & 1 \\ 1 & 1 & -4 & 0 \\ 1 & 1 & 0 & -2 \end{vmatrix}$$

$$= 0 - \begin{vmatrix} 1 & 1 & 1 \\ 1 & -4 & 0 \\ 1 & 0 & -2 \end{vmatrix} + \begin{vmatrix} 1 & -2 & 1 \\ 1 & 1 & 0 \\ 1 & 1 & -2 \end{vmatrix} - \begin{vmatrix} 1 & -2 & 1 \\ 1 & 1 & -4 \\ 1 & 1 & 0 \end{vmatrix}$$

$$= 0 - [8 + 0 + 0 - (-4 + 0 - 2)] + [-2 + 1 + 0 - (1 + 0 + 4)]$$

$$\qquad\qquad\qquad\qquad - [0 + 1 + 8 - (1 - 4 + 0)]$$

$$= 0 - 14 - 6 - 11 = -31$$

$\Delta_3 > 0$, $\Delta_4 < 0$, so the point $(15, 9, 11)$ is a local maximum of the function $f(x, y, z) = -x^2 - 2y^2 - z^2 + xy + z$ subject to $x + y + z = 35$.

If utility analysis is generalized to the case of n commodities, the utility function is given by

$$U = f(q_1, q_2, \ldots, q_n)$$

where $q_1, q_2, \ldots, q_n$ are the quantities of the n commodities, and the budget constraint is given by

$$y - \sum_{i=1}^{n} p_i q_i = 0$$

where $p_1, p_2, \ldots, p_n$ are the unit prices of the n commodities. Then the function to be maximized is

$$F = f(q_1, q_2, \ldots, q_n) - \lambda\left(y - \sum_{i=1}^{n} p_i q_i\right)$$

and, for maximization,

$$\frac{\partial F}{\partial q_i} = f_i + \lambda p_i = 0 \qquad i = 1, 2, \ldots, n$$

$$\frac{\partial F}{\partial \lambda} = -\left(y - \sum_{i=1}^{n} p_i q_i\right) = 0$$

The demand curves for the n commodities can be obtained by solving for the q's. The conditions

$$\frac{\partial F}{\partial q_i} = f_i + \lambda p_i = 0 \qquad i = 1, 2, \ldots, n$$

can be written as

$$-\frac{\partial q_i}{\partial q_j} = \frac{p_j}{p_i} \qquad \text{for all } i \text{ and } j$$

That is, the rate of substitution of commodity i for commodity j must equal the price ratio $\dfrac{p_j}{p_i}$. The second-order conditions for maximization require that the principal minors of the bordered Hessian determinant must alternate in sign; that is,

$$\begin{vmatrix} 0 & -p_1 & -p_2 \\ -p_1 & f_{11} & f_{12} \\ -p_2 & f_{21} & f_{22} \end{vmatrix} > 0 \qquad \begin{vmatrix} 0 & -p_1 & -p_2 & -p_3 \\ -p_1 & f_{11} & f_{12} & f_{13} \\ -p_2 & f_{21} & f_{22} & f_{23} \\ -p_3 & f_{31} & f_{32} & f_{33} \end{vmatrix} < 0$$

$$\cdots (-1)^n \begin{vmatrix} 0 & -p_1 & -p_2 & \cdots & -p_n \\ -p_1 & f_{11} & f_{12} & \cdots & f_{1n} \\ -p_2 & f_{21} & f_{22} & \cdots & f_{2n} \\ \vdots & \vdots & \vdots & & \vdots \\ -p_n & f_{n1} & f_{n2} & \cdots & f_{nn} \end{vmatrix} > 0$$

□ KUHN-TUCKER CONDITIONS

Consider a function of n variables $f(x_1, x_2, \ldots, x_n)$ subject to the constraint $g(x_1, x_2, \ldots, x_n) \leq 0$. A point $x^* = (x_1^*, x_2^*, \ldots, x_n^*)$ is a local maximum of $f(x_1, x_2, \ldots, x_n)$ subject to $g(x_1, x_2, \ldots, x_n)$ only if there exists a nonnegative λ such that λ and $(x_1^*, x_2^*, \ldots, x_n^*)$ satisfy the Kuhn-Tucker conditions:

$$h_i = \frac{\partial f}{\partial x_i} - \lambda \frac{\partial g}{\partial x_i} = 0 \qquad i = 1, 2, \ldots, n$$

$$\lambda g(x_1, x_2, \ldots, x_n) = 0$$

$$g(x_1, x_2, \ldots, x_n) \leq 0$$

These conditions are also sufficient if $f(x_1, x_2, \ldots, x_n)$ is concave and the constraint is concave. Since a maximum point of $f(x_1, x_2, \ldots, x_n)$ is a minimum point of $-f(x_1, x_2, \ldots, x_n)$, this result is also applicable to minimizing a convex function subject to a convex constraint.

NOTE: A function $f(x_1, x_2, \ldots, x_n)$ is convex in a region if for any two points $(\tilde{x}_1, \tilde{x}_2, \ldots, \tilde{x}_n)$ and $(\bar{x}_1, \bar{x}_2, \ldots, \bar{x}_n)$,

$$f[(1 - t)\tilde{x}_1 + t\bar{x}_1, \ldots, (1 - t)\tilde{x}_n + t\bar{x}_n]$$

$$\leq (1 - t)f(\tilde{x}_1, \tilde{x}_2, \ldots, \tilde{x}_n) + tf(\bar{x}_1, \bar{x}_2, \ldots, \bar{x}_n)$$

The function is strictly convex if $\leq$ can be replaced by $<$; the function is concave if $\leq$ can be replaced by $\geq$ and strictly concave if $\leq$ can be replaced by $>$.

The method of Lagrange multipliers can be modified to determine the maximum or minimum of a function of n variables subject to one inequality constraint in a manner similar to the modification for a function of two variables subject to one inequality constraint. Assume that the inequality constraint holds as an equality constraint and obtain the maximum using the method of Lagrange multipliers: If $\lambda > 0$, this maximum is also the maximum subject to the inequality constraint; if $\lambda \leq 0$, the maximum determined without regard to the constraint satisfies the constraint and is thus also the constrained maximum. Corresponding statements hold for determining the minimum of a function of n variables subject to one inequality constraint.

Examples

Find the minimum of $f(x_1, x_2, x_3) = x_1x_2 + x_1x_3 + x_2x_3$ subject to the constraint $x_1x_2x_3 \geq 125$.

Assuming the inequality constraint to hold as an equality constraint, $\lambda = \frac{2}{5}$ (see page 603). Since $\lambda > 0$, the minimum $(5, 5, 5)$ assuming the equality constraint is also the minimum assuming the inequality constraint.

Alternatively, using the Kuhn-Tucker conditions,

$$\frac{\partial f}{\partial x_1} - \lambda \frac{\partial g}{\partial x_1} = x_2 + x_3 - \lambda x_2 x_3 = 0$$

$$\frac{\partial f}{\partial x_2} - \lambda \frac{\partial g}{\partial x_2} = x_1 + x_3 - \lambda x_1 x_3 = 0$$

$$\frac{\partial f}{\partial x_3} - \lambda \frac{\partial g}{\partial x_3} = x_1 + x_2 - \lambda x_1 x_2 = 0$$

$$\lambda(x_1 x_2 x_3 - 125) = 0$$

$$x_1 x_2 x_3 \geq 125$$

Either $\lambda = 0$ or $x_1 x_2 x_3 - 125 = 0$. If $\lambda = 0$,

$$x_2 + x_3 = 0$$

$$x_1 + x_3 = 0$$

$$x_1 + x_2 = 0$$

and $x_1 = x_2 = x_3 = 0$; but then $x_1 x_2 x_3 \geq 125$ is not satisfied. If $x_1 x_2 x_3 - 125 = 0$,

$$\frac{x_2 + x_3}{x_2 x_3} = \frac{x_1 + x_3}{x_1 x_3} = \frac{x_1 + x_2}{x_1 x_2}$$

and $x_1 = x_2 = x_3 = 5$; this solution satisfies the Kuhn-Tucker conditions. Thus, as above, the minimum of $f(x_1, x_2, x_3) = x_1 x_2 + x_1 x_3 + x_2 x_3$ subject to $x_1 x_3 x_3 \geq 25$ is $x_1 = x_2 = x_3 = 5$.

Find the maximum of $f(x, y, z) = -x^2 - 2y^2 - z^2 + xy + z$ subject to the constraint $x + y + z \leq 35$.

Assuming the inequality constraint to hold as an equality constraint, $\lambda = -21$ (see page 604). Since $\lambda < 0$, the unconstrained maximum is also the maximum subject to the inequality constraint.

$$\frac{\partial f}{\partial x} = -2x + y \qquad \frac{\partial^2 f}{\partial x^2} = -2 \qquad \frac{\partial^2 f}{\partial x \, \partial y} = 1$$

$$\frac{\partial f}{\partial y} = -4y + x \qquad \frac{\partial^2 f}{\partial y^2} = -4 \qquad \frac{\partial^2 f}{\partial x \, \partial z} = 0$$

$$\frac{\partial f}{\partial z} = -2z + 1 \qquad \frac{\partial^2 f}{\partial z^2} = -2 \qquad \frac{\partial^2 f}{\partial y \, \partial z} = 0$$

If $\frac{\partial f}{\partial x} = 0$, $\frac{\partial f}{\partial y} = 0$, $\frac{\partial f}{\partial z} = 0$, then

$$x = y = 0 \qquad z = 1$$

$$\Delta_1 = -2$$

$$\Delta_2 = \begin{vmatrix} -2 & 1 \\ 1 & -4 \end{vmatrix} = 8 - 1 = 7$$

$$\Delta_3 = \begin{vmatrix} -2 & 1 & 0 \\ 1 & -4 & 0 \\ 0 & 0 & -2 \end{vmatrix} = -16 - (-2) = -14$$

$\Delta_1 < 0$, $\Delta_2 > 0$, $\Delta_3 < 0$ so the point $(0, 0, 1)$ is a maximum.

Alternatively, using the Kuhn-Tucker conditions,

$$\frac{\partial f}{\partial x} - \lambda \frac{\partial g}{\partial x} = -2x + y - \lambda = 0$$

$$\frac{\partial f}{\partial y} - \lambda \frac{\partial g}{\partial y} = -4y + x - \lambda = 0$$

$$\frac{\partial f}{\partial z} - \lambda \frac{\partial g}{\partial z} = -2z + 1 - \lambda = 0$$

$$\lambda(x + y + z - 35) = 0 \qquad x + y + z \le 35$$

Either $\lambda = 0$ or $x + y + z - 35 = 0$. If $\lambda = 0$,

$$x = y = 0 \qquad z = 1$$

and $x + y + z \le 35$ is satisfied. Thus, as above, the maximum of $f(x, y, z) = -x^2 - 2y^2 - z^2 + xy + z$ subject to the constraint $x + y + z \le 35$ is $x = y = 0$, $z = 1$.

PROBLEMS

1. Determine the values of x_1, x_2, and x_3 that minimize the function

$$f(x_1, x_2, x_3) = x_1^2 + 4x_2^2 + x_3^2 - 4x_1x_2 - 6x_3$$

   subject to the constraint $x_1 + x_2 + x_3 = 15$.

2. Determine the values of x_1, x_2, and x_3 that maximize the function

$$f(x_1, x_2, x_3) = 6x_1x_2 + 4x_2x_3 + 6x_2 - 3x_3^2 - x_2^2$$

   subject to the constraint $x_1 + 2x_2 + x_3 = 75$.

3. Determine the values of x_1, x_2, and x_3 (if any) that maximize or minimize the function

$$f(x_1, x_2, x_3) = x_1x_2 + 10x_1 - x_1^2 - x_2^2 - x_3^2$$

4. Determine the values of x, y, and z (if any) that maximize or minimize the function

$$f(x, y, z) = e^{4x^2 + 2y^2 + z^2 - 5xy - 4z}$$

5. Determine the values of x_1, x_2, and x_3 that minimize the function

$$f(x_1, x_2, x_3) = x_1^2 + x_2^2 + x_3^2 + x_1x_2x_3$$

   subject to the constraint $x_1x_2x_3 = 1000$.

6. Determine the values of x_1, x_2, and x_3 that minimize the function

$$f(x_1, x_2, x_3) = 5x_1^2 + 10x_2^2 + x_3^2 - 4x_1x_2 - 2x_1x_3 - 36x_2$$

   subject to the constraint $x_1 + x_2 + x_3 = 3$.

7. Determine the values of x, y, and z (if any) that maximize or minimize the function

$$f(x, y, z) = e^{-x^2 - 2y^2 - z^2 - 2xy}$$

8. Determine the values of x_1, x_2, and x_3 (if any) that maximize or minimize the function

$$f(x_1, x_2, x_3) = x_1^2 + x_2^2 + 7x_3^2 - x_1x_2$$

9. Determine the values of x_1, x_2, and x_3 that minimize the function

$$f(x_1, x_2, x_3) = x_1^2 + 4x_2^2 + x_3^2 - 4x_1x_2 - 6x_3$$

   subject to the constraint $x_1 + x_2 + x_3 \ge 15$ (see Problem 1).

10. Determine the values of x_1, x_2, and x_3 that maximize the function

$$f(x_1, x_2, x_3) = 6x_1x_2 + 4x_2x_3 + 6x_2 - 3x_3^2 - 2x_2^2$$

subject to the constraint $x_1 + 2x_2 + x_3 \leq 75$ (see Problem 2).

11. Determine the values of x_1, x_2, and x_3 that minimize the function

$$f(x_1, x_2, x_3) = x_1^2 + x_2^2 + x_3^2 + x_1x_2x_3$$

subject to the constraint $x_1x_2x_3 \leq 1000$ (see Problem 5).

12. Determine the values of x_1, x_2, and x_3 that minimize the function

$$f(x_1, x_2, x_3) = 5x_1^2 + 10x_2^2 + x_3^2 - 4x_1x_2 - 2x_1x_3 - 36x_2$$

subject to the constraint $x_1 + x_2 + x_3 \geq 3$ (see Problem 6).

ANSWERS TO ODD-NUMBERED PROBLEMS

1. $x_1 = 8, x_2 = 4, x_3 = 3$

3. $x_1 = \frac{20}{3}, x_2 = \frac{10}{3}, x_3 = 0$ (maximize)

5. $x_1 = x_2 = x_3 = 10$

7. $x = y = z = 0$ (maximize)

9. $x_1 = 8, x_2 = 4, x_3 = 3$

11. no finite maximum

■ 8.2 INPUT-OUTPUT ANALYSIS

Input-output analysis traces the flow of production to show how production of primary, intermediate, and finished goods is affected by a change in the demand for final goods. The primary purpose of input-output analysis is to calculate the output levels in various industries that would be required by particular levels of final goods demand. Input-output analysis can also be discussed in terms of sectors of the economy, either for a closed model where the output for a sector is equal to the sum of its inputs in the other sectors or for an open model including final demand in addition to demands from other sectors.

Assume that an economy is divided into n industries and that each industry produces only one type of output. Industries are usually related in the sense that each must use some of the others' products in order to operate. In addition, an economy must usually produce some finished products for final demand. Input-output analysis determines the production of each of the industries if final demand changes, assuming the structure of the economy does not change. It is convenient to tabulate the data for input-output analysis as shown in Table 8.1, where b_{ij} is the dollar amount of the products of industry i used by industry j, h_i is the final demand for the products of industry i, and $x_1 = \sum_{j=1}^{n} b_{ij} + h_i$ is the total output of industry i.

Table 8.1

Producer	User 1	User 2 $\cdots$ n	Final demand	Total output
1	b_{11}	$b_{12} \cdots b_{1n}$	h_1	x_1
2	b_{21}	$b_{22} \cdots b_{2n}$	h_2	x_2
$\vdots$	$\vdots$	$\vdots \quad \vdots$	$\vdots$	$\vdots$
n	b_{n1}	$b_{n2} \cdots b_{nn}$	h_n	x_n

The structure of the economy can now be described by the technological matrix

$$\mathbf{A} = (a_{ij})$$

where $a_{ij} = \dfrac{b_{ij}}{x_j}$ = dollar value of the output of industry i that industry j must purchase to produce one dollar's worth of its own products. Note that this definition of a_{ij} assumes that the purchases of intermediate product of an industry are proportional to the level of output of the industry; that is,

$$\frac{\text{sales of industry } i}{\text{sales of industry } j} = (a_{ij})(\text{output of industry } j)$$

This assumption of constant proportionality between inputs and outputs is standard for input-output analysis.

Thus the ith industry must produce outputs

$$a_{i1}x_1 + a_{i2}x_2 + \cdots + a_{in}x_n \quad \text{for } i = 1, 2, \ldots, n$$

in order to supply the needs of all industries. The interindustry demand vector $\mathbf{X}$ can thus be written as $\mathbf{AX}$, where

$$\mathbf{A} = \begin{pmatrix} a_{11} & a_{12} \cdots a_{1n} \\ a_{21} & a_{22} \cdots a_{2n} \\ \vdots & \vdots \quad \vdots \\ a_{n1} & a_{n2} \cdots a_{nn} \end{pmatrix} \quad \text{and} \quad \mathbf{X} = \begin{pmatrix} x_1 \\ x_2 \\ \vdots \\ x_n \end{pmatrix}$$

the production of the economy must be adjusted to fulfill both interindustry needs and final demand. If the final demand vector is

$$\mathbf{H} = \begin{pmatrix} h_1 \\ h_2 \\ \vdots \\ h_n \end{pmatrix} \quad h_i \geq 0 \quad i = 1, 2, \ldots, n$$

this requirement can be written

$$\mathbf{X} = \mathbf{AX} + \mathbf{H}$$

Thus

$$(\mathbf{I} - \mathbf{A})\mathbf{X} = \mathbf{H}$$

and

$$\mathbf{X} = (\mathbf{I} - \mathbf{A})^{-1}\mathbf{H}$$

the matrix $\mathbf{I} - \mathbf{A}$ is known as the *Leontief matrix*.

There are a number of mathematical and practical problems in input-output analysis. For example, the technological matrix must be such that each of the x_i's is nonnegative; otherwise, the solution is not economically meaningful. There are also problems concerning industry classification and stability of the technological matrix.

Given a set of positive final demands, consider the problem of determining the conditions under which there is a unique set of positive production levels consistent with the set of final demands. First, since $(\mathbf{I} - \mathbf{A})^{-1}$ must exist, $|\mathbf{I} - \mathbf{A}|$ must be nonzero. In addition, each element of $(\mathbf{I} - \mathbf{A})^{-1}$ must be nonnegative, since otherwise an increase in final demand would result in a decrease in production at some point in the production process. It can be shown that, in order for positive gross-output levels to be associated with any given set of positive demands, the following conditions are required

$$1 > a_{ij} \geq 0 \qquad \text{all } i \text{ and } j$$
$$|\mathbf{I} - \mathbf{A}| > 0$$

Since any k-industry subset of the n industries must be able to satisfy interindustry demands with some surplus to satisfy demands external to the k industries, all principal minors of the n industry Leontief determinant

$$\mathbf{I} - \mathbf{A} = \begin{vmatrix} 1 - a_{11} & -a_{12} & \cdots & -a_{1n} \\ -a_{21} & 1 - a_{22} & \cdots & -a_{2n} \\ \vdots & \vdots & & \vdots \\ -a_{n1} & -a_{n2} & \cdots & 1 - a_{nn} \end{vmatrix}$$

must be positive.

Examples

Consider a very simple hypothetical economy of two industries, A and B, represented in Table 8.2, where data are in millions of dollars of products.

Table 8.2

Producer	User A	B	Final demand	Total output
A	500	350	150	1000
B	320	360	120	800

Determine the output vector of the economy if final demand changes to 200 for A and 100 for B.

$$A = \begin{pmatrix} \frac{1}{2} & \frac{7}{16} \\ \frac{8}{25} & \frac{9}{20} \end{pmatrix}$$

$$I - A = \begin{pmatrix} \frac{1}{2} & -\frac{7}{16} \\ -\frac{8}{25} & \frac{11}{20} \end{pmatrix}$$

$$(I - A)^{-1} = \frac{200}{27} \begin{pmatrix} \frac{11}{20} & \frac{7}{16} \\ \frac{8}{25} & \frac{1}{2} \end{pmatrix}$$

NOTE: $|I - A| = \frac{1}{2} \cdot \frac{11}{20} - \frac{7}{16} \cdot \frac{8}{25} = \frac{27}{200}$.

As must be the case,

$$X = (I - A)^{-1}H = \frac{200}{27} \begin{pmatrix} \frac{11}{20} & \frac{7}{16} \\ \frac{8}{25} & \frac{1}{2} \end{pmatrix} \begin{pmatrix} 150 \\ 120 \end{pmatrix} = \begin{pmatrix} 1000 \\ 800 \end{pmatrix}$$

And, if $H = \begin{pmatrix} 200 \\ 100 \end{pmatrix}$, then

$$X = (I - A)^{-1}H = \frac{200}{27} \begin{pmatrix} \frac{11}{20} & \frac{7}{16} \\ \frac{8}{25} & \frac{1}{2} \end{pmatrix} \begin{pmatrix} 200 \\ 100 \end{pmatrix} = \begin{pmatrix} 1138\frac{8}{9} \\ 844\frac{4}{9} \end{pmatrix}$$

That is, industry A must have an output of $1138\frac{8}{9}$ and industry B must have an output of $844\frac{4}{9}$, where output is given in millions of dollars of products.

Consider a very simple hypothetical economy of three industries, A, B, and C, represented in Table 8.3, where data are in millions of dollars of products.

Table 8.3

Producer	User A	B	C	Final demand	Total output
A	90	150	225	75	540
B	135	150	300	15	600
C	270	200	300	130	900

Determine the output vector of the economy if final demand changes to (a) 50 for A, 10 for B, and 100 for C; (b) 100 for A, 20 for B, and 60 for C; (c) 80 for A, 100 for B, and 120 for C.

$$A = \begin{pmatrix} \frac{1}{6} & \frac{1}{4} & \frac{1}{4} \\ \frac{1}{4} & \frac{1}{4} & \frac{1}{3} \\ \frac{1}{2} & \frac{1}{3} & \frac{1}{3} \end{pmatrix}$$

$$(\mathbf{I} - \mathbf{A}) = \begin{pmatrix} \frac{5}{6} & -\frac{1}{4} & -\frac{1}{4} \\ -\frac{1}{4} & \frac{3}{4} & -\frac{1}{3} \\ -\frac{1}{2} & -\frac{1}{3} & \frac{2}{3} \end{pmatrix}$$

$$(\mathbf{I} - \mathbf{A})^{-1} = \frac{864}{109} \begin{pmatrix} \frac{7}{18} & \frac{1}{4} & \frac{13}{48} \\ \frac{1}{3} & \frac{31}{72} & \frac{49}{144} \\ \frac{11}{24} & \frac{29}{72} & \frac{9}{16} \end{pmatrix}$$

NOTE: $|\mathbf{I} - \mathbf{A}| = \frac{5}{6} \cdot \frac{3}{4} \cdot \frac{2}{3} - \frac{1}{4} \cdot \frac{1}{3} \cdot \frac{1}{4} - \frac{1}{2} \cdot \frac{1}{3} \cdot \frac{1}{4}$

$$- \left(\frac{1}{4} \cdot \frac{3}{4} \cdot \frac{1}{2} + \frac{1}{3} \cdot \frac{1}{3} \cdot \frac{5}{6} + \frac{2}{3} \cdot \frac{1}{4} \cdot \frac{1}{4} \right)$$

$$= \frac{109}{864}$$

$c_{11} = (-1)^{1+1} \begin{vmatrix} \frac{3}{4} & -\frac{1}{3} \\ -\frac{1}{3} & \frac{2}{3} \end{vmatrix} = \frac{7}{18}$ $c_{23} = (-1)^{2+3} \begin{vmatrix} \frac{5}{6} & -\frac{1}{4} \\ -\frac{1}{2} & -\frac{1}{3} \end{vmatrix} = \frac{29}{72}$

$c_{12} = (-1)^{1+2} \begin{vmatrix} -\frac{1}{4} & -\frac{1}{3} \\ -\frac{1}{2} & \frac{2}{3} \end{vmatrix} = \frac{1}{3}$ $c_{31} = (-1)^{3+1} \begin{vmatrix} -\frac{1}{4} & -\frac{1}{4} \\ \frac{3}{4} & -\frac{1}{3} \end{vmatrix} = \frac{13}{48}$

$c_{13} = (-1)^{1+3} \begin{vmatrix} -\frac{1}{4} & \frac{3}{4} \\ -\frac{1}{2} & -\frac{1}{3} \end{vmatrix} = \frac{11}{24}$ $c_{32} = (-1)^{3+2} \begin{vmatrix} \frac{5}{6} & -\frac{1}{4} \\ -\frac{1}{4} & -\frac{1}{3} \end{vmatrix} = \frac{49}{144}$

$c_{21} = (-1)^{2+1} \begin{vmatrix} -\frac{1}{4} & -\frac{1}{4} \\ -\frac{1}{3} & \frac{2}{3} \end{vmatrix} = \frac{1}{4}$ $c_{33} = (-1)^{3+3} \begin{vmatrix} \frac{5}{6} & -\frac{1}{4} \\ -\frac{1}{4} & \frac{3}{4} \end{vmatrix} = \frac{9}{16}$

$c_{22} = (-1)^{2+2} \begin{vmatrix} \frac{5}{6} & -\frac{1}{4} \\ -\frac{1}{2} & \frac{2}{3} \end{vmatrix} = \frac{31}{72}$

As must be the case,

$$\mathbf{X} = (\mathbf{I} - \mathbf{A})^{-1}\mathbf{H} = \frac{864}{109} \begin{pmatrix} \frac{7}{18} & \frac{1}{4} & \frac{13}{48} \\ \frac{1}{3} & \frac{31}{72} & \frac{49}{144} \\ \frac{11}{24} & \frac{29}{72} & \frac{9}{16} \end{pmatrix} \begin{pmatrix} 75 \\ 15 \\ 130 \end{pmatrix} = \begin{pmatrix} 540 \\ 600 \\ 900 \end{pmatrix}$$

(a) If $\mathbf{H} = \begin{pmatrix} 50 \\ 10 \\ 100 \end{pmatrix}$,

$$\mathbf{X} = (\mathbf{I} - \mathbf{A})^{-1}\mathbf{H} = \frac{864}{109} \begin{pmatrix} \frac{7}{18} & \frac{1}{4} & \frac{13}{48} \\ \frac{1}{3} & \frac{31}{72} & \frac{49}{144} \\ \frac{11}{24} & \frac{29}{72} & \frac{9}{16} \end{pmatrix} \begin{pmatrix} 50 \\ 10 \\ 100 \end{pmatrix}$$

$$= \begin{pmatrix} 388.62 \\ 435.96 \\ 819.08 \end{pmatrix}$$

(b) If $\mathbf{H} = \begin{pmatrix} 100 \\ 20 \\ 60 \end{pmatrix}$,

$$X = (I - A)^{-1}H = \tfrac{864}{109}\begin{pmatrix} \tfrac{7}{18} & \tfrac{1}{4} & \tfrac{13}{48} \\ \tfrac{1}{3} & \tfrac{31}{72} & \tfrac{49}{144} \\ \tfrac{11}{24} & \tfrac{29}{72} & \tfrac{9}{16} \end{pmatrix}\begin{pmatrix} 100 \\ 20 \\ 60 \end{pmatrix}$$

$$= \begin{pmatrix} 476.70 \\ 494.31 \\ 694.68 \end{pmatrix}$$

(c) If $H = \begin{pmatrix} 80 \\ 100 \\ 120 \end{pmatrix}$,

$$X = (I - A)^{-1}H = \tfrac{864}{109}\begin{pmatrix} \tfrac{7}{18} & \tfrac{1}{4} & \tfrac{13}{48} \\ \tfrac{1}{3} & \tfrac{31}{72} & \tfrac{49}{144} \\ \tfrac{11}{24} & \tfrac{29}{72} & \tfrac{9}{16} \end{pmatrix}\begin{pmatrix} 80 \\ 100 \\ 120 \end{pmatrix}$$

$$= \begin{pmatrix} 702.39 \\ 876.33 \\ 1053.21 \end{pmatrix}$$

PROBLEMS

1. A simple hypothetical economy of three industries, A, B, and C, is represented in the following table (data are in millions of dollars of products):

Producer	User			Final demand	Total output
	A	B	C		
A	80	100	100	40	320
B	80	200	60	60	400
C	80	100	100	20	300

Determine the output vector for the economy if the final demand changes to (a) 120 for A, 40 for B, and 10 for C; (b) 60 for A, 60 for B, and 60 for C.

2. A simple hypothetical economy of two industries, A and B, is represented in the following table (data are in tens of millions of dollars of products):

Producer	User		Final demand	Total output
	A	B		
A	14	6	8	28
B	7	18	11	36

Determine the output vector for the economy if the final demand changes to
(a) 16 for A and 3 for B; (b) 2 for A and 4 for B.

3. A simple hypothetical economy of two industries, A and B, is represented
in the following table (data are in millions of dollars of products):

Producer	User		Final demand	Total output
	A	B		
A	150	240	210	600
B	200	120	160	480

Determine the output vector for the economy if the final demand changes to
(a) 100 for A and 200 for B; (b) 50 for A and 60 for B.

4. A simple hypothetical economy of three industries, A, B, and C, is represented
in the following table (data are in tens of millions of dollars of products):

Producer	User			Final demand	Total output
	A	B	C		
A	5	4	3	3	15
B	3	10	6	1	20
C	3	4	4	1	12

Determine the output vector for the economy if the final demand changes to
(a) 1 for A, 2 for B, and 10 for C; (b) 2 for A, 3 for B, and 2 for C.

ANSWERS TO ODD-NUMBERED PROBLEMS

1. (a) 481.74 for A, 469.57 for B, and 371.74 for C
   (b) 469.56 for A, 542.61 for B, and 469.56 for C

3. (a) 442.11 for A and 463.16 for B
   (b) 170.53 for A and 155.79 for B

■ 8.3 LINEAR PROGRAMMING

Many problems in business are concerned essentially with the allocation of
limited resources—money, personnel, materials, machines, space, time—in
order to maximize some measure of performance or minimize some measure

of cost. The mathematical techniques for planning such allocation are referred to as *mathematical programming*; the special case in which the measure of performance or cost is a linear function of the controllable variables and the restrictions on the availability or utilization of resources are expressible as linear equations or inequalities is referred to as *linear programming*.

More specifically, the general linear programming problem involves maximizing or minimizing a linear function of several *primary variables*, referred to as an *objective function*, subject to a set of linear equalities or inequalities referred to as *constraints*. None of the variables may be negative. (Note, however, that a negative variable can be written as the difference of two positive variables.)

Mathematically, the linear programming problem for maximization is written

$$\text{Maximize an objective function } Z = c_1 X_1 + c_2 X_2 + \cdots + c_n X_n$$

subject to the constraints

$$a_{11} X_1 + a_{12} X_2 + \cdots + a_{1n} X_n \le b_1$$
$$a_{21} X_1 + a_{22} X_2 + \cdots + a_{2n} X_n \le b_2$$
$$\vdots$$
$$a_{m1} X_1 + a_{m2} X_2 + \cdots + a_{mn} X_n \le b_m$$
$$X_j \ge 0 \qquad j = 1, 2, \ldots, n$$

This may be written more compactly as

$$\text{Maximize } Z = \sum_{j=1}^{n} c_j X_j$$

subject to $\sum_{j=1}^{n} a_{ij} X_j \le b_i \qquad \text{for } i = 1, 2, \ldots, m$

$$X_j \ge 0 \qquad \text{for } j = 1, 2, \ldots, n$$

and, in matrix notation, as

$$\text{Maximize } \mathbf{Z} = \mathbf{CX}$$

subject to $\mathbf{AX} \le \mathbf{B}, \mathbf{X} \ge \mathbf{O}$, where

$$\mathbf{C} = (c_1, c_2, \ldots, c_n)$$

$$\mathbf{X} = \begin{pmatrix} x_1 \\ x_2 \\ \vdots \\ x_n \end{pmatrix}$$

$$\mathbf{A} = \begin{pmatrix} a_{11} & a_{12} & \cdots & a_{1n} \\ a_{21} & a_{22} & \cdots & a_{2n} \\ \vdots & & & \\ a_{m1} & a_{m2} & \cdots & a_{mn} \end{pmatrix}$$

$$\mathbf{B} = \begin{pmatrix} b_1 \\ b_2 \\ \cdot \\ \cdot \\ b_m \end{pmatrix}$$

Similarly, a linear programming problem involving minimization may be stated in matrix notation as

$$\text{Minimize } \mathbf{Z} = \mathbf{CX}$$

subject to $\mathbf{AX} \geq \mathbf{B}$, $\mathbf{X} \geq 0$. These formulations can be referred to as the standard forms for the problems of linear maximization and minimization, respectively, because the constraint inequalities are all expressed in the form $\leq$ for the maximization problem and in the form $\geq$ for the minimization problem. In order to write a problem in standard form, it may be necessary to reverse the direction of an inequality by multiplying by a negative one. Recall, for example that,

$$a_{11}x_1 + a_{12}x_2 \leq b$$

can be written

$$-a_{11}x_1 - a_{12}x_2 \geq -b$$

Although the standard form may be convenient, it is not necessary for the solution of a linear programming problem. The standard form is necesssary for obtaining the dual, as discussed later in this section.

It can be shown that when there are m constraints in a linear programming problem, there are at most m variables or allocations in its solution. Various methods are available for determining which combination of m of the X_j's maximizes the objective function Z. Linear programming problems involving no more than two primary variables can be solved geometrically; although algebraic solution is usually more efficient even for these problems, geometric solution is intuitively appealing and helps develop a basic understanding which can be applied to more complicated problems. For this reason, it is discussed below. There are several algebraic methods for solving linear programming problems; for more complicated problems involving many variables and many constraints, the *simplex method* is the most efficient of these. The simplex method is an iterative computational routine based on matrix algebra which develops successively better. solutions until the optimal solution is obtained. Most computer program packages include a program for simplex solution of linear programming problems.

□ *GEOMETRIC SOLUTION*

Linear programming problems are solved geometrically by graphing the inequality constraints as equalities and thus determining a polygon of feasible solutions. A solution is said to be *feasible* if it satisfies all the constraints of a linear programming problem. Once the polygon of feasible solutions has been obtained, the next step is to determine which feasible solution optimizes the objective function and is thus the solution of the problem. The following theorem is used to reduce the number of feasible solutions to be checked.

THEOREM: If there is a unique solution which maximizes or minimizes a linear objective function, then that solution must be a vertex (or corner) of the polygon of feasible solutions; if there is more than one solution, at least two of the solutions must correspond to adjacent vertices of the polygon of feasible solutions.

Thus the value of the objective function need be computed only for solutions corresponding to vertices of the polygon of feasible solutions in order to determine the optimal solution. (In some cases certain of these solutions are clearly inferior to others and the corresponding objective functions need not be computed.)

Examples

A manufacturer produces bicycles and motor scooters, each of which must be processed through two machine centers. Machine center 1 has a maximum of 120 hours available and machine center 2 has a maximum of 180 hours available. Manufacturing a bicycle requires 6 hours in machine center 1 and 3 hours in machine center 2; manufacturing a motor scooter requires 4 hours in machine center 1 and 10 hours in machine center 2. If profit is \$45 for a bicycle and \$55 for a motor scooter, determine the number of bicycles and motor scooters that should be manufactured in order to maximize profit.

If X_1 = number of bicycles and X_2 = number of motor scooters, the problem can be stated as follows:

$$\text{Maximize } Z = 45X_1 + 55X_2$$

subject to $6X_1 + 4X_2 \leq 120$, $3X_1 + 10X_2 \leq 180$, and $X_1, X_2 \geq 0$. The polygon of feasible solutions is obtained by graphing the equations

$$6X_1 + 4X_2 = 120$$
$$3X_1 + 10X_2 = 180$$
$$X_1 = 0$$
$$X_2 = 0$$

Any point lying in or on the edge of the shaded polygon in Fig. 8.1 corresponds to a pair of values X_1 and X_2 which satisfies the constraints of the problem and thus is a feasible solution. The optimal solution corresponds to one of the vertices of the polygon; the objective function must thus be evaluated for the solutions (0, 0), (0, 18), (10, 15), and (20, 0).

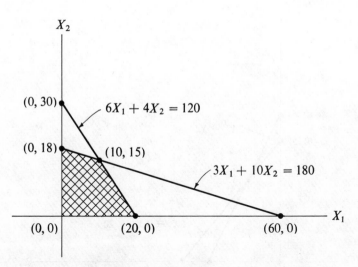

FIGURE 8.1

Since $(0, 0)$ is clearly inferior to $(0, 18)$, it need not be considered.

Solution	$Z = 45X_1 + 55X_2$
$(0, 18)$	\$ 990
$(10, 15)$	\$1275
$(20, 0)$	\$ 900

Thus the optimal solution is $(10, 15)$; that is, manufacture 10 bicycles and 15 motor scooters.

A company produces two commodities in quantities X_1 and X_2, respectively, and wishes to minimize Cost $= 2X_1 + 10X_2$ subject to the constraints

$$2X_1 + X_2 \leq 6$$
$$5X_1 + 4X_2 \geq 20$$
$$X_1, X_2 \geq 0$$

Determine the optimal quantities of each commodity to be produced and the associated cost.

The polygon of feasible solutions is obtained by graphing the equations

$$2X_1 + X_2 = 6$$
$$5X_1 + 4X_2 = 20$$
$$X_1 = 0$$
$$X_2 = 0$$

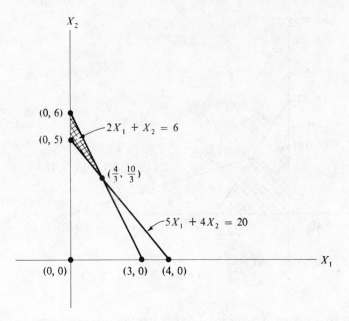

FIGURE 8.2

Any point lying in or on the edge of the shaded polygon in Fig. 8.2 corresponds to a feasible solution. The optimal solution is one of the vertices $(0, 5)$, $(0, 6)$, and $(\frac{4}{3}, \frac{10}{3})$.

Solution	$Z = 2X_1 + 10X_2$
$(0, 5)$	\$50
$(\frac{4}{3}, \frac{10}{3})$	\$36

Note that $(0, 6)$ need not be evaluated, since clearly it is associated with a higher cost than $(0, 5)$. The optimal solution is $(\frac{4}{3}, \frac{10}{3})$; that is, produce $\frac{4}{3}$ units of the first commodity and $\frac{10}{3}$ units of the second commodity. The associated cost is \$36.

□ THE SIMPLEX METHOD

The simplex method solves linear programming problems by obtaining a feasible solution and, by an iterative procedure, improving this solution until the optimal solution is obtained. The computational routine of the simplex method is based on matrix algebra and consists essentially of obtaining an inverse matrix in order to solve a set of simultaneous linear equations.

For simplex solution it is necessary to write the constraint inequalities as equalities (that is, equations) by adding positive variables, referred to as *slack variables*, to the left-hand side of the inequalities. For a maximization problem written in standard form, one slack variable is added to the left-hand side of each inequality. If the slack variable added to the ith equation is denoted by X_{n+i}, the problem can be rewritten as follows:

$$\text{Maximize } Z = c_1 X_1 + c_2 X_2 + \cdots + c_n X_n$$

subject to

$$a_{11} X_1 + a_{12} X_2 + \cdots + a_{1n} X_n + X_{n+1} = b_1$$
$$a_{21} X_1 + a_{22} X_2 + \cdots + a_{2n} X_n + X_{n+2} = b_2$$
$$\vdots$$
$$a_{m1} X_1 + a_{m2} X_2 + \cdots + a_{mn} X_n + X_{n+m} = b_m$$
$$X_j \geq 0 \qquad j = 1, 2, \ldots, n + m$$

In this problem there are n variables and m constraints. The addition of slack variables results in m equations involving $m + n$ unknowns. Note that the slack variables are omitted from the objective function or, equivalently, are given a value of zero in the objective function.

If an inequality is of the form $\geq$, a positive slack variable is subtracted from the left-hand side of the inequality; this slack variable is given a value of zero in the objective function. In order to obtain a feasible solution, an artificial variable is added to the left-hand side of the inequality; this artificial variable is given a value of $-M$ in the objective function for a maximization problem and a value of $+M$ in the objective function for a minimization problem, where M is very large in absolute value. The artificial variable is thus assigned a value in the objective function that precludes its appearance in the final solution. For example, if an inequality is of the form

$$a_{11} X_1 + a_{12} X_2 + \cdots + a_{1n} X_n \geq b_1$$

a slack variable X_{n+1} may be subtracted and an artificial variable X_{n+2} added

$$a_{11} X_1 + a_{12} X_2 + \cdots + a_{1n} X_n - X_{n+1} + X_{n+2} = b_1$$

where the value of X_{n+1} in the objective function is zero and the value of X_{n+1} in the objective function is $-M$ for maximization and $+M$ for minimization.

For convenience, the data are arranged in a simplex tableau on which the computational routine is performed. The initial tableau for the maximization problem stated above is of the form shown in Table 8.4. In the simplex method, two rows are usually included in addition to the data tableau; these are the Z_j row, representing the total profit from the solution, and the $C_j - Z_j$ row, representing the net profit from adding one unit of a variable.

The simplex method consists of the following basic steps, which are illustrated in detail in the examples:

1. Add the necessary slack and artificial variables to convert inequalities to equalities.

2. Arrange the data in a simplex tableau.

3. Determine a feasible solution from the simplex tableau.

4. Check the solution for optimality.

5. If the solution is not optimal, determine from the tableau the entering variable and the departing variable for the next solution.

6. Compute the entries for the revised tableau.

7. Check the solution of the revised tableau for optimality.

8. Repeat this procedure (steps 5 through 7) until the optimal solution is obtained.

Table 8.4

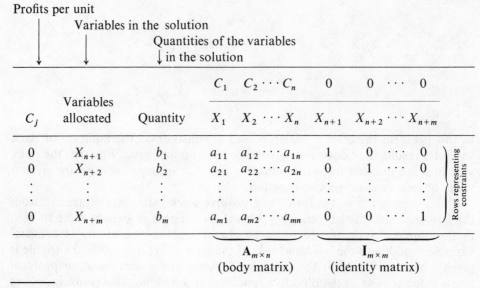

Profits per unit

Variables in the solution

Quantities of the variables in the solution

C_j	Variables allocated	Quantity	C_1 X_1	C_2 X_2	$\cdots$ C_n $\cdots X_n$	0 X_{n+1}	0 X_{n+2}	$\cdots$ 0 $\cdots X_{n+m}$
0	X_{n+1}	b_1	a_{11}	a_{12}	$\cdots a_{1n}$	1	0	$\cdots$ 0
0	X_{n+2}	b_2	a_{21}	a_{22}	$\cdots a_{2n}$	0	1	$\cdots$ 0
.	.	.	.	.	.	.	.	.
.	.	.	.	.	.	.	.	.
0	X_{n+m}	b_m	a_{m1}	a_{m2}	$\cdots a_{mn}$	0	0	$\cdots$ 1

$\underbrace{\qquad}$ Rows representing constraints

$\mathbf{A}_{m \times n}$ (body matrix) $\mathbf{I}_{m \times m}$ (identity matrix)

Example

Consider the problem of the manufacturer of bicycles and motor scooters (see page 618). Adding the slack variables X_3 and X_4, the linear programming problem can be stated as follows:

$$\text{Maximize } Z = 45X_1 + 55X_2$$

subject to

$$6X_1 + 4X_2 + X_3 = 120$$
$$3X_1 + 10X_2 + X_4 = 180$$
$$X_1, X_2, X_3, X_4 \geq 0$$

The initial simplex tableau is shown in Table 8.5. Note the following character-istics of the initial simplex tableau:

Table 8.5

C_j	Variables allocated	Quantity	$45 X_1	$55 X_2	$0 X_3	$0 X_4
$0	X_3	120	6	4	1	0
$0	X_4	180	3	10	0	1
	Z_j	$0	$0	$0	$0	$0
	$C_j - Z_j$		$45	$55	$0	$0

↑
Optimal column

1. Any unknown that occurs in one equation occurs (implicitly at least) in all equations; the unknowns that do not appear explicitly in an equation are considered to have zero coefficients in that equation. Thus the zeros in the X_4 column of the first row and the X_3 column of the second row correspond to those in the equations

$$6X_1 + 4X_2 + X_3 + 0X_4 = 120$$

$$3X_1 + 10X_2 + 0X_3 + X_4 = 180$$

2. The initial tableau is constructed for the solution having zero profit. The objective function can be written

$$Z = 45X_1 + 55X_2 + 0X_3 + 0X_4$$

If $X_3 = 120$ and $X_4 = 180$, then $X_1 = X_2 = 0$ and Z is also zero. This solution is obviously not optimal, but provides a convenient initial feasible solution.

The necessary slack variables are included, the data are arranged in a simplex tableau, and an initial feasible solution is indicated in the tableau (steps 1 through 3). The solution is now checked for optimality.

Step 4. Check for optimality: The $C_j - Z_j$ row gives the net profit from adding one unit of a variable. For a maximization problem, the presence of at least one positive number in the $C_j - Z_j$ row thus indicates that profit can be improved; absence of positive numbers in the $C_j - Z_j$ row indicates that profit cannot be improved; that is, the optimal solution has been obtained. For a minimization problem, the presence of at least one negative number in the $C_j - Z_j$ row indicates that cost can be decreased; absence of negative numbers in the $C_j - Z_j$ row indicates that cost cannot be decreased; that is, the optimal solution has been obtained. In this example, there are positive numbers in the $C_j - Z_j$ row of the initial tableau, so the corresponding solution is not optimal.

Step 5. Entering and departing variables: The largest contribution to profit per unit (\$55) is made by variable X_2, so it is the entering or replacing variable. To determine the departing variable, the quantities of X_3 and X_4 in the initial tableau are divided respectively by their corresponding entries in the optimal column:

$$X_3 \text{ row: } \frac{120 \text{ hours available}}{4 \text{ hours per unit}} = 30 \text{ units of } X_2$$

$$X_4 \text{ row: } \frac{180 \text{ hours available}}{10 \text{ hours per unit}} = 18 \text{ units of } X_2$$

The variable corresponding to the smaller positive ratio is the departing or replaced variable; thus X_4 is the replaced variable in the example. (Note that 18 is the largest number of units of X_2 than can be added without violating the constraints.)

Step 6. Recompute the simplex tableau: The X_2 row of the revised tableau is computed by dividing each number in the replaced row X_4 by the element in the optimal column of the replaced row, which is 10 in this example (Table 8.6).

Table 8.6

C_j	Variables allocated	Quantity	$45 X_1	$55 X_2	$0 X_3	$0 X_4
$0	X_3	48	(2⁴⁄₅)	0	1	$-\frac{2}{5}$
$55	X_2	18	(3⁄10)	1	0	$\frac{1}{10}$
	Z_j	$990	$\frac{33}{2}$	$55	$0	$\frac{11}{2}$
	$C_j - Z_j$		$\frac{57}{2}$	$0	$0	$-\frac{11}{2}$

Thus the entries in the X_2 row are

$$\frac{180}{10} = 18 \qquad \frac{3}{10} \qquad 1 \qquad 0 \qquad \frac{1}{10}$$

All the remaining rows of the variables in the tableau are computed using the formula

$$\begin{pmatrix} \text{Element in} \\ \text{new row} \end{pmatrix} = \begin{pmatrix} \text{element in} \\ \text{old row} \end{pmatrix} - \begin{pmatrix} \text{element of old row} \\ \text{in the optimal} \\ \text{column} \end{pmatrix} \begin{pmatrix} \text{corresponding} \\ \text{element in} \\ \text{replacing row} \end{pmatrix}$$

In this example, the only remaining variable row is X_3; its entries in the revised tableau are

$$120 - (4 \times 18) = 48$$
$$6 - (4 \times \tfrac{3}{10}) = \tfrac{24}{5}$$
$$4 - (4 \times 1) = 0$$
$$1 - (4 \times 0) = 1$$
$$0 - (4 \times \tfrac{1}{10}) = -\tfrac{2}{5}$$

Z_j is the total profit for the solution $= 0 \cdot 48 + 55 \cdot 18 = 990$

$$\left. \begin{aligned} Z_j \text{ for } X_1 &= (0)(\tfrac{24}{5}) + (55)(\tfrac{3}{10}) = \tfrac{33}{2} \\ Z_j \text{ for } X_2 &= (0)(0) + (55)(1) = 55 \\ Z_j \text{ for } X_3 &= (0)(1) + (55)(0) = 0 \\ Z_j \text{ for } X_4 &= (0)(-\tfrac{2}{5}) + (55)(\tfrac{1}{10}) = \tfrac{11}{2} \end{aligned} \right\} \begin{aligned} &\text{profit given up by adding} \\ &\text{one unit of the variable} \end{aligned}$$

The $C_j - Z_j$ row gives the net profit per unit (profit per unit minus profit given up by adding one unit). The positive entry $\$\frac{57}{2}$ in the revised tableau indicates that the solution can be improved by the inclusion of variable X_1. Checking to see which variable is to be omitted (although it is obviously X_3 in this example):

$$X_3: \frac{48}{\frac{24}{5}} = 10$$

$$X_2: \frac{18}{\frac{3}{10}} = 60$$

The smallest positive ratio corresponds to X_3, and X_3 is thus the departing variable. The simplex tableau is recomputed the same way as in the preceding stage (see Table 8.7). The absence of positive entries in the $C_j - Z_j$ row indicates

Table 8.7

C_j	Variables allocated	Quantity	$45 X_1	$55 X_2	$0 X_3	$0 X_4
$45	X_1	10	1	0	$\frac{5}{24}$	$-\frac{1}{12}$
$55	X_2	15	0	1	$-\frac{1}{16}$	$\frac{1}{8}$
	Z_j	$1275	$45	$55	$\frac{95}{16}$	$\frac{25}{8}$
	$C_j - Z_j$		$0	$0	$-\frac{95}{16}$	$-\frac{25}{8}$

that the optimal solution has been obtained: Manufacture 10 bicycles and 15 motor scooters, as obtained above using the geometric method.

Note the following characteristics of the simplex tableau:

1. Slack and artificial variables are included in the constraint equations as follows: If an inequality constraint is of the form $\leq$, a slack variable is added and is given a value of zero in the objective function for both maximization and minimization problems. If an inequality constraint is of the form $\geq$, a slack variable is subtracted and is given a value of zero in the objective function for both maximization and minimization problems; in addition, an artificial variable is added and is given a value in the objective function of $-M$ for maximization problems and $+M$ for minimization problems.

2. The elements of the body and identity matrices of the simplex tableau represent marginal rates of substitution between the variables in the solution and the variables heading the columns. For example, in Table 8.6, X_3 must be decreased by $\frac{24}{5}$ units if 1 unit of X_1 is added; X_3 must be increased by $\frac{2}{5}$ units if 1 unit of X_4 is added, and so forth. Note that a variable always has a marginal rate of substitution of 1 with itself and a marginal rate of substitution of 0 with a variable with which it is not substitutable.

3. The body matrix of the initial tableau has become an identity matrix in the final tableau; the identity matrix of the initial tableau has become the inverse of the initial body matrix in the final tableau.

4. In the final tableau, the $C_j - Z_j$ row consists of zero or negative numbers for a maximization problem and of zero or positive numbers for a minimization problem.

Example

Consider the problem of cost minimization discussed above (see page 619). Adding the slack variables X_3 and X_4 and the artificial variable X_5, the linear programming problem can be stated as follows.

$$\text{Minimize } Z = 2X_1 + 10X_2 + MX_4$$

subject to

$$2X_1 + X_2 + X_3 = 6$$
$$5X_1 + 4X_2 - X_4 + X_5 = 20$$
$$X_1, X_2, X_3, X_4, X_5 \geq 0$$

The initial simplex tableau is shown in Table 8.8.

Table 8.8

C_j	Variables allocated	Quantity	$2 X_1	$10 X_2	$0 X_3	$0 X_4	$M X_5
$0	X_3	6	2	1	1	0	0
$M	X_5	20	5	4	0	-1	1
	Z_j	$20M	$5M	$4M	$0	$-M	$M
	$C_j - Z_j$		$2 - 5M	$10 - 4M	$0	$M	$0

↑
Optimal column

The variable to enter at the next step is X_1 and the variable to be replaced is X_3 since

$$X_3: \quad \frac{6}{2} = 3$$
$$X_5: \quad \frac{20}{5} = 4$$

The revised simplex tableau is shown in Table 8.9.

Table 8.9

C_j	Variables allocated	Quantity	$2 X_1	$10 X_2	$0 X_3	$0 X_4	$M X_5
$2	X_1	3	1	$\frac{1}{2}$	$\frac{1}{2}$	0	0
$M	X_5	5	0	$\frac{3}{2}$	$-\frac{5}{2}$	-1	1
	Z_j	$6 + 5M	$2	$1 + 3M/2	$1 - 5M/2	$-M	$M
	$C_j - Z_j$		$0	$9 - 3M/2	$-1 + 5M/2	$M	$0

↑
Optimal column

The variable to enter at the next step is X_2 and the variable to be replaced is X_5 since

$$X_1: \quad \frac{3}{\frac{1}{2}} = 6$$

$$X_5: \quad \frac{5}{\frac{3}{2}} = \frac{10}{3}$$

The revised simplex is shown in Table 8.10. The absence of negative entries in

Table 8.10

C_j	Variables allocated	Quantity	$2 X_1	$10 X_2	$0 X_3	$0 X_4	$M X_5
$2	X_1	$\frac{4}{3}$	1	0	$\frac{4}{3}$	$\frac{1}{3}$	$-\frac{1}{3}$
$10	X_2	$\frac{10}{3}$	0	1	$-\frac{5}{3}$	$-\frac{2}{3}$	$\frac{2}{3}$
	Z_j	$36	$2	$10	$-14	$-6	$6
	$C_j - Z_j$		$0	$0	$14	$6	$M-6

the $C_j - Z_j$ row indicates that the optimal solution has been obtained: manufacture $\frac{4}{3}$ units of the first commodity and $\frac{10}{3}$ units of the second commodity at a cost of $36, as determined above by the graphical method.

There are several variations of the standard simplex method, although none differs substantially from the one discussed above. In addition, there are some linear programming problems for which the coefficients in the constraints have special forms and special cases of the simplex method, which require less computation, can be used. The simplex method must also be modified if the solution is required to be a set of integers.

□ *THE DUAL OF A LINEAR PROGRAMMING PROBLEM*

Corresponding to every linear programming problem is a second linear programming problem referred to as the *dual*. When the initial or *primal* problem involves maximization (minimization) of an objective function, the dual problem involves the minimization (maximization) of an objective function. The number of variables in the dual problem is equal to the number of constraints in the primal problem. The following table summarizes the correspondence between the primal and dual problems.

Primal Problem	*Dual Problem*
Constants in constraints	Coefficients in objective function
Coefficients in objective function	Constants in constraints
Inequality signs of constraints	Inequality signs reversed
ith row of coefficients in constraints	ith column of coefficients in constraints

The dual of the linear programming problem stated above can thus be stated as follows:

$$\text{Minimize } Z_{\text{dual}} = b_1 Y_1 + b_2 Y_2 + \cdots + b_m Y_m$$

subject to

$$a_{11} Y_1 + a_{21} Y_2 + \cdots + a_{m1} Y_1 \geq c_1$$

$$a_{12} Y_1 + a_{22} Y_2 + \cdots + a_{m2} Y_m \geq c_2$$
$$\vdots$$
$$a_{1n} Y_1 + a_{2n} Y_2 + \cdots + a_{mn} Y_m \geq c_m$$
$$Y_j \geq 0 \quad j = 1, 2, \ldots, m$$

Thus if a linear programming problem, written in standard form, is

$$\text{Maximize } \mathbf{CX}$$

subject to

$$\mathbf{AX} \leq \mathbf{B}$$
$$\mathbf{X} \geq \mathbf{0}$$

then its dual, written in standard form, is

$$\text{Minimize } \mathbf{BY}$$

subject to

$$\mathbf{A'Y} \geq \mathbf{C}$$
$$\mathbf{Y} \geq \mathbf{0}$$

and, similarly, if a linear programming problem, written in standard form, is

$$\text{Minimize } \mathbf{CX}$$

subject to

$$\mathbf{A\dot{X}} \geq \mathbf{B}$$
$$\mathbf{X} \geq \mathbf{0}$$

then its dual, written in standard form, is

$$\text{Maximize } \mathbf{BY}$$

subject to

$$\mathbf{A'Y} \leq \mathbf{C}$$
$$\mathbf{Y} \geq \mathbf{0}$$

Example

Write the dual of each of the following linear programming problems.

(a) Min $5X_1 + 9X_2$

subject to
$$3X_1 + 2X_2 \leq 6$$
$$5X_1 + X_2 \geq 10$$
$$X_1 + 10X_2 \geq 9$$
$$X_1 \geq 0, \quad X_2 \geq 0$$

(b) Max $X_1 + 9X_2 + 15X_3$

subject to
$$3X_1 + 2X_2 \geq 11$$
$$X_1 + X_2 + X_3 \geq 15$$
$$8X_2 + 7X_3 \leq 25$$
$$X_1 \geq 0, \quad X_2 \geq 0, \quad X_3 \geq 0$$

(a) Writing the problem in standard form,
$$\text{Min } 5X_1 + 9X_2$$

subject to

$$-3X_1 - 2X_2 \leq -6$$
$$5X_1 + X_2 \geq 10$$
$$X_1 + 10X_2 \geq 9$$
$$X_1 \geq 0, \quad X_2 \geq 0$$

and its dual is
$$\text{Max } -6Y_1 + 10Y_2 + 9Y_3$$

subject to

$$-3Y_1 + 5Y_2 + Y_3 \leq 5$$
$$-2Y_1 + Y_2 + 10Y_3 \leq 9$$
$$Y_1 \geq 0, \quad Y_2 \geq 0, \quad Y_3 \geq 0$$

(b) Writing the problem in standard form,
$$\text{Max } X_1 + 9X_2 + 15X_3$$

subject to

$$-3X_1 - 2X_2 \geq -11$$
$$-X_1 - X_2 - X_3 \geq -15$$
$$8X_2 + 7X_3 \leq 25$$
$$X_1 \geq 0, \quad X_2 \geq 0, \quad X_3 \geq 0$$

and its dual is
$$\text{Min } -11Y_1 - 15Y_2 + 25Y_3$$

subject to

$$-3Y_1 - Y_2 \geq 1$$
$$-2Y_1 - Y_2 + 8Y_3 \geq 9$$
$$-Y_2 + 7Y_3 \geq 15$$
$$Y_1 \geq 0, \quad Y_2 \geq 0, \quad Y_3 \geq 0$$

Solution of the dual problem also provides the solution of the primal problem; if $m < n$, solution of the dual problem requires less computation and is therefore usually preferable. The solution of the dual problem provides *implicit* or *imputed prices* that would lead to an efficient allocation of resources. The following table summarizes the correspondence between the primal and dual solutions.

Primal Problem	Dual Problem
Value of objective function	Value of objective function
Criteria for primary variables	Solutions for slack variables
Criteria for slack variables	Solutions for primary variables
Solutions for primary variables	−Criteria for slack variables
Solutions for slack variables	−Criteria for primary variables

Examples

For the maximization problem on page 622

$$\text{Max } Z = 45X_1 + 55X_2$$

subject to

$$6X_1 + 4X_2 \leq 120$$
$$3X_1 + 10X_2 \leq 180$$
$$X_1, X_2 \geq 0$$

the dual is given by

$$\text{Min } 120Y_1 + 180Y_2$$

subject to

$$6Y_1 + 3Y_2 \geq 45$$
$$4Y_1 + 10Y_2 \geq 55$$
$$Y_1, Y_2 \geq 0$$

and, with slack and artificial variables, by

$$\text{Min } 120Y_1 + 180Y_2 + MY_4 + MY_6$$

subject to

$$6Y_1 + 3Y_2 - Y_3 + Y_4 = 45$$
$$4Y_1 + 10Y_2 - Y_5 + Y_6 = 55$$
$$Y_1, Y_2, Y_3, Y_4, Y_5, Y_6 \geq 0$$

The final tableau of the simplex solution of the dual is given in Table 8.11. Note the correspondence between Tables 8.7 and 8.11 with respect to the properties listed above.

Table 8.11

C_j	Variables allocated	Quantity	$120 Y_1	$180 Y_2	$0 Y_3	$M Y_4	$0 Y_5	$M Y_6
$120	Y_1	$\frac{95}{16}$	1	0	$-\frac{5}{24}$	$\frac{5}{24}$	$\frac{1}{16}$	$-\frac{1}{16}$
$180	Y_2	$\frac{25}{8}$	0	1	$\frac{1}{12}$	$-\frac{1}{12}$	$-\frac{1}{8}$	$\frac{1}{8}$
	Z_j	$1275	$120	$180	$-10	$10	$-15	$15
	$C_j - Z_j$		$0	$0	$10	$M-10	$15	$M-15

For the minimization problem on page 625

$$\text{Min } 2X_1 + 10X_2$$

subject to

$$2X_1 + X_2 \le 6$$
$$5X_1 + 4X_2 \ge 20$$
$$X_1, X_2 \ge 0$$

the dual is given by

$$\text{Max } -6Y_1 + 20Y_2$$

subject to

$$-2Y_1 + 5Y_2 \le 2$$
$$-Y_1 + 4Y_2 \le 10$$
$$Y_1, Y_2 \ge 0$$

and, with slack and artificial variables, by

$$\text{Max } -6Y_1 + 20Y_2$$

subject to

$$-2Y_1 + 5Y_2 + Y_3 = 2$$
$$-Y_1 + 4Y_2 + Y_4 = 10$$
$$Y_1, Y_2, Y_3, Y_4 \ge 0$$

The final tableau of the simplex solution of the dual is given in Table 8.12. Note the correspondence between Tables 8.10 and 8.12 with respect to the properties listed above.

Table 8.12

C_j	Variables allocated	Quantity	$\$-6$ Y_1	$\$20$ Y_2	$\$0$ Y_3	$\$0$ Y_4
$20	Y_2	6	0	1	$-\frac{1}{3}$	$\frac{2}{3}$
$-6	Y_1	14	1	0	$-\frac{4}{3}$	$\frac{5}{3}$
	Z_j	$36	$-6	$20	$\$\frac{4}{3}$	$\$\frac{10}{3}$
	$C_j - Z_j$			$0	$0	$-\frac{4}{3}$	$-\frac{10}{3}$

Thus the dual problem is completely symmetric to the primal problem and the solution of one problem gives full information as to the solution of the other problem. The dual problem can provide a much simpler computational routine than the primal problem when the simplex tableau of the dual has fewer rows than the simplex tableau of the primal.

PROBLEMS

1. A company manufactures two types of novelty souvenirs made of plywood. Souvenirs of type A require 5 minutes each for cutting and 10 minutes each for assembling; souvenirs of type B require 8 minutes each for cutting and 8 minutes each for assembling. There are 3 hours and 20 minutes available for cutting and 4 hours available for assembling. The profit is 50¢ for each type A souvenir and 60¢ for each type B souvenir. How many souvenirs of each type should the company manufacture in order to maximize profit?

2. Determine the values of x and y that maximize the function

$$f(x, y) = 0.4x + 0.9y$$

subject to the constraints

$$5x + 3y \leq 30 \qquad 7x + 2y \leq 28$$

3. Determine the values of x_1 and x_2 that maximize the function

$$f(x, x_2) = 3x_1 + 5x_2$$

subject to the constraints

$$x_1 + 2x_2 \leq 10 \qquad 3x_1 + x_2 \leq 10$$

4. Determine the values of x_1 and x_2 that maximize the function

$$f(x_1, x_2) = 3x_1 + 6x_2$$

subject to the constraints

$$2x_1 + 5x_2 \leq 20 \qquad 2x_1 + 2x_2 \leq 10$$

5. Determine the values of x and y that maximize the function

$$f(x, y) = 3x + 2y$$

subject to the constraints

$$x + y \leq 7 \qquad 2x + 3y \leq 16$$

6. A manufacturer of a line of hair shampoos is planning a production run for products A (for dry hair) and B (for oily hair). There are sufficient ingredients on hand for 60,000 bottles of each shampoo but there are only 60,000 bottles into which either shampoo can be put. It takes 4 hours to prepare enough shampoo to fill 1000 bottles of shampoo A and 3 hours to prepare enough shampoo to fill 1000 bottles of shampoo B; there are 200 hours available for preparation. Profit is 9 cents a bottle for shampoo A and 7 cents a bottle for shampoo B. How should production be scheduled to maximize profit?

7. The Tr-Ply Company manufactures two types of heavy-duty wood crates. The profit on each crate of type 1 is $\$9$ and the profit on each crate of type 2 is $\$12$. Each crate must go through two production lines; a total of 10 hours are available on production line A and a total of 12 hours are available on

production line *B*. Each crate of type 1 requires 2 hours on line *A* and 4 hours on line *B*. Each crate of type 2 requires 5 hours on line *A* and 3 hours on line *B*. Determine the number of crates of each type that should be produced in order to maximize the associated profit.

8. The UP-DOWN Ladder Company can manufacture three types of ladders; profit is $5 per ladder of type 1, $7 per ladder of type 2, and $8 per ladder of type 3. Each ladder must be processed through three centers according to the following requirements:

	Center 1 (min)	Center 2 (min)	Center 3 (min)
Type 1	4	5	6
Type 2	5	7	9
Type 3	6	7	7
Total available	80	100	120

In order to maximize profit, determine the number of ladders of each type that should be manufactured.

9. The Capsize Yachting Company produces two models of racing boats. Their profit is $520 for Model 1 and $450 for Model 2. Model 1 requires 40 hours for cutting and assembling and 24 hours for finishing. Model 2 requires 25 hours for cutting and assembling and 30 hours for finishing. There are 400 hours available for cutting and assembling and 360 hours available for finishing. Determine the optimal number of each model for the company to produce and the resulting profit.

10. The Duoply Company can make three products; their profit is $10 per unit for Product 1, $14 per unit for Product 2, and $15 per unit for Product 3. Each of these products is manufactured using three raw materials according to the following requirements:

	Material 1	Material 2	Material 3
Product 1	3 lb/unit	4 lb/unit	5 lb/unit
Product 2	5 lb/unit	7 lb/unit	7 lb/unit
Product 3	4 lb/unit	8 lb/unit	6 lb/unit
Total lb available	220	280	320

Determine the optimal product mix.

11. College Publishers, Inc. plans to use one section of its plant to produce two textbooks. The profit is $2 for Textbook 1 and $3 for Textbook 2. Textbook 1 requires 4 hours for printing and 6 hours for binding. Textbook 2 requires 5 hours for printing and 3 hours for binding. There are 200 hours available for printing and 210 hours available for binding. Determine the optimal number of each textbook for the publishers to produce and their resulting profit.

12. Obtain the solution for the following linear programming problem.

$$\text{Maximize } 6X_1 + 3X_2$$

subject to

$$4X_1 + X_2 \leq 12$$
$$2X_1 + 2X_2 \leq 10$$
$$2X_1 + 4X_2 \geq 8$$
$$X_1, X_2 \geq 0$$

13. Obtain the solution for the following linear programming problem.

$$\text{Minimize } 12X_1 - 5X_2$$

subject to

$$X_1 - 2X_2 \geq 3$$
$$X_1 - X_2 \geq 4$$
$$X_1 \geq 1$$
$$X_1, X_2 \geq 0$$

Write the duals of the following linear programming problems

14. Max $X_1 + X_2 + 5X_3$

   subject to $4X_1 + 3X_2 + X_3 \leq 10$
   $$2X_1 + 10X_2 + 3X_3 \geq 15$$
   $$X_1, X_2, X_3 \geq 0$$

15. Min $3X_1 + 5X_2 + X_3$

   subject to $X_1 + X_2 + X_3 \geq 6$
   $$3X_1 + 8X_2 + 9X_3 \leq 50$$
   $$6X_1 + 7X_3 \geq 12$$
   $$12X_2 + 4X_3 \geq 15$$
   $$X_1, X_2, X_3 \geq 0$$

16. Max $5X_1 - 6X_2 + 10X_3$

   subject to $X_1 + X_2 + X_3 \geq 15$
   $$2X_1 + 3X_2 + 4X_3 \leq 35$$
   $$3X_1 - 4X_2 + 6X_3 \leq 30$$
   $$X_1 - X_2 \geq 0$$
   $$X_1, X_2, X_3 \geq 0$$

17. Min $2X_1 + 10X_2$

   subject to $X_1 + X_2 + X_3 \geq 5$
   $$3X_1 - 2X_2 + 6X_3 \leq 20$$
   $$X_2 + 3X_3 \geq 10$$
   $$X_1, X_2, X_3 \geq 0$$

18. Max $8X_1 - 3X_2$

   subject to $9X_1 + 2X_2 \leq 20$
   $$10X_1 + 3X_2 \leq 32$$
   $$X_1, X_2 \geq 0$$

19. Max $5X_1 + 3X_2 + 14X_3$

   subject to $2X_1 + X_2 + 3X_3 \leq 14$
   $$X_1 + 3X_2 + 2X_3 \leq 15$$
   $$X_1 + X_2 + X_3 \geq 8$$
   $$X_1, X_2, X_3 \geq 0$$

20. Min $6X_1 - 3X_2 + 4X_3$

   subject to $3X_1 + 6X_2 + 2X_3 \leq 30$
   $$5X_1 + X_2 + 6X_3 \geq 25$$
   $$X_1, X_2, X_3 \geq 0$$

---

1. 8 type A and 20 type B

3. $x_1 = 2$, $x_2 = 4$

5. $x = 7$, $y = 0$

7. $\frac{15}{7}$ type 1, $\frac{8}{7}$ type 2, profit \$33

9. 5 Model 1, 8 Model 2, profit \$6200

11. 0 Textbook 1, 40 Textbook 2, profit \$120

13. $X_1 = 4$, $X_2 = 0$, min $Z = 48$

15. Max $6Y_1 - 50Y_2 + 12Y_3 + 15Y_4$

   subject to $Y_1 - 3Y_2 + 6Y_3 \leq 3$
   $$Y_1 - 8Y_2 + 12Y_3 \leq 5$$
   $$Y_1 - 9Y_2 + 7Y_3 + 4Y_4 \leq 1$$
   $$Y_1, Y_2, Y_3, Y_4 \geq 0$$

17. Max $5Y_1 - 20Y_2 + 10Y_3$

   subject to $Y_1 - 3Y_2 \leq 2$
   $$Y_1 + 2Y_2 + Y_3 \leq 10$$
   $$Y_1 - 6Y_2 + 3Y_3 \leq 0$$
   $$Y_1, Y_2, Y_3 \geq 0$$

19. Min $14Y_1 + 15Y_2 - 8Y_3$

   subject to $2Y_1 + Y_2 - Y_3 \geq 5$
   $$Y_1 + 3Y_2 - Y_3 \geq 3$$
   $$3Y_1 + 2Y_2 - Y_3 \geq 14$$
   $$Y_1, Y_2, Y_3 \geq 0$$

■ 8.4 GAME THEORY

Game theory was developed for the purpose of analyzing competitive situations involving conflicting interests. In the situations considered by game theory, there are two or more persons with different objectives, each of whose action influences, but does not completely determine, the outcome of the game; furthermore, each person is assumed to know his opponent's objectives. Game theory provides solutions to such games, assuming that each of the players wishes to maximize his minimum expected profits or, equivalently, minimize his maximum expected losses. This criterion, which is based on a somewhat conservative view of the problem, is referred to as the *minimax* or *maximin criterion* and is the basis for the *theory of games of strategy* originally developed by John von Neumann and Oskar Morganstern and subsequently extended by research in various areas of application.

Note that the theory of games assumes a particular type of situation involving maximizing the expected value of a decision made under uncertainty. Decisions made under uncertainty are often thought of as involving only one person making a decision—the events which, together with the decision, influence the result are thought of as being controlled by some random nonrational device. Most recreational games such as tick-tack-toe, checkers, backgammon, chess, poker, bridge, and other card games can be analyzed as games of strategy. As usually formulated, gambling games such as dice and roulette are not games of strategy —a person playing one of these games is "playing against the odds," not against a rational opponent. The applications of game theory are not limited to parlor games but include competitive situations in economics, business, warfare, and social behavior.

There are several fundamental characteristics by which games are classified for solution. The most important of these are (1) the number of persons, (2) the nature of the payoff, and (3) the number of available strategies.

● Number of Persons

Games are classified according to the number of distinct sets of interests or objectives present in the game. From the game theory point of view, the number of persons in the game is not necessarily the same as the number of people playing the game—that is, if two or more players form a coalition in which they agree to pool their winnings or losses, game-theory analysis treats them as a single person.

Most of the work done thus far in game theory deals with two-person games and the discussion in the following sections is confined to this case. Analysis of games involving more than two persons is usually very difficult. Note that many situations that are not strictly two-person games may be analyzed as though they were—for example, the interests in a game of cards can be considered as "his" and "everybody else's."

● The Payoff

Games are also classified with respect to the nature of the payoff, that is, what happens at the end of the game. The distinction in this respect is between zero-sum games and non-zero-sum games. If the sum of the payoffs to all players of a game is zero, counting winnings as positive and losses as negative, then the game is *zero-sum*; otherwise, it is *non-zero-sum*. Thus in a zero-sum game anything won by one player is lost by another player. The importance of this distinction lies in the fact that a zero-sum game is a closed system and a non-zero-sum game is not. Almost all parlor games are zero-sum, and many other situations can be analyzed as zero-sum games. Most of the work in game theory has concerned zero-sum games and the discussion in the following sections will be confined to such games. Note that a non-zero-sum game may be made zero-sum by adding a fictitious player, say Nature, but this necessitates a more difficult analysis, especially if the original game was a two-person game.

● **Strategies**

In game theory a strategy for a particular player is a plan which specifies his action for every possible action of his opponent—that is, a strategy is a complete plan for playing the game, without any connotation of skillfulness on the part of the player. In a game completely amenable to analysis it is possible (conceptually, if not actually) to foresee all eventualities and thus to catalogue all possible strategies. Games are classified according to the number of strategies available to each player: if player 1 has m possible strategies and player 2 has n possible strategies and they are the only players, then the game is $m \times n$, that is, m by n. The important distinction for classifying games on the basis of strategies is between finite games and infinite games. If the greatest number of strategies available to any player is finite, then the game is *finite*; if at least one player has an infinite number of available strategies, then the game is *infinite*. The theory of infinite games is very difficult and will not be discussed. For the analysis of finite games, it is convenient to distinguish three cases: those in which the player having the least number of strategies has two, three, or more than three.

In summary, the discussion in following sections will generally concern finite, zero-sum, two-person games.

● **The Game Matrix**

A problem is usually set up for game-theory analysis in the form of a game matrix. A *game matrix* or *payoff matrix* is a rectangular array of the payoffs, where the rows represent the strategies of one player and the columns represent the strategies of the other player; thus an $m \times n$ game is represented by an $m \times n$ game matrix. It is conventional to write the payoffs from the point of view of the player whose strategies are associated with the rows of the matrix; the payoffs for the other player, in a zero-sum game, are then given by the negative of this matrix.

Game theory thus assumes that the strategies available to each player can be enumerated and that the corresponding payoffs can be expressed in meaningful, although not necessarily monetary, units. This information is sufficient for solution of the game—that is, for determining which choice of strategies each player should make—assuming that each player wishes to maximize his minimum expected winnings or minimize his maximum expected losses. The minimax theorem, the key result of the theory of games, states that such a minimax solution exists for every finite zero-sum two-person game. Note that minimax is not the only possible criterion for solving a game matrix and that its use leads to a conservative theory, since the opponent is assumed to be skillful and to use his best strategy.

The *value* of a game is the expected or average payoff per play over a long series of plays, assuming that both players consistently use their optimum strategies. It is conventional to regard value from the point of view of the player whose strategies correspond to the rows of the payoff matrix. A game is said to be *fair* if its value is zero; in a fair game neither player has an advantage. In a game that is not fair one player will win from the other in the long run if both play their optimum strategies—if the value of the game is positive, the row player has the advantage; if the value of the game is negative, the column player has the advantage.

● **Saddle Points**

If a game matrix contains an entry that is simultaneously a maximum of row minima and a minimum of column maxima, this minimax entry is said to be a *saddle point* of the game and the game is said to be *strictly determined*. In this case, according to the criterion of game theory, the *optimum strategies* for the respective players are represented by the row and column whose intersection is the saddle point. The value of a strictly determined game is the value of its saddle point.

The first step in the solution of a matrix game is to check for the existence of a saddle point—if one is found, the game is solved; if not, further analysis is necessary. Checking for a saddle point is usually done by writing the row minimum beside each row and the column maximum at the bottom of each column and then determining the maximum of the minima and the minimum of the maxima. A saddle point can also be determined by checking for an entry which is simultaneously the minimum of the row in which it occurs and the maximum of the column in which it occurs (see Table 8.13).

Table 8.13

Player Y

	1	2	$\cdots$	n	
1	a_{11}	a_{12}	$\cdots$	a_{1n}	$\min_j a_{1j}$
2	a_{21}	a_{22}	$\cdots$	a_{2n}	$\min_j a_{2j}$
Player X $\vdots$	$\vdots$	$\vdots$	a_{ij}	$\vdots$	$\vdots$ $\max_i \min_j a_{ij}$
m	a_{m1}	a_{m2}	$\cdots$	a_{mn}	$\min_j a_{mj}$
	$\max_i a_{i1}$	$\max_i a_{i2}$	$\cdots$	$\max_i a_{in}$	

$$\min_j \max_i a_{ij}$$

Example

Check the following games for saddle points.

(a)

12	2	25	−10
16	③	4	10
−2	−1	26	0
14	−4	8	6

2
3
−2
−4

max min = 3

16   3   26   10
min max = 3

There is a saddle point at the intersection of the second row (player X's optimum strategy) and the second column (player Y's optimum strategy); the value of the game is 3.

(b)

−15	22	10	8	6	−14	−8
−3	4	−6	0	−4	22	−10
−2	3	4	10	−1	0	⊝−6

−15
−10   max min = −6
−6

−2   22   10   10   6   22   −6
min max = −6

There is a saddle point at the intersection of the third row (player X's optimum strategy) and the seventh column (player Y's optimum strategy); the value of the game is −6.

(c)

−3	2	4
6	1	3
3	10	12
5	0	−2
0	−4	6

−3
1
3   max min = 3
−2
−4

6   10   12
min max = 6

There is no saddle point.

(d)

2	0	6	−4	8	10	25	−10	12	14
−14	−2	0	14	9	12	15	0	−10	−3

−10
−14   max min = −10

2   0   6   14   9   12   25   0   12   14
min max = 0

There is no saddle point.

□ *SOLUTION OF TWO-PERSON TWO-STRATEGY GAMES*

The basic concepts of game-theory analysis discussed in previous sections are illustrated in the following sections for two-person two-strategy games—that is, for games in which at least one of the two players has only two strategies. By convention, the strategies for player X are listed and indexed in a column along the left edge of the game matrix and the strategies for player Y are listed and indexed in a row along the top edge. The payoffs are to player X—that is, a positive number indicates a payoff from player Y to player X and a negative number indicates a payoff from player X to player Y.

● 2 × 2 Games

The most easily analyzed two-strategy games are 2 × 2—that is, games for which each player has only two possible strategies. Solution of 2 × 2 subgames is also frequently necessary as a step in the solution of larger (2 × n or m × 2) two-strategy games.

Examples

The game

Player Y

1   2

Player X 1 | ⓪ | 1 |
2 | −3 | 10 |

is strictly determined and fair. Player X's optimum strategy is 1; player Y's optimum strategy is 1.

The game

Player Y

1   2

Player X 1 | 5 | ② |
2 | −7 | −4 |

is strictly determined, but not fair (its value is 2). Player X's optimum strategy is 1; player Y's optimum strategy is 2.

The game

Player Y

1   2

Player X 1 | 0 | 1 |
2 | 2 | 0 |

is not strictly determined.

THEOREM: The 2×2 matrix game

$$G = \begin{array}{|c|c|} \hline a & b \\ \hline c & d \\ \hline \end{array}$$

is nonstrictly determined if and only if one of the following two conditions is satisfied:

(1) $a < b, a < c, d < b,$ and $d < c.$
(2) $a > b, a > c, d > b,$ and $d > c.$

That is, a 2×2 matrix game is nonstrictly determined if and only if the two entries on one diagonal of the matrix are each greater than each of the two entries on the other diagonal.

In a nonstrictly determined game there is no clearly optimum strategy for either player to use consistently—and, furthermore, consistent use of any particular strategy by either player can be capitalized on by the other player. There is thus an important difference between strictly determined and nonstrictly determined games: In a strictly determined game there is an optimum strategy for each player and no "security measures" are necessary; in a nonstrictly determined game optimal play involves preventing the opponent from knowing what strategy one plans to use on a given play. This is accomplished by selecting the strategy to be used for each play at random, according to probabilities that can be computed from the game matrix. Such a strategy, which consists of a probability mixture of more than one (pure) strategy, is called a *mixed strategy*.

The solution of a 2×2 nonstrictly determined game consists of a pair of probabilities p_1 and $p_2 = 1 - p_1$ with which player X selects at random his strategies 1 and 2, respectively, and a pair of probabilities q_1 and $q_2 = 1 - q_1$ with which player Y selects at random his strategies 1 and 2, respectively. These probabilities provide the optimum mixed strategies—that is, the strategies by which each player, respectively, can maximize his minimum expected profits or minimize his maximum expected losses against optimal play by the other player.

The value of p_1 can be obtained by equating the two possible expected payoffs for player X and solving for p_1, since for any other p_1 one or the other of the two expected payoffs is less and thus the minimax criterion is violated. Similarly, q_1 can be obtained by equating the two possible expected payoffs for player Y and solving.

If

$$G = \begin{array}{|c|c|} \hline a & b \\ \hline c & d \\ \hline \end{array}$$

represents the game matrix, then the expected payoff to player X is

$$ap_1 + c(1 - p_1)$$

if player Y uses strategy 1 and is

$$bp_1 + d(1 - p_1)$$

if player Y uses strategy 2. Thus, equating the expected payoffs,

$$ap_1 + c(1 - p_1) = bp_1 + d(1 - p_1)$$
$$p_1(a - b - c + d) = d - c$$
$$p_1 = \frac{d - c}{a - b - c + d}$$

$$p_2 = 1 - p_1 = \frac{a - b}{a - b - c + d}$$

Similarly, equating the (negative) expected payoffs to player Y,

$$aq_1 + b(1 - q_1) = cq_1 + d(1 - q_1)$$

$$a_1(a - b - c + d) = d - b$$

$$q_1 = \frac{d - b}{a - b - c + d}$$

$$q_2 = 1 - q_1 = \frac{a - c}{a - b - c + d}$$

The value of a game has the same meaning for strictly and nonstrictly determined games: The value of a game is the payoff that a player can expect to obtain per play—on the average a player cannot win more than the value of a game unless his opponent plays poorly, nor can he win less than the value of a game unless he plays poorly.

The value of the game $G = \begin{array}{|c|c|} \hline a & b \\ \hline c & d \\ \hline \end{array}$ (to player X) is

$$v = ap_1 + c(1 - p_1) = bp_1 + d(1 - p_1)$$

$$= -[aq_1 + b(1 - q_1)] = -[cq_1 + d(1 - q_1)]$$

$$= \frac{ad - bc}{a - b - c + d}$$

The negative of this quantity is the payoff to player Y.

Examples

The game $\begin{array}{|c|c|} \hline 2 & 0 \\ \hline 0 & 2 \\ \hline \end{array}$ is nonstrictly determined. The optimum mixed strategies are

$$p_1 = \tfrac{2}{4} = \tfrac{1}{2}$$

$$p_2 = \tfrac{2}{4} = \tfrac{1}{2}$$

$$q_1 = \tfrac{2}{4} = \tfrac{1}{2}$$

$$q_2 = \tfrac{2}{4} = \tfrac{1}{2}$$

and the value is $\tfrac{4}{4} = 1$ (that is, the game is biased in favor of player X).

The game $\begin{array}{|c|c|} \hline -1 & 0 \\ \hline 0 & -2 \\ \hline \end{array}$ is nonstrictly determined. The optimum mixed strategies

are

$$p_1 = \tfrac{-2}{-3} = \tfrac{2}{3}$$

$$p_2 = \tfrac{-1}{-3} = \tfrac{1}{3}$$

$$q_1 = \frac{-2}{-3} = \frac{2}{3}$$

$$q_2 = \frac{-1}{-3} = \frac{1}{3}$$

and the value is $v = \frac{2}{-3} = -\frac{2}{3}$ (that is, the game is biased in favor of player Y).

The game
$$\begin{array}{|c|c|} \hline 7 & -6 \\ \hline 5 & 8 \\ \hline \end{array}$$
is nonstrictly determined. The optimum mixed strategies are

$$p_1 = \frac{3}{16}$$

$$p_2 = \frac{13}{16}$$

$$q_1 = \frac{14}{16} = \frac{7}{8}$$

$$q_2 = \frac{2}{16} = \frac{1}{8}$$

and the value is $v = \frac{86}{16} = 5\frac{3}{8}$ (that is, the game is biased in favor of player X).

The game
$$\begin{array}{|c|c|} \hline 10 & -30 \\ \hline -10 & 20 \\ \hline \end{array}$$
is nonstrictly determined. The optimum mixed strategies are

$$p_1 = \frac{30}{70} = \frac{3}{7}$$

$$p_2 = \frac{40}{70} = \frac{4}{7}$$

$$q_1 = \frac{50}{70} = \frac{5}{7}$$

$$q_2 = \frac{20}{70} = \frac{2}{7}$$

and the value is $v = -\frac{100}{70} = -1\frac{3}{7}$ (that is, the game is biased in favor of player Y).

The play of a game is not affected by adding a constant to all payoffs or by multiplying all payoffs by a positive constant. The value of the game is affected by the same transformation as that applied to the payoffs of the game matrix.

Example

For each of the games

$$G_1 = \begin{array}{|c|c|} \hline 8 & 1 \\ \hline 4 & 6 \\ \hline \end{array}$$

$$G_2 = \begin{array}{|c|c|} \hline 11 & 4 \\ \hline 7 & 9 \\ \hline \end{array}$$

$$G_3 = \begin{array}{|c|c|} \hline 16 & 2 \\ \hline 8 & 12 \\ \hline \end{array}$$

$p_1 = \frac{2}{9}$, $p_2 = \frac{7}{9}$, $q_1 = \frac{5}{9}$, $q_2 = \frac{4}{9}$. Note that $G_2 = G_1 + 3$; the value of G_1 is $4\frac{8}{9}$ and the value of G_2 is $7\frac{8}{9}$. $G_3 = 2G_1$; the value of G_1 is $4\frac{8}{9}$ and the value of G_3 is $9\frac{7}{9}$.

● Solution of 2 × 2 Games by Matrix Algebra

The optimum strategies and the value of a nonstrictly determined 2 × 2 game can be obtained using matrix algebra as follows: If the payoff matrix is represented by

$$A = \begin{pmatrix} a_{11} & a_{12} \\ a_{21} & a_{22} \end{pmatrix}$$

then X's optimum strategies are given by

$$(p_1, p_2) = \frac{(1, 1)(\text{adj } A)}{(1, 1)(\text{adj } A)\begin{pmatrix} 1 \\ 1 \end{pmatrix}}$$

Y's optimum strategies are given by

$$(q_1, q_2) = \frac{(1, 1)(\text{adj } A)'}{(1, 1)(\text{adj } A)\begin{pmatrix} 1 \\ 1 \end{pmatrix}}$$

and the value of the game is given by

$$v = \frac{|A|}{(1, 1)(\text{adj } A)\begin{pmatrix} 1 \\ 1 \end{pmatrix}}$$

Alternatively, the value of the game is given by

$$v = (p_1, p_2) \begin{pmatrix} a_{11} & a_{12} \\ a_{12} & a_{22} \end{pmatrix} \begin{pmatrix} q_1 \\ q_2 \end{pmatrix}$$

We shall now reconsider the examples on pages 642 and 643.

Examples

The game $\begin{array}{|c|c|} \hline 2 & 0 \\ \hline 0 & 2 \\ \hline \end{array}$ is nonstrictly determined.

$$(p_1, p_2) = \frac{(1, 1)(\text{adj } A)}{(1, 1)(\text{adj } A)\begin{pmatrix} 1 \\ 1 \end{pmatrix}}$$

$$= \frac{(1, 1)\begin{pmatrix} 2 & 0 \\ 0 & 2 \end{pmatrix}}{(1, 1)\begin{pmatrix} 2 & 0 \\ 0 & 2 \end{pmatrix}\begin{pmatrix} 1 \\ 1 \end{pmatrix}} = \frac{(2, 2)}{4} = (\tfrac{1}{2}, \tfrac{1}{2})$$

$$(q_1, q_2) = \frac{(1, 1)(\text{adj } \mathbf{A})'}{(1, 1)(\text{adj } \mathbf{A})\begin{pmatrix} 1 \\ 1 \end{pmatrix}}$$

$$= \frac{(1, 1)\begin{pmatrix} 2 & 0 \\ 0 & 2 \end{pmatrix}}{(1, 1)\begin{pmatrix} 2 & 0 \\ 0 & 2 \end{pmatrix}\begin{pmatrix} 1 \\ 1 \end{pmatrix}} = \frac{(2, 2)}{4} = (\tfrac{1}{2}, \tfrac{1}{2})$$

$$v = \frac{|\mathbf{A}|}{(1, 1)(\text{adj } \mathbf{A})\begin{pmatrix} 1 \\ 1 \end{pmatrix}}$$

$$= \frac{4}{4} = 1$$

Alternatively,

$$v = (p_1, p_2) \begin{pmatrix} a_{11} & a_{12} \\ a_{21} & a_{22} \end{pmatrix}\begin{pmatrix} q_1 \\ q_2 \end{pmatrix}$$

$$= (\tfrac{1}{2}, \tfrac{1}{2}) \begin{pmatrix} 2 & 0 \\ 0 & 2 \end{pmatrix}\begin{pmatrix} \tfrac{1}{2} \\ \tfrac{1}{2} \end{pmatrix}$$

$$= 1$$

(as obtained above using algebraic methods).

The game $\begin{array}{|c|c|} \hline -1 & 0 \\ \hline 0 & -2 \\ \hline \end{array}$ is nonstrictly determined.

$$(p_1, p_2) = \frac{(1, 1)(\text{adj } \mathbf{A})}{(1, 1)(\text{adj } \mathbf{A})\begin{pmatrix} 1 \\ 1 \end{pmatrix}}$$

$$= \frac{(1, 1)\begin{pmatrix} -2 & 0 \\ 0 & -1 \end{pmatrix}}{(1, 1)\begin{pmatrix} -2 & 0 \\ 0 & -1 \end{pmatrix}\begin{pmatrix} 1 \\ 1 \end{pmatrix}} = \frac{(-2, -1)}{-3} = (\tfrac{2}{3}, \tfrac{1}{3})$$

$$(q_1, q_2) = \frac{(1, 1)(\text{adj } \mathbf{A})'}{(1, 1)(\text{adj } \mathbf{A})\begin{pmatrix} 1 \\ 1 \end{pmatrix}}$$

$$= \frac{(1, 1)\begin{pmatrix} -2 & 0 \\ 0 & -1 \end{pmatrix}}{(1, 1)\begin{pmatrix} -2 & 0 \\ 0 & -1 \end{pmatrix}\begin{pmatrix} 1 \\ 1 \end{pmatrix}} = \frac{(-2, -1)}{-3} = (\tfrac{2}{3}, \tfrac{1}{3})$$

$$v = \frac{|\mathbf{A}|}{(1, 1)(\text{adj } \mathbf{A})\begin{pmatrix} 1 \\ 1 \end{pmatrix}}$$

$$= \frac{2}{-3} = -\tfrac{2}{3}$$

Alternatively,

$$v = (p_1, p_2) \begin{pmatrix} a_{11} & a_{12} \\ a_{21} & a_{22} \end{pmatrix} \begin{pmatrix} q_1 \\ q_2 \end{pmatrix}$$

$$= (\tfrac{2}{3}, \tfrac{1}{3}) \begin{pmatrix} -1 & 0 \\ 0 & -2 \end{pmatrix} \begin{pmatrix} \tfrac{2}{3} \\ \tfrac{1}{3} \end{pmatrix}$$

$$= -\tfrac{2}{3}$$

(as obtained above using algebraic methods).

The game $\begin{array}{|c|c|} \hline 7 & -6 \\ \hline 5 & 8 \\ \hline \end{array}$ is nonstrictly determined.

$$(p_1, p_2) = \frac{(1, 1)(\text{adj } \mathbf{A})}{(1, 1)(\text{adj } \mathbf{A})\begin{pmatrix} 1 \\ 1 \end{pmatrix}}$$

$$= \frac{(1, 1)\begin{pmatrix} 8 & 6 \\ -5 & 7 \end{pmatrix}}{(1, 1)\begin{pmatrix} 8 & 6 \\ -5 & 7 \end{pmatrix}\begin{pmatrix} 1 \\ 1 \end{pmatrix}} = \frac{(3, 13)}{16} = (\tfrac{3}{16}, \tfrac{13}{16})$$

$$(q_1, q_2) = \frac{(1, 1)(\text{adj } \mathbf{A})'}{(1, 1)(\text{adj } \mathbf{A})\begin{pmatrix} 1 \\ 1 \end{pmatrix}}$$

$$= \frac{(1, 1)\begin{pmatrix} 8 & -5 \\ 6 & 7 \end{pmatrix}}{(1, 1)\begin{pmatrix} 8 & 6 \\ -5 & 7 \end{pmatrix}\begin{pmatrix} 1 \\ 1 \end{pmatrix}} = \frac{(14, 2)}{16} = (\tfrac{7}{8}, \tfrac{1}{8})$$

$$v = \frac{|\mathbf{A}|}{(1, 1)(\text{adj } \mathbf{A})\begin{pmatrix} 1 \\ 1 \end{pmatrix}}$$

$$= \frac{86}{16} = \tfrac{43}{8}$$

Alternatively,

$$v = (p_1, p_2) \begin{pmatrix} a_{11} & a_{12} \\ a_{21} & a_{22} \end{pmatrix} \begin{pmatrix} q_1 \\ q_2 \end{pmatrix}$$

$$= (\tfrac{3}{16}, \tfrac{13}{16}) \begin{pmatrix} 7 & -6 \\ 5 & 8 \end{pmatrix} \begin{pmatrix} \tfrac{7}{8} \\ \tfrac{1}{8} \end{pmatrix}$$

$$= \tfrac{43}{8}$$

(as obtained above using algebraic methods).

The game

10	-30
-10	20

is nonstrictly determined.

$$(p_1, p_2) = \frac{(1, 1)(\text{adj } \mathbf{A})}{(1, 1)(\text{adj } \mathbf{A})\begin{pmatrix} 1 \\ 1 \end{pmatrix}}$$

$$= \frac{(1, 1)\begin{pmatrix} 20 & 30 \\ 10 & 10 \end{pmatrix}}{(1, 1)\begin{pmatrix} 20 & 30 \\ 10 & 10 \end{pmatrix}\begin{pmatrix} 1 \\ 1 \end{pmatrix}} = \frac{(30, 40)}{70} = (\tfrac{3}{7}, \tfrac{4}{7})$$

$$(q_1, q_2) = \frac{(1, 1)(\text{adj } \mathbf{A})'}{(1, 1)(\text{adj } \mathbf{A})\begin{pmatrix} 1 \\ 1 \end{pmatrix}}$$

$$= \frac{(1, 1)\begin{pmatrix} 20 & 10 \\ 30 & 10 \end{pmatrix}}{(1, 1)\begin{pmatrix} 20 & 30 \\ 10 & 10 \end{pmatrix}\begin{pmatrix} 1 \\ 1 \end{pmatrix}} = \frac{(50, 20)}{70} = (\tfrac{5}{7}, \tfrac{2}{7})$$

$$v = \frac{|\mathbf{A}|}{(1, 1)(\text{adj } \mathbf{A})\begin{pmatrix} 1 \\ 1 \end{pmatrix}}$$

$$= \frac{-100}{70} = -\tfrac{10}{7}$$

Alternatively,

$$v = (p_1, p_2) \begin{pmatrix} a_{11} & a_{12} \\ a_{21} & a_{22} \end{pmatrix}\begin{pmatrix} q_1 \\ q_2 \end{pmatrix}$$

$$= (\tfrac{3}{7}, \tfrac{4}{7}) \begin{pmatrix} 10 & -30 \\ -10 & 20 \end{pmatrix}\begin{pmatrix} \tfrac{5}{7} \\ \tfrac{2}{7} \end{pmatrix}$$

$$= -\tfrac{10}{7}$$

(as obtained above using algebraic methods).

● **2 × n Games and m × 2 Games**

In $2 \times n$ games and $m \times 2$ games one player has two strategies and the other player has more than two strategies; the solution of a $2 \times n$ game or an $m \times 2$ game can be reduced to the solution of a 2×2 subgame.

As in the solution of 2×2 games, the first step is to check for a saddle point—if one exists, the optimum (pure) strategies and the value of the game are thus determined.

Examples

The game

4	4
5	3
6	⑤
1	3
5	4

has a saddle point at the intersection of the third row (player X's optimal strategy) and the second column (player Y's optimal strategy); the value of the game is 5.

The game

1	7	⓪	3
4	8	−1	6

has a saddle point at the intersection of the first row (player X's optimal strategy) and the third column (player Y's optimal strategy); the value of the game is zero.

● **Dominance**

In an $m \times m$ matrix game, row i is said to *majorize* or to *dominate* row h if every entry in row i is as large or larger than the corresponding entry in row h. Similarly, column j is said to *minorize* or to be *dominated* by column k if every entry in column j is as small as or smaller than the corresponding entry in column k. Note that any majorized row or minorized column can be omitted from the matrix game without affecting its solution, since such strategies are clearly not optimal. Thus, if a $2 \times n$ or an $m \times 2$ game does not have a saddle point, that is, is not strictly determined, all majorized rows and minorized columns should be eliminated as the next step in the solution.

The solution of a $2 \times n$ game consists of probabilities p_1 and $p_2 = 1 - p_1$ with which player X selects, at random, his strategies 1 and 2, respectively, and probabilities $q_1, q_2, \ldots, q_n$ (where $\sum_{i=1}^{n} q_i = 1$) with which player Y selects, at random, his strategies $1, 2, \ldots, n$, respectively. Similarly, the solution of an

Examples

The game
2	5
4	3
3	6
5	4
4	4

(rows 1, 2, and 5 struck through) has no saddle point.

However, row 3 dominates row 1 and row 4 dominates rows 2 and 5. Thus the game is reduced, for calculation, to the subgame

3	6
5	4

The game
−6	−1	1	4	7	4	3
7	−2	6	3	−2	−5	7

(columns 3, 4, 5, 7 struck through) has no saddle point.

However, columns 3, 4, 5, and 7 dominate column 2. Thus the game is reduced, for calculation, to the subgame

−6	−1	4
7	−2	−5

$m \times 2$ game consists of probabilities $p_1, p_2, \ldots, p_m$ (where $\sum\limits_{i=1}^{m} p_i = 1$) for player X and probabilities q_1 and $q_2 = 1 - q_1$ for player Y.

After dominance has been used to reduce a $2 \times n$ or an $m \times 2$ game for calculation, all possible 2×2 games derived from the matrix of this reduced game can be solved. The value of the original game is the value of one of these derived 2×2 games and the optimal strategies of the original game are also those of that derived 2×2 game, extended for one player by the addition of zeros. Which of the derived games provides the solution of the original game can be determined either by trial and error or graphically.

The trial-and-error procedure consists of solving the derived 2×2 games until one is found for which the two-strategy player does at least as well (usually better) against all his opponent's other strategies as he does against the pair appearing in the 2×2 subgame. When such a game is determined, its solution provides the solution of the original game.

Examples

In the first example above, only one 2×2 subgame remained:

3	6
5	4

Its solution is $p_1 = \frac{1}{4}$, $p_2 = \frac{3}{4}$; $q_1 = \frac{1}{2}$, $q_2 = \frac{1}{2}$; and the solution of the 5×2 game is thus $p_1 = 0$, $p_2 = 0$, $p_3 = \frac{1}{4}$, $p_4 = \frac{3}{4}$, $p_5 = 0$; $q_1 = \frac{1}{2}$, $q_2 = \frac{1}{2}$. For both games, $v = \frac{9}{2}$.

In the second example above, a 2×3 subgame remained:

-6	-1	4
7	-2	-5

and thus there are three 2×2 games for possible solution. The first of these 2×2 games,

-6	-1
7	-2

has the solution $p_1 = \frac{9}{14}$, $p_2 = \frac{5}{14}$; $q_1 = \frac{1}{14}$, $q_2 = \frac{13}{14}$; its value is $-\frac{19}{14}$.

Against the other remaining strategy of player Y, column 3 of the reduced game, $p_1 = \frac{9}{14}$, $p_2 = \frac{5}{14}$ has the value

$$\tfrac{9}{14}(4) + \tfrac{5}{14}(-5) = \tfrac{11}{14}$$

which is greater than $-\frac{19}{14}$, so the solution of this 2×2 game extended is the solution of the original game:

$$p_1 = \tfrac{9}{14} \qquad p_2 = \tfrac{5}{14}$$

$$q_1 = \tfrac{1}{14} \qquad q_2 = \tfrac{13}{14} \qquad q_3 = q_4 = q_5 = q_6 = q_7 = 0$$

NOTE: The 2×2 game

$\;\;\;\;$	-1	4
	-2	-5

has a saddle point; thus $p_1 = 1$, $p_2 = 0$, and the value of the game is -1. Against the other remaining strategy of player Y, column 1 of the reduced game, $p_1 = 1$, $p_2 = 0$ has the value -6, which is *not* greater than -1, so the solution of this game is *not* the solution of the original game. The 2×2 game

-6	4
7	-5

has the solution $p_1 = \frac{6}{11}$, $p_2 = \frac{5}{11}$, and the value of the game is $\frac{1}{11}$. Against the other remaining strategy of player Y, column 2 of the reduced game, $p_1 = \frac{6}{11}$, $p_2 = \frac{5}{11}$ has value $-\frac{16}{11}$, which is *not* greater than $\frac{1}{11}$, so the solution of this game is *not* the solution of the original game.

● Graphical Solution

Graphically, the 2×2 game whose solution is the solution of a $2 \times n$ game is determined as follows. Plot the payoffs of the n strategies of player Y on separate vertical axes and connect the pairs of points by straight lines; locate the highest point on the line segments that form the lower boundary of the graph. The lines that intersect at this point identify the strategies player Y should use in his optimum strategy. Note that it may be possible to reduce the game by dominance before doing graphical analysis.

Example

In the game

2	−2	3	7	6
6	5	1	4	0

column 5 is dominated by column 4. The 2×2 game to be solved is (see Fig. 8.3)

−2	3
5	1

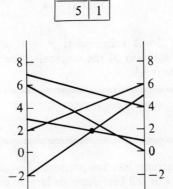

FIGURE 8.3

The solution of this 2×2 subgame is $p_1 = \frac{4}{9}$, $p_2 = \frac{5}{9}$; $q_1 = \frac{2}{9}$, $q_2 = \frac{7}{9}$; its value is $\frac{17}{9}$. Thus the solution of the original game is $p_1 = \frac{4}{9}$, $p_2 = \frac{5}{9}$; $q_1 = 0$, $q_2 = \frac{2}{9}$, $q_3 = \frac{7}{9}$, $q_4 = 0$, $q_5 = 0$; its value is $\frac{17}{9}$.

Similarly, for an $m \times 2$ game, the payoffs of the m strategies of player X are plotted and the lines that intersect at the lowest point on the line segments that form the upper boundary of the figure identify the strategies player X should use in his optimum strategy.

Examples

In the game

−3	6
6	3
8	−2

the 2×2 game to be solved is (see Fig. 8.4)

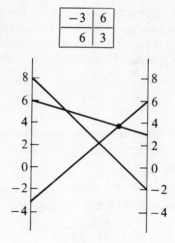

-3	6
6	3

FIGURE 8.4

The solution of this 2×2 subgame is $p_1 = \frac{1}{4}$, $p_2 = \frac{3}{4}$; $q_1 = \frac{1}{4}$, $q_2 = \frac{3}{4}$; its value is $\frac{15}{4}$. Thus the solution of the original game is $p_1 = \frac{1}{4}$, $p_2 = \frac{3}{4}$, $p_3 = 0$; $q_1 = \frac{1}{4}$, $q_2 = \frac{3}{4}$; its value is $\frac{15}{4}$.

An automobile manufacturer has five proposed designs for next year's new cars. Which of these is likely to sell best depends largely on whether his competitor's standard model is excellent, good, fair, or poor. If the model is excellent, his profit (millions of dollars) will be 100, 150, 50, 125, and 90, respectively; if the model is good, his profit will be 80, 55, 55, 60, and 70, respectively; if the model is fair, his profit will be 150, 100, 100, 100, and 125, respectively; if the model is poor, his profit will be 50, 80, 25, 80, and 75, respectively. What design should he choose in order to maximize his minimum expected profit?

Competitor's model

		Excellent	Good	Fair	Poor
	1	100	80	150	50
	2	~~150~~	~~55~~	~~100~~	~~80~~
Design	3	~~50~~	~~55~~	~~100~~	~~25~~
	4	125	60	100	80
	5	90	70	125	75

The 2×2 game to be solved is (see Fig. 8.5)

80	50
70	75

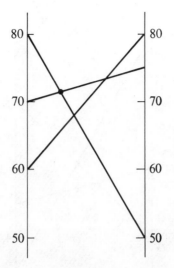

FIGURE 8.5

The solution of this 2 × 2 subgame is $p_1 = \frac{1}{7}$, $p_2 = \frac{6}{7}$. Thus the manufacturer should produce model 1 with probability $\frac{1}{7}$ and model 5 with probability $\frac{6}{7}$.

The Defense Department plans to award a contract for a new missile range at one of two locations, A or B. A real estate speculator intends to invest $5000 in land—all at location A, all at location B, or half at each location. If he buys at location A, the land will be worth $10,000 if the missile range is built there, but $3000 if it is built at location B. If he buys at location B, the land will be worth $4000 if the missile range is built at location A and $8000 if it is built at location B. If he buys at both locations, the land will be worth $6000 if the missile range is built at location A and $5000 if it is built at location B. In order to maximize his minimum expected profits, what should the speculator do?

| | | Missile range | |
		A	B
	A	10,000	3,000
Investment	B	4,000	8,000
	A and B	6,000	5,000

The 2 × 2 subgame to be solved is (see Fig. 8.6)

10,000	3,000
4,000	8,000

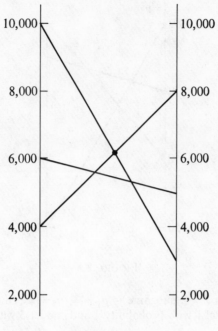

FIGURE 8.6

The solution of this 2×2 subgame is $p_1 = \frac{4}{11}$, $p_2 = \frac{7}{11}$. Thus the speculator should invest his money in property A with probability $\frac{4}{11}$ and property B with probability $\frac{7}{11}$.

☐ *SOLUTION OF LARGER GAMES*

For 3×3 and larger games, if there is no saddle point and if the original game cannot be reduced to a smaller game by dominance, linear programming provides the best method of solution. Linear programming is concerned with the problem of maximizing or minimizing a linear function whose variables are restricted to values satisfying a system of linear constraints. A matrix game can be expressed as a problem of this type, since each player is concerned with maximizing the value of the game to himself but is subject to the constraints imposed by the payoff matrix.

If, as above, the payoff matrix is represented by

$$\mathbf{A} = \begin{pmatrix} a_{11} & a_{12} \cdots a_{1n} \\ a_{21} & a_{22} \cdots a_{2n} \\ \vdots & \vdots & \vdots \\ a_{m1} & a_{m2} \cdots a_{mn} \end{pmatrix}$$

and Y's optimum strategies are represented by $(q_1, q_2, \ldots, q_n)$, the inequalities which express the expectations of Y are given by

$$a_{11}q_1 + a_{12}q_2 + \cdots + a_{1n}q_n \leq v$$
$$a_{21}q_1 + a_{22}q_2 + \cdots + a_{2n}q_n \leq v$$
$$\vdots$$
$$a_{m1}q_1 + a_{m2}q_2 + \cdots + a_{mn}q_n \leq v$$
$$q_1 + q_2 + \cdots + q_n = 1$$

Substituting $\bar{q}_i = \dfrac{q_i}{v}$,

$$a_{11}\bar{q}_1 + a_{12}\bar{q}_2 + \cdots + a_{1n}\bar{q}_n \leq 1$$
$$a_{21}\bar{q}_1 + a_{22}\bar{q}_2 + \cdots + a_{2n}\bar{q}_n \leq 1$$
$$\vdots$$
$$a_{m1}\bar{q}_1 + a_{m2}\bar{q}_2 + \cdots + a_{mn}\bar{q}_n \leq 1$$
$$\bar{q}_1 + \bar{q}_2 + \cdots + \bar{q}_n = \frac{1}{v}$$

Player Y's objective is to minimize v or, equivalently, maximize $\dfrac{1}{v}$. Thus the solution of the matrix game can be written as a linear programming problem as follows:

$$\text{Maximize } \bar{q}_1 + \bar{q}_2 + \cdots + \bar{q}_n$$

subject to

$$a_{11}\bar{q}_1 + a_{12}\bar{q}_2 + \cdots + a_{1n}\bar{q}_n \leq 1$$
$$a_{21}\bar{q}_1 + a_{22}\bar{q}_2 + \cdots + a_{2n}\bar{q}_n \leq 1$$
$$\vdots$$
$$a_{m1}\bar{q}_1 + a_{m2}\bar{q}_2 + \cdots + a_{mn}\bar{q}_n \leq 1$$
$$\bar{q}_1 + \bar{q}_2 + \cdots + \bar{q}_n = \frac{1}{v}$$

or, more concisely,

$$\text{Maximize } \sum_{i=1}^{n} \bar{q}_i$$

subject to

$$\sum_{j=1}^{n} a_{ij}\bar{q}_j \leq 1 \qquad \text{for } i = 1, 2, \ldots, m$$
$$\sum_{j=1}^{n} \bar{q}_j = \frac{1}{v}$$

PROBLEMS

Find the optimum strategies for the players of each of the following matrix games using the minimax criterion.

1.

8	10	13	16	9
10	12	6	15	10
16	18	9	13	25
4	9	18	20	6

4.

14	3	5	8	4
−3	−1	6	−2	5
2	12	10	13	16

2.

5	8	7
−1	−3	10
2	12	−6

5.

15	−20	−12	3
4	2	−10	−6
20	−18	−15	−8
−12	8	−10	6
10	9	−11	4

3.

10	8	6	2
15	12	2	4
−4	6	−3	1
12	−2	8	−6
16	13	7	12

6.

3	10	20	18	0
−9	−8	46	10	4
2	0	17	18	0
−1	1	13	5	3

Find the optimum strategies for the players of each of the following matrix games using the minimax criterion and determine the value of each game.

7.

7	−1	7
10	−2	−5
9	5	6

11.

12	−10	8	−6	7	−11
18	2	−3	−4	8	10
5	−3	14	0	−10	−12
3	12	16	1	8	2
−15	16	12	−2	9	−9

8.

3	5	2	1
0	4	8	3
2	7	14	9

12.

10	8	11	−2
14	6	−5	5
9	7	5	−4
15	4	−3	3

9.

5	4	−2	1
7	−6	3	6
12	8	10	9
6	18	−9	14

13.

4	6
9	5
3	1
7	8
10	2

10.

3	−10	−5
2	−4	−3
4	−5	−2
−6	−4	0
10	−8	1

14.

6	−10	12	25	0	5	3	−2
2	−8	4	−6	−7	9	4	10

15.

0	2
1	3
-1	0
2	0

16.

9	-5	7	1	-3
-10	4	-8	-6	2

17. A contractor is going to build a large number of houses for a housing development. Four types of houses have been discussed: colonial, ranch, split-level, and contemporary; the development committee will choose two of these types for the contractor to construct. The contractor has the opportunity to buy materials in carload lots, thus saving considerable money, but he must order in advance of the committee's decision and can order only one type of material. If the committee chooses colonial and ranch, the contractor will make an (extra) profit (in thousands of dollars) of 125, 120, 60, and 50 if he orders colonial, ranch, split-level, and contemporary materials, respectively. If the committee chooses colonial and split-level, he will make 90, 40, 80, 75, respectively; if the committee chooses colonial and contemporary, he will make 150, 30, 75, 100, respectively; if the committee chooses ranch and split level, he will make 70, 70, 75, 65, respectively; if the committee chooses ranch and contemporary, he will make 90, 80, 80, 120, respectively; if the committee chooses split-level and contemporary, he will make 80, 40, 130, and 80, respectively. How should the contractor order to maximize his minimum expected extra profit?

18. A plant manager must set up his reactors to produce a certain type of polythene using either process 1, 2, 3, 4, or 5. Unfortunately, the chemical raw material varies in nitrogen content and may contain 3, 4, 5, or 6% nitrogen. The nitrogen content affects the relative efficiency of the five processes. With 3% nitrogen, the five processes have an output of 50, 45, 60, 50, and 30 tons, respectively. With 4% nitrogen, the outputs are 60, 70, 75, 90, and 60 tons, respectively; with 5% nitrogen, the outputs are 30, 55, 60, 45, and 70 tons, respectively; with 6% nitrogen, the outputs are 45, 80, 80, 65, and 85 tons, respectively. Testing for nitrogen content is too expensive to be practical. What process should the plant manager use to maximize the minimum expected output?

19. A firm builds construction machinery whose performance depends on the reliability of a gasoline motor. The firm can buy an expensive motor, fully guaranteed including replacement costs, for $500; the firm can also buy a moderately expensive motor for $400, guaranteed for half its cost and the cost of replacement, so that a failure means the firm pays $600 for the motor; or the firm can buy a cheaper motor for $300—if it buys this cheaper motor it can either guarantee replacement for a total cost of $700, or it can pay $50 to have the motor examined before installation, so total cost, if the motor is defective, is $650. To minimize maximum expected costs, what should the firm do?

20. Mr. Smith and Mr. Jones each have a small hothouse in which they grow plants to sell. Each of them grows either tomatoes, flowers, or strawberries in any particular year but they are very secretive about their plans. If Mr. Smith grows tomatoes, his profit is $100 if Mr. Jones grows tomatoes, $150 if Mr. Jones grows strawberries, and $200 if Mr. Jones grows flowers. If Mr. Smith grows strawberries, his profit is $180, $125, $200 if Mr. Jones

grows tomatoes, strawberries, flowers, respectively. If Mr. Smith grows flowers, his profit is $140, $125, $100 if Mr. Jones grows tomatoes, strawberries, flowers, respectively. For each to maximize his minimum expected profit, what should Mr. Smith and Mr. Jones grow?

21. Mr. Reno has decided to bet $5 on a basketball game between Anglewood and Barleyville. Mr. Las and Mr. Vegas have each offered Mr. Reno a bet. Mr. Las wants to bet on Barleyville and is willing to pay Mr. Reno $10 if Anglewood wins and collect $5 if Barleyville wins. Mr. Vegas wants to bet on Anglewood and is willing to pay Mr. Reno $4 if Barleyville wins and collect $5 if Anglewood wins. If he wants to maximize his minimum expected winnings, what should Mr. Reno do?

22. Casey has a concession at the Yankee Stadium for the sale of sunglasses and umbrellas. He has observed that he can sell about 500 umbrellas when it rains, and about 100 when it shines; and in the latter case he can also dispose of 1000 sunglasses. Umbrellas cost $0.50 and sell for $1.00; glasses cost $0.20 and sell for $0.50. He is willing to invest $250 in the project. Assuming that everything that isn't sold is a total loss, what should he purchase to maximise his minimum expected profit?

23. Mr. Hilton Conrad is faced with the following decision: The State Medical Society would like to use his hotel for their annual convention; they would essentially take over all facilities of the hotel (so business from other sources would be negligible) and would pay $20,000 for this privilege. Ordinarily the hotel would do $10,000 business during the time the convention would be in session; however, there is a chance that the World Series will be played in the city at that time and, in this event, the hotel would do $50,000 business. Should Mr. Hilton Conrad accept or decline the Medical Society's offer in order to maximize his minimum expected business?

24. An investor has a choice of buying one of three stocks: A, B, or C. The outcome of his purchase depends on whether a particular company executes a merger, divests itself of a subsidiary, or maintains the status quo. In case of a merger, stock A results in a gain of 20, stock B in a loss of 25, and stock C in a gain of 12. In case of divesting, stock A results in a loss of 5, stock B in a loss of 10, and stock C in a loss of 12. If the status quo is maintained, stock A results in a gain of 5, stock B in a gain of 30, and stock C in a loss of 4 (amounts are in thousands of dollars). (a) In order to maximize his minimum expected gains, what stock should the investor buy? (b) If divesting were impossible, but the gains and losses from the other possibilities were unchanged, what stock should he buy to maximize his minimum expected gains?

25. A commuter must decide what to do about buying insurance for his car. He will definitely carry liability insurance, but the car is rather old and he is not sure whether or not collision insurance is worthwhile. He can either carry no collision insurance, buy a $50 deductible policy for $60, or buy a full-coverage policy for $70. The commuter drives this car only to and from work and he thinks one of three things will happen during the year: He will have no accident, he will have one minor accident not exceeding $50 damage, or he will have one more serious accident not exceeding $250 damage (the car is worth only about $400 so this is not unreasonable optimism). The commuter realizes he could possibly have more than one accident during the year, but on the basis of his past performances he is willling to assume that he won't. What should he do to minimize his maximum expected cost?

26. In the summer Mr. Smith is considering the winter coal problem. During a normal winter, it takes about 15 tons of coal to heat his shop, but he has observed extremes where as little as 10 tons or as much as 20 tons were used. The price per ton seems to fluctuate with the weather, being $10, $15, and $20 a ton during mild, normal, and severe winters, respectively. He can buy now at $10 a ton. Mr. Smith considers three possible alternatives: to buy 10, 15, or 20 tons now and the rest, if any, later. Assuming that all coal not used is a total loss (Mr. Smith plans to sell the shop in the spring), what should he do to minimize his maximum expected cost?

27. A student must decide how to study for a final exam in history. He studies differently for true-false, multiple-choice, and essay exams, and he doesn't know which type this exam will be. The student thinks that if he studies for a true-false test, he will score 85 on a true-false test, 80 on a multiple-choice test, and 75 on an essay test. If he studies for a multiple-choice test, he will score 85 on a true-false test, 90 on a multiple-choice test, and 85 on an essay test. If he studies for an essay test, he will score 80 on a true-false test, 90 on a multiple-choice test, and 90 on an essay test. To maximize his minimum expected score, for what type of test should the student study?

28. A service station must have its service and parking area plowed after every heavy snowfall. The manager can pay $5 every time the area needs plowing; he can buy a contract for $25 which provides plowing for up to and including six snowfalls, with each additional plowing at a cost of $3; or he can buy a contract for $30 which provides plowing as many times as it is needed. What should the manager do to minimize his maximum expected cost of plowing if he is willing to assume (based on past records) that there will be between 3 and 8 (inclusive) snowfalls during the winter?

ANSWERS TO ODD-NUMBERED PROBLEMS

1. $p_1 = p_2 = 0, p_3 = \frac{2}{3}, p_4 = \frac{1}{3}$
$q_1 = \frac{3}{7}, q_2 = 0,$
$\qquad q_3 = \frac{4}{7}, q_4 = q_5 = 0$

3. $p_1 = p_2 = p_3 = 0, p_4 = \frac{5}{19},$
$\qquad\qquad p_5 = \frac{14}{19}$
$q_1 = q_2 = 0, q_3 = \frac{18}{19}, q_4 = \frac{1}{19}$

5. $p_1 = 0, p_2 = 1, \ p_3 = p_4 = p_5 = 0$
$q_1 = q_2 = 0, q_3 = 1, q_4 = 0$

7. $p_1 = p_2 = 0, p_3 = 1$
$q_1 = 0, q_2 = 1, q_3 = 0$
$v = 5$

9. $p_1 = p_2 = 0, \ p_3 = \frac{27}{29}, p_4 = \frac{2}{29}$

$q_1 = 0, q_2 = \frac{19}{29}, q_3 = \frac{10}{29}, q_4 = 0$
$v = \frac{252}{29}$

11. $p_1 = p_2 = p_3 = 0, p_4 = 1, p_5 = 0$
$q_1 = q_2 = q_3 = 0, q_4 = 1,$
$\qquad\qquad q_5 = q_6 = 0$
$v = 1$

13. $p_1 = 0, p_2 = \frac{1}{5}, p_3 = 0,$
$\qquad\qquad p_4 = \frac{4}{5}, p_5 = 0$
$q_1 = \frac{3}{5}, q_2 = \frac{2}{5}$
$v = \frac{37}{5}$

15. $p_1 = 0, p_2 = \frac{1}{2}, p_3 = 0, p_4 = \frac{1}{2}$
$q_1 = \frac{3}{4}, q_2 = \frac{1}{4}$
$v = \frac{3}{2}$

17. buy for colonial with probability $\frac{3}{14}$ and for split-level with probability $\frac{11}{14}$

19. buy expensive motor

21. bet Las with probability $\frac{3}{8}$ and Vegas with probability $\frac{5}{8}$

23. accept offer of a convention

25. buy full coverage

27. study for multiple-choice test

■ 8.5 MARKOV CHAINS

Sequences of observations or experimental outcomes are sometimes considered to be independent; that is, the probability of observing any particular outcome is assumed to be constant. The simplest generalization of this model permits the probability of the outcome for any experiment or observation to depend on the outcome of the immediately preceding observation, but not on the outcomes of other prior observations. A process (sequence) of this type is said to be a *Markov chain process*, *Markov chain*, or *Markov process*.

□ DEFINITION OF A MARKOV CHAIN

Suppose that the outcome of each of a sequence of experiments or observations is one of a finite number of possible outcomes $a_1, a_2, \ldots, a_r$. The probability of outcome a_j for any given experiment or observation depends on at most the outcome of the immediately preceding observation. Assume that there are given numbers p_{ij} which represent the probability of outcome a_j for any particular observation given that outcome a_i occurred for the immediately preceding observation. The outcomes $a_1, a_2, \ldots, a_r$ are called *states* and the numbers p_{ij} are called *transition probabilities* of a Markov chain. If it is assumed that the process begins in some particular state, then the probabilities of various sequences of observations can be calculated. Thus a Markov chain is specified by defining its possible states, specifying the initial probability distribution for these states, and specifying the transition matrix.

Note the implicit assumption that the transition probabilities are constant over time. When the transition probabilities are constant from one observation to another of the sequence, the Markov process is said to be *stationary*. A Markov process whose transition probabilities are not constant over time is said to be *nonstationary* or *time-dependent*; the mathematics of such processes is extremely difficult.

The transition probabilities can be shown by a square matrix. For a Markov process with states $a_1, a_2, \ldots, a_r$, the matrix of transition probabilities is

$$\mathbf{P} = \{p_{ij}\} = \begin{pmatrix} p_{11} & p_{12} \cdots p_{1r} \\ p_{21} & p_{22} \cdots p_{2r} \\ \vdots & \vdots & \vdots \\ p_{r1} & p_{r2} \cdots p_{rr} \end{pmatrix}$$

Note that the sum of the elements in each row of the matrix $\mathbf{P}$ is 1, since the elements of the ith row represent the probabilities for all possible transitions when the process is in state a_i. That is,

$$\sum_{j=1}^{r} p_{ij} = 1 \qquad \text{for } i = 1, 2, \ldots, r$$

Thus if the probability distribution of the states on trial n is $(p_1, p_2, \ldots, p_r)$, the probability distribution of the states on trial $n + 1$ is

$$(p_1, p_2, \ldots, p_r) \begin{pmatrix} p_{11} & p_{12} \cdots p_{1r} \\ p_{21} & p_{22} \cdots p_{2r} \\ \vdots & \vdots \qquad \vdots \\ p_{r1} & p_{r2} \cdots p_{rr} \end{pmatrix} = \left(\sum_{i=1}^{r} p_i p_{i1}, \sum_{i=1}^{r} p_i p_{i2}, \ldots, \sum_{i=1}^{r} p_i p_{ir} \right)$$

□ STEADY STATE OR EQUILIBRIUM

As shown by the discussion of the preceding section, the probability distribution of the outcomes for the nth observation of a Markov process is the product of the initial probability vector and the nth power of the transition matrix. Under some rather nonrestrictive mathematical assumptions, it can be shown that a Markov process approaches a steady state or equilibrium as the number of observations increases, that is, as n approaches infinity. By definition, when a Markov process is in equilibrium, the probability of each possible state or outcome is constant from observation to observation. The Markov processes used to describe situations in business and economics almost invariably fulfill the mathematical assumptions for equilibrium, and the probability distribution of the states in equilibrium is frequently the most interesting property of these processes.

It can be shown that if a Markov chain approaches a steady or equilibrium state as the number of observations or transitions approaches infinity, the stationary (equilibrium) probability distribution of its states is unique and depends only on the transition matrix and not on the initial probability distribution of the states. Any particular Markov chain is, of course, in one particular state for any given observation. The physical (and computational) significance of stationarity thus becomes apparent only if a number of Markov processes are in the same equilibrium state simultaneously. In this case if there are N such processes and p_i is the equilibrium probability of state i, $p_i N$ of the processes are expected to be in state i for any given observation. Thus, if N is large, a state of macroscopic equilibrium is maintained by a large number of transitions in opposite directions. Most statistical equilibria in physics are of this kind.

Computationally, the stationary probability distribution $(p_1, p_2, \ldots, p_r)$ of the states of a Markov chain is obtained by solving the equations given in matrix form by

$$(p_1, p_2, \ldots, p_r) \begin{pmatrix} p_{11} & p_{12} \cdots p_{1r} \\ p_{21} & p_{22} \cdots p_{2r} \\ \vdots & \vdots \qquad \vdots \\ p_{r1} & p_{r2} \cdots p_{rr} \end{pmatrix} = (p_1, p_2, \ldots, p_r)$$

where p_i is the probability of being in state i, $i = 1, \ldots, r$ and $\sum_{i=1}^{r} p_i = 1$. This involves solution of the r independent linear equations

$$\sum_{i=1}^{r} p_i p_{ij} = p_j \qquad \text{for } j = 1, 2, \ldots, r \ (r - 1 \text{ of which are independent})$$

$$\sum_{i=1}^{r} p_i = 1$$

Note that these equations actually define equilibrium: If $(p_1, p_2, \ldots, p_r)$ is the probability distribution of the states for a given observation, the product

$$(p_1, p_2, \ldots, p_r) \begin{pmatrix} p_{11} & p_{12} \cdots p_{1r} \\ p_{21} & p_{22} \cdots p_{2r} \\ \vdots & \vdots & \vdots \\ p_{r1} & p_{r2} \cdots p_{rr} \end{pmatrix}$$

gives the probability distribution of the states for the next observation. If that distribution is also $(p_1, p_2, \ldots, p_r)$, the same as for the preceding observation, the system is in equilibrium.

Examples

On September 1, of the subscribers in a fixed area the Herald has $\frac{1}{2}$, the Tribune has $\frac{1}{4}$, and the Gazette has $\frac{1}{4}$. During the month of September, the Herald retains $\frac{7}{8}$ of its subscribers and loses $\frac{1}{8}$ of them to the Tribune; the Tribune retains $\frac{1}{12}$ of its subscribers and loses $\frac{3}{4}$ of them to the Herald and $\frac{1}{6}$ of them to the Gazette; the Gazette retains $\frac{1}{3}$ of its subscribers and loses $\frac{1}{2}$ of them to the Herald and $\frac{1}{6}$ of them to the Tribune. Assume there are no new subscribers and that none quit subscribing. (a) What proportion of the subscribers does each paper have on October 1? (b) If the same pattern of gains and losses continues for October, what proportion of the subscribers does each paper have on November 1? (c) If the same pattern of gains and losses continues each month, what proportion of the subscribers will each paper have in the long run (that is, in equilibrium)?

The transition matrix is

$$\begin{array}{c} \\ \text{Herald} \\ \text{Tribune} \\ \text{Gazette} \end{array} \begin{array}{c} \text{Herald} \quad \text{Tribune} \quad \text{Gazette} \\ \begin{pmatrix} \frac{7}{8} & \frac{1}{8} & 0 \\ \frac{3}{4} & \frac{1}{12} & \frac{1}{6} \\ \frac{1}{2} & \frac{1}{6} & \frac{1}{3} \end{pmatrix} \end{array}$$

(a)

$$(\tfrac{1}{2}, \tfrac{1}{4}, \tfrac{1}{4}) \begin{pmatrix} \frac{7}{8} & \frac{1}{8} & 0 \\ \frac{3}{4} & \frac{1}{12} & \frac{1}{6} \\ \frac{1}{2} & \frac{1}{6} & \frac{1}{3} \end{pmatrix} = (\tfrac{3}{4}, \tfrac{1}{8}, \tfrac{1}{8})$$

Thus on October 1, of the subscribers, the Herald has $\frac{3}{4}$, the Tribune has $\frac{1}{8}$, and the Gazette has $\frac{1}{8}$.

(b)

$$(\tfrac{3}{4}, \tfrac{1}{8}, \tfrac{1}{8}) \begin{pmatrix} \frac{7}{8} & \frac{1}{8} & 0 \\ \frac{3}{4} & \frac{1}{12} & \frac{1}{6} \\ \frac{1}{2} & \frac{1}{6} & \frac{1}{3} \end{pmatrix} = (\tfrac{13}{16}, \tfrac{1}{8}, \tfrac{1}{16})$$

Thus on November 1, of the subscribers, the Herald has $\frac{13}{16}$, the Tribune has $\frac{1}{8}$, and the Gazette has $\frac{1}{16}$.

(c)

$$(p_1, p_2, p_3) \begin{pmatrix} \frac{7}{8} & \frac{1}{8} & 0 \\ \frac{3}{4} & \frac{1}{12} & \frac{1}{6} \\ \frac{1}{2} & \frac{1}{6} & \frac{1}{3} \end{pmatrix} = (p_1, p_2, p_3)$$

$$\tfrac{7}{8}p_1 + \tfrac{3}{4}p_2 + \tfrac{1}{2}p_3 = p_1$$

$$\tfrac{1}{8}p_1 + \tfrac{1}{12}p_2 + \tfrac{1}{6}p_3 = p_2$$

$$\tfrac{1}{6}p_2 + \tfrac{1}{3}p_3 = p_3$$

$$p_1 + p_2 + p_3 = 1$$

$$-p_1 + 6p_2 + 4p_3 = 0$$

$$3p_1 - 22p_2 + 4p_3 = 0$$

$$p_2 - p_3 = 0$$

$$p_1 + p_2 + p_3 = 1$$

$$\begin{pmatrix} 1 & 1 & 1 & \bigm| & 1 \\ 0 & 1 & -4 & \bigm| & 0 \\ -1 & 6 & 4 & \bigm| & 0 \end{pmatrix}$$

$$\begin{pmatrix} 1 & 1 & 1 & \bigm| & 1 \\ 0 & 1 & -4 & \bigm| & 0 \\ 0 & 7 & 5 & \bigm| & 1 \end{pmatrix}$$

$$\begin{pmatrix} 1 & 0 & 5 & \bigm| & 1 \\ 0 & 1 & -4 & \bigm| & 0 \\ 0 & 0 & 33 & \bigm| & 1 \end{pmatrix}$$

$$\begin{pmatrix} 1 & 0 & 0 & \bigm| & \frac{28}{33} \\ 0 & 1 & 0 & \bigm| & \frac{4}{33} \\ 0 & 0 & 1 & \bigm| & \frac{1}{33} \end{pmatrix}$$

Thus in the long run, of the subscribers, the Herald will have 84.9%, the Tribune will have 12.1%, and the Gazette will have 3.0%.

In the community of Gardenville each year 5% of the residents in the city proper move to the suburbs and 2% of the people in the suburbs move to the city. Assuming that the total number of people in the community remains constant, determine the long-run proportions of city and suburban residents.

The transition matrix is

$$\begin{array}{cc} & \text{City} \quad \text{Suburbs} \\ \begin{array}{c} \text{City} \\ \text{Suburbs} \end{array} & \begin{pmatrix} 0.95 & 0.05 \\ 0.02 & 0.98 \end{pmatrix} \end{array}$$

and the equilibrium probabilities are determined by

$$(p_1, p_2) \begin{pmatrix} 0.95 & 0.05 \\ 0.02 & 0.98 \end{pmatrix} = (p_1, p_2)$$

$$0.95p_1 + 0.02p_2 = p_1$$

$$0.05p_1 + 0.98p_2 = p_2$$

$$p_1 + p_2 = 1$$

$$-5p_1 + 2p_2 = 0$$

$$5p_1 - 2p_2 = 0$$

$$p_1 + p_2 = 1$$

$$\left(\begin{array}{cc|c} 1 & 1 & 1 \\ -5 & 2 & 0 \end{array} \right)$$

$$\left(\begin{array}{cc|c} 1 & 1 & 1 \\ 0 & 7 & 5 \end{array} \right)$$

$$\left(\begin{array}{cc|c} 1 & 1 & 1 \\ 0 & 1 & \frac{5}{7} \end{array} \right)$$

$$\left(\begin{array}{cc|c} 1 & 0 & \frac{2}{7} \\ 0 & 1 & \frac{5}{7} \end{array} \right)$$

Thus, eventually, of the people in the community $\frac{2}{7}$ are city residents and $\frac{5}{7}$ are residents of the suburbs. Note that in this equilibrium state each year $0.05 \times \frac{2}{7} = \frac{1}{70}$ of the people move from the city to the suburbs and $0.02 \times \frac{5}{7} = \frac{5}{70}$ of the people move from the suburbs to the city—the numbers of city and suburban residents thus are unchanged or stable.

A broker is studying the price movements of various stocks on the market and is particularly interested in a company called Astronaut Instruments. He has observed that if this stock goes up on a given day, then the next day it has a 50 : 50 chance of going up again, a $\frac{1}{3}$ chance of staying the same price, and a $\frac{1}{6}$ chance of going down. If the stock stays the same on a given day, then it is equally likely to go up, stay the same, or go down the next day. If the stock goes down on a given day, then the next day it has a 50 : 50 chance of going down again, a $\frac{1}{3}$ chance of staying the same price, and a $\frac{1}{6}$ chance of going up. What proportion of the time (in the long run) does the stock go up, stay the same, and go down?

The transition matrix is

	Up	Same	Down
Up	$\frac{1}{2}$	$\frac{1}{3}$	$\frac{1}{6}$
Same	$\frac{1}{3}$	$\frac{1}{3}$	$\frac{1}{3}$
Down	$\frac{1}{6}$	$\frac{1}{3}$	$\frac{1}{2}$

and the equilibrium probabilities are determined by

$$(p_1, p_2, p_3) \begin{pmatrix} \frac{1}{2} & \frac{1}{3} & \frac{1}{6} \\ \frac{1}{3} & \frac{1}{3} & \frac{1}{3} \\ \frac{1}{6} & \frac{1}{3} & \frac{1}{2} \end{pmatrix} = (p_1, p_2, p_3)$$

$$\tfrac{1}{2}p_1 + \tfrac{1}{3}p_2 + \tfrac{1}{6}p_3 = p_1$$

$$\tfrac{1}{3}p_1 + \tfrac{1}{3}p_2 + \tfrac{1}{3}p_3 = p_2$$

$$\tfrac{1}{6}p_1 + \tfrac{1}{3}p_2 + \tfrac{1}{2}p_3 = p_3$$

$$p_1 + p_2 + p_3 = 1$$

$$-3p_1 + 2p_2 + p_3 = 0$$

$$p_1 - 2p_2 + p_3 = 0$$

$$p_1 + 2p_2 - 3p_3 = 0$$

$$p_1 + p_2 + p_3 = 1$$

$$\begin{pmatrix} 1 & 1 & 1 & 1 \\ 1 & 2 & -3 & 0 \\ 1 & -2 & 1 & 0 \end{pmatrix}$$

$$\begin{pmatrix} 1 & 1 & 1 & 1 \\ 0 & 1 & -4 & -1 \\ 0 & -3 & 0 & -1 \end{pmatrix}$$

$$\begin{pmatrix} 1 & 0 & 5 & 2 \\ 0 & 1 & -4 & -1 \\ 0 & 0 & -12 & -4 \end{pmatrix}$$

$$\begin{pmatrix} 1 & 0 & 0 & \tfrac{1}{3} \\ 0 & 1 & 0 & \tfrac{1}{3} \\ 0 & 0 & 1 & \tfrac{1}{3} \end{pmatrix}$$

Thus, in the long run, the stock goes up $\tfrac{1}{3}$ of the time, stays the same $\tfrac{1}{3}$ of the time, and goes down $\tfrac{1}{3}$ of the time.

PROBLEMS

1. A country has a three-party political system and the results of elections follow a definite pattern: If a party wins an election, its chance of winning the next election are 50 : 50 and if it loses the next election, each of the other two parties has a 50 : 50 chance of winning. What proportion of the elections does each party win over a long period of time?

2. A trucking company offers its drivers three approved routes between two cities: over the Mystic Bridge, on the Interstate Parkway, and on Route 1. If a trucker goes on the Mystic Bridge the chance of his getting into a traffic jam is $\tfrac{1}{3}$; if he does get in a traffic jam, the next day he takes the Interstate Parkway with probability $\tfrac{2}{3}$ and Route 1 with probability $\tfrac{1}{3}$; if he doesn't get in a traffic jam, the next day he takes the Mystic Bridge again with probability $\tfrac{1}{2}$, the Interstate Parkway with probability $\tfrac{1}{6}$, and Route 1 with probability $\tfrac{1}{3}$. If he takes the Interstate Parkway the chance of his getting into a traffic jam is $\tfrac{1}{2}$; if he does get in a traffic jam, the next day he takes the Mystic Bridge; if he

doesn't get in a traffic jam, the next day he takes the Mystic Bridge, the Interstate Parkway, and Route 1 with equal probability. If he takes Route 1, the trucker is invariably late, so he never takes Route 1 two days in a row and the next day he takes the Mystic Bridge with probability $\frac{1}{3}$ and the Interstate Parkway with probability $\frac{2}{3}$. What proportion of the time does the trucker go on the Mystic Bridge, the Interstate Parkway, and Route 1, respectively?

3. Every year the Smith family goes on a vacation—a camping trip (preferred by the children), a visit to the city (preferred by Mrs. Smith), or a winter vacation (preferred by Mr. Smith). They never take the same kind of vacation 2 years in a row. Each year they flip a coin to decide which of the two types of vacation they did not take the previous year they will take that year. What proportion of the time do the Smiths go on a camping trip, visit the city, and take a winter vacation?

4. A mechanic has a very unreliable automobile. Every morning he goes out to the garage hopefully to start it—some days it starts by itself, some days it starts if he gets a push from a neighbor, other days no amount of pushing is effective and the service station must be called. If it starts one day, the chances are $\frac{1}{2}$ it will start, $\frac{1}{3}$ it must be pushed, and $\frac{1}{6}$ the service station must be called the next day. If it is pushed one day, the chances are $\frac{1}{3}$ it will start and $\frac{2}{3}$ the service station must be called the next day (it is never pushed 2 days in a row). If the service station is called one day, the chances are $\frac{5}{6}$ it will start and $\frac{1}{6}$ it must be pushed the next day (the service station is never needed 2 days in a row). In the long run, what proportion of the days will the auto start, be this pushed, and need the service station?

5. The students of Professor Geology never know what's going to happen in class—the professor may give them a surprise quiz, take them on a field trip, discuss the daily assignment, or deliver a lecture. If he gives a quiz one day, the next day there is always a field trip. If there is a field trip one day, there is never a quiz or a field trip the next day, but discussing the assignment and a lecture are equally likely. If he discusses the assignment one day, there is $\frac{1}{4}$ chance of a quiz, $\frac{1}{4}$ chance of a field trip, $\frac{1}{6}$ chance of discussing the assignment, and $\frac{1}{3}$ chance of a lecture the next day. If he lectures one day, there is $\frac{1}{4}$ chance of a quiz, $\frac{1}{8}$ chance of a field trip, $\frac{1}{8}$ chance of discussing the assignment, and $\frac{1}{2}$ chance of a lecture the next day. One of the students has calculated that they can expect quizzes $\frac{43}{287}$ of the days, field trips $\frac{72}{287}$ of the days, discussion of the assignment $\frac{60}{287}$ of the days, and lectures $\frac{112}{287}$ of the days. Is this correct?

6. Mr. S (who prefers steak), Mr. C (who prefers chicken), and Mr. H (who prefers ham) are invited frequently to the home of a friend who serves only these three entrees. They have decided to bet before each dinner engagement on which entree will be served. Suppose that if the hostess serves steak on one occasion, she never serves it next time; she tosses a fair coin and serves chicken if it comes up heads and ham if it comes up tails. If she serves chicken on one occasion, then the next time she tosses two dice and serves chicken if the dice come up the same; if the dice come up different on the first toss, she tosses them again and serves steak if they come up the same and ham otherwise. If she serves ham on one occasion, then the next time she draws a card randomly from a deck and serves chicken if it is a diamond and steak otherwise. If each man always bets on his preference, what proportion of the time (in the long run) will each win?

7. Every summer the Stormy Lakes Yachting Association must decide whether to

hold its annual regatta in June, July, or August. If the regatta is in June, the probability of good weather is $\frac{3}{4}$; if there is good weather, the next year the regatta will be held in June with probability $\frac{2}{3}$, in July with probability $\frac{1}{6}$, and in August with probability $\frac{1}{6}$; if there is bad weather, the next year the regatta will be held in July and August with equal probabilities. If the regatta is in July, good and bad weather are equally probable; if there is good weather, the next year the regatta will be held in July; if there is bad weather, the regatta will be held in August with probability $\frac{2}{3}$ and in June with probability $\frac{1}{3}$. If the regatta is in August, the probability of good weather is $\frac{2}{5}$; if there is good weather, the next year the regatta will be held in July and August with equal probabilities; if there is bad weather, the regatta will be held in June with probability $\frac{1}{3}$ and in July with probability $\frac{2}{3}$. What proportion of the time is the regatta held in June, July, and August, respectively?

8. A scientific book club has three mailing lists: a selected list consisting of members of 3 years or more of active membership, a membership list consisting of current members, and an augmented list consisting of current members and others who have shown interest in the club's activities in the past. For each new publication, it must be decided which list to use for mailing the sales literature. If after the preceding mailing there were too few copies ordered, the secretary uses the member list with probability $\frac{1}{4}$ and the augmented list with probability $\frac{3}{4}$; if after the preceding mailing there was a satisfactory response, the secretary uses the member list and the augmented list with equal probability; if after the preceding mailing, the publication was oversold, the secretary uses the selected list with probability $\frac{1}{3}$ and the member list with probability $\frac{2}{3}$. If the selected list is used, there are too few sold, or a satisfactory number sold with equal probability; if the member list is used, there are too few sold with probability $\frac{1}{4}$ and an adequate sale with probability $\frac{3}{4}$; if the augmented list is used, there is an adequate sale with probability $\frac{1}{3}$ and an oversale with probability $\frac{2}{3}$. What proportion of the time are the sales too small, adequate, and an oversale, respectively?

9. A housewife always buys one of three brands of detergent: A, B, or C. Which brand she buys depends partly on which (if any) of the three companies are having a promotional campaign (free combs, plastic roses, etc.) The companies time these campaigns at random, paying no attention to whether or not the competition is running one at the same time. Company A runs a campaign $\frac{1}{2}$ of the time, company B runs a campaign $\frac{1}{3}$ of the time, and company C runs a campaign $\frac{1}{3}$ of the time. If she buys brand A one time, the next time she buys brand A if brand A is running a campaign or if none of the brands is running a campaign, she buys brand B if brand B is running a campaign but brand A is not, and she buys brand C if brand C is running the only campaign at the time. If she buys brand B one time, the next time she buys brand A if it is running the only campaign at the time and brand B otherwise. If she buys brand C one time, the next time she buys brand A if it is running the only campaign at the time, brand C if it is running a campaign and B is not, and brand B otherwise. What proportion of the time does the housewife buy brands A, B, and C, respectively?

HELPFUL HINT: From $P(A) = \frac{1}{2}, P(B) = \frac{1}{3}, P(C) = \frac{1}{3}$ given above, the following probabilities can be obtained with a little arithmetic:

$$P(A \text{ only}) = \tfrac{2}{9} \qquad P(A \text{ and } C, \text{ not } B) = \tfrac{1}{9}$$

$$P(B \text{ only}) = \tfrac{1}{9} \qquad P(B \text{ and } C, \text{ not } A) = \tfrac{1}{18}$$

$$P(C \text{ only}) = \tfrac{1}{9} \qquad P(A, B \text{ and } C) = \tfrac{1}{18}$$

$$P(A \text{ and } B, \text{ not } C) = \tfrac{1}{9} \qquad P(\text{no campaign}) = \tfrac{2}{9}$$

10. Computeronics Corporation orders 2-foot lengths of wire for use in its experimental models from a supplier who claims that the wire has a specified strength desired by the Computeronics engineers. Each shipment is classified by the engineers who use it as satisfactory in strength (no report is made to the supplier), below standard (the supplier is notified by letter that the shipment was not as claimed), or unacceptable (the shipment is returned and a replacement which has been subjected to a 100% test is sent by the supplier in accordance with the guarantee). The classification depends upon the extent to which a shipment fulfills or fails to fulfill the supplier's claim regarding strength. The engineers have observed that if a shipment is classified as satisfactory, the next shipment is satisfactory $\tfrac{4}{5}$ of the time, below standard $\tfrac{3}{20}$ of the time, and unacceptable $\tfrac{1}{20}$ of the time; if a shipment is classified as below standard, the next shipment is satisfactory $\tfrac{19}{20}$ of the time, below standard $\tfrac{1}{20}$ of the time, and never unacceptable. What proportion of the shipments is satisfactory, below standard and unacceptable in the long run, respectively?

ANSWERS TO ODD-NUMBERED PROBLEMS

1. $\tfrac{1}{3}, \tfrac{1}{3}, \tfrac{1}{3}$

3. $\tfrac{1}{3}, \tfrac{1}{3}, \tfrac{1}{3}$

5. yes

7. $\tfrac{24}{91}, \tfrac{42}{91}, \tfrac{25}{91}$

9. $\tfrac{4}{9}, \tfrac{31}{63}, \tfrac{4}{63}$

ALGEBRA REVIEW PROBLEMS

EXPONENTS

I. PROBLEMS   Write the following in radical form.

    1. $k^{3/2}$ **2.** $(ab)^{3/4}$ **3.** $(m - n^2)^{-1/2}$ **4.** $6y^{1/5}$ **5.** $-4xy^{1/2}$

    6. $(xy)^{2/3}$ **7.** $(x - y)^{5/6}$ **8.** $(a + 5y)^{1/2}$ **9.** $k^{1/2} - m^{1/2}$

    10. $(4x - 6y)^{3/7}$ **11.** $y^{-2/3}$ **12.** $(a^2 - b^2)^{-1/2}$

ANSWERS   **1.** $\sqrt{k^3}$ **2.** $\sqrt[4]{a^3 b^3}$ **3.** $\dfrac{1}{(m - n^2)^{1/2}} = \dfrac{1}{\sqrt{m - n^2}}$ **4.** $6\sqrt[5]{y}$

    5. $-4x\sqrt{y}$ **6.** $\sqrt[3]{x^2 y^2}$ **7.** $\sqrt[6]{(x - y)^5}$ **8.** $\sqrt{a + 5y}$

    9. $\sqrt{k} - \sqrt{m}$ **10.** $\sqrt[7]{(4x - 6y)^3}$ **11.** $\dfrac{1}{\sqrt[3]{y^2}}$ **12.** $\dfrac{1}{\sqrt{a^2 - b^2}}$

II. PROBLEMS   Write the following with positive fractional exponents.

    1. $\sqrt{4^3}$ **2.** $\dfrac{1}{\sqrt{m - 1}}$ **3.** $\sqrt[3]{5x^2}$ **4.** $\sqrt[3]{ab}$ **5.** $\sqrt[5]{x^4}$ **6.** $\dfrac{x}{\sqrt[5]{y}}$

669

7. $x\sqrt[3]{a^2b^3}$ **8.** $\sqrt{x} - 5\sqrt{y}$ **9.** $\dfrac{2}{\sqrt{x+y}}$ **10.** $\dfrac{1}{\sqrt[3]{x}}$ **11.** $\sqrt[3]{x-y}$

12. $\sqrt[5]{7ab^2}$ **13.** $8\sqrt{m}$ **14.** $\dfrac{-6x}{\sqrt[3]{a^2b}}$ **15.** $-4\sqrt[5]{x^3y}$

ANSWERS   **1.** $4^{3/2}$ **2.** $\dfrac{1}{(m-1)^{1/2}}$ **3.** $(5x^2)^{1/3} = 5^{1/3}x^{2/3}$ **4.** $(ab)^{1/3}$ **5.** $x^{4/5}$

6. $\dfrac{x}{y^{1/5}}$ **7.** $xa^{2/3}b$ **8.** $x^{1/2} - 5y^{1/2}$ **9.** $\dfrac{2}{(x+y)^{1/2}}$ **10.** $\dfrac{1}{x^{1/3}}$

11. $(x-y)^{1/3}$ **12.** $7^{1/5}a^{1/5}b^{2/5}$ **13.** $8m^{1/2}$ **14.** $\dfrac{-6x}{a^{2/3}b^{1/3}}$

15. $-4x^{3/5}y^{1/5}$

III. PROBLEMS   In the following, determine the root indicated.

1. $\sqrt[5]{-32}$ **2.** $\sqrt{9}$ **3.** $\sqrt[4]{x^8y^4}$ **4.** $-\sqrt[3]{27x^3}$ **5.** $-\sqrt{16}$

6. $-\sqrt{a^8y^4}$ **7.** $\sqrt[3]{-27}$ **8.** $\sqrt[3]{\frac{27}{125}x^3y^9}$ **9.** $-\sqrt{a^4b^6}$

10. $\sqrt[3]{27a^6}$

ANSWERS   **1.** -2 **2.** 3 **3.** x^2y **4.** $-3x$ **5.** -4 **6.** $-a^4y^2$ **7.** -3

8. $\frac{3}{5}xy^3$ **9.** $-a^2b^3$ **10.** $3a^2$

IV. PROBLEMS   Change the following to simplest form.

1. $\sqrt{300}$ **2.** $\sqrt{5xy}\sqrt{5x}$ **3.** $\sqrt{2x^5y^2}$ **4.** $-\sqrt{300}$ **5.** $\sqrt{k^4}$

6. $-\sqrt{m^3}$ **7.** $\sqrt{9x^5}$ **8.** $-\sqrt{9x^4}$ **9.** $-\sqrt{24x^6}$ **10.** $\sqrt{8}\sqrt{2}$

11. $\sqrt{ab}\sqrt{a^5b}$ **12.** $\sqrt[4]{a^3}\sqrt[4]{a}$ **13.** $\sqrt[3]{3}\sqrt[3]{9}$ **14.** $\sqrt{400}$

15. $\sqrt{300}$ **16.** $\sqrt[3]{a^7y}$

ANSWERS   **1.** $\sqrt{100}\sqrt{3} = 10\sqrt{3}$ **2.** $\sqrt{25x^2y} = \sqrt{25x^2}\sqrt{y} = 5x\sqrt{y}$

3. $\sqrt{x^4y^2}\sqrt{2x} = x^2y\sqrt{2x}$ **4.** $-\sqrt{100}\sqrt{3} = -10\sqrt{3}$ **5.** k^2

6. $-m\sqrt{m}$ **7.** $3x^2\sqrt{x}$ **8.** $-3x^2$ **9.** $-\sqrt{(4)(6)x^6} = -2x^3\sqrt{6}$

10. $\sqrt{(8)(2)} = 4$ **11.** $\sqrt{a^6b^2} = a^3b$ **12.** $\sqrt[4]{a^4} = a$ **13.** $\sqrt[3]{27} = 3$

14. $\sqrt{4(10)^2} = 2(10) = 20$ **15.** $\sqrt{3(10)^2} = 10\sqrt{3}$ **16.** $a^2\sqrt[3]{ay}$

V. PROBLEMS   Rationalize the denominator in the following.

1. $\sqrt{\frac{1}{6}}$ **2.** $\dfrac{\sqrt{6x}\sqrt{3x}}{\sqrt{9}}$ **3.** $\sqrt[5]{\frac{3}{a^3}}$ **4.** $\sqrt{\frac{1}{8}}$ **5.** $\dfrac{-1}{\sqrt{3}}$ **6.** $-\sqrt{\frac{e}{m}}$

7. $\dfrac{-ab}{\sqrt{b}}$ 8. $\dfrac{1}{\sqrt[3]{9}}$

ANSWERS   1. $\dfrac{\sqrt{1}}{\sqrt{6}} = \dfrac{\sqrt{1}}{\sqrt{6}}\dfrac{\sqrt{6}}{\sqrt{6}} = \dfrac{\sqrt{6}}{6}$ 2. $\dfrac{\sqrt{18x^2}}{\sqrt{9}} = \sqrt{\dfrac{9}{9}\cdot 2x^2} = x\sqrt{2}$

3. $\dfrac{\sqrt[5]{3}}{\sqrt[4]{a^3}} = \dfrac{\sqrt[5]{3}}{\sqrt[5]{a^3}}\dfrac{\sqrt[5]{a^2}}{\sqrt[5]{a^2}} = \dfrac{\sqrt[5]{3a^2}}{a}$ 4. $\dfrac{\sqrt{2}}{4}$ 5. $\dfrac{-\sqrt{3}}{3}$

6. $\dfrac{-\sqrt{e}\sqrt{m}}{\sqrt{m}\sqrt{m}} = \dfrac{-\sqrt{em}}{m}$ 7. $\dfrac{-ab\sqrt{b}}{b} = -a\sqrt{b}$ 8. $\dfrac{1\sqrt[3]{3}}{\sqrt[3]{9}\sqrt[3]{3}} = \dfrac{\sqrt[3]{3}}{3}$

VI. PROBLEMS   Simplify the following.

1. $(2a^2b)(2ab^2)$ 2. $(-3x^3y^4)(7y^3xz)$ 3. $(x^{1/2})(yx^{1/2})$ 4. $\dfrac{x^4}{x^7}$

5. $\dfrac{8a^4b^2}{4a^2b}$ 6. $\dfrac{12x^3y^3z^3}{-6xyz}$ 7. $\dfrac{48x^{3/2}y^{3/5}}{16x^{1/2}y^{1/5}}$ 8. $(3x^2)^2$ 9. $(3ab^{1/2})^2$

10. $(x^{2/3}y^{4/3})^3$ 11. $(x^{2/3}y^{4/3})^{3/2}$ 12. $\dfrac{(x^{1/2}\cdot y^4)^2}{(x^{2/3}\cdot y)^3}$ 13. $\dfrac{(x^n)^{3/2}}{x^{n/2}}$

14. $(y^k\cdot y^{k/2})^4$ 15. $(x^2)^{n/2}\cdot(y^{2n})^{2/n}$ 16. $\left(\dfrac{x^n}{y}\right)^{1/2}\cdot\left(\dfrac{y}{x^{2n}}\right)^{3/2}$

17. $\left(\dfrac{a^m b^{2m}}{b^{4m}}\right)^{1/m}$ 18. $6x^{-2/3}$ 19. $6a^{-2}b^3$ 20. $\frac{3}{5}x^{-2}$

21. $\dfrac{6a^{-3}x^2}{3y^2c^{-4}}$ 22. $(a^2b^{-3})^{-1}$ 23. $x^0\cdot y^n$ 24. $\dfrac{4^{-1}a\cdot b^{-3}}{(2ab)^{-4}}$ 25. $\dfrac{x^{-2}y^{-1}}{3y}$

26. $a^{-1}+b^{-2}$ 27. $(n^{-1}+n^{-2})^{-1}$ 28. $\left(\dfrac{n^{1-a}}{n^{2-a}}\right)^{-2}$ 29. $(x)(x^{2/3})$

30. $n^{3/5}(n+n^{2/5})$ 31. $(a+b)^{1/2}[(a+b)^{1/2}-(a+b)]$

32. $a^{-1/2}(a^{3/2}-a+6)$

ANSWERS   1. $4a^3b^3$ 2. $-21x^4y^7z$ 3. xy 4. $x^{-3}=\dfrac{1}{x^3}$ 5. $2a^2b$

6. $-2x^2y^2z^2$ 7. $3xy^{2/5}$ 8. $9x^4$ 9. $9a^2b$ 10. x^2y^4 11. xy^2

12. $\dfrac{xy^8}{x^2y^3} = \dfrac{y^5}{x}$ 13. $x^{3n/2-n/2}=x^n$ 14. $y^{4k}\cdot y^{4k/2}=y^{6k}$ 15. $x^n\cdot y^{4n/n}=x^n y^4$

16. $\dfrac{x^{n/2}}{y^{1/2}}\cdot\dfrac{y^{3/2}}{x^{6n/2}}=x^{-5n/2}\cdot y=\dfrac{1}{x^{5n/2}}\cdot y=\dfrac{y}{x^{5n/2}}$ 17. $\dfrac{ab^2}{b^4}=a\cdot b^{-2}=\dfrac{a}{b^2}$

18. $\dfrac{6}{x^{2/3}}$ 19. $\dfrac{6b^3}{a^2}$ 20. $\frac{3}{5}\cdot\dfrac{1}{x^2}=\dfrac{3}{5x^2}$

21. $\left(\dfrac{6 \cdot 1}{a^3} \cdot x^2\right) \div \left(\dfrac{3y^2 \cdot 1}{c^4}\right) = \dfrac{6x^2}{a^3} \cdot \dfrac{c^4}{3y^2} = \dfrac{6x^2 c^4}{3y^2 a^3}$ **22.** $a^{-2}b^3 = \dfrac{b^3}{a^2}$ **23.** y^n

24. $\dfrac{\frac{1}{4} \cdot a \cdot b^{-3}}{(2ab)^{-4}} = a \div 4b^3 \cdot 16a^4b^4 = 4a^5 \cdot b$

25. $\dfrac{1}{x^2} \cdot \dfrac{1}{y} \div 3y = \left(\dfrac{1}{x^2 y}\right)\left(\dfrac{1}{3y}\right) = \dfrac{1}{3x^2 y^2}$

26. $\dfrac{1}{a} + \dfrac{1}{b^2}$ to get common denominator: $\dfrac{(b^2)1}{(b^2)a} + \dfrac{(a)1}{(a)b^2} = \dfrac{b^2 + a}{ab^2}$

27. $\left(\dfrac{1}{n} + \dfrac{1}{n^2}\right)^{-1}$ to get common denominator: $\left(\dfrac{(n)1}{(n)n} + \dfrac{1}{n^2}\right)^{-1} = \left(\dfrac{n+1}{n^2}\right)^{-1} =$

$\dfrac{1}{n+1} \div \dfrac{1}{n^2} = \dfrac{1}{n+1} \cdot \dfrac{n^2}{1} = \dfrac{n^2}{n+1}$

28. $(n^{(1-a)-(2-a)})^{-2} = (n^{-1})^{-2} = n^2$ **29.** $(x^{3/3})(x^{2/3}) = x^{5/3}$

30. $n^{3/5}(n^{5/5} + n^{2/5}) = n^{8/5} + n$

31. $(a+b)^{2/2} - [(a+b)^{1/2} + (a+b)^{2/2}] = (a+b) - (a+b)^{3/2}$

32. $a - a^{1/2} + 6a^{-1/2}$

EXPONENTIAL FUNCTIONS

PROBLEMS   ANSWERS

1. Find the second component of each of the following ordered pairs if $y = 2^x$: $(-3,\ )$, $(0,\ )$, $(3,\ )$, $(6,\ )$.

1. $y = 2^{-3} = \frac{1}{8}$; $y = 2^0 = 1$; $y = 2^3 = 8$; $y = 2^6 = 64$

2. Find the second component of each of the following ordered pairs if $f(x) = (\frac{1}{2})^x$: $(-3,\ )$, $(0,\ )$, $(3,\ )$, $(5,\ )$.

2. $f(x) = (\frac{1}{2})^{-3} = \dfrac{1}{1^3} \div \dfrac{1}{2^3} = 1(\frac{8}{1}) = 8$;

$f(x) = (\frac{1}{2})^0 = 1$; $f(x) = (\frac{1}{2})^3 = \dfrac{1}{2^3}$

$= \frac{1}{8}$; $f(x) = (\frac{1}{2})^5 = \dfrac{1}{2^5} = \frac{1}{32}$

3. State the equations $a = b^x$ if $b = 10,\ e,\ \frac{1}{10}, \dfrac{1}{e}$.

3. $a = 10^x$; $a = e^x$; $a = (\frac{1}{10})^x = 10^{-x}$;

$a = \left(\dfrac{1}{e}\right)^x = e^{-x}$

EXPONENTIAL AND LOGARITHMIC FUNCTIONS

I. PROBLEMS   Express the following exponential statements in logarithmic notation.

1. $5^2 = 25$ **2.** $3^{-2} = \frac{1}{9}$ **3.** $16^{1/4} = 2$ **4.** $3^2 = 9$ **5.** $2^3 = 8$

6. $(\frac{1}{3})^2 = \frac{1}{9}$ **7.** $10^2 = 100$ **8.** $10^3 = 1000$ **9.** $10^{-1} = 0.1$

10. $10^0 = 1$

ANSWERS   **1.** $\log_5 25 = 2$ **2.** $\log_3 \frac{1}{9} = -2$ **3.** $\log_{16} 2 = \frac{1}{4}$ **4.** $\log_3 9 = 2$

5. $\log_2 8 = 3$ **6.** $\log_{1/3} \frac{1}{9} = 2$ **7.** $\log_{10} 100 = 2$ **8.** $\log_{10} 1000 = 3$.

9. $\log_{10} 0.1 = -1$ **10.** $\log_{10} 1 = 0$

II. PROBLEMS   Express the following logarithmic statements in exponential notation.

1. $\log_{1/5} 125 = -3$ **2.** $\log_4 16 = 2$ **3.** $\log_3 27 = 3$ **4.** $\log_6 36 = 2$

5. $\log_{10} 1000 = 3$ **6.** $\log_{1/3} \frac{1}{9} = 2$ **7.** $\log_{12} 144 = 2$ **8.** $\log_e e = 1$

ANSWERS   **1.** $(\frac{1}{5})^{-3} = 125$ **2.** $4^2 = 16$ **3.** $3^3 = 27$ **4.** $6^2 = 36$ **5.** $10^3 = 1000$

6. $(\frac{1}{3})^2 = \frac{1}{9}$ **7.** $12^2 = 144$ **8.** $e^1 = e$

III. PROBLEMS   Find the value of x, y, or z for the following.

1. $\log_4 16 = x$ **2.** $\log_6 216 = y$ **3.** $\log_{10} 1 = x$ **4.** $\log_4 4 = z$

5. $\log_{10} 100 = y$ **6.** $\log_{10} 0.1 = y$ **7.** $\log_{10} 0.01 = x$ **8.** $\log_4 \frac{1}{4} = z$

9. $\log_3 27 = x$ **10.** $\log_{12} 144 = y$ **11.** $\log_4 x = 2$ **12.** $\log_3 x = 2$

13. $\log_2 4 = y$ **14.** $\log_6 36 = z$ **15.** $\log_x 10 = \frac{1}{2}$ **16.** $\log_3 27 = y$

ANSWERS   **1.** $x = 2$ **2.** $y = 3$ **3.** $x = 0$ **4.** $z = 1$ **5.** $y = 2$ **6.** $y = -1$

7. $x = -2$ **8.** $z = -1$ **9.** $x = 3$ **10.** $y = 2$ **11.** $x = 16$

12. $x = 9$ **13.** $y = 2$ **14.** $z = 2$ **15.** $x = 100$ **16.** $y = 3$

IV. PROBLEMS   Write the following as the sum or difference of simpler logarithmic quantities. (Remember the rules of logarithmic computation.)

1. $\log_a \left(\frac{mn}{x}\right)^{1/3}$ **2.** $\log_x (abc)$ **3.** $\log_n \left(\frac{a}{b}\right)$ **4.** $\log_x \sqrt[5]{y}$ **5.** $\log_a n^5$

6. $\log_a x^5 y^2$ **7.** $\log_a \sqrt{\frac{m}{n}}$ **8.** $\log_4 \sqrt{a} \sqrt[5]{b^2}$ **9.** $\log_3 \sqrt{a(a-b)}$

10. $\log_{10} \sqrt[5]{\frac{ab^2}{c}}$

ANSWERS **1.** $\log_a \left(\dfrac{mn}{x}\right)^{1/3} = \frac{1}{3} \log_a \left(\dfrac{mn}{x}\right) = \frac{1}{3}(\log_a m + \log_a n - \log_a x)$

2. $\log_x a + \log_x b + \log_x c$ **3.** $\log_n a - \log_n b$ **4.** $\frac{1}{5} \log_x y$

5. $5 \log_a n$ **6.** $5 \log_a x + 2 \log_a y$ **7.** $\frac{1}{2}(\log_a m - \log_a n)$

8. $\frac{1}{2} \log_4 a + \frac{1}{5}(2 \log_4 b) = \frac{1}{2} \log_4 a + \frac{2}{5} \log_4 b$ **9.** $\frac{1}{2} \log_3 a + \frac{1}{2} \log_3 (a - b)$

10. $\frac{1}{5} \log_{10} a + \frac{2}{5} \log_{10} b - \frac{1}{5} \log_{10} c$

SELECTED REFERENCES

MATHEMATICS

Aitken, A. C. *Determinants and Matrices.* Edinburgh: Oliver & Boyd, 1942.

Birkhoff, G., and S. MacLane. *A Survey of Modern Algebra.* New York: Macmillan, 1941.

Britton, J. R., R. B. Kriegh, and Leon W. Rutland. *Calculus and Analytic Geometry.* San Francisco, Calif.: Freeman, 1966.

Browne, E. T. *Introduction to the Theory of Determinants and Matrices.* Chapel Hill: The University of North Carolina Press, 1958.

Buck, R. C. *Advanced Calculus.* New York: McGraw-Hill, 1956.

Burkill, J. C. *The Theory of Ordinary Differential Equations.* Edinburgh: Oliver & Boyd, 1956.

Cameron, E. A., and E. T. Browne. *College Algebra.* New York: Holt, Rinehart & Winston, 1956.

Coask, H. *Ordinary Differential Equations.* Cambridge, Mass.: M.I.T. Press, 1968.

Coddington, E. A., and N. Levinson. *Theory of Ordinary Differential Equations.* New York: McGraw-Hill, 1955.

Courant, R. *Differential and Integral Calculus.* New York: Interscience Publishers, 1937.

Courant, R. *Differential and Integral Calculus,* translated by E. J. McShane, Vols. I and II. New York: Interscience, 1955 printing.

Dwyer, P. S. *Linear Computations.* New York: Wiley, 1951.

Ford, L. R. *Differential Equations.* New York: McGraw-Hill, 1933.

Frazer, R. A., W. J. Duncan, and A. R. Collar, *Elementary Matrices.* London: Cambridge University Press, 1946.

Frazer, R. A., W. J. Duncan, and A. R. Collar. *Elementary Matrices and Some Applications to Dynamic and Differential Equations.* London: Cambridge University Press, 1950.

Golomb, M., and M. Shanks. *Elements of Ordinary Differential Equations.* New York: McGraw-Hill, 1953.

Granville, W. A., P. F. Smith, and W. R. Longley. *Elements of the Differential and Integral Calculus,* New Rev. Ed. Boston: Ginn, 1957.

Hadley, G. *Linear Algebra.* Reading, Mass.: Addison-Wesley, 1961.

Ince, E. L. *Integration of Ordinary Differential Equations.* Edinburgh: Oliver & Boyd, 1952.

Jolley, L. B. W. *Summation of Series,* Rev. Ed. New York: Dover, 1961.

Jordon, C. *Calculus of Finite Differences.* New York: Chelsea, 1950.

Kaplan, W. *Advanced Calculus.* Reading, Mass.: Addison-Wesley, 1952.

Kemeny, J. G., J. L. Snell, and G. L. Thompson. *Finite Markov Chains.* Englewood Cliffs, N.J.: Prentice-Hall, 1960.

Kuhn, H. W., and A. W. Tucker, eds. *Linear Inequalities and Related Systems.* Princeton, N.J.: Princeton University Press, 1956.

Lang, S. *A First Course in Calculus.* Reading, Mass.: Addison-Wesley, 1964.

Love, C. E. *Differential and Integral Calculus.* New York: Macmillan, 1947.

Luce, R. D., and H. Raiffa. *Games and Decisions.* New York: Wiley, 1957.

MacDuffee, C. C. *The Theory of Matrices.* New York: Chelsea, 1946.

McKinsey, J. C. C. *Introduction to the Theory of Games.* New York: McGraw-Hill, 1952.

Mason, T. E., and C. T. Hazard. *Brief Analytic Geometry,* 3rd Ed. Boston: Ginn, 1957.

Mirsky, L. *An Introduction to Linear Algebra,* 2nd Ed. New York: Oxford University Press, 1961.

Nelson, A. L., K. W. Folley, and M. Coral. *Differential Equations.* Boston: D. C. Heath, 1952.

Orchard-Hays, W. *Advanced Linear Programming Computer Techniques.* New York: McGraw-Hill, 1968.

Osgood, W. F. *Advanced Calculus.* New York: Macmillan, 1925.

Perlis, S. *Theory of Matrices.* Reading, Mass.: Addison-Wesley, 1952.

Peterson, T. S. *Elements of Calculus.* New York: Harper & Row, 1950.

Randolph, J. F. *Calculus.* New York: Macmillan, 1952.

Richardson, C. H. *An Introduction to the Calculus of Finite Differences.* New York: Van Nostrand, Reinhold, 1954.

Saltz, D. *An Introduction to Analysis.* Englewood Cliffs, N.J.: Prentice-Hall, 1965.

Sisam, C. S., and W. F. Atchison. *Analytic Geometry.* New York: Holt, Rinehart & Winston, 1955.

Smail, L. L. *Calculus.* New York: Appleton-Century-Crofts, 1949.

Spitzbart, A., and R. H. Bardell. *College Algebra and Plane Trigonometry.* Reading, Mass.: Addison-Wesley, 1964.

Steen, F. H., and D. H. Ballou. *Analytic Geometry.* Boston: Ginn, 1946.

Stoll, R. F. *Linear Algebra and Matrix Theory.* New York: McGraw-Hill, 1952.

Thomas, G. B., Jr. *Calculus and Analytic Geometry*. Reading, Mass.: Addison-Wesley, 1953.

Thrall, R. M., and L. Tornheim. *Vector Spaces and Matrices*. New York: Wiley, 1957.

Vajda, S. *The Theory of Games and Linear Programming*. London: Methuen, 1956.

Widder, D. W. *Advanced Calculus*. Englewood Cliffs, N.J.: Prentice-Hall, 1947.

Wooton, W., and I. Drooyan. *Intermediate Algebra*. Belmont, Calif.: Wadsworth, 1962.

Wylie, C. R., Jr. *Calculus*. New York: McGraw-Hill, 1953.

APPLICATIONS OF MATHEMATICS
IN BUSINESS AND ECONOMICS

Arrow, K., and others. *Studies in Linear and Non-Linear Programming*. Stanford, Calif.: Stanford University Press, 1958.

Arrow, K., and S. Karlin. *Studies in the Mathematical Theory of Inventory and Production*. Stanford, Calif.: Stanford University Press, 1958.

Bierman, H., C. P. Bonini, Jr., and W. H. Hausman. *Quantitative Analysis for Business Decisions*. Homewood, Ill.: Irwin, 1969.

Boulding, K. E., and W. A. Spivey. *Linear Programming and the Theory of the Firm*. New York: Macmillan, 1960.

Bowen, E. K. *Mathematics—With Applications in Management and Economics*. Homewood, Ill.: Irwin, 1963.

Buffa, E. S. *Production Inventory System: Planning and Control*. Homewood, Ill.: Irwin, 1962.

Carr, C. R., and C. W. Howe. *Introduction to Quantitative Decision Procedures in Management and Economics*. New York: McGraw-Hill, 1964.

Charnes, A., W. W. Cooper, and A. Henderson. *An Introduction to Linear Programming*. New York: Wiley, 1953.

Chung, An-Min. *Linear Programming*. Columbus, Ohio: Merrill, 1963.

Churchman, C. W., R. L. Ackoff, and E. L. Arnoff. *Introduction to Operations Research*. New York: Wiley, 1957.

Crum, W. L., and J. A. Schumpeter. *Rudimentary Mathematics for Economists and Statisticians*. New York: McGraw-Hill, 1946.

Daus, P. H., and W. M. Whyburn. *Algebra With Applications to Business and Economics*. Reading, Mass.: Addison-Wesley, 1961.

Daus, P. H., and W. H. Whyburn. *Introduction to Mathematical Analysis*. Reading, Mass.: Addison-Wesley, 1958.

Dean, B. V., M. W. Sasieni, and S. K. Gupta. *Mathematics for Modern Management*. New York: Wiley, 1963.

Dorfman, R. *Application of Linear Programming to the Theory of the Firm*. Berkeley: University of California Press, 1951.

Dorfman, R., P. A. Samuelson, and R. Solow. *Linear Programming and Economic Analysis*. New York: McGraw-Hill, 1958.

Fetter, R. B., and W. C. Band. *Decision Models for Inventory Management*. Homewood, Ill.: Irwin, 1961.

Fowler, F. P., Jr., and E. W. Sandberg. *Basic Mathematics for Administration.* New York: Wiley, 1962.

Garvin, W. W. *Introduction to Linear Programming.* New York: McGraw-Hill, 1960.

Glicksman, A. M. *Linear Programming and The Theory of Games.* New York: Wiley, 1963.

Goldberg, S. *Introduction to Difference Equations.* New York: Wiley, 1958.

Grawoig, D. E. *Decision Mathematics.* New York: McGraw-Hill, 1967.

Hadley, G. *Linear Programming.* Reading, Mass.: Addison-Wesley, 1962.

Holt, C. C., F. Modigliani, J. F. Muth, and H. A. Simon, with contributions by C. P. Bonini and P. R. Winters. *Planning Production, Inventories, and Work Force.* Englewood Cliffs, N.J.: Prentice-Hall, 1960.

Horowitz, I. *An Introduction to Quantitative Business Analysis.* New York: McGraw-Hill, 1965.

Horst, P. *Matrix Algebra for Social Scientists.* New York: Holt, Rinehart & Winston, 1963.

Howell, J. E., and D. Teichroew. *Mathematical Analysis for Business Decisions.* Homewood, Ill.: Irwin, 1963.

Intriligator, M. D. *Mathematical Optimization and Economic Theory.* Englewood Cliffs, N.J.: Prentice-Hall, 1971.

Karlin, S. *Mathematical Methods and Theory in Games, Programming and Economics.* Reading, Mass.: Addison-Wesley, 1959.

Kemeny, J. G., J. L. Snell, and G. L. Thompson. *Introduction to Finite Mathematics,* 2nd Ed. Englewood Cliffs, N.J.: Prentice-Hall, 1966.

Levin, R. I., and C. A. Kirkpatrick. *Quantitative Approaches to Management,* 2nd Ed. New York: McGraw-Hill, 1971.

Llewellyn, R. W. *Linear Programming.* New York: Holt, Rinehart & Winston, 1964.

Managerial Economics and Operations Research: A Nonmathematical Introduction, Edwin Mansfield, ed. New York: Norton, 1966.

Martin, J. J. *Bayesian Decision Problems and Markov Chains.* New York: Wiley, 1967.

Naddor, E. *Inventory Systems.* New York: Wiley, 1966.

Naylor, T. H., and E. T. Byrne. *Linear Programming: Methods and Cases.* Belmont, Calif.: Wadsworth, 1963.

Nemhaueser, G. L. *Introduction to Dynamic Programming.* New York: Wiley, 1966.

Saaty, T. L. *Mathematical Methods of Operations Research.* New York: McGraw-Hill, 1959.

Sasaki, Kyohei. *Introduction to Finite Mathematics and Linear Programming.* Belmont, Calif.: Wadsworth, 1970.

Sasieni, M., A. Yaspan, and L. Friedman. *Operations Research—Methods and Problems.* New York: Wiley, 1959.

Spivey, A. *Linear Programming.* New York: Macmillan, 1963.

Teichroew, D. *An Introduction to Management Science, Deterministic Models.* New York: Wiley, 1964.

Tintner, G., and C. B. Millham. *Mathematics and Statistics for Economists.* New York: Holt, Rinehart & Winston, 1970.

Vajda, S. *The Theory of Games and Linear Programming.* London: Methuen, 1967.

ECONOMICS

Ackley, G. *Macroeconomic Theory*. New York: Macmillan, 1961.

Allen, C. L. *Elementary Mathematics of Price Theory*. Belmont, Calif.: Wadsworth, 1962.

Allen, R. G. D. *Mathematical Analysis for Economists*. London: Macmillan, 1947.

Allen, R. G. D. *Mathematical Economics*. New York: St. Martin's, 1956.

Baumol, W. J. *Economic Dynamics*. New York: Macmillan, 1951.

Baumol, W. J. and R. Turvey, *Economic Dynamics*. New York: Macmillan, 1959.

Baumol, W. J. *Economic Theory and Operations Analysis*. Englewood Cliffs, N.J.: Prentice-Hall, 1961.

Beach, E. F. *Economic Models*. New York: Wiley, 1957.

Boulding, K. E. *Economic Analysis,* 3rd Ed. New York: Harper & Row, 1955.

Braff, A. J. *Microeconomic Analysis*. New York: Wiley, 1969.

Bushaw, D. W., and R. W. Clower. *Introduction to Mathematical Economics*. Homewood, Ill.: Irwin, 1957.

Cyert, R. M., and J. G. March. *A Behavioral Theory of the Firm*. Englewood Cliffs, N.J.: Prentice-Hall, 1963.

Dernburg, T. F., and D. M. McDougall. *Macroeconomics*. New York: McGraw-Hill, 1968.

Dernburg, T. F., and J. D. Dernburg. *Macroeconomic Analysis*. Reading, Mass.: Addison-Wesley, 1969.

Domar, E. *Essays in the Theory of Economic Growth*. New York: Oxford University Press, 1957.

Duesenberry, J. S. *Business Cycles and Economic Growth*. New York: McGraw-Hill, 1958.

Harrod, R. *Dynamic Economics*. New York: Macmillan, 1948.

Henderson, J. M., and R. E. Quandt. *Microeconomic Theory, A Mathematical Approach,* 2nd Ed. New York: McGraw-Hill, 1971.

Keynes, J. M. *The General Theory of Employment Interest and Money*. New York: Harcourt, Brace, Jovanovich, 1935.

Kooros, A. *Elements of Mathematical Economics*. Boston: Houghton Mifflin, 1965.

Metzler, L. A. "The Nature and Stability of Inventory Cycles," *Review of Economics and Statistics,* 1941.

Neumann, J. von, and O. Morgenstern. *Theory of Games and Economic Behavior*. Princeton, N.J.: Princeton University Press, 1954.

Samuelson, P. A. *Foundations of Economic Analysis*. Cambridge, Mass.: Harvard University Press, 1947.

Samuelson, P. A. *Economics: Introductory Analysis,* 4th Ed. New York: McGraw-Hill, 1958.

Schultz, H. *The Theory and Measurement of Demand*. Chicago: University of Chicago Press, 1938.

Stonier, A. W., and D. C. Hague. *A Textbook of Economic Theory*. Edinburgh: Longmans, Tenth Impression, 1960.

Wold, H., and L. Juréen. *Demand Analysis*. New York: Wiley, 1953.

INDEX